Biological and Biochemical Bases of Behavior

BIOLOGICAL
AND
BIOCHEMICAL
BASES OF
BEHAVIOR

Edited by

Harry F. Harlow and Clinton N. Woolsey

Madison

The University of Wisconsin Press

1965

Published by the University of Wisconsin Press
P.O. Box 1379, Madison, Wisconsin 53701

Copyright © 1958 by the Regents of the University of Wisconsin

Printed in the United States of America

Second printing, 1959
Third printing, 1962
Fourth printing, 1965

Library of Congress Catalog Card Number 58–13447

Contributors

FRANK A. BEACH
Department of Psychology
Yale University
New Haven, Connecticut

EDWARD L. BENNETT
Radiation Laboratory
University of California
Berkeley, California

JOSEPH V. BRADY
Department of Experimental Psychology
Neuropsychiatry Division
Walter Reed Institute of Research
Walter Reed Army Medical Center
Washington, D. C.

IRVING T. DIAMOND
Department of Psychology
University of Chicago
Chicago, Illinois

HARRY F. HARLOW
Department of Psychology
University of Wisconsin
Madison, Wisconsin

D. O. HEBB
Department of Psychology
McGill University
Montreal, Canada

HERBERT JASPER
Montreal Neurological Institute
Montreal, Canada

DAVID KRECH
Department of Psychology
University of California
Berkeley, California

JOHN C. LILLY
Chief, Section on Cortical Integration
Laboratory of Neurophysiology
Research Branch
National Institutes of Health
Bethesda, Maryland

H. W. MAGOUN
Department of Anatomy
University of California
Los Angeles, California

DONALD R. MEYER
Department of Psychology
The Ohio State University
Columbus, Ohio

WILLIAM D. NEFF
Department of Psychology
University of Chicago
Chicago, Illinois

JAMES OLDS
Psychology Department
University of Michigan
Ann Arbor, Michigan

KARL H. PRIBRAM
Director of Research and Laboratories
The Institute of Living
Hartford, Connecticut

AUSTIN H. RIESEN
Department of Psychology
University of Chicago
Chicago, Illinois

JERZY E. ROSE
Department of Physiology, School of Medicine
The Johns Hopkins University
Baltimore, Maryland

MARK R. ROSENZWEIG
Department of Psychology
University of California
Berkeley, California

R. W. SPERRY
Division of Biology
California Institute of Technology
Pasadena, California

DONALD B. TOWER
Chief, Section of Clinical Neurochemistry
National Institute of Neurological Diseases and Blindness
Bethesda, Maryland

CLINTON N. WOOLSEY
Department of Physiology
University of Wisconsin
Madison, Wisconsin

One of the most important developments in the biological sciences during the last fifty years has been the growth of interdisciplinary research. The correlation of physiological and anatomical data is an excellent example of this trend. A somewhat more recent, but equally impressive, movement has been the correlation of behavior with data obtained from other biological sciences—anatomy, embryology, physiology, pharmacology, and biochemistry. The information that has come from these interdisciplinary researches has not only been of great importance in its own right, but has in turn stimulated research within the individual disciplines.

In order to summarize and correlate ongoing programs within the areas of anatomy, physiology, biochemistry, and behavior involving researches in a host of laboratories, the Symposium on Interdisciplinary Research was arranged. The participants and the discussants are eminent authorities within their own disciplines, and in addition they are men recognized for their many contributions in interareal researches.

The present volume is a collection of papers presented by the speakers at this Symposium. The original plan was to include the comments prepared by the discussants and the transcripts of the general discussion, which proved so valuable and stimulating. Unfortunately, limitations imposed by publication costs made this impossible, and the discussions were of necessity omitted.

A large part of the credit for the success of the Symposium must be given to the cochairmen, Dr. John D. Benjamin and Dr. Douglas D. Bond, who directed with patient sagacity the presentation of the papers and the subsequent discussions. The discussants who contributed so ably included Dr. Harlow W. Ades, Dr. Konrad Akert, Dr. Edward L. Bennett, Dr. K. L. Chow, Dr. Glen Finch, Dr. Vernon B. Mountcastle, Dr. James O'Leary, Dr. Eli Robins, the late Dr. Paul H. Settlage, Dr. Richard L. Solomon, and Dr. Hans-Lukas Teuber.

The impetus for the formation of this Symposium came as a result of conferences in the Subcommittee to Explore the Relation between the Biochemical and Biological Sciences to Mental Health, of the Mental Health Study Section. The Symposium was made possible by a grant from the Research Committee of the University of Wisconsin from funds supplied by the Wisconsin Alumni Research Foundation, and by a grant from the National Institute of Mental Health. We wish to acknowledge the generosity of these two sponsors and to express appreciation to the many local staff members who planned and arranged the program and made available the needed supporting facilities.

HARRY F. HARLOW
CLINTON N. WOOLSEY

Madison, Wisconsin
January, 1958

Table of Contents

List of Illustrations

PLATES

List of Tables

Biological and Biochemical Bases of Behavior

Harry F. Harlow

Behavioral Contributions
to Interdisciplinary Research

The original research reported in this paper was supported in part by Atomic Energy Commission Contract AT(11–1)–64, Project No. 11, and in part by funds received from the Graduate School of the University of Wisconsin.

Every human being throughout his life has been a student of animal behavior, and the animal which he has most commonly studied is man. Furthermore, most human beings have studied, with varying degrees of interest and intensity, a generous sample of this species of mammal, and their behavioral studies have frequently taken interdisciplinary form as they correlated, often with more enthusiasm than accuracy, the observed behaviors with the anatomical and physiological variables of sex, facial form, body build, complexion, perspiration rate, and vasomotor patterns.

But no normal human being limits his behavioral studies to the analysis of responses made by other human beings. Primitive man's survival was and is dependent upon knowledge of the behavior of other animals, and without this knowledge he would not be able to feast on some of the animal forms inhabiting his environment, nor keep from being eaten by others. Civilized man studies the behavior of other animals from need, if professionally involved, and from curiosity, if not. To children in all cultures the behavior of the nonhuman animals is now and must have been in the past a continual source of delightful wonderment.

Not only is the study of behavior the common property of all men, but it approaches being the common property of all the disciplines forming the family of biological sciences. The pure behaviorist, the psychologist, studies behavior like the true artist studies art—for its own sake. Most biological scientists—the anatomists, physical anthropologists, zoologists, physiologists, and biochemists—correlate behaviors with other variables, and in so far as they work along these lines, they achieve interdisciplinary research. This does not mean, of course, that interdisciplinary research between or among biological sciences of necessity involves behavioral measures. Correlations between chemical and anatomical, chemical and physiological, and anatomical and physiological variables may be made without direct measures of, or reference to, behavior, but even in such studies the implications for behavior are frequently obvious and usually

3

little distance removed. It is a safe generalization, I believe, to state that the universal common interest of the biological scientists is behavior, the single characteristic which best defines and differentiates the living animal.

In spite of the universality of behavior study this investigative area was the last of the biological sciences to be incorporated formally and recognized as an independent science. Only during the last fifty or seventy-five years, depending upon the historical criterion taken, has a self-conscious, and sometimes embarrassed, science of behavior existed, even though the historical antecedents of behavior science can be traced almost as far back as human records go. Because there is no biological science whose variables cannot or need not be related to behavioral variables, the existence of an ordered and formal behavioral science is doubtless a strong incentive for interdisciplinary studies.

No psychologist, or, at least, no nonparanoid psychologist, believes that behavior study, or even good behavior study, is the private domain of the psychologist. The zoologists, the ethologists, and the naturalists have conducted many highly effective behavior studies for many years, and, by and large, have demonstrated more enthusiasm, productivity, and ingenuity in the study of animal behavior under natural environmental conditions than have the psychologists. Furthermore, many naturalistic studies have formed the basis for interesting and ingenious interdisciplinary researches, such as those correlating light duration, gonadal size, and homing behavior in the junco.

PSYCHOLOGICAL CONTRIBUTIONS

The primary contribution of the psychologist to behavioral science lies in the fact that he has adapted behavioral analysis to laboratory situations; indeed, it is almost the trade-mark of the psychologically oriented behavior scientist that he leaves the laboratory only for avocational purposes, and in some tragic cases, not even for these. Geographically the psychologist seldom wanders far afield, and the tests that he devises are products of his laboratory researches and are designed for other laboratory investigations.

Likewise, most tests and apparatus devised by the anatomists, physiologists, and biochemists are designed for use in the laboratory situation. For these reasons the tests and techniques of psychologists tend to be well adapted to the needs of scientists in related fields, and the techniques developed by men in the related fields can be used effectively by psychologists for correlational analysis.

Ordinarily, the behavioral techniques used by the psychologist engaging in interdisciplinary research are the same as those used by the psychologist studying behavior for its own sake. It is obvious that no interdisciplinary research can be better than the behavioral measures which provide its dependent variable or variables. Yet the fact remains that the behavioral methods used in interdisciplinary research are commonly inferior to the behavorial methods available at the time, and there are many illustrations—even in our current literature—of the use of behavioral techniques outmoded by two or more decades. No doubt this is equally true of the anatomical, physiological, and biochemical methods used by the behavior scientists, and to a certain extent it is inevitable. At best there is temporal lag in interdisciplinary information; there is also a tendency to utilize outmoded techniques in an honest effort to relate new researches to the data obtained from antedated experiments; and the sheer excitement and challenge of interdisciplinary research may lead the investigator to feel that technical excellence is of secondary importance. Probably the best safeguard against correlating results obtained from outmoded techniques lies in the formation of research teams representing members of both or all the disciplines whose data are to be related. Doubtless, there will always be some scientists who can be adequate lovers to all the beckoning scientific Loreleis, but the demands of intellectual polygyny lie beyond the physiological capabilities of most.

Interdisciplinary research in the biological sciences may be thought of as reducing or enhancing anatomical, physiological, and biochemical capabilities of the animal and determining the effect of the alteration of these biological variables on behavior measures. We excise the prefrontal areas, thereby reducing the capabilities of the brain, and relate this change to the delayed response; we render the male ːat blind, deaf, and anosmic, and determine the effects of reduction of sensory capacities on pattern and frequency of sex behavior; we inject testosterone propionate and relate this enhanced biochemical variable to the hopeful behavior of the senile rat. Considering interdisciplinary research from this point of view is more than proper and perhaps the most efficient way to regard the activities undertaken.

But from a purely psychological point of regard we can consider the alteration of any and all variables in related fields as merely extending the scope and domain of comparative psychology. Bilateral removal of the temporal lobe in the monkey produces a new species or subspecies of primate that behaves differently on our tests from all or most other monkey species! The injection of testosterone propionate in the rat does nothing but produce a new subspecies of *Mus norvegicus* more temporally resistant to certain aspects of the aging process. Implantation of electrodes into the septal region of the rat produces a species endowed with unusual responsiveness to human control. Perhaps there is little or no real difference between the two viewpoints even though the first point of regard emphasizes the role and importance of the neurochemical variables, and the second point of view, the role and importance of the behavioral measures.

We have already indicated that the use of behavior tests by biological scientists far antedates the appearance of the professional psychologist. What, then, has the psychologist contributed above and beyond the tests and test procedures that existed before?

One contribution of the psychologist has been the production of tests and test procedures that give highly reliable results so that significant differences can be established between and among experimental and control groups. Such methodological advancements make possible a degree of quantification that would not otherwise exist and also make practical the use of relatively small groups of subjects and relatively short test intervals, even though in some cases these relatively short test intervals should be measured in terms of weeks or months. Since interdisciplinary researches may involve preparations whose production is extremely time-consuming, the development of the reliable test or test battery is a contribution of major importance.

In spite of methodological and procedural improvements, behavioral data collection is still a time-consuming and costly process. There is every reason to believe, however, that much behavioral testing will become progressively more mechanized and that the experimenter will be partially superseded by automation. This trend began at least as early as the Tryon maze, a rat maze that was completely automatic as long as an experimenter was always available to maintain the machine and assist the animal. Probably the greatest trend toward automation has come with the development of the Skinner Box, which has reached such a high degree of precision that a laboratory equipped with a row of boxes and unlimited electronic engineering support can, on simple problems, obtain an almost unlimited amount of data. Up to the present time automation has been little used by those who have chosen to select their apparatus in terms of their problems, rather than their problems in terms of their apparatus, and particularly on tests of complex learning functions has labor-saving apparatus been rare. It would, however, be an unwise man who would predict that robotism has reached its zenith, and robotism is obviously desirable if precision is not impaired and range of problems not restricted.

Before and after the advent of psychologists, scientists have devised behavioral tests which presumably measure a category defined by such common-sense terms as thinking, learning, emotion, motivation, or drive. Until relatively recently little consideration was given to the scientific meaningfulness of these categories, and the degree to which any or all tests measured these categories, if they had more than fictional existence. The statistical demonstration of the reliability or unreliability within tests automatically led to measures of reliability between tests, that is, validity. Disturbingly low correlations were obtained between existing measures of animal learning in such generally employed situations as the maze, the problem box, and the discrimination apparatus, even though high or moderately high intraproblem reliability measures were demonstrable. Similar results have been found for drive or other motivational measures; high reliability between varying measures of some drive, such as the sex drive, may exist, but low interdrive correlations are obtained.

Although the psychologist has gone far to solve the problem of test reliability, the problem of test validity remains difficult and challenging. There is every reason to believe that continuing progress will be made along this line. We have at Wisconsin, for example, data analyses which enable us to predict for a wide range of tests, extending from spatial discrimination to the very complex multiple-sign tests, both positive and negative transfer among analyzable factors underlying the learning. This permits us within reasonable limits both to predict and explain the nature of intertest correlations and to describe common factors and distinctive elements within a large family of learning tests.

Factor-analysis studies have been made and are being made, and these studies give, and will continue to give, information concerning the degree of relatedness of various motivational and learning measures. Factor-analysis techniques have their limitations in that they merely indicate interrelationships exist; they do not reveal the nature of the interrelations. But in spite of any limitation of the technique, these studies clearly demonstrate that psychologists are attacking the problem of test validity and making progress. Because the behavioral measure is the dependent variable for many interdisciplinary researches, the problem of test validity assumes paramount importance for interdisciplinary research.

The large variety of behavior tests, the arrangements of tests into orderly batteries, and the systematic scaling of many tests for difficulty represent additional psychological achievements. Test development is no part-time job, and it could not be efficient, and certainly not systematic, until it was accepted by some group as a major responsibility.

CONTRIBUTIONS OF INTERDISCIPLINARY RESEARCH

Another, and very fundamental, contribution that the psychologist is making to interdisciplinary research is that of focusing attention on the temporal and experiential variables in behavior. The importance of these variables may be illustrated by interdisciplinary studies correlating cortical injury with behavioral deficit. Following bilateral destruction of the lateral surface of the prefrontal areas in monkeys, there is either total loss or drastic impairment of the capacity to solve delayed-response problems. If, however, testing on delayed response is subsequently continued for prolonged periods of time, a very considerable fraction of the operated subjects will regain a moderate or even high level of performance on the delayed-response test (9). Following unilateral hemispherectomy in monkeys, significant impairment can be demonstrated in object-discrimination learning-set formation, but these differences disappear with time and training (13). With extensive bilateral damage to the lateral surface of the temporal lobes of monkeys, severe impairment of object-discrimination learning-set formation results, but after a year of additional testing this deficit disappears (22).

The importance of the temporal variable alone has been demonstrated in an ingenious experiment by Stewart and Ades (21). These investigators showed that monkeys fail to retain a form discrimination habit if areas 18 and 19 are removed by a two-stage operation, with the stages seven days or less apart, but they do not lose this habit when the two stages are separated by more than seven days.

The effect of brain destruction cannot be related merely to the locus of the lesion; the animal's history must be taken into account. Thus, we see that the temporal and experiential variables can be of extreme importance in interpreting interdisciplinary research. This is an example of psychological variables, discovered through interdisciplinary research, that could conceivably influence anatomical thinking.

Conversely, the introduction of nonpsychological variables may forcibly alter psychological thinking and theorizing. A classic example of this is the information obtained by analysis of the delayed response in the bilateral prefrontal monkey preparation. Because the ability of any animal to perform successfully on delayed-response tests decreases as a function of the delay interval, it has always been assumed that delayed response was primarily a "memory" test. But when the delayed-response performance of normal monkeys was compared with that of prefrontal monkeys, it was found by Harlow and Meyer (unpublished study) that the statistical significance of the differences decreased as the delay increased. Memory function is certainly no more affected by the operation than is the ability to obtain and to respond properly to the information given at the time of the stimulus presentation and problem setting. With these data available from the operated animals, it becomes clear that the original information-getting variable is of great importance. In retrospect, it is now obvious why even normal animals must be intensively trained on very low levels of delay before they can perform effectively with longer delays. Information-getting has always been a very important aspect of the de-layed-response situation, and it is subject to marked learning. Yet little was made of this point, and no theoretical significance was attached to it, until the operative data forced it upon our attention.

In the semi-suicidal search for operational orderliness biologists and psychologists have conceptualized unlearned behaviors as simple and stereotyped, and learned behaviors as complex and variable. Until res-cued by interdisciplinary research, they bolstered their misconceptions with fictitious anatomical support and assigned unlearned behaviors to subcortical centers and learned behaviors to the cerebral cortex. But in-terdisciplinary researches by Beach (7) have unequivocally demonstrated that unlearned maternal behavior may be drastically impaired by com-paratively small cortical lesions, lesions so small that they would cer-tainly not affect learned brightness discriminations (6) and probably not affect, or little affect, simple maze learning. These interdisciplinary data strongly suggest that we should reappraise unlearned and learned re-sponses in terms of their relative simplicity and stereotypy; perhaps it would be well to re-examine the value of this nearly universally accepted dichotomous classification.

Still another example indicates the effect interdisciplinary research can exert on psychological theory. In 1949 Harlow (12) pointed out that animals trained on a series of problems of a given class improve progress-ively and may eventually solve new ones in a single trial. To many psy-chologists, this phenomenon described as learning-set formation has offered little theoretical difficulty if it was assumed that there is no funda-mental difference between intraproblem and interproblem learning. But recent interdisciplinary researches suggest that the differences in the two kinds of learning may be even more drastic than we first surmised. Rio-pelle, Alper, Strong, and Ades (19), and subsequently Meyer in researches to be presented at these meetings, have discovered that the integrity of learning-set formation may be dependent upon different cortical centers from those necessary for single-problem learning. Even though our psy-chological analyses had suggested fundamental differences between intra-problem and interproblem learning, and even though differences are clearly demonstrated by our ongoing researches on the development of behavioral capacities in the infant monkey, the contribution made by combining physiological and anatomical techniques with the behavioral is very great.

It is easy when one plans and conducts interdisciplinary research to think in terms of the correlations which will be established. But I am convinced by results such as those which I have cited that interdisciplinary research leads to far more than correlations. Inevitably, there arises new information specific to the individual disciplines which are involved, and these data may be as important as, or even more important than, the correlational data themselves.

HISTORICAL BASIS OF INTERDISCIPLINARY RESEARCH

From the historical point of view, it is interesting to note that man has engaged in interdisciplinary research—or interdisciplinary speculation—for as long as, or longer than, we have written records. These efforts have resulted from observations that have either followed the production of anatomical and physiological alterations in animals, or followed observations of the effects of accidents and combat, the so-called experiments of nature.

Almost twenty-four centuries ago Hippocrates noted in support of his theory that an excess of the humor phlegm was the cause of epilepsy, that, upon cutting open the head of an epileptic animal, particularly a goat, one finds "the brain humid, full of sweat, and having a bad smell" (3, p. 364) and generalized his observations to epileptic persons. The Greek, Erasistratus, living in the third century B.C., concluded that complexity of the convolutions of the brain and mentality are closely related, coming to this conclusion apparently from correlating anatomical dissections with general observations of men and other animals (4, pp. 121–22). Galen, the Roman physician living in the second century A.D., conducted a series of experiments involving precise and limited destruction of, or damage to, particular parts of the nervous system (16, p. 28), and these researches may be regarded as beginning the traditions of precise experimental interdisciplinary investigations in the biological science area.

Equally time-honored as source materials for interdisciplinary correlations are the data derived from accidents, illness, and combat. Thus, Hippocrates noted in his discussion of head wounds that "for the most part, convulsions seize the other side of the body for, if the wound be situated on the left side, the convulsions will seize the right side of the body; or if the wound be on the right side of the head, the convulsion attacks the left side of the body" (1, p. 464).

Some five hundred years later the same phenomenon was again reported by Aretaeus, who wrote:

" . . . if the head be primarily affected on the right side, the left side of the body will be paralyzed; and the right, if on the left side. The cause of this is the interchange in the origins of the nerves, for they do not pass along on the same side, the right on the right side, until their terminations; but each of them passes over to the other side from that of its origin, decussating each other in the form of the letter X" (2, p. 306).

Without doubt the same discovery had been made and reported many times during the five centuries separating the two physicians, but this is no criticism of Aretaeus, for the mass of scientific literature had doubtless reached such proportions by the second century A.D. that no one possibly could have been familiar with all of it. In actual fact, and in fairness to Aretaeus, there is every reason to believe that he was familiar with Hippocrates' writing and that he regarded his own work as confirming that of the master.

An unusually interesting neurological observation was made by the famous physicist Robert Boyle, who reported "the remarkable case of a knight who, following a depressed fracture of the skull, experienced an enduring 'dead palsy,' *i.e.*, motor and sensory paralysis, of the arm and leg. . . ." Eventually a surgeon explored the wound, and "the motor and sensory symptoms disappeared within a few hours after the spicule of bone pressing on the brain had been removed" (11, p. 399).

It is, of course, commonly known that the experiments of nature—even if man had a helping hand in many of them—served as the initial source for many scientific discoveries in the biological sciences. Gall localized cortical motor aphasia from observations of a Frenchman suffering from a sword wound. Panizza, in 1855, localized visual functions in the posterior part of the cerebrum on the basis of observation and subsequent pathological study of two patients, one blinded by an apoplectic stroke and the other by an injury. Fritsch localized the motor area by observing the behavior of a German Uhlan struck down during the Franco-Prussian war, and Broca and his predecessors localized aphasia in the third convolution of the left frontal lobe from observations of diseased or injured people.

Observations and experiments relating the effects of injury or disease of the frontal lobes of the brain to learned and motivated behaviors has resulted in a wealth of literature, wealth being considered from a quantitative rather than qualitative point of view. Because every conceivable function, known or unknown, has been localized in this area by one savant or another, it is likely that at least one authority was correct even though our knowledge of the actual roles of these areas is so limited that the correct savant must still remain nameless.

LABORATORY INVESTIGATIONS OF THE EXPERIMENTS OF NATURE

Returning to the observations by Robert Boyle concerning the injured knight, one recalls the extreme severity of the symptoms as long as the spicule of bone remained and the rapid alleviation of symptoms after the bone fragment was removed. This is an example of a phenomenon doubtless observed countless times previously and countless times since. No authority has discussed the implications of these described phenomena with either more enthusiasm or insight than Dr. Hebb, who wrote in 1949 that "it has been discovered that a comparatively small region of pathological change, producing hypersynchrony, may have a much more deteriorating effect on behavior than a complete loss of the tissue concerned" (14, p. 282).

Dr. Hebb illustrates this point in a dramatic manner by contrasting the loss in patients in which residual tumor apparently remained after bilateral frontal lobectomy (as the Brickner case [8] and the Nickols and Hunt case [17]) with the patient from whom Dr. Penfield apparently removed all pathological tissue by bilateral prefrontal lobectomy. This latter case was a youth who, following skull fracture, developed severe epilepsy, dangerous combativeness, and tested below IQ 70 on an intelligence test. After operation the IQ score rose to 96, the psychotic behavior disappeared, and the young man enlisted in the Canadian Army and served satisfactorily overseas for more than ten months.

Although Dr. Hebb is scrupulously careful not to deny intellectual or learning functions to the frontal lobes, the contrast in behavioral loss following the large surgical ablation compared with loss in the presence of small regions of pathological tissue is striking. One cannot help but wonder whether, if Dr. Penfield continues to refine his surgical methods, he cannot remove the entire neocortex with no deficit resulting other than transient motor impairment. At the very least it appears that Einstein was needlessly generous in bequeathing his entire brain to science.

The contrast between the nature and extent of behavioral changes following surgical and pathological lesions has brought sharply to attention the fact that although cerebral surgical techniques have dramatically improved in the last quarter-century, relatively little attention has been given to the laboratory production of pathological lesions. There are suggestions in the literature concerning the production of pathological lesions by such procedures as CO_2 asphyxiation, temporary ligation of carotid and vertebral arteries, anoxic anoxia, and total-head X irradiation, but precise and definitive experiments are rare.

In 1941 Barrera, Kopeloff, and Kopeloff (5) reported experimental studies on 102 monkeys in which irritative lesions were induced or attempted by implantation over the motor area of discs containing chemical agents such as silver oxide or alumina cream, or immunological agents as white of egg (given to an animal previously sensitized to it) or

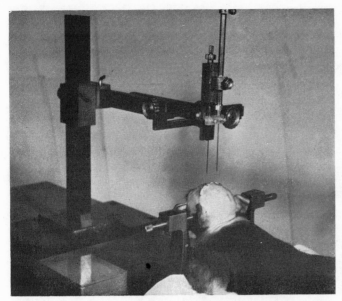

Plate 1.—Stereotaxic instrument in position for insertion of cobalt 60 needles.

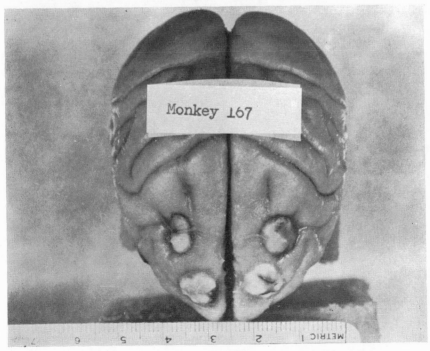

Plate 2.—Lesions produced by 8,000-r. doses delivered by cobalt 60 needles.

Plate 3.—Successful response in crossed-strings test.

heat-killed typhoid bacilli incorporated in aquaphor. These procedures resulted in chronic and recurring spasms, tremors, and seizures in some experimental subjects. The data as summarized by the authors show:

There did not seem to be a direct quantitative relationship between the extent of chronic pathologic involvement and the occurrence of seizures. Some brains with a relatively mild chronic, proliferative meningocortical cicatrix were associated clinically with chronic or recurrent seizures related topographically to the area of scar; other brains with similar pathologic changes were never associated with seizures, even during long periods of observation. . . . From examination of a large number of cases, it may be stated that pathologic changes have always been found to accompany seizures, but that seizures have not always accompanied pathologic changes, no matter how severe (5, p. 733).

Dr. Pribram (18) has reported a series of two experiments, one with a population of two baboons, and the other with a population of one baboon, in which five silver discs approximately 1 mm. in diameter filled with aluminum hydroxide paste were placed over or near each prefrontal area. The animals after implantation were tested for retention on 10-sec. delayed response and a red-green discrimination. One baboon with silver discs in the prefrontal areas showed immediate total behavioral loss followed by recovery during the subsequent month and progressively severe resumption of the deficit beginning during the fourth month. The baboon with the silver discs implanted near, but not within, the prefrontal areas showed no immediate loss but transient loss four months later. The third baboon, which, like the first, had the silver discs in the prefrontal areas, showed no behavioral loss. Baboons 2 and 3, however, both showed greater behavior loss to metrazol than did a control subject, which suddenly appeared on page 3 but whose genus and test history were not specified. Pribram properly concludes: "These experiments demonstrate that marked impairment of performance may result from a lesion which causes only minimal damage to the anatomical organization of the cerebral cortex . . . it is most likely that the symptoms produced by these lesions can be attributed to interference with the normal patterning of neuronal discharge" (18, p. 318). The most serious limitation of the technique would appear to be the great behavior variability among subjects, a condition not explicable in terms of the site of the irritative agent.

Chow (10) subsequently extended Pribram's experiment by placing from four to nine discs with aluminum hydroxide cream in front of the lunate sulcus and testing the effect of these implantations on the retention of a single brightness discrimination, a color discrimination, and a pattern discrimination. The monkeys showed perfect retention on all tests from the second day after implantation through 18 months of testing even though the animals had EEG anomalies and epileptic seizures. In summary, Chow points out: "Irritative foci experimentally induced in the preoccipital region are as ineffective in producing visual disturbances as the ablation of that region. It is possible, however, that the irritation produced by the aluminum hydroxide cream differs qualitatively from that produced by pathological tissue, i.e., tumor, abscess, atrophy, etc." (10, p. 7).

Several years ago in the search for a technique capable of producing irritative lesions which would give rise to some invariant syndrome with a predictable temporal course, we initiated a series of studies on the effect of transient implantation of radioactive cobalt needles in the cerebral cortex of monkeys. The technique of implantation, which was developed and described by Settlage and Bogumill (20), involves irradiating the tissues by means of a stereotaxic instrument, substituting cobalt 60 needles for the conventional electrode (see Plate 1). This technique makes possible the production of precise cortical or subcortical lesions, as is shown in Plate 2.

Our initial experiments were, of course, completely exploratory because limited information existed concerning the effect of cobalt 60 on cortical tissue, and no information existed concerning the effect of cortical irradiation on learned behaviors of monkeys. In our first three preliminary experiments the needles were left in place long enough to deliver a dosage of 8,000 r. at a distance of 5 mm. from the cobalt source, and the needles were placed so that the cobalt source was at the cortical surface. In these experiments two needles were applied bilaterally to the prefrontal areas in two experiments and bilaterally to the posterior temporal lobes in the third study.

Behaviorally, we aspired to develop a test battery making possible daily assessment of a range of learned behaviors, and after preliminary experimentation we developed the following test battery: 20, 10-sec. delayed-response trials, 10 two-trial discrimination tests, and 10 trials on a crossed-strings test.

In the delayed-response test two identical stimulus objects are placed behind the foodwells of a Klüver-type tray, which is beyond the monkey's reach, and food is placed in one of these wells in full view of the animal. Both stimuli are then moved over the two foodwells, a 10-sec. delay period is interposed, the tray pushed forward, and the monkey permitted to make a choice. Figure 1 shows identical stimuli in position over the foodwells of a test tray used with the Wisconsin General Test Apparatus.

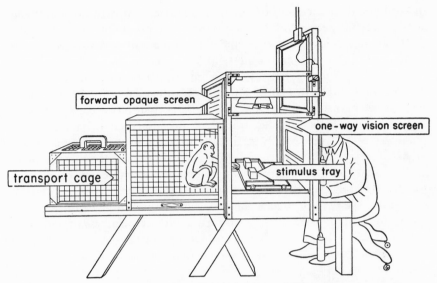

forward opaque screen

one-way vision screen

transport cage

stimulus tray

Fig. 1.—Delayed-response trial using Wisconsin General Test Apparatus.

The two-trial discrimination test utilizes the same basic apparatus, but the two stimuli differ in multiple physical characteristics, and a screen prevents the monkey's seeing the placement of the food or arrangement of the stimuli. On trial 1, food is put in one foodwell, and both foodwells are covered by the stimuli. The problem is then presented to the animal. A single choice is permitted, which is rewarded or not rewarded, depending upon the object displaced. Trial 2 is arranged like trial 1 except for the fact that the position of the correct object is reversed on half the problems. Trial 2 is the measure of the ability of the animal to learn in a single trial which stimulus object is correct. With each new problem a new pair of stimulus objects is used.

The cross-strings test is illustrated in Plate 3. Solution of the problem requires consistent response to the baited string. Half the time the string which is baited is the left one, and half the time the string in the right-hand position is the correct one.

There is a rationale for the selection of all these tests. Successful performance on delayed-response tests is more dependent upon integrity of the prefrontal areas than any other cortical locus. Two-trial discrimination performance is particularly dependent upon integrity of the posterior portion of the lateroventral portions of the temporal lobes, and crossed-strings solution is known to be lost temporarily following unilateral occipital lobectomy and probably lost temporarily following serious unilateral damage to the frontal eye fields, that is, among other things it is a precise measure of homonymous hemianopsia. It should be emphasized that delayed response and discrimination performance are impaired only if the lesions are bilateral.

To utilize such a battery so as to measure continuous behavior changes in a single animal or a group of animals requires that the subjects perform prior to irradiation at a level approaching perfection, demonstrating little interday variation. Because such behavior can be obtained only from highly trained and experienced, laboratory-wise monkeys, research on these problems poses difficult logistic problems.

The first three preliminary experiments were conducted on a single subject, No. 167, which previously had had two years' continuous testing on a wide variety of problems. The results obtained from all these experiments were highly similar, and Figure 2 gives typical results obtained

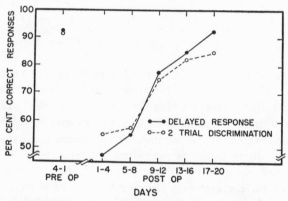

Fig. 2.—Effect of bilateral temporal implantation of cobalt 60 needles on delayed response and two-trial discrimination problems.

on delayed response and discrimination tests. Recovery on the crossed-strings test was usually more rapid. Cortical irradiation of an adequate dosage from localized sources results in complete loss of all measured laboratory-learned behaviors, followed by continuous recovery, which is complete or nearly complete within a 10- to 20-day interval. We have called this the "cortical irradiation syndrome." Whether or not the severity of the imposed deficits and the speed of recovery are influenced by the localization of the radiation source is by no means established because we still lack fundamental information necessary to make such research efficient. Such scanty evidence as we have, however, does suggest that cortical localization of the radiation source may be a factor of importance in determining rate of recovery among the various behavioral measures utilized. Nevertheless, it seems quite unlikely that the high degree of separation of behavioral test results that follow differential surgical lesions will ever be found to follow the use of differentially localized sources of cobalt 60 irradiation.

On the basis of three subsequent experiments conducted on a total of five monkeys, it appears that the same syndrome can be produced by unilateral implantation at a lower dosage level. A single dose of 4,000 r. at a distance of 5 mm. from the radiation source of one needle produces the same irradiation syndrome as was obtained with two needles bilaterally implanted until a dosage of 8,000 r. at a 5-mm. distance had been delivered through each needle. Consequently, we shall now refer to the single-needle, 4,000-r. dosage at a distance of 5 mm. from the radiation source as the "standard radiation dosage."

A series of additional tests now nearing completion suggests that we may be near determination of the minimal dosage which will produce our syndrome of drastic learning loss. By word of caution I state that these experiments have been made using temporal lobe implantations in monkeys which had previously been subjected to one or more prefrontal implantations, and each of the tests has been made on a single monkey. The strength of all dosage levels is given in terms of roentgens as a distance of 5 mm. from the radiation source. A dosage of 2,000 r. delivered by a single needle in one temporal lobe does not produce the syndrome. Likewise, two needles, each delivering 2,000 r., applied either to one temporal lobe or bilaterally, fail to induce the syndrome. No measurable change results in any tested laboratory-learned behavior. Furthermore, a dosage of 3,000 r. delivered by a single needle in one temporal lobe does not produce the syndrome, nor do 3,000-r. dosages delivered by each of two needles implanted in a single temporal lobe result in the cortical irradiation syndrome. None of the animals used in these experiments showed any indication of loss on any learning test, and even though single monkeys served as subjects, their six to seven years of continuous laboratory learning prior to irradiation had rendered them stable and effective subjects. It should be stated, however, that both the monkeys subjected to 3,000-r. dosages gave indications of behavioral alterations other than accuracy of performance on tests. Their motivational level appeared to be slightly depressed in that they were sometimes slow to initiate a trial, and they exhibited a degree of cage restlessness not previously noted in them or in the 2,000-r. animals. Thus, it is likely that the critical dose lies between 3,000 and 4,000 r. and may well be definable within a 250- to 500-r. differential.

It is perfectly obvious that a level of irradiation sufficient to produce cortical lesions may adversely affect learned behaviors through various channels. The necrotic tissue might produce toxic, mechanical, or local circulatory effects which would lead to behavioral impairment; radiation from the high-energy cobalt 60 source obviously does not stop at the site of the lesions but, instead, decreases in strength as a function of the inverse square law, and total amount of irradiation of cerebral tissues may be the primary cause of behavioral failure; finally, the loss may be attributable to some such mechanism as that which von Monakow called "diaschisis." The acute, localized cell destruction may transmit, through association or commissural pathways, atypical discharge patterns giving rise to the so-called "reverberations at a distance," which in turn lead to behavioral decrement.

In an effort to make at least one test of the effect of the radioactively produced necrotic tissue, an experiment was conducted with six rhesus monkeys, the same six monkeys that we previously stated had given many of the best years of their lives to the solution of psychological problems. The three experimental animals were given the standard dosage in the right prefrontal lobe; a hemispherical block of tissue with a radius of 5 to 6 mm. from the needle point was then removed. This block is as large as, or larger than, the maximal lesion size produced by the radiation. The control subjects were given no radiation but were subjected to the same operative procedures to produce equivalent lesions.

The results of this experiment are unequivocal. The control group showed no significant loss on any test and probably no loss of any kind. The experimental group, on the other hand, suffered deficits on all tests

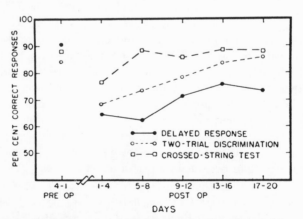

Fig. 3.—Performance following unilateral prefrontal lobe irradiation and subsequent extirpation of the predicted necrotic tissue.

(Fig. 3), and these deficits were at least as severe as would be predicted had the monkeys been irradiated and the necrotic tissue left in place. Actually, the deficit on the delayed-response test (Fig. 4) was surprisingly severe and more persistent than the loss previously found after irradiation only. Although not shown on the figures, all the monkeys subsequently recovered completely, attaining stable and nearly perfect levels of performance on the three tests.

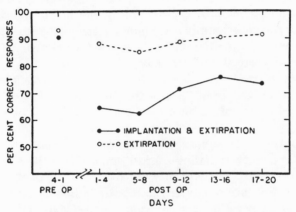

Fig. 4.—Effect on delayed-response performance of cobalt 60 implantation and subsequent cortical extirpation compared with effect of extirpation only.

It is quite obvious from the above experiment that the learning-loss syndrome is not dependent upon the existence of the necrotic tissue or any secondary effect resulting from it. Furthermore, in view of the relatively small amount of tissue involved and the fact that no tissue could have been necrotic for more than 4 or 5 hr., it seems unlikely that the existence of necrotic tissue prior to the extirpation was a significant factor in the production of the observed deficits.

There are theoretical reasons for doubting that the cortical irradiation syndrome is produced by the direct effect of gamma rays on the cortical centers essential for the regulation of the tested behaviors. If we place a cobalt needle on the surface of one prefrontal area, it is approximately 25 mm. distant from the contralateral prefrontal area and from 35 to 45 mm. distant from the ipsilateral and contralateral posterior temporal lobes. Because radiation dosage decreases as a function of the inverse square of the distance, a dose of 4,000 r. at 5 mm. from a radiating source placed on one prefrontal area should produce a dosage level of less than 200 r. on the contralateral prefrontal area and a dosage level of less than 100 r. and less than 50 r. on the ipsilateral and contralateral posterior temporal lobes, respectively. In view of the fact that total-body X-radiation dosages, including total head, of 400 r. have no effect on learned behaviors, it is hard to believe that our described syndrome results from inactivation of essential cortical centers by direct gamma irradiation.

Nevertheless, we ran a number of experiments designed to test the hypothesis of inactivation of essential centers through gamma rays. By placing cobalt needles 5 mm. from the cortex, tissue damage can be prevented or certainly minimized, and by increasing the number of needles, the amount of radiation can be systematically varied. One needle 5 mm. from a cortical surface delivers to the immediately subjacent cortex only a quarter of the dosage delivered by a needle placed at the surface, but at a distance of 25 mm. the ratio has shrunk to about 2 to 1, and at a distance of 35 to 45 mm. the difference in dose level is negligible.

Two monkeys were subjected to our standard dosage from each of two needles, with the radiating source 5 mm. above the surface of the prefrontal cortex, and subsequently tested on the standard test battery. Absolutely no evidence of any deficit appeared, the monkeys performing for 20 days at, or near, perfect performance levels on all tests. A single monkey was then subjected to the same procedures except that it was given the standard radiation dosage from each of four needles with the radiating surface 5 mm. from the left prefrontal area, and its subsequent performance on delayed-response, two-trial discrimination, and crossed-strings tests was equal or superior to that of any normal monkey ever tested. It is certain that the dosage level to the theoretically critical cortical centers in the contralateral hemisphere was higher in this animal than in any experimental monkey which suffered from the syndrome, and it is very certain that the total dosage delivered to the entire cortical surface or the entire cerebral mass was greater in this subject than in many animals demonstrating the cortical radiation syndrome.

Finally, we have already mentioned that 2,000-r. dosages delivered bilaterally at or near critical temporal centers produced no effect even though the dose level at these critical temporal centers must have been twenty-five or fifty times as great as the dosage level delivered to these centers from a single 4,000-r. source located in a prefrontal area.

It is entirely possible that the syndrome could be produced by edema, or increased cerebrospinal fluid pressure, or some other debilitating effect. In our preliminary experiments, when we subjected the animals to a bilateral dosage of 8,000 r. at 5 mm. from the needle, the animals showed obvious signs of debility, and by refusals to work gave evidence of motivational loss. In our first experiment we found our monkey prostrate on the cage floor on days 5 and 6 and presumed that it was near death. When taken off the cage floor to the test room, it made no balks for the first time since irradiation, and recovery of efficient delayed-response performance began. It is possible that this is to be attributed to the laying-on of hands or possibly the monkey was cheered by the obvious faith we demonstrated in it. At 4,000-r. dose levels delivered at the cortical surface, no motivational problem exists, and there are no behavioral signs indicating the existence of debilitating effects. The monkeys seem to be healthy and happy, and if I may be permitted to drift into neurological terminology, it appears that only their minds are missing.

We are still continuing the search for the causes of the peripatetic mentality. We have completed tests on a single monkey in which the *corpus callosum* was sectioned 20 days before the standard radiation dosage was given, the needle being placed on the surface of one prefrontal area. The results are presented in Figure 5, and they are different

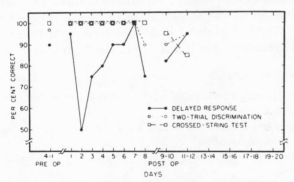

Fig. 5.—Effect of unilateral cobalt 60 implantation following callosal section.

from any results obtained to date. On the first postradiation day there was no loss on any test and no loss has ever appeared on two-trial discriminations or crossed-strings tests. Delayed-response performance dropped to chance on the second day, progressively improved, and probably returned to normal by the fifth day, a recovery more rapid than ever found in an animal radiated with the standard dosage and having its *corpus callosum* intact. The interpretation of the transient delayed-response loss is difficult because the collosal section itself produced drastic

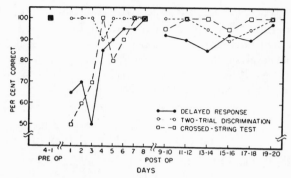

Fig. 6.—Effect of section of the *corpus callosum* on performance on the learning test battery.

delayed-response and string-test loss but no impairment whatsoever on the two-trial discriminations (see Fig. 6).

Regardless of the final outcome of these researches the experiment provides strong, presumptive evidence that commissural fibers and presumably the impulses conveyed over them play a very important role in the production of the cortical irradiation syndrome. In a day and age, and Symposium, in which the association and commissural fibers are described as if they had outlived their usefulness, it is cheering to find that they play some role even if it is that of the Devil instead of the saint.

REFERENCES

1 Adams, F. (Trans.) *The genuine works of Hippocrates.* London: C. and J. Polard, 1849. 2 vols.

2 ———. (Ed. and Trans.) *The extant works of Aretaeus, the Cappadocian.* London: Wertheimer, 1856.

3 ———. (Trans.) *The genuine works of Hippocrates.* Baltimore: Williams and Wilkins, 1939.

4 Baas, J. H. *Outlines of the history of medicine and the medical profession.* Translated by H. E. Handerson. New York: J. H. Vail, 1889.

5 Barrera, S. E., L. M. Kopeloff, and N. Kopeloff. Brain lesions associated with experimental "epileptiform" seizures in the monkey. *Amer. J. Psychiat.,* 1944, *100:* 727–37.

6 Beach, F. A., Jr. The neural basis of innate behavior: I. Effects of cortical lesions upon the maternal behavior pattern in the rat. *J. comp. Psychol.,* 1937, *24:* 393–40.

7 ———. The neural basis of innate behavior: II. Relative effects of partial decortication in adulthood and infancy upon the maternal behavior of the primiparous rat. *J. genet. Psychol.,* 1938, *53:* 109–48.

8 Brickner, R. M. *The intellectual functions of the frontal lobes.* New York: Macmillan, 1936.

9 Campbell, R. J., and H. F. Harlow. Problem solution by monkeys following bilateral removal of the prefrontal areas. V. Spatial delayed reactions. *J. exp. Psychol.,* 1945, *35:* 110–26.

10 Chow, K. L., and W. D. Obrist. EEG and behavioral changes on application of Al(OH)₃ cream on preoccipital cortex of monkeys. *A.M.A. Arch. Neurol. Psychiat.,* 1954, *72:* 80–87.

11 Fulton, J. F. *Physiology of the nervous system.* New York: Oxford Univer. Press, 1938.

12 Harlow, H. F. The formation of learning sets. *Psychol. Rev.,* 1949, *56:* 51–65.

13 ———. Functional organization of the brain in relation to mentation and behavior. In: *The biology of mental health and disease.* New York: Hoeber, 1952, pp. 244–64.

14 Hebb, D. O. *The organization of behavior.* New York: Wiley, 1949.

15 Lashley, K. S. *Brain mechanisms and intelligence.* Chicago: Univer. Chicago Press, 1929.

16 Mettler, C. C. *History of medicine.* Philadelphia: Blakiston, 1947.

17 Nichols, I. C., and J. McV. Hunt. A case of partial bilateral frontal lobectomy. *Amer. J. Psychiat.,* 1940, *96:* 1063–87.

18 Pribram, K. H. Some aspects of experimental psychosurgery: The effects of scarring frontal cortex on complex behavior. *Surg. Forum,* 1950, 315–18.

19 Riopelle, A. J., R. G. Alper, P. N. Strong, and H. W. Ades. Multiple discrimination and patterned string performance of normal and temporal-lobectomized monkeys. *J. comp. physiol. Psychol.,* 1953, *46:* 145–49.

20 Settlage, P. H., and G. Bogumill. Use of radioactive cobalt for the production of brain lesions in animals. *J. comp. physiol. Psychol.,* 1955, *48:* 208-10.

21 Stewart, J. W., and H. W. Ades. The time factor in reintegration of a learned habit lost after temporal lobe lesions in the monkey (*Macaca mulatta*). *J. comp. physiol. Psychol.,* 1951, *44:* 479–86.

22 Warren, J. M., and H. F. Harlow. Learned discrimination performance by monkeys after prolonged postoperative recovery from large cortical lesions. *J. comp. physiol. Psychol.,* 1952, *45:* 119–26.

Non-Specific Brain Mechanisms

Aided by grants from the Commonwealth Fund and the National Institute of Neurological Diseases and Blindness, United States Public Health Service.

Within recent years, interest in spinal reflexes or specifically sensory or motor systems of the brain has been extended to include study of relatively nonspecific neural mechanisms involved in functions previously receiving attention chiefly from investigators in psychology. As a result, boundaries between neurophysiology and psychology are in some areas commencing to lose sharp definition and increasingly to overlap. One program in this development has utilized electrical recording techniques to examine features of the brain's activity during arousal to wakefulness or alerting to attention.

ASCENDING RETICULAR SYSTEM AND WAKEFULNESS

This work began with the chance observation that direct stimulation of the central reticular core of the brain stem (Plate 4) reproduced those alterations in cortical electrical activity encountered in awakening from sleep or alerting to attention (Plate 6), in which patterns of high voltage, slow waves, and spindle bursts in the EEG become replaced by low-voltage fast discharge (41). This evoked electrocortical alteration was manifest over wide areas of the hemisphere, being most pronounced and persisting longest in frontal regions. It was mediated by diffusely distributed ascending connections, some of which appeared to reach the cortex through relays in the nonspecific thalamic nuclei, while the remainder traversed extra-thalamic routes through the subthalamus and internal capsule.

The functional significance of this ascending reticular system for behavior was tested by exciting it through chronically implanted electrodes in naturally sleeping animals (Fig. 10 and Plate 9), with consequent behavioral awakening or arousal (42). Conversely, the production of large experimental lesions in its cephalic portion resulted in chronic loss of wakefulness, the animals appearing as though asleep, anesthetized, or comatose for as long as they could be nursed to survival (Plate 5). Serial EEGs of monkeys with such central cephalic lesions of the brain stem were of the coma or stupor type and, though classical afferent paths to the cortex were intact and viable, peripheral stimulation of the most vigorous sort was no longer capable of evoking generalized EEG or behavioral arousal (8, 9, 10, 11).

This latter observation suggested that the arousing properties of afferent stimulation might be mediated by collateral connections from direct lemniscal paths, turning into the ascending reticular system in the brain stem (Fig. 7 and Plate 7). In preparations without central anesthesia, potentials evoked by somatic and auditory stimulation could be recorded widely through the central brain stem, and further exploration has shown that all sensory modalities make such collateral reticular

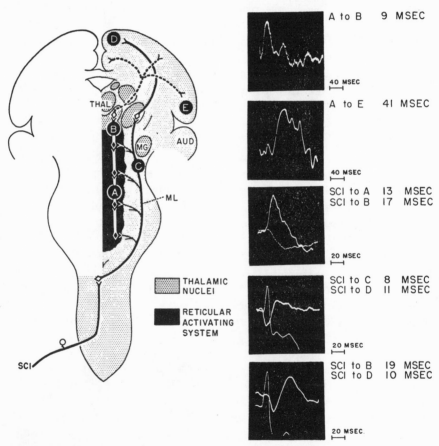

Fig. 7.—Diagram showing somatic afferent path making collateral connections with ascending reticular system (black) in brain stem, with potentials evoked and recorded at labeled sites with latencies indicated. From French, Verzeano, and Magoun (9).

connections. While early work emphasized the long latency, wave-like form, and prolonged recovery time of these evoked potentials, together with the interaction of discharge initiated from various peripheral sources, more recent study suggests that several component types may be differentiated. By direct test, these extralemniscal connections with the reticular formation can be shown to mediate generalized EEG arousal, though this change may also be induced in the circumscribed sensory regions of the cortex by excitation of each of the classical afferent paths (27).

Unit analysis of excitation induced in the ascending reticular system by single afferent shocks (Fig. 8) has revealed a complex cycle of repeti-

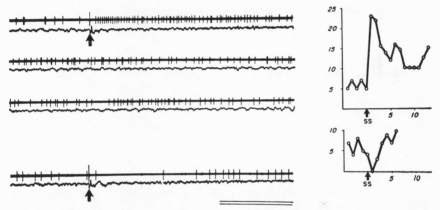

Fig. 8.—Unit activity in central cephalic brain stem (upper) and cortical EEG (lower beam) upon single-shock sciatic stimuli. Graphs show spikes per second (vertical) and time in seconds (horizontal). From Machne, Calma, and Magoun (32).

tive discharge associated with the evoked potential, subsequent increased frequency of firing, or a reduction of spontaneous activity (32). Most commonly, brief repetitive afferent stimulation led to prolonged increased frequency of unit firing, to rates of 30-60/sec, together with the recruitment of previously silent units (Plate 8).

CORTICIFUGAL PROJECTIONS TO CENTRAL BRAIN STEM

An ascending reticular system subserving arousal or attention would seem likely to receive inflows from central as well as peripheral sources. Corticifugal projections to the central brain stem have been demonstrated both by Jasper and his associates (26) and by Bremer and Terzuolo (4). Further investigation by French, Hernández-Peón, and Livingston (7) has shown that associational areas of frontal, cingulate, pari-

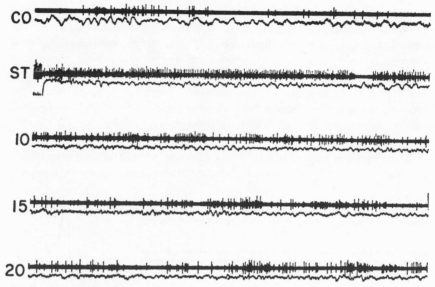

Fig. 9.—Unit activity in central cephalic brain stem (upper) and cortical EEG (lower beam) before (*CO*), at the conclusion of repetitive sciatic stimulation (*ST*), and 10, 15, and 20 sec. later. From Machne, Calma, and Magoun (32).

eto-occipital, and temporal cortex, as well as sensory and motor regions, project diffusely to common portions of the central cephalic brain stem (Fig. 9). Considerable overlap exists in these projections, and interaction of discharge initiated from different parts of the cortex, and from peripheral sources as well, can readily be demonstrated (22). More focal facilitation or inhibition of reticular transmission can be observed, however (1). When conditions are appropriate for its testing, generalized EEG arousal can be induced by stimulating certain of these cortical areas (Fig. 10), in particular, those of the temporal lobe (44).

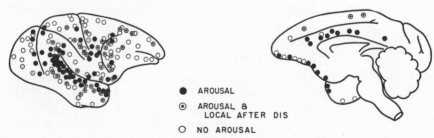

1   10.—Lateral and medial views of monkey's cortex with symbols indicating sites whose stimulation evoked EEG arousal. From Segundo, Naquet, and Buser (44).

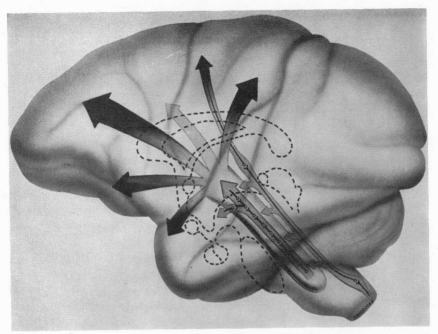

Plate 4.—View of monkey brain showing ascending reticular system receiving collaterals from somatic afferent pathway in the brain stem and projecting diffusely to the cortex. From Magoun (38).

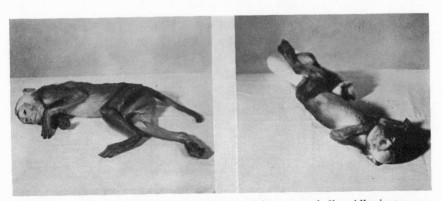

Plate 5.—Photographs of monkey with extensive injury to cephalic midbrain tegmentum. From French and Magoun (8).

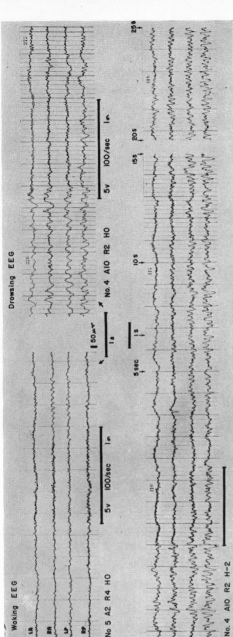

Plate 6.—Effect of stimulating ascending reticular system (signal) upon electrocorticogram of monkey under local anesthesia and syncurine. From French, von Amerongen, and Magoun (11).

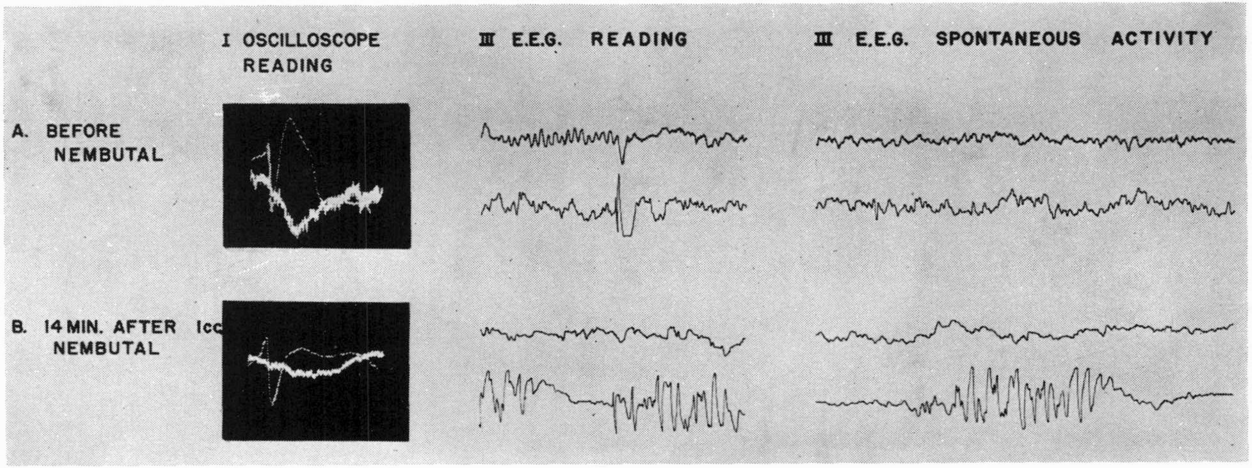

Plate 7.—Oscilloscopic and ink-written records showing effect of barbiturate anesthesia upon potentials evoked in the central brain stem (heavy beam and upper EEG trace) and somatic cortex (light beam and lower EEG trace) by single sciatic shocks. From French, Verzeano, and Magoun (10).

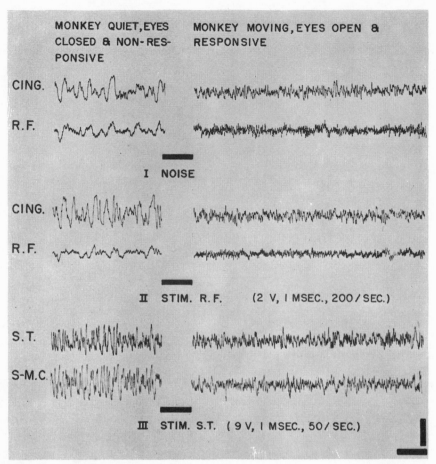

Plate 8.—Behavioral and EEG arousal by noise (I), brain-stem (II), and cortical (III) stimulation. Abbreviations are: *CING,* cingulate gyrus; *RF,* central cephalic brain stem; *ST,* superior temporal gyrus; *SMC,* sensorimortor cortex. From Segundo, Arana, and French (42).

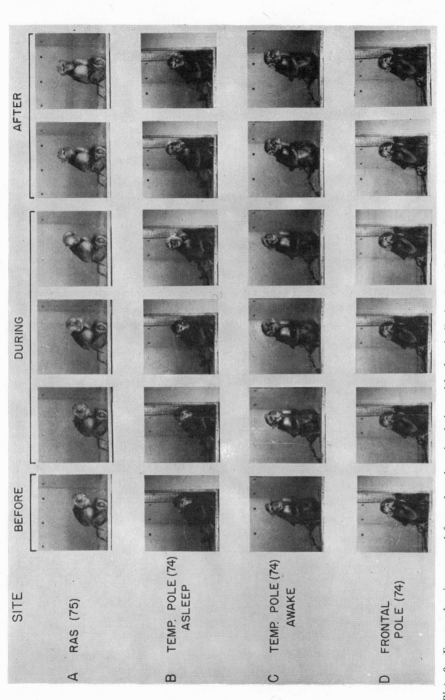

Plate 9.—Frames showing arousal from sleep by stimulation with chronically implanted electrodes. Horizontal strips show monkey before, during, and after stimulating: *A*, central cephalic brain stem; *B*, temporal pole while asleep; *C*, temporal pole while awake; and *D*, frontal pole, which fails to awaken animal. From Segundo, Arana, and French (42).

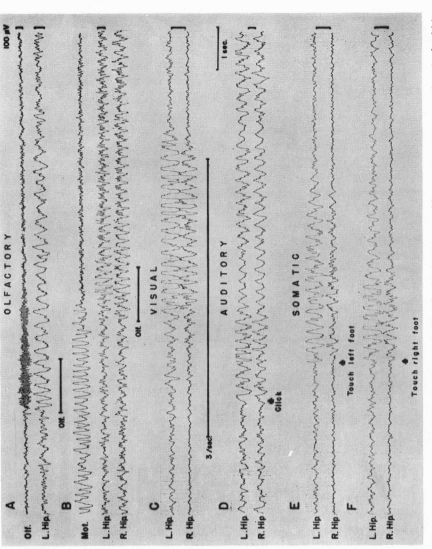

Plate 10.—Electrical activity of olfactory bulb (*olf.*), hippocampus (*hip.*), and motor cortex (*mot.*) of rabbit, showing alterations induced by arousing stimuli (signal) of several modalities. From Green and Arduini (17).

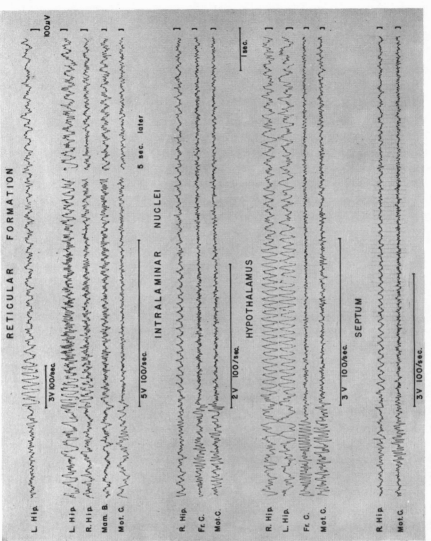

Plate 11.—Electrical activity of hippocampus (*hip.*), mammillary body (*mam.*) and motor (*mot.*) or frontal (*fr.*) cortex of rabbit, showing alterations induced by stimulation (signal) of brain-stem areas indicated. From Green and Arduini (17).

With the use of chronically implanted electrodes, stimulating these cortical areas in naturally sleeping monkeys evoked behavioral awakening (Plate 9). Their stimulation in the waking monkey caused it to behave as though confronted with an alerting or alarming situation. Exciting the somatic or visual sensory cortex in the wide-awake animal induced behavior suggesting the experience of subjective impressions. The same or far more intense stimuli applied to these functionally specific areas during sleep were, by contrast, devoid of any obvious consequence. It would appear, therefore, that excitation of cortical sensory areas is not by itself sufficient either to induce arousal or to cause sensation. For the latter to occur, a simultaneous background of wakefulness appears indispensable (42).

CENTRAL INFLUENCES ON AFFERENT TRANSMISSION

From the classical studies of Adrian and others, it is clear that variations in the frequency of receptor discharge signal intensity of afferent stimulation and, if such stimulation is maintained, accommodation. Transmission of afferent impulses from receptors to receiving areas of the cortex has been conceived as stereotyped, however, and little subject to central neural influences. Demonstrations by Granit and Kaada (14) of pronounced centrifugal effects upon afferent discharge from the muscle spindle, led Hagbarth and Kerr (21) to explore the effect of excitation of the brain-stem reticular formation, or of cortical or cerebellar regions projecting to it, upon somatic afferent transmission at the first central relay in the spinal cord. A pronounced reduction of amplitude of afferent potentials was encountered (Fig. 11), and similar inhibitory influences upon transmission have since been observed in the olfactory bulb (28) and in the posterior column nuclei, nucleus of the spinal fifth tract, and dorsal cochlear nucleus (24). Except in the retina, where Granit (12) has observed potentiation, nonspecific influences thus seem generally capable of reducing afferent transmission at the first central relay, and this influence is evidently a tonic one, for enhancement of evoked afferent discharge at these sites follows central brain stem injury or anesthesia (Fig. 12).

In addition to lower relays in the neuraxis, transmission in each of the classical afferent pathways (except the olfactory one) has the common feature of relay to the cortex by a specific thalamic nucleus. By contrast with lower stations, reticular influences upon thalamic transmission in the somatic pathway led to more pronounced alterations in temporal features than in amplitude (30). Reticular stimulation induced abbreviation of latency, as well as duration of discharge and recovery time, to-

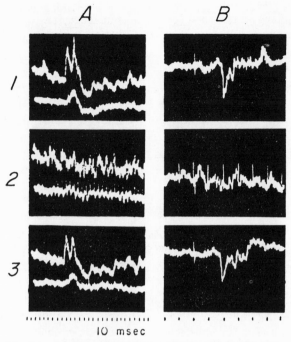

Fig. 11.—*A*, effect of stimulating sensory cortex (2) upon an afferent volley evoked at lumbar dorsal root and recorded from ventral column of cord (upper) and midbrain (lower beam). *B*, an afferent response recorded from cerebellar vermis depressed by similar stimulation (2). From Hagbarth and Kerr (21).

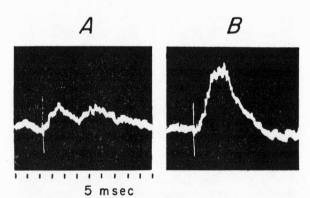

Fig. 12.—Effect of high cord section upon ventral column response to lumbar dorsal root stimulus. *A*, before, and *B*, 1 hr. after transection. From Hagbarth and Kerr (21).

gether with obliteration of facilitatory periods in the recovery cycle, the latter raising some question of the importance in alert wakefulness of the 10/sec excitability cycle which augments in-phase afferent signals during anesthesia (6).

While the functional significance of these novel observations will require much further study, it appears that they may contribute to understanding of the mechanisms of focus of attention and habituation. With chronically implanted electrode techniques, Hernández-Peón, Scherrer, and Jouvet (25) have observed that discharge evoked in the dorsal cochlear nucleus of the cat by serially repeated clicks becomes markedly reduced in amplitude during an interval when the animal's attention is attracted by visual or olfactory stimulation. If nonspecific influences are involved in this effect, they may provide a means by which the brain is able to exclude irrelevant afferent information during the focus of attention.

Possibly allied to this is a type of learning called "habituation," by which the brain ultimately ceases to attend to monotonously repeated, afferent information. Nonspecific brain mechanisms have been shown to be involved by Sharpless and Jasper (45), and Hernández-Peón and Scherrer (23) have found that reduction in evoked potentials at the dorsal cochlear nucleus, associated with habituation to repeated clicks, is reversed by central brain-stem lesions or anesthesia. These latter categories of experimentation particularly emphasize the great desirability of increasing the scope of interdisciplinary research in the field between neurophysiology and physiological psychology.

SUBCORTICAL RELATIONS WITH RHINENCEPHALIC STRUCTURES

Antedating the cerebral development of the neocortex was the phylogenetically old establishment of the paleocortical hippocampus, which, with its basal ganglion, the amygdala, served as the highest forebrain mechanism regulating subcortical function (Fig. 13).

The work of Green and Arduini (17) has shown that when electrical patterns of the neocortex and hippocampus are recorded simultaneously in the rabbit, the two often exhibit inverse relationships, fast discharge in the neocorticogram being associated with large, slow-wave activity in the hippocampus and vice versa. The contrasting patterns of spontaneous activity in these two parts of the forebrain are more striking still during arousal to afferent stimulation (Plate 10). Neocortical desynchronization is invariably accompanied in the hippocampus by a train of sinusoidal slow waves of large amplitude and 3-6/sec rhythm. This response

POSSIBLE PATHWAYS IN HIPPOCAMPAL
AROUSAL   REACTION

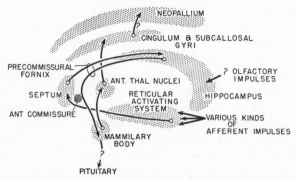

Fig. 13.—Diagram showing possible pathways in hippocampal arousal. From Green and Arduini (17).

is generalized in the hippocampus and identical for all modalities of stimulation. It is obtained most readily in the rabbit, is often partially obscured by fast activity in the cat, and is difficult to observe at all in the monkey.

Like that of the neocortical EEG, this hippocampal arousal pattern can readily be evoked by direct stimulation of the central cephalic brain stem, as well as by excitation of the preoptic region and septum (Plate 11). It appears to be mediated by a cephalic projection of the ascending reticular system directed through the dorsal fornix to the hippocampus. The slow-wave discharge is reflected centrifugally through the fornix proper and can be recorded from the mammillary body, the mammillo-thalamic tract, and, with wide pickups, from areas of the neocortex.

Functional relationships between the hippocampus and entorhinal area are greatly in need of study as potentially direct links between paleo- and neocortex. Recent observations by Carreras *et al.* (5) indicate that delimited ablation of the entorhinal cortex in the rabbit converts the slow-wave pattern of hippocampal arousal to low-voltage fast discharge like that of the neocortex. Green and Arduini (17) earlier concluded that the hippocampal arousal pattern was uninfluenced by total decortication, however, and more recent study has not revealed specific influences of entorhinal ablations upon it.

The high-frequency electrical activity of the deep-lying nuclear masses of the amygdala is relatively imperturbable and shows no conspicuous alteration with EEG changes between relaxation and arousal (2).

Afferent or central brain-stem stimulation fails to evoke clear-cut changes, but prolonged increase in the rate of unit-firing can be observed with microelectrode recording (33). It would appear that the amygdala may secondarily be subject to afferent or central influences through the hippocampus (16) or neocortex of the superior gyrus and tip of the temporal lobe (43).

As observed with electrical recording techniques, experimentally induced amygdaloid seizures propagate most conspicuously to the basal forebrain and cephalic brain stem. Such seizures propagate also to the hippocampus and to the temporal cortex outside the auditory area. Striking, indeed, is their failure to involve the large remainder of the cerebral cortex (2). At present the amygdala would appear potentially able to command somatic, visceral, and endocrine regulating mechanisms of the cephalic brain stem and to be itself subject to influence both by the hippocampus and temporal cortex.

SUMMARY

From a number of recent studies, conceptions of brain organization have been enlarged by identification of nonspecific neural mechanisms lying between the sensory and motor systems of classical neurophysiology and richly interconnected with them. Reciprocal ascending and descending connections between these nonspecific neural mechanisms in the brain stem and wide areas of the hemispheres, including both neo- and paleocortex, are involved in arousal to wakefulness and alerting to attention. Further study of these nonspecific neural mechanisms may be expected to be rewarding in relating brain organization and behavior.

REFERENCES

In an effort to limit the bibliography, reference has been made primarily to papers from this laboratory. Most of these contain extensive references to related work by others.

1　Adey, R. W., R. B. Livingston, and J. P. Segundo. Corticifugal influences on intrinsic brain stem induction in the cat and monkey. *J. Neurophysiol.*, 1957, *20:* 1–16.

2　Arana-Iníguez, R., D. J. Reis, R. Naquet, and H. W. Magoun. Propagation of amygdaloid seizures. *Acta Neurol. Latino-Amer.*, 1955, *1:* 109–22.

3　Arduini, A., and M. G. Arduini. Effect of drugs and metabolic alterations on brain stem arousal mechanism. *J. Pharmachol.*, 1954, *110:* 76–85.

4　Bremer, F., and C. Terzuolo. Nouvelles recherches sur le processus physiologique du réveil. *Arch. int. Physiol.*, 1953, *61:* 86–90.

5　Carreras, M., G. Macchi, F. Angeleri, and M. Urbani. Sull' attività elettrica

34   H. W. Magoun

della formazione Ammonica. Effetti determinati dall'ablazione della corteccia entorinale. *Boll. Soc. ital. Biol. sper.,* 1955, *31:* sep.

6   Chang, H. -T. The repetitive discharges of corticothalamic reverberating circuit. *J. Neurophysiol.,* 1950, *13:* 235–58.

7   French, J. D., R. Hernández-Peón, and R. B. Livingston. Projections from cortex to cephalic brain stem (reticular formation) in monkey. *J. Neurophysiol.,* 1955, *18:* 74–95.

8   French, J. D., and H. W. Magoun. Effects of chronic lesions in central cephalic brain stem of monkeys. *Arch. Neurol. Psychiat., Chicago,* 1952, *68:* 591–604.

9   French, J. D., M. Verzeano, and H. W. Magoun. An extralemniscal sensory system in the brain. *Arch. Neurol. Psychiat., Chicago,* 1953, *69:* 505–18.

10 ———. A neural basis of the anesthetic state. *Arch. Neurol. Psychiat., Chicago,* 1953, *69:* 519–29.

11 French, J. D., F. K. von Amerongen, and H. W. Magoun. An activating system in brain stem of monkey. *Arch. Neurol. Psychiat., Chicago,* 1952, *68:* 577–90.

12 Granit, R. Centrifugal and antidromic effects on ganglion cells of retina. *J. Neurophysiol.,* 1955, *18:* 388–411.

13 ———. *Receptors and sensory perception.* New Haven: Yale Univer. Press, 1955.

14 Granit, R., and B. R. Kaada. Influence of stimulation of central nervous structures on muscle spindles in cat. *Acta physiol. scand.,* 1952, *27:* 130–60.

15 Green, J. D. Neural pathways to the hypophysis. Chap. I in *Hypothalamic-hypophysical interrelations.* Springfield, Ill.: Charles C Thomas, 1956.

16 Green, J. D., and W. R. Adey. Electrophysiological studies of hippocampal connections and excitability. *Electroenceph. clin. Neurophysiol.,* 1956, *8:* 245–63.

17 Green, J. D., and A. A. Arduini. Hippocampal electrical activity in arousal. *J. Neurophysiol.,* 1954, *17:* 533–57.

18 Green, J. D., and X. Machne. Unit activity of rabbit hippocampus. *Amer. J. Physiol.,* 1955, *181:* 219–24.

19 Green, J. D., and T. Shimamoto. Hippocampal seizures and their propagation. *Arch. Neurol. Psychiat., Chicago,* 1953, *70:* 687–702.

20 Gunn, C. G., S. Eliasson, and J. D. French. Cortical projections to the septum. *Fed. Proc.,* 1955, *14:* 66 (Abstract).

21 Hagbarth, K. -E., and D. I. B. Kerr. Central influences on spinal afferent conduction. *J. Neurophysiol.,* 1954, *17:* 295–307.

22 Hernández-Peón, R., and K. -E. Hagbarth. Interaction between afferent and cortically induced reticular responses. *J. Neurophysiol.,* 1955, *18:* 44–55.

23 Hernández-Peón, R., and H. Scherrer. "Habituation" to acoustic stimuli in cochlear nucleus. *Fed. Proc.,* 1955, *14:* 71 (Abstract).

24 ———. Inhibitory influence of brain stem reticular formation upon synaptic transmission in trigeminal nucleus. *Fed. Proc.,* 1955, *14:* 71 (Abstract).

25 Hernández-Peón, R., H. Scherrer, and M. Jouvet. Modification of electric activity in cochlear nucleus during attention in unanesthetized cats. *Science,* 1956, *123:* 331–32.

26 Jasper, H., C. Ajmone-Marsan, and J. Stoll. Corticofugal projections to the brain stem. *Arch. Neurol. Psychiat., Chicago,* 1952, *67:* 155–71.

27 Jasper, H., R. Naquet, and E. E. King. Thalamocortical recruiting responses in sensory receiving areas in the cat. *Electroenceph. clin. Neurophysiol.,* 1955, *7:* 99–114.

28 Kerr, D. I. B., and K. -E. Hagbarth. An investigation of olfactory centrifugal fiber system. *J. Neurophysiol.,* 1955, *18:* 362–74.

29 King, E. E. Differential action of anesthetics and interneuron depressants upon EEG arousal and recruitment responses. *J. Pharmacol.,* 1956, *116:* 404–17.

30 King, E. E., R. Naquet, and H. W. Magoun. Alterations in somatic afferent transmission through the thalamus by central mechanisms and barbiturates. *J. Pharmacol.,* 1957, *119:* 48–63.

31 Lindsley, D. B., L. H. Schreiner, W. B. Knowles, and H. W. Magoun. Behavioral and EEG changes following chronic brain stem lesions in the cat. *Electroenceph. clin. Neurophysiol.,* 1950, *2:* 483–98.

32 Machne, X., I. Calma, and H. W. Magoun. Unit activity of central cephalic brain stem in EEG arousal. *J. Neurophysiol.,* 1955, *18:* 547–58.

33 Machne, X., and J. P. Segundo. Unit activity in the amygdaloid complex of the cat. *Fed. Proc.,* 1955, *14:* 96 (Abstract).

34 Magoun, H. W. Caudal and cephalic influences of the brain stem reticular formation. *Physiol. Rev.,* 1950, *30:* 459–74.

35 ———. The ascending reticular activating system. *Res. Publ. Ass. nerv. ment. Dis.,* 1952, *30:* 480–92.

36 ———. An ascending reticular activating system in the brain stem. *Harvey Lect.* Ser. 47, 1951–52. New York: Academic Press, 1953, p. 53–71.

37 ———. Physiological interrelationships between cortex and subcortical structures. *Electroenceph. clin. Neurophysiol.,* 1953, Suppl. No. 4, 163–67.

38 ———. The ascending reticular system and wakefulness. In J. F. Delafresnaye (Ed.), *Brain mechanism and consciousness.* Oxford: Blackwell, 1954, p. 1–20.

39 ———. A neural basis for the anesthetic state. In *Symposium on sedative and hypnotic drugs.* Baltimore: Williams and Wilkins, 1954, p. 1–19.

40 ———. Ascending reticular system and anesthesia. *Neuropharmacology:* transactions of the first conference, 1955, *1:* 145–61.

41 Moruzzi, G., and H. W. Magoun. Brain stem reticular formation and activation of the EEG. *Electroenceph. clin. Neurophysiol.,* 1949, *1:* 455–73.

42 Segundo, J. P., R. Arana, and J. D. French. Behavioral arousal by stimulation of the brain in the monkey. *J. Neurosurg.,* 1955, *12:* 601–13.

43 Segundo, J. P., R. Naquet, and R. Arana. Subcortical connections from temporal cortex of monkey. *Arch. Neurol. Psychiat. Chicago,* 1955, *73:* 515–24.

44 Segundo, J. P., R. Naquet, and P. Buser. Effects of cortical stimulation on electrocortical activity in monkeys. *J. Neurophysiol.*, 1955, *18*: 236–45.

45 Sharpless, S., and H. H. Jasper. Habituation of the arousal reaction. *Brain*, 1956, *79*: 655–80.

46 Shimamoto, T., and M. Verzeano. Relations between caudate and diffusely projecting thalamic nuclei. *J. Neurophysiol.*, 1954, *17*: 278–88.

47 Starzl, T. E., and H. W. Magoun. Organization of the diffuse thalamic projection system. *J. Neurophysiol.*, 1951, *14*: 133–46.

48 Starzl, T. E., C. W. Taylor, and H. W. Magoun. Ascending conduction in reticular activating system, with special reference to the diencephalon. *J. Neurophysiol.*, 1951, *14*: 461–77.

49 ———. Collateral afferent excitation of reticular formation of brain stem. *J. Neurophysiol.*, 1951, *14*: 479–96.

50 Starzl, T. E., and D. G. Whitlock. Diffuse thalamic projection system in the monkey. *J. Neurophysiol.*, 1952, *15*: 449–68.

Reticular-Cortical Systems and Theories
of the Integrative Action of the Brain

Neurophysiological studies of the so-called "unspecific" projection systems interconnecting the cerebral cortex with the diencephalon and brain stem have provided some new principles for theories of the integrative action of the brain. The broad functional significance of these findings in the attempt to understand the neurophysiological basis of mental processes and behavior requires closely coördinated research in experimental psychology and neurophysiology as sponsored by this Symposium.

The need for new conceptions of brain function, as opposed to the old reflex-circuit or chain-association theories, was forcefully brought out in a previous symposium of this nature (14). Reflex theories of the integrative action of the nervous system, from Sherrington's classical treatise to the most recent elaboration of dynamic reverberating circuit theories developed by McCulloch (14) must still be considered an essential basic structure of the mechanisms of at least the more automatic types of behavior. However, a simple pyramiding mosaic of interacting specific reflexes does not provide a good working model of the integrative action of the brain as a whole. Lashley has given an excellent critique of this point of view with alternative suggestions providing a more dynamic theory of many simultaneously and constantly interacting systems but still without making use of the functional properties of the reticular system. Most important for the present discussion is Lashley's conclusion that "every bit of evidence available indicates a dynamic, constantly active system, or, rather a composite of many interacting systems. . . . Only when methods of analysis of such systems have been devised will there be progress toward understanding of the physiology of the cerebral cortex" (14, p. 135).

Reference should perhaps be made as well to a more recent symposium, the Laurentian Conference (4), in which Dr. Lashley also took part. Here it was attempted to bring evidence from psychology, neurophysiology, neuroanatomy, neurosurgery, psychiatry, and electroencephalography to bear upon the problem of the functional significance of the brain stem reticular system in conscious mental processes. A wealth of new data was presented, but divergent viewpoints were expressed with regard to its interpretation.

ANATOMICAL CONSIDERATIONS

Neurophysiologists concerned with functional properties of the central nervous system are very much dependent upon neuroanatomy for a firm basis for their investigations. One can hardly speak of this association as an "interdisciplinary coöperation" any more. As a matter of fact, the leading anatomists today seem to be among our best neurophysiologists, and some neurophysiologists are leaders in neuroanatomical investigation.

Anatomists have long known that the reticular system must have rather unusual properties in view of the many collateral connections with the principal sensory and motor pathways.

Ramón y Cajal has described it (22, p. 958), and although it is not necessary to quote him it should be noted that Cajal recognized that all parts of the reticular system did not have the same function since there were different connections with different parts.

Of particular interest is a little-known paper on the reticular system, published in an obscure journal in 1932 (2), by the late Professor William F. Allen, former head of the Department of Anatomy of the University of Oregon Medical School. The opening paragraph of this paper bears quotation.

It is known from embryology that most of the left over cells of the brain stem and spinal cord which are not concerned in the formation of motor root nuclei and purely sensory relay nuclei are utilized in the production of the formatio reticularis. This is a very old structure phylogenetically. It is but little differentiated in the lower vertebrates, where it apparently serves as an effective mechanism which enables these animals to adapt themselves properly to their various inside and outside conditions. In the higher vertebrates there is but little reticular formation in the spinal cord, but considerable in both the median and lateral portions of the medulla, pons and midbrain, where for the most part it exists anatomically in its original undifferentiated state. Reticular formation surrounds or partially surrounds the sensory nuclei of the thalamus, and when considered phylogenetically the nucleus ruber, substantia nigra and other differentiated hypothalamic and midbrain nuclei should probably be considered as specialized derivatives (p. 490).

Professor Allen then goes on to describe the many collaterals from the principal sensory and motor pathways and including the *brachium conjunctivum,* as well as collaterals from corticofugal pathways which apparently end in the reticular formation. He makes the remarkable prediction that, in view of the many afferent connections to the *formatio reticularis* from the cerebrum, from the colliculi, *corpora striata,* and especially the diverse and extensive connections from the cerebellum, it would seem that considerable portions of the *formatio reticularis* function as efferent centers for tonic impulses. "It may be that there are separate areas for inhibition as well as for augmentation. . . . The extensive distribution of the reticular formation through the brain stem and spinal cord may be used to good advantage in the summation and recruitment phenomena" (p. 494). Professor Allen, therefore, had foreseen much of the eventual significance of the reticular system which was demonstrated later by Professor Magoun and his colleagues.

One might say, in a general way, therefore, that the reticular formation, extending from the thalamus down into the medulla, is represented by all those neuronal structures which are not included in the specific afferent and efferent pathways. This is a rather loose definition, for there are many structures which are not part of known afferent or efferent pathways and yet which one would not like to include in the reticular system, such as, for example, the pulvinar and *n. medialis dorsalis* of the thalamus. Further discussion of the so-called association systems as intermediate between the specific and the unspecific projection systems will be described later.

The reticular system is not truly an anatomical entity from the morphological standpoint. This was pointed out in detail by Olszewski in a recent discussion of the cytoarchitecture of the human reticular formation, in which he describes many distinguishable nuclei in the brain stem throughout what is functionally the reticular system (21, p. 54). Olszewski believes that the use of the term reticular formation is probably ill-advised for, from an anatomical point of view, it seems to be composed of many nuclei of different structure and, therefore, probably of different function. It may be wise, therefore, for neurophysiologists to be constantly alert to possible functional differences between the different parts of the reticular system which can be distinguished by cytoarchitectural methods.

The conception of Professor Allen, based upon a more comprehensive view of neural pathways and connections, rather than upon detailed cytoarchitectural morphology, corresponds more closely with the reticular system identified by electrophysiological methods. It is of particular interest that Professor Allen recognized the homology of the intralaminar and reticular nuclei of the thalamus with the more commonly recognized reticular system of the lower brain stem as a part of a continuous system extending throughout the entire central core of the neuraxis. This does

not imply that different parts of the system do not have specialized properties as well as common functional characteristics. Much of the detailed
fine organization within the system has yet to be worked out from both
anatomical and physiological points of view.

Detailed neuroanatomical studies of the thalamic reticular system have
been recently pursued by Rose (25), Droogleever-Fortuyn (5), Nauta and
Whitlock (20), and by Nashold (19). In the last-mentioned study it was
shown that there were definite retrograde degenerative changes in the
intralaminar nuclei of the thalamus following complete decortication,
but that these changes did not follow the same pattern as those for specific nuclei. Complete degeneration occurred only when sectioning the
anterior limb of the internal capsule, just ventromedial to the caudate
nucleus. This confirms the previous neurophysiological studies showing
that the principal rostral pathway of the recruiting system of the thalamus passes in this vicinity.

It is proposed by Nashold and Olszewski that the reason for the lack
of complete degeneration with cortical excisions is due to the presence
of collaterals in this system, some of which go to subcortical structures.
This is shown in the diagram borrowed from Nashold's thesis (Fig. 14).

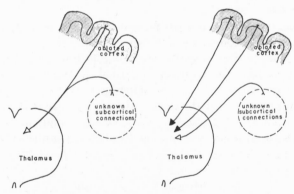

Fig. 14.—Diagrammatic representation of arrangement of
thalamocortical projection fibers which might explain
partial retrograde degeneration as seen in the intralami-
nal regions of the thalamus following restricted excision
of the neocortex. To the left is shown a neurone with a
collateral to a subcortical structure which may preserve
it from complete degeneration following cortical excision
alone. An alternative explanation would be that some
neurones project only to subcortical structures while others
project only to the cortex, as shown at the right. From
Nashold (19).

This may well explain some of the discrepancy in previous results, since it seems that projections from the thalamus to the cortex over the diffuse projection system are more likely to have important collaterals than are the simple, direct projections from the sensory relay nuclei, for example. The course of the pathways of the thalamic reticular system from the rostral *centrum medianum* through the mesial portion of the thalamus, passing into the wings of the intralaminar nuclei and into *ventralis anterior* and *nucleus reticularis,* have now been confirmed in both electrographic and anatomical studies.

The work of Nauta and Whitlock with the special silver method is of particular importance in this connection. There remains some doubt, however, as to how the unspecific fibers from the thalamus reach all parts of the cortex, since this was not clear in Nauta's studies and has not been adequately worked out in studies of retrograde degeneration. The most likely assumption now is that they are distributed with a predominance of rostrally oriented fibers through the anterior pole of the thalamus but passing laterally for the posteriorly directed fibers into the *nucleus reticularis* and then back to join the specific projections to the parietal and temporal occipital areas of the cortex. This would fit the electrographic studies of Hanbery, Marsan, and Dilworth (7), as well as the more recent studies of Jasper, Naquet, and King (12).

From available evidence it seems now to be well established that the projections from the thalamus to the cortex of the reticular system are at least partially independent of the specific projection fibers and pass over a different route all the way to the cortex. This does not rule out the possibility that the intralaminar thalamic system also acts as an intra-thalamic association system, interconnecting the specific nuclei within the thalamus as well. The work of Nauta would certainly suggest that this is true, and some electrophysiological evidence would also suggest it, especially with regard to the association nuclei, *medialis dorsalis,* and *pulvinar.*

EVIDENCE FROM HUMAN ELECTROENCEPHALOGRAPHY

Since it was largely observations of the changes in electrical activity of the human brain in response to sensory stimulation and in various states of consciousness which led to the conception of an ascending reticular system controlling cortical activity, it may be well to review some of the evidence which has been obtained in man before citing experimental observations in animals.

It was Hans Berger, commonly known as the father of electroencephalography, who first pointed out that the electrical activity of the cortex as a whole is altered by sensory stimuli in the awaking human brain. It was immediately apparent that significant responses of the brain to sensory stimuli are far more complex than the simple projection of afferent impulses upon the appropriate sensory receiving areas of the cortex. In fact, the arrival of volleys of afferent impulses to local sensory receiving areas is hardly detectable in the background of continuous electrical activity constantly observed from the human cerebral cortex. The most obvious and significant changes in the electrical activity of the human cortex occur not necessarily with specific sensory stimuli, but are dependent upon the meaning of these stimuli to the subject.

Berger was quick to recognize that the changes he observed seemed more closely related to attention to stimulus situations, rather than to the nature or intensity of the stimulus as such. This was equivalent to saying that it was the arousal value or attention value of the stimulus which determined whether or not it would produce a significant alteration in the electrical activity of the cortex in man. This was manifest in the now familiar arrest of the 10/sec alpha rhythm of the brain with attention or alerting of the subject. Berger thought that this blocking or arrest of the alpha rhythm represented an inhibitory process involving large areas of the cortex so that the focusing of attention could be more easily directed toward one small area containing the functional circuits needed for a given attentive process.

The relationship between the alpha rhythm in man and processes of attention was soon confirmed in the experiments of Adrian and Mathews. In these classical pioneer studies it was shown that, although visual stimuli seemed to be effective in arresting the occipital alpha rhythm, it was the attention to visual processes that was the critical factor in this arrest of the alpha rhythm.

It will be recalled that Adrian showed that shifting the attention from a visual to an auditory stimulus caused the alpha rhythm to return in the occipital region. It was also shown that attempting to see in a totally darkened room was almost as effective as actual visual stimulus in producing the arrest of the occipital alpha rhythm. This suggests a certain direction of the attending process from one functional system in the cortex to another.

The necessary conclusions which must be drawn from these observations of the reaction of the human alpha rhythm were clearly expressed in Adrian's Waynflete Lectures (1).

The alpha rhythm may be regarded, therefore, as associated with the inattentive state and as occurring in regions of the brain which are playing no part in mental activity because attention is directed elsewhere. . . . The onset of the rhythm seems to be determined by some central influence, and the direction of attention seems to be determined also by a balancing of claims which must take place in some central region to decide which part of the cortex shall be set free from the alpha rhythm for the use of the mind. . . . The mechanism which determines whether we can be conscious, with the power of directing our attention and analyzing the sensory messages, or whether we are asleep or stunned, involves some part of this central brain stem region . . . though the control is not due to an isolated group of nerve cells and the whole mechanism certainly involves both the cortex and the optic thalamus as well as the brain stem (pp. 76–78).

Curiously, Adrian did not mention at this time the previously published experiments of Morison and Dempsey (17) on the control of the alpha rhythm by electrical stimulation of the intralaminar system of the thalamus, which were the first direct demonstration that there exists a special thalamocortical projection system which may fulfill the role of at least part of the central controlling mechanism postulated by Adrian. The relationship to attention and states of consciousness was not apparent until later work (11, 9), which related the intralaminar system of the thalamus, not only to the control of the alpha rhythm, but also to the neuronal system most probably involved in the generation of the wave and spike discharge of petit mal epilepsy, a type of seizure which is unique in its principal effect upon consciousness.

It was later shown in studies by Jasper and Andrews that the beta rhythm at about 20-25/sec recorded from the central area in man was not necessarily affected by attention to visual stimuli but was blocked by tactile stimulation or voluntary movement. Here, again, we have evidence for a local direction of the attentive process. More conclusive confirmation of this latter observation was obtained by Dr. Penfield, recording from the exposed cerebral cortex in man. With electrodes placed clearly on the precentral gyrus, following its identification by electrical stimulation, it was possible to study this process more precisely.

Movement of the fingers of one hand serves to block the rhythmic activity from the pre- and postcentral gyri for the hand area. In some patients this blocking reaction was observed to be most clearly present in the hand area alone, while in others it tended to extend further into the adjacent leg and face areas of the pre- and postcentral gyri. It was possible, however, for this reaction to occur only in the sensorimotor area, without affecting the alpha rhythm simultaneously recorded from the parietal zone immediately posterior to the postcentral gyrus. This was not always true, however, since in some patients blocking of activity in the sensorimotor cortex was accompanied by a block of the much larger alpha rhythm in the parietal cortex adjacent.

It was obvious that this response to voluntary movement was a very labile phenomenon which might include more than the particular area concerned in the movement itself but might involve a reaction in other parts of the motor system and even extend further into the parietal area adjacent. It was possible, however, in some experiments to demonstrate that opening and closing the eyes would arrest the posterior parietal or occipital alpha rhythm without affecting the sensorimotor rhythms, while attention to movement of the hand would affect the sensorimotor activity. This was obviously related to attention or preparation for movement, for in movement, such as clenching of the fist, the effect was seen only on the initiation of the movement and not during the sustained movement. Also, it was clear that preparation to move upon command was sufficient to cause a change in the electrical activity, though no movement could be observed. These results again confirm that this type of change in the electrical activity of the cortex is clearly related to attention or to the impulses involved in the voluntary initiation of movement. It is also clear that this may not involve the brain as a whole but may be directed upon functional sectors of the cortex independent of activity in other regions.

These observations required the postulation of some neurophysiological mechanism which provides a very labile and quickly changing direction of control of the electrical activity of particular functional areas of the brain and which can quickly be directed over very wide areas by the fluctuations of a patient's attention. The most logical postulation would be that there is some central controlling system of neurones with projections which are widespread to all areas of cortex which could mediate such a mechanism as would be required by these observations made on the surface of the cortex.

It should be pointed out, however, that the results from human electroencephalographic studies have shown that the response of the cortex to arousing stimuli are not always as simple as the blocking of the alpha or beta rhythms. It was pointed out as early as 1936 (8) from both human and animal studies that the form of change in electrical activity of the cortex in response to significant afferent stimuli depended upon the excitatory state of the cortex at the time of arrival of the stimulus. This has been borne out by many subsequent studies on patients in different states of consciousness. We will cite a few representative examples.

During drowsiness, especially marked in patients with narcolepsy, who find it difficult to keep awake during an EEG examination, stimuli which tend to arouse the patients produce a return of the alpha rhythm rather than cause its disappearance. This is spoken of in common EEG parlance as a "paradoxical response to stimulation." These patients may

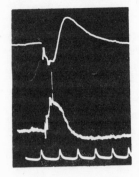

Plate 12.—Evoked potential recorded from the somatosensory (I) cortex of the cat in response to a single shock to the sensory relay nucleus of the thalamus (*ventralis posterior*). The upper record shows the classical surface positive-negative complex as recorded with a gross electrode on the surface. Beneath is shown the record obtained simultaneously from a microelectrode 0.9 mm. beneath the surface. Note that the surface positive wave has become reversed to a deep negative wave with a unit spike at its peak. Cal. below is 10 msec.

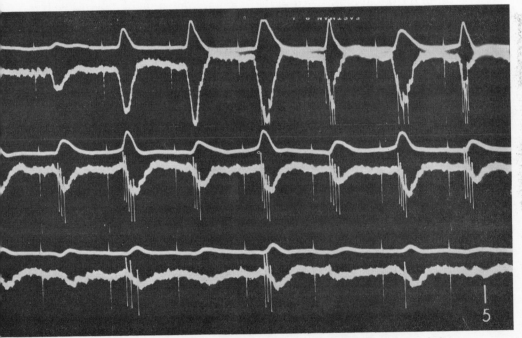

Plate 13.—Typical recruiting response recorded from the somatosensory cortex of the cat in response to stimulation of *n. centralis lateralis* of the thalamus. The first line is the surface record with a gross electrode. Below is the microelectrode record from a depth of 1.0 mm. recorded simultaneously. Note the recruiting positive waves in the depth with unit spikes appearing on the crest of the fifth wave. Stimulus repetition rate 8/sec. This was probably recorded from inside a cell.

show a decrease or absence of alpha rhythm very soon after closing the eyes. Upon opening the eyes the alpha rhythm returns. This is, of course, the reverse of the usual normal response in the alert, conscious individual.

Other interesting variations in the so-called arousal response are found in patients in various states of stupor or coma. These patients often show continuous very slow waves in their EEG instead of the usual 10/sec alpha rhythm. There are even times when the electrical activity decreases to a very low level. When they are showing the large slow-wave disturbances at 1-3/sec, sensory stimuli may cause their disappearance with a flattening of the record, even though they do not seem to be actually awakened from their coma or stupor.

It was pointed out many years ago in interesting studies by Fischgold and his colleagues in Paris (6) that even in conditions of stupor or coma the arousal value of a stimulus was not necessarily related to its intensity, but, rather, to its significance to the individual. He showed, for example, in his famous patient Pierre Dupont, that the record went on unchanged throughout many meaningless auditory stimuli, and even pinching the patient produced very little change. When the patient's name was called the record immediately changed from one of slow waves to one with lower voltage and more rapid activity. This illustrated that even during stupor the brain was responding to a pattern of sounds whose significance had been learned, rather than to the simple sensory stimulus itself.

In states of coma one also sees the opposite effect of sensory stimulation. Frequently a stimulus will induce a burst of slow waves rather than block them (16). This seems to depend upon the level of the state of consciousness at the time of the stimulation, or perhaps better, "the excitatory state" of the cortex. This is just another illustration of the fact that the response of the brain to a sensory stimulation is dependent upon how this stimulus affects the existing activity, which is always present before the impulses arrive in response to a given afferent volley.

There are other pathological conditions which show interesting responses to arousing stimuli. The most dramatic, perhaps, is the wave and spike discharge of the petit mal seizure. During this electrical discharge, which seems to involve in a synchronous 3/sec beat homologous areas of frontal and parietal cortex, the patient usually has some impairment of consciousness. This may not always be true, but in the typical attack there is a loss of responsiveness, which is more or less complete and is usually associated with amnesia. During the relatively mild attacks, however, the attack may be arrested, and the wave and spike caused to disappear by sensory stimuli, which alert the patient. Thus, a very abnormal epileptiform discharge of the brain as a whole responds to significant arousing stimuli, as does the normal alpha rhythm. This is just another illustration of the presence of a mechanism in the brain capable of exerting very rapid control on widespread areas of both hemispheres, not only to permit the remarkable 3/sec beat of the wave and spike activity during the seizure, but to arrest it suddenly from all areas in both hemispheres, in response to a sensory stimulus. It is obvious that neuronal circuits other than those which project specific afferent impulses to sensory receiving areas must be involved in this type of reaction of the brain to sensory volleys.

EVIDENCE FROM LOCAL ELECTRICAL STIMULATION OF THE THALAMUS IN ANIMALS

The principal experimental evidence for possible functional significance of the thalamic reticular system arises from results of detailed local electrical stimulation of different points in the thalamus with stimulating electrodes directed with the stereotaxic instrument, followed by anatomical control of the site stimulated. While the thalamus or reticular system is being stimulated, the electrical activity from numerous areas of cortex are being recorded simultaneously in order to map out the cortical responsive areas to different points of stimulation in the thalamus, and to determine the form of the cortical response in each area.

Electrical stimulation usually consists of brief electrical pulses of about 1 msec. in duration administered through a concentric or very closely spaced bipolar stimulating electrode which will minimize the spread of current from the point stimulated. Frequencies of stimulation vary from single shocks, spaced several seconds apart, to repetitive stimulation at several hundred cycles per second. Intensities of stimulation usually are effective between 1 and 5 or 6 v. for pulses of 1 msec. or less in duration.

The most favorable animal preparations for this type of work in the cat or the monkey are those very lightly anesthetized with Dial or Nembutal, or perhaps even better, the animals prepared previously by electrocoagulation of the mesial portion of the midbrain reticular system and then allowed to recover from the anesthetic. This blocks the desynchronizing action or activation of the thalamic reticular system from ascending fibers from the midbrain reticular system, which allows one to get responses without the interference of the constant high level of activity in an unanesthetized animal.

When exploring the different points within the thalamus with this method, it is immediately apparent that there are large areas in the thalamus which produce local cortical responses in a precisely organized topographic relationship to the point stimulated in the thalamus. This is most clearly demonstrated when stimulating the sensory relay nuclei with local responses in sensory receiving areas of the cortex. In these areas localization may be very precise, and movement of the stimulation point by a fraction of a millimeter in the thalamus will shift the cortical site of maximum response one or more millimeters in distance across the surface.

The precision of projection from the association nuclei, namely, *medialis dorsalis* and the pulvinar and lateral nuclear complexes, is not as discrete as from sensory relay nuclei but is nevertheless clearly a localized projection to frontal and temporoparietal areas. Stimulation within these specific nuclei, without searching carefully over the cortical surface, may fail to yield any apparent response if the electrodes do not happen to be situated precisely on a responding area of the cortex.

In marked contrast with the localization of responses from specific nuclear stimulation, one finds that there are certain restricted areas within the thalamus which tend to give more widespread cortical responses. This has given the impression that the unspecific projection system in the intralaminar portions of the thalamus did not have any localized organization of projection to the cortex. It has been thought by some (28, 29) that projection was largely limited to the association areas of the cortex, the motor cortex, and the anterior cingulate gyrus, omitting completely all sensory areas of cortex. Also, it was believed that this unspecific projection system behaved in an all-or-none fashion and projected to all these areas regardless of the point in the thalamus stimulated. It is of considerable importance to know, therefore, whether or not in the thalamic reticular system we have a mechanism which behaves in a mass all-or-none manner affecting principally the motor and association areas of the cortex, for this would have definite implications in regard to its functional importance.

In other studies (9, 10) it seemed that the projections from the unspecific system included also the sensory areas of cortex, though responses were more readily obtained in other areas. It was not clear why there seemed to be this discrepancy in results until the recent controlled studies carried out with Naquet and King at Professor Magoun's laboratory (12), showed that there were several reasons for the lack of consistent responses from sensory receiving areas of the cortex. In order to record an unspecific type of response in sensory receiving areas, it was necessary to search through the thalamus to find precisely the right point of stimulation, for in some parts of the intralaminar system there seemed to be very little tendency for responses to be observed in sensory areas, while in other parts they were clearly obtained.

If an animal were subjected to sensory stimulation while stimulating the unspecific thalamic system, or if the specific nuclei, such as the lateral geniculate bodies, were stimulated at the same time, it was possible to mask completely or partially, at least, the response of the unspecific system. For example, in an environment which is rather noisy it was very difficult, if not impossible, to obtain unspecific responses from the auditory area. Stimulation of the optic nerve or the lateral geniculate body, or photic stimulation administered to the eyes would interfere with responses in the visual receiving area.

Destruction of the sensory relay nuclei of the thalamus facilitated greatly the demonstration of unspecific cortical responses in their respective areas of cortical projection. It seemed obvious, therefore, that the failure to observe unspecific afferents arriving in these areas was due to competition from specific afferents, and when this competition was eliminated, it could be shown that there were projection fibers to sensory areas from the unspecific system of the thalamus.

Before going further into the analysis of the nature and functional characteristics of the thalamic reticular system, I should say a few words about the difference in the form of the cortical response when the specific and unspecific thalamic projection systems are stimulated. I need not describe in detail the response obtained from the specific projection system, for it will be dealt with undoubtedly by other papers in this Symposium. I will mention briefly, however, that the form of the cortical response when association nuclei of the thalamus are being stimulated is similar to that obtained when the sensory relay nuclei are stimulated. There may be some difference in the relative predominance of the initial surface positive wave.

The form of the characteristic response from stimulating the unspecific thalamic projection system consists of very little observable potential following only a single shock. With repetitive stimulation at frequencies close to the frequency of the spontaneous rhythmic activity of the cortex, namely, at about 6-12/sec, there occurs a recruiting response with an increase in the voltage of the responses following the first two or three shocks, with a maximum response appearing after several repetitive stimuli and then, even though the stimulus is maintained at the same frequency and intensity, the response may decrease and then increase again in an envelope-type of waxing and waning, similar to the spindles seen in the spontaneous electrical activity of the cortex. This recruiting onset and waxing and waning in amplitude are very characteristic features of the response from the unspecific system. A most important feature also is the fact that the most prominent wave of the response is a surface negative wave, sometimes preceded by a very inconspicuous surface positive component.

Perhaps the most striking distinguishing feature of recruiting responses is the latency between the thalamic shock and the cortical response. These latencies are surprisingly long, though they differ, depending on the cortical area from which the records are being taken, in relation to the thalamic site stimulated. Latencies have been shown to vary from about 8 or 10 msec. to as much as 30 or 40 msec. This is in contrast with the latency for specific thalamocortical responses, which are usually of the order of 1 msec. It should be pointed out, however, that there are some definite similarities in the form of cortical response to repetitive stimulation at about 6-10 or 6-12/sec. There is a recruiting or augmenting type of response to the stimulation of specific thalamic nuclei, and this may wax and wane in amplitude to some extent; except for the latency of the initial phase of this response, it might well be confused in a local area with the recruiting response. The augmenting response, however, is a local projection to a cortical area a little larger than that from which primary specific evoked potentials are obtained.

It is important to emphasize that the unspecific system does not respond in an all-or-none manner with just supraliminal intensities of stimulation. There is a definite organization with a rostrally oriented projection of the mesial intralaminar nuclei, with some nuclei projecting to the rhinencephalon (e.g., reuniens) while the lateral portions (*n. centralis lateralis* and the dorsolateral portion of *n. ventralis anterior*) project to sensory and posterior temporoparietal areas.

In fact, it is very difficult to obtain any recruiting response from visual, auditory, and posterior parietal cortex unless one stimulates the *n. centralis lateralis* or its vicinity. However, it is also quite clear that there are very close interconnections between the different parts of the system, and it can be brought into rhythmic synchrony with more intense stimulation of the mesial intralaminar regions. Then the recruiting response is observed in wide areas of the cortex, often bilaterally, tending to time the rhythmic activity of the cortex with the stimulation of a small area within the thalamic reticular system. Although there is a definite topographical organization, it is not as point-to-point precise as is the projection of the specific system, and the interconnections between different parts of it are much more intimate, with marked tendency for mutual facilitation and synchronization within the different parts of the system, making a closely integrated network of neurones but with capability of independent action, at least to certain regions of the cortex.

Under most conditions it must be acknowledged also that recruiting responses are easier to elicit and of larger voltage usually in the frontal and motor cortex and the anterior cingulate region than in sensory areas and the posterior parietal areas. The parietal area is also much more readily brought into the rhythmic beat of the intermittent stimulation of the recruiting system than are the sensory areas. It may well be that the number of projections to motor, anterior cingulate, and frontal and parietal cortex from the unspecific system is greater than that to the sensory areas, though this is difficult to ascertain with certainty because of the competition with specific afferents to the sensory areas blocking out the electrical evidence of recruiting responses in these zones.

A very intimate relationship has been shown between the thalamic recruiting system and those portions of the brain stem more inferiorly placed in the basal diencephalon, tegmentum, and midbrain. Simultaneous rapid electrical stimulation of midbrain reticular formation, for example, prevents completely the appearance of recruiting responses from stimulation of the intralaminar nuclei of the thalamus. There are obviously important anatomical relatitonships between these two systems. However, the topographically organized aspect of the projections and the individual responses to single shocks and to repetitive stimulation in this particular manner are properties which obtain only in the thalamic portion of the system and cannot be shown for the reticular system at the tegmental and midbrain levels.

At lower levels there seems to be little evidence of local effects upon the cortex, although it is true that the so-called "arousal blocking reaction" is more readily observed in frontal and motor cortices than in the posterior or more caudal areas of cerebral cortex, though it is frequently seen in all.

There is lateralization, however, of the midbrain reticular system, since it is possible to produce unilateral arousal effects which are seen only in one hemisphere following a lesion which interrupts the conduction, forward in the thalamus, of the activity from one side. A unilateral lesion of the brain stem at the level of the superior colliculus, for example, produces an animal which will show signs of cortical awakening in the spontaneous activity of the cortex only on the uninjured side, the side ipsilateral to the lesion remaining apparently unaffected by the stimuli which cause arousal, such as pain or sound.

THE ADRENALINE-SENSITIVE PORTION OF THE RETICULAR ACTIVATING SYSTEM

It has been shown by Bonvallet, Dell, and Hiebel (3) that there is a portion of the reticular system located in the upper midbrain and basal diencephalon which is sensitive to adrenaline and which seems to mediate the cortical arousal effects of adrenaline. Lesions within this system prevent the cortex from showing the activation response to intravenous adrenaline. This work has been confirmed recently in our laboratories by Dr. Rothballer (26), who, in addition to confirming the results of Bonvallet, Dell, and Hiebel, has been able to show that the adrenaline-sensitive area of the brain stem can be demonstrated by local microinjection with the needle directed by the stereotaxic instrument. Dr. Rothballer has permitted me to show two of his illustrations. Figure 15 shows the adrenaline type of long-latency and sustained cortical activation produced by intravenous injection of adrenaline. Response to local injection of adrenaline is also shown in Figure 16.

Mapping the areas of the brain stem of the cat which show activation due to local adrenaline injection shows that the sensitive area extends to

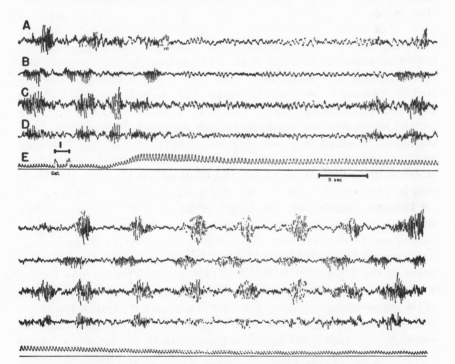

Fig. 15.—Arousal response of the cortex in response to intravenous injection of adrenaline in the cat following small electro-coagulation of the caudal midbrain. *A* and *B* are from the left hemisphere, *C* and *D* are from the right side. The blood pressure is recorded on channel *E* (cal. is 55 mm. Hg). The line at *I* is the period of injection of adrenaline.

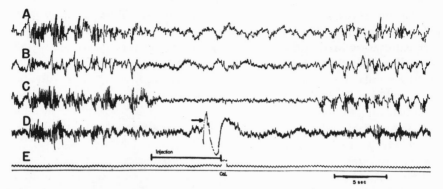

Fig. 16.—Activation of the cortical electrogram by means of local microinjection of adrenaline (8 gamma) into the tegmentum of the midbrain. *A* and *B* are records from the cortex of the left hemisphere; *C* is from the right hemisphere; *D* is taken from the tip of the injection artifact. Blood pressure is shown in Channel *E*. From Rothballer (26).

the caudal pole of the thalamus in the center median. It is clear, however, that none of the more rostral portions of the thalamic reticular system are adrenaline-sensitive. This demonstrates, therefore, another striking difference between the brain stem reticular system and the thalamic reticular system: The latter is insensitive to local adrenaline injection, while there are obviously cells in the upper midbrain and basal diencephalon which are peculiarly sensitive to adrenaline and are excited to long-sustained effect on the cortex of the activation or arousal type which is quite different from the effect due to thalamic stimulation. It may be that the more rostral parts of the arousal system, including cortical projection systems, are cholinergic, as suggested by Rinaldi and Himwich.

MICROELECTRODE STUDIES OF SPECIFIC AND UNSPECIFIC THALAMOCORTICAL RESPONSES

In collaboration with Dr. Li (15), we have been studying for some time the response of the somatosensory and other cortical areas of the cat to thalamic stimulation by the use of microelectrodes, recording from different depths within the cortex, measured with a micrometer. I cannot give the details of these studies, which are to be published elsewhere, but a summary is pertinent to our present discussion.

With microelectrodes it is possible, not only to map out the usual relatively slow responses to thalamic stimulation and to discover their distribution in the different layers of the cortex from the surface to the depth, but it is also possible to record the response or discharge of individual nerve cells. This individual cortical cell unit discharge is characterized by very brief spikes of less than 1 msec. in duration, as compared with the wave type of response which may last from 15 to 20 or more microseconds. The contrast between these two types of response, namely, from units and from other groups of elements in the cortex, probably dendrites and fibers, is shown in Plate 12.

The surface negative recruiting potential, when analyzed with microelectrodes at various depths of the cortex, is shown to be inverted in many instances, to become a deep positive wave, out of phase with the surface negative response. This is a gradual change and most commonly observed at a depth of about 0.6 to 1 mm. beneath the surface. In some experiments, the shifting in phase from the surface to the depth, is not as clear as for the evoked potential in response to specific sensory volleys, but, as shown in Plate 12, in general, the response does turn over and shows the maximum tendency for reversal in about the third layer of the cortex. The recruiting response shows the same intracortical distribution as does the spontaneous alpha rhythm.

It is obvious in some experiments, however, that there is much more to the recruiting response than is first seen in records from gross electrodes on the surface. One finds earlier phases in the depths, with a shorter latency than one sees on the surface with gross electrodes. This suggests that some of the delay of 20 to 30 msec. seen in the recruiting response may actually be an elaboration of this response in the depth of the cortex, rather than a delay in the thalamus.

However, not all the delay in thalamocortical response in the recruiting system takes place in the cortex. Expecially when recording from posterior areas, we have recorded, with microelectrodes, delays up to 20 msec. with no shorter-latency initial responses found in the depths. This raises the question as to whether or not the shorter latencies seen with microelectrodes, particularly in motor cortex, are due to simultaneous stimulation of specific and unspecific projection fibers.

The most interesting feature of the microelectrode analysis is the recording of the discharge of single cortical cells. We have done this both with extracellular recording, where several units may appear in the record, or, in a few instances, we were successful in recording the recruiting response from microelectrodes situated inside single cortical cells. An example of unicellular recording of a recruiting response is shown in Plate 13. It is clear that with the development of the surface cortical recruiting response there tends to occur a discharge of cortical cells in certain layers on the crest of the negative wave of the response. With intracellular recording this appears to be an intracellularly positive wave with gradually increasing repetitive discharge of a single cell as the positive wave is increased with repetitive stimulation. In the waning phase of the recruiting response, when the intracellular negative wave begins to decline in amplitude, the repetitive discharge of the unit continues, however, not simply related to the height of the intracellular negative wave. It would seem that this wave of recruited depolarization has to reach a certain threshold before the cell discharges, and then, following its discharge, the cell is more excitable and will fire after the depolarization has reached a level below its threshold value.

In our experience we have never been able to obtain discharge of cortical cells tò both the unspecific and specific thalamic stimulation. Those units which will fire with a very short latency following a single shock to the sensory relay nucleus of the thalamus cannot be fired by stimulating the unspecific thalamic projection system. Conversely, those units which fire with unspecific stimulation, in the recruiting response, cannot be fired directly by a volley from the sensory relay nucleus. There is, however, an interaction between the two projection systems. With proper pairing of stimuli to specific and unspecific regions of the thalamus it can be shown that a unit will respond more frequently at a higher frequency if preceded by a conditioning shock to the unspecific system. This facilitatory interaction is the only type that we have seen in microelectrode studies with intracellular recording. In other experiments, however, we have been able to show that there are certain units, recorded extracellularly, which may be arrested in their firing during a recruiting response or during a specific afferent volley. Thus, it seems that certain units in the cortex may be inhibited, while others may be facilitated by volleys from the thalamus, either specific or unspecific.

The importance of these findings is to show that the afferent terminals from the unspecific system must have a different distribution and effect on the matrix of the cortex than do the terminals from the specific projection system. Even the cells which they excite directly are distinct. Interactions, therefore, which occur must occur by interrelations between units in the cortex which are separately activated. This may not be an entirely valid statement, since some interaction may be shown to occur when there is no evidence for actual discharge of cells in response to unspecific thalamic stimulation. This suggests that there may be excitatory changes occurring, possibly on the dendrites of cells, which may regulate the excitability of cells without actually being mediated by activation of cells to discharge. This would indicate· a modulating effect of the unspecific system upon the excitability of specific cortical synapses.

THE ADAPTATION OF THE RETICULAR SYSTEM
TO REPEATED SENSORY STIMULATION

One of the most curious features of the naturally occurring response of the brain stem reticular system to repeated sensory stimulation is its rapid adaptation. An initial startling stimulus is always far more effective than the same stimulus repeated or expected. For example, if a sound is administered to a sleeping animal, the animal will be awakened on the first administration of the stimulus. If the subject is allowed to go to sleep again and the same sound repeated, it may be again awakened with the characteristic changes in the electrical activity of the cortex. If this is repeated many times, however, sometimes only 10 or 12 times, this stimulus loses its effectiveness for arousal, and the animal sleeps right through the stimulus. Then, however, if the stimulus is changed, for example, if instead of using a 500-cycle tone, one uses a tone of 100 cycles, then the animal will be awakened as though to the first sound stimulus, as shown in Figure 17, This seems to be a kind of learning process, in which the animal learns to ignore a repeated stimulus, the response to which has

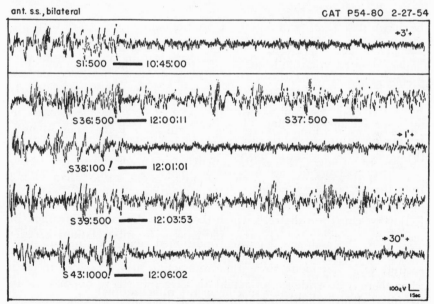

Fig. 17.—Habituation of arousal responses to a tone of 500 cycles after repetition 37 (S37:500). Then a 100-cycle tone presented for the first time produces arousal. The 500-cycle tone then tested again has no effect (fourth line) while 1000 cycles presented for the first time produces a good arousal reaction (last line). From Sharpless and Jasper (27).

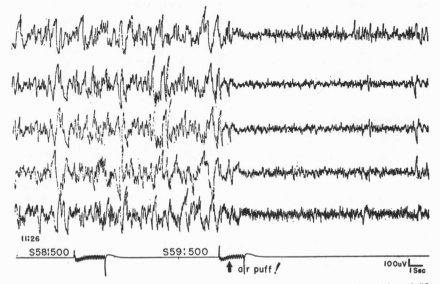

11:26

S58:500   S59:500

↑ a|r puff ✏

100uv L____
         1 Sec

Fig. 18.—Habituation of arousal to a 500-cycle tone, showing presentations 58 and 59, with prompt arousal to a puff of air on the nose. After Sharpless and Jasper (27).

become extinguished, but to be alerted by a novel stimulus. This learned adaptation or habituation is not only frequency-specific but also modality-specific, as shown in Figure 18.

This is merely an experimental demonstration of the commonly observed fact that monotonous stimuli tend to lose their effectiveness in claiming our attention or in arousing us from sleep. It makes an interesting experimental tool, however, under controlled conditions, to study the property of adaptation in the reticular system. Of course, one has to prove that this does occur in the reticular system, rather than in the sensory receptors, or in their pathways to the cortex or to the reticular system.

In a number of studies carried out by Dr. Sharpless (27) in our laboratories, it has been shown that this conditioned adaptation to unresponsiveness to arousal by specific tonal frequencies is not associated with a marked alteration in the response of the auditory cortex to the sound. Furthermore, it is frequency specific in the intact animal.

When a pattern of several tones is used in sequence to make a simple melody or a variation in frequency, adaptation occurs to the tonal pattern. After this has been well established, one finds that an isolated tone, which was formerly a part of the pattern, will cause arousal. Furthermore, reversing the sequence of tones in the pattern will also cause arousal. It seems that the adaptation, then, has occurred to the pattern of the tones rather than to specific tonal elements in it.

This is the beginning of an experimental approach to the commonly known fact that stimuli which cause awakening are those which are conditioned by some previous experience to be of arousal value to the individual. Once this conditioning has occurred, it is retained, even in sleep, so that certain stimuli which have significance will awaken a sleeping individual while others, even though much louder, may not disturb sleep. This differential type of adaptation to the stimulus patterns in our environment is a most important feature of the response of the brain to stimulus situations and may teach us much regarding how the brain differentiates between significant and insignificant stimulus patterns.

We have found that such differential adaptation to patterns is not possible without the cerebral cortex, though in the cat adaptation to specific tones takes place even though all auditory cortex has been removed bilaterally. However, the essential mechanism of the response still seems to lie in the brain stem reticular system, for, following lesions in this system, arousal itself becomes difficult or impossible. Loss of frequency-specific habituation occurs with lesions involving the brachium of the inferior colliculus, and posterior medial geniculate complex.

THE RETICULAR SYSTEM AND CONDITIONING OR LEARNING

It will be recalled that positive conditioning of the alpha blocking reaction, or attentive reaction, of the brain has been studied in some detail. With Shagass we have shown that all various forms of Pavlovian conditioning may be demonstrated by using the blocking of the alpha rhythm as a conditioned response. More recently, in collaboration with Dr. Morrell (18) in our laboratories, the conditioning of the corticogram in monkeys has been undertaken and found to be a very useful technique for the study of temporary connection formation in the brain. Once again it has been found that at the beginning of the conditioning process a more generalized blocking reaction occurs, which, with repeated conditioning, may be restricted to a relatively local region of the cortex.

The blocking reaction is only one aspect of the conditioning process, however, since a positive conditioned response, namely, an increase in the discharge of the cortex, can also be conditioned. The initial effect, however, is always the blocking reaction. This indicates quite clearly that not only is a mechanism operating which is similar to that in arousal in conditioning processes, but that the initial more generalized effect changes to a more localized one with repetition.

Also, it seems that this general activation effect always precedes learning in a conditioning situation, so that one must assume that, if this effect is due to the reticular system, this system participates in the initial processes of learning in new connection formation, although after a habit has been very well formed, the connection may occur in a relatively automatic fashion, with little evidence of the attentive response in the electrogram. It may return later in the experiment, however, in an unpredictable fashion.

DISCUSSION AND CONCLUSIONS

Speculation about the psychological implications of recent anatomical and neurophysiological observations on the structure and functional properties of the brain stem reticular system may be useful as a guide to working hypotheses, though the gaps between neurophysiological observations and psychological phenomena must still be bridged with rather tenuous theories. In the first place, it is necessary to avoid the more philosophical considerations of the ultimate nature of "consciousness." It is not possible, however, to omit data derived from subjective experience even though we realize that interpolation is hazardous from behavior and verbal reports to subjective experiences. This age-old problem of scientific method is particularly acute in attempting to correlate conscious mental experience with neurophysiological data.

In this discussion we must emphasize that it is with *conscious* experience that we are dealing. Most of the activity in the nervous system, which determines behavior and mental processes, goes on without awareness. The stream of our consciousness in only a minute sampling of the multitude of simultaneously active cells and circuits in the complex machinery of the mind.

Much of the function of the reticular system is also undoubtedly unconscious as, for example, the regulation of muscle tone and posture and its participation in integrated functions of the autonomic nervous system. The ascending reticular system, that portion intimately related to the cerebral cortex, seems to be most closely associated with what we generally recognize as conscious behavior. This is manifest in relation to states of coma or sleep in contrast with wakefulness, and in relation to attention in the waking individual. Attention seems most likely to be a further differentiation of the gross generalized arousal mechanism permitting focussed "arousal" in restricted assemblies of neurones with momentary exclusion of the rest.

It now seems clearly established that generalized arousal, as in awakening from sleep, is dependent upon activity within the mesencephalic and caudal portions of the diencephalic reticular system. There is less certainty regarding the more highly integrated functions of the centrencephalic system of Penfield. According to the latter hypothesis, sensation results not from the arrival of sensory impulses to sensory receiving areas of the cortex. Cortical sensory areas are only relays to corticofugal projections to the centrencephalic system of the brain stem. It is only after this projection that conscious sensation is presumed to occur. It is now well established that anesthesia, which precludes conscious sensation, does not block the arrival of impulses to the sensory cortex. Evoked potentials in the reticular system are readily abolished by anesthesia.

The fact that the thalamic reticular system seems to possess a certain degree of topographical organization relative to its cortical projections may provide a neurophysiological basis for the direction of attention. It would be necessary, however, for information elaborated in the cortex to be available to the reticular system if the system is to function in this capacity. It now seems that many corticofugal projections do exist, but we have not found them to be particularly strong from sensory receiving areas, especially for the visual system. The most important corticofugal projections seem to arise from areas which are not primarily sensory in function: frontal, cingulate, temporal, parietal, and area 19 of the occipital lobe. It seems likely that these elaborative areas may form an intermediary system between the primary sensory cortex and projection to the centrencephalic system.

Other proposed functions of the centrencephalic system require much further study, such as its function in the initiation of voluntary movement and in the recall of memories. We believe, however, that it provides a much more fruitful working hypothesis than the older reflex chain association theories, which have failed so often to account for even the more simple integrative functions of the brain.

The highest level of integration must occur in that system of neurones with the greatest number of confluent disparate convergent afferent and efferent connections. Integrative processes depend upon spaciotemporal impulse patterns processed at various levels, including cortex, and then some significant signal projected to the centrencephalic system of the brain stem for final coördination with signals from multiple simultaneously active systems to give coherent unity or direction to behavior and conscious mental life. The brain stem reticular system seems to possess many of the required properties for such a system of neurones with central integrative functions.

REFERENCES

1 Adrian, E. D. *The physical background of perception,* Oxford: The Clarendon Press, 1947.
2 Allen, W. F. Formatio reticularis and reticulospinal tracts, their visceral

functions and possible relationships to tonicity and clonic contractions. *J. Wash. Acad. Sci.*, 1932, *22:* 490–95.

3 Bonvallet, M., P. Dell, and G. Hiebel. Tonus sympathique et activité électrique corticale. *Electroencéph. clin. Neurophysiol.*, 1954, *6:* 119–44.

4 Delafresnaye, J. F. (Ed.) *Brain mechanisms and consciousness.* Oxford: Blackwell, 1954.

5 Droogleever-Fortuyn, J. On the configuration and the connections of the medioventral area and the midline cells in the thalamus of the rabbit. *Folia. psychiat. neerl.*, 1950, *53:* 213–54.

6 Fischgold, H., and G. C. Lairy-Bounes. Réaction d'arrêt et d'éveil dans les lésions du tronc cérébral et des hémisphères. *Rev. neurol.*, 1952, *87:* 603–4 (Abstract).

7 Hansbery, J. W., C. Ajmone-Marsan, and M. Dilworth. Pathways of the non-specific thalamo-cortical projection system. *Electroenceph. clin. Neurophysiol.*, 1954, *6:* 103–18.

8 Jasper, H. H. Cortical excitatory state and synchronism in the control of bioelectric autonomous rhythms. *Cold Spr. Harb. Symp. Quant. Biol.*, 1936, *4:* 320–38.

9 ———. Diffuse projection systems: The integrative action of the thalamic reticular system. *Electroenceph. clin. Neurophysiol.*, 1949, *1:* 405–20.

10 Jasper, H. H., and C. Ajmone-Marsan. Thalamocortical integrating mechanisms. *Res. Publ. Ass. nerv. ment. Dis.*, 1952, *30:* 493–512.

11 Jasper, H. H., and J. Droogleever-Fortuyn. Experimental studies on the functional anatomy of petit mal epilepsy. *Res. Publ. Ass. nerv. ment. Dis.*, 1947, *26:* 272–98.

12 Jasper, H., R. Naquet, and E. E. King. Thalamocortical recruiting responses in sensory receiving areas in the cat. *Electroenceph. clin. Neurophysiol.*, 1955, *7:* 99–114.

13 Jasper, H., and W. Penfield. Electrocorticograms in man: Effect of voluntary movement upon the electrical activity of the precentral gyrus. *Arch. Psychiat. Nervenkr.*, 1949, *183:* 163–74.

14 Jeffrees, L. A. (Ed.) *Cerebral mechanisms in behavior: The Hixon symposium.* New York: Wiley, 1951.

15 Li, C.-L., C. Cullen, and H. H. Jasper. Laminar microelectrode analysis of cortical unspecific recruiting responses and spontaneous rhythms. *J. Neurophysiol.*, 1956, *19:* 131–43.

16 Li, C.-L., H. Jasper, and L. Henderson, Jr. The effect of arousal mechanisms on various forms of abnormality in the electronencephalogram. *Electroenceph. clin. Neurophysiol.*, 1952, *4:* 513–26.

17 Morison, R. S., and E. W. Dempsey. A study of thalamo-cortical relations. *Amer. J. Physiol.*, 1942, *135:* 281–92.

18 Morrell F., and H. H. Jasper. Conditioning of cortical electrical activity in the monkey. *Proc. Amer. EEG. Soc.*, 1955, *9.*

19 Nashold, B. S. Observations on the thalamocortical projections. Unpublished master's thesis, McGill Univer., 1954.

20 Nauta, W. J. H., and D. G. Whitlock. An anatomical analysis of the non-specific thalamic projection system. In J. F. Delafresnaye (Ed.), *Brain mechanisms and consciousness*. Oxford: Blackwell, 1954, pp. 81–116.

21 Olszewski, J. The cytoarchitecture of the human reticular formation. In J. F. Delafresnaye (Ed.), *Brain mechanisms and consciousness*. Oxford: Blackwell, 1954, pp. 54–80.

22 Ramón y Cajal, S. *Histologie du système nerveux de l'homme et des vertébrés*. Vol. I. Paris: A. Maloine, 1909. (Traduite de l'espanol par L. Azoulay.)

23 Rinaldi, F., and H. E. Himwich. Alerting responses and actions of atropine and cholinergic drugs. *Arch. Neurol. Psychiat., Chicago*, 1955, *73:* 387–95.

24 ———. Cholinergic mechanism involved in function of mesodiencephalic activating system. *Arch. Neurol. Psychiat., Chicago*, 1955, *73:* 396–402.

25 Rose, J. E. The cortical connections of the reticular complex of the thalamus. *Res. Publ. Ass. nerv. ment. Dis.*, 1952, *30:* 454–79.

26 Rothballer, A. B. Studies on the adrenaline sensitive component of the reticular activating system. Unpublished master's thesis, McGill Univer., 1955.

27 Sharpless, S., and H. H. Jasper. Habituation of the arousal reaction. *Brain,* 1956, *79:* 655–80.

28 Starzl, T. E., and H. W. Magoun. Organization of the diffuse thalamic projection system. *J. Neurophysiol.*, 1951, *14:* 133–46.

29 Starzl, T. E., and D. G. Whitlock. Diffuse thalamic projection system in monkey. *J. Neurophysiol.*, 1952, *15:* 449–68.

Clinton N. Woolsey

Organization of Somatic Sensory and Motor Areas of the Cerebral Cortex

Supported by research grants from the National Institute of Neurological Diseases and Blindness (B-35 and B-732), the Alfred Laukhuff Trust Fund, and the Research Committee of the University of Wisconsin out of funds provided by the Wisconsin Alumni Research Foundation.

The purpose of this paper is to discuss the present status of the problem of localization in somatic sensory and motor centers of the cerebral cortex. This is relevant to the subject of this Symposium because in any behavioral study involving the method of ablation it is essential that the lesions be placed according to anatomical or functional definitions of regions to be removed and spared.

We are all aware of the lack of general agreement on anatomical criteria for parcellation of cortical cytoarchitectural fields (9, 11, 13, 16, 18, 23, 24, 36) and the difficulties of determining with certainty the precise limits of homologous areas of cortex in different species. However, the electrophysiological technique for defining the afferent projection areas has provided a new method for study of localization of function in the cortex and, because it yields a very detailed story of the relations of specific parts of peripheral sensory mechanisms to specific parts of the central receiving areas, it provides not only the means of determining the extent of cortex concerned with a given sensory mechanism but, from the detailed pattern of organization of the system, it permits clear identifications of homologous parts in different species. This enables one to sidestep the immediate necessity of establishing homologies by anatomical criteria. The method provides, in fact, a new base of departure for comparative cytoarchitectural studies and for more precise studies of thalamocortical relations, through placement of lesions in physiologically identified portions of cortical fields in various species of mammals. The opportunities for interdisciplinary research between the fields of physiology and anatomy are, in consequence, great. The method is also of value in determining the boundaries of cortical fields in behavioral studies involving local cortical destruction. Thus, by defining with the evoked potential technique the various cortical receiving areas and by the method of electrical stimulation the motor projection areas, one can determine the maximal extent of tissue potentially remaining in the category of

63

"associational" cortex. As a matter of fact, the method has already greatly restricted the amount of cortex which can be appropriately classed as associational, because it has revealed within the classical association areas the existence of additional well-organized receiving areas with independent afferent projection pathways. These are the "second" somatic, visual and auditory receiving areas (2, 3, 44, 65).

The wealth of detail in the organization of the cortical afferent areas revealed by the evoked potential method has led to a re-examination of cortical motor systems by the electrical stimulation technique (63). By examining the "motor areas" in the detailed manner found productive in the afferent studies, new relationships have been established in the motor systems, the precentral and supplementary motor areas have been differentiated and the sensory and motor studies together have given rise to clearer conceptions of the basic plan of organization of the sensory and the motor systems and of their evolution in the mammalian series.

Moreover, it has now been firmly established that the afferent areas are not strictly afferent nor are the motor areas entirely motor. The afferent areas (SI and SII; postcentral and "second" sensory) have well-organized motor outflows which are still functional months after complete removal of the motor areas of the frontal lobe (64), while at the same time it appears that afferent connections to the frontal motor areas exist independently of the parietal afferent paths (28). Thus, the concept that the rolandic region is indeed a sensorimotor system, as held by pre-Sherringtonian workers, is reaffirmed, but with the considerable difference that the region is not an undifferentiated entity but one compounded of a number of distinguishable, individually complete, though interrelated, sensory-motor and motor-sensory representations. These facts appear to us to have important consequences for studies of the role of cortex in neurological and behavioral functions—studies which will require the close cooperation of anatomist, physiologist and behaviorist, or the mastery of multiple techniques by single individuals. Some interdisciplinary investigations based on the newer functional maps in which our laboratory has participated have already been reported (47, 48, 49); others are being discussed in this Symposium (Meyer; Rose and Woolsey).

THE PATTERNS OF LOCALIZATION
IN SOMATIC AFFERENT AREAS I AND II AND
IN THE PRECENTRAL AND SUPPLEMENTARY MOTOR AREAS

In reviewing some of the evidence upon which the foregoing generalizations are based, we shall keep in mind the overall picture and proceed in discussion from the whole to its parts.

Figures 19 through 22 are general diagrams illustrating the evolution of the rolandic sensory and motor fields from rat and rabbit through cat, to monkey and their relations to visual, auditory and "association" cortex.

These diagrams undertake to represent the general arrangement of the somatotopical organization of the areas concerned. The orientations, proportions and relations of parts to one another are essentially correct. The diagrams are inadequate to the actual facts in that they do not indicate the successive overlap which is characteristic of the organization of the central nervous system. This overlap is minimal between the major subdivisions of each area. The nature of the overlap is best visualized through study of detailed figurine charts, such as those of Figures 23 and 24. For rat and cat, somatic sensory areas I and II (SI and SII) and the "precentral" motor area (MI) are delineated; for rabbit and monkey these areas, plus the supplementary motor area (MII), are shown. In addition, the visual and auditory fields are outlined for rat, rabbit and cat and the anterolateral boundary of visual area I on the lateral aspect of the hemisphere of the monkey is indicated.

The basic plan of organization of these four rolandic areas is best seen in the rabbit diagram. In essence SI and SII, and MI and MII are laid down as mirror image patterns on opposite sides of the line separating SI and MI, which corresponds to the bottom of the central sulcus of the monkey. Centers for the apices of the limbs in all four areas are nearest this line, while centers for the dorsal aspect of the animal are farther away. The symmetry is not quite complete, since SII is near the head end of SI, while MII is near the tail end of MI.

Of particular significance in the evolution of these fields is the central position of the hand areas of SI and MI. In the primates the hand achieves a high degree of corticalization in the precentral and the postcentral fields. Because of the central location of the hand areas, the simple basic pattern of organization seen in the rodent, where the parts are represented in relation to one another much as they exist in the actual animal, apparently becomes distorted in evolution as cortical representation for the hand increases, with the result that in chimpanzee (57) and in man (31) the sensory and the motor face areas lose continuity with the centers for occiput and neck, which remain associated with the trunk representations. In macaque (Figs. 22, 23, 24) this separation of face from occiput has taken place in the postcentral gyrus but in the precentral field the motor pattern still hangs together as it does in lower forms. Evidence for a transitional status in the postcentral area in the smooth-brained marmoset has been reported and illustrated elsewhere (56). That this separation of cortical centers for face and occiput is not the result of an *en bloc*

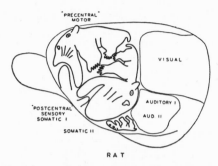

RAT

Fig. 19.—Diagram of rat cortex, showing general arrangement of somatic sensory areas I (SI) and II (SII), the "precentral" motor area (MI) and the gross positions of the visual and auditory areas.

reversal of the projections of the cervical segments upon the cortex as was once suggested (62), but rather is due to expansion of the hand area and disruption thereby of the cortical pattern (56), is supported by the finding (50) that the trigeminal nerve projects not only to the lower, classical face area but also to the "upper" head area, where not only the occiput but other parts of the head and face are represented (62). The suggestion of

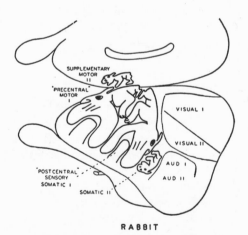

RABBIT

Fig. 20.—Diagram of rabbit cortex, showing locations and general plans of organization of "precentral" (MI) and supplementary (MII) motor areas, "postcentral" sensory (SI) and second somatic (SII) sensory areas, the visual (VI and VII) and auditory areas (AI and AII).

Petit-Dutaillis *et al.,* (33) that the upper head area of primates corresponds to the lateral face area of lower forms, while the lateral face area of primates is an elaboration of the second somatic sensory system in relation to speech function, is not in accord with our studies on the second somatic area nor with our detailed studies of somatic area I in a number of species.

Figure 19 is based on data collected by LeMessurier (25) and by Woolsey and LeMessurier (61) for the afferent systems and by Settlage, Bingham, Suckle, Borge and Woolsey (41) for the "precentral" motor area. Detailed figurine maps of somatic sensory areas I and II and of the precentral motor area of the rat have been published elsewhere together with maps of the visual and the auditory areas (56). A supplementary motor area has not yet been sought in this species.

Figure 20 summarizes the data of several studies on the rabbit. The only one of these which has been published in full is that on the visual areas (46). The somatic afferent areas were defined by Woolsey and Wang (66); the precentral and supplementary motor areas were charted by Meyer and Woolsey, while the auditory areas were determined by focal stimulations of cochlear nerve fibers in the spiral osseous lamina by Ostenso, Lende and Woolsey.

Figure 21 for the cat is derived from the studies of Talbot and Marshall (45) on visual area I and of Talbot (44) on visual area II, from the

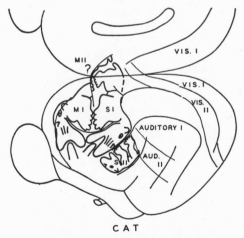

C A T

Fig. 21.—Diagram of cat cortex, showing locations and general arrangements of the precentral (MI) motor area, the "postcentral" (SI) and second (SII) somatic sensory areas, visual (VI and VII) and auditory (AI and AII) fields.

studies of Woolsey and Walzl (65) and of Rose (36) on the auditory system, from unpublished data on somatic afferent areas I and II by Woolsey, Hayes, Cranston and Luethy and from motor data of a study by Borge (10). As in rat and rabbit, SI and MI in cat are arranged in a mirror image fashion but the "precentral" motor centers for the posterior half of the body are almost entirely enfolded within the cruciate sulcus. The supplementary motor area should lie near the label "MII?", although no serious attempt to define this area in the cat has yet been made.

MONKEY

Fig. 22.—Diagram of monkey cortex, showing locations and general plans of organization of the supplementary motor (MII), the precentral motor (MI), the postcentral tactile (SI) and the second sensory (SII) areas. The latter lies largely on the upper bank of the sylvian fissure adjacent to the insula and the auditory area on the lower bank (not illustrated). The anterolateral boundary of the first visual area (VI) is shown by the thin line, with an asterisk placed at the center of the macular projection area.

Figure 22 shows for the monkey the general plans of organization of the precentral (MI) and supplementary (MII) motor areas as these were defined by Woolsey, *et al.* (63), of the postcentral sensory area (SI) of Woolsey, Marshall and Bard (62) and of the second somatic sensory area (SII) as reported by Woolsey (53, 54, 60). The latter lies for the most part on the upper bank of the sylvian fissure adjacent to the insula and auditory cortex. Only a part of the face subdivision is exposed near the lower end of the central sulcus. The question marks near SI are intended to indicate that no connection has yet been established between the "upper" head area and the laterally situated face area and that discontinuity exists between the pre- and postaxial representations for the leg and between centers for the sacral and the thoracolumbar portions of the dorsal surface, apparently as a consequence of the marked development of centers for the digits of the hindlimb (Fig. 24). Since in the precentral motor area there is continuity of centers for the dorsal axial musculature from tail to neck along the rostral border of the area (Fig. 23), it is still possible that a similar continuous, but tenuous, representation for the skin of the back may exist along the caudal border of SI, but to date it has not been possible to demonstrate this. One may point out that the precentral motor and the postcentral tactile maps (Figs. 23 and 24) differ in their anteroposterior extents, the former being considerably wider. The greater width of the precentral motor area, established by the identification of centers for the epaxial musculature, has only recently been demonstrated (63). Thus the "old" motor map of area 4 (20) resembles more closely the postcentral tactile map than does the "new" motor map. This again suggests that the tactile map may still be incomplete along its caudal boundary and calls for further study of this problem. In chimpanzee and man, where the distances are still greater, the discontinuities of the localization patterns are still more striking.

The figurine maps of Figures 23 and 24 provide a comparison of the patterns of organization of the precentral motor area (Fig. 23) and the postcentral tactile areas (Fig. 24) of *Macaca mulatta*. The motor map is reproduced from *Patterns of Organization in the Central Nervous System* (63); the tactile map is based on data used originally to construct the map for Bard's Harvey Lecture (6; see also 7) and presented with details of individual experiments by Woolsey, Marshall and Bard (62). It has been completely redrawn in our present style of map making. The scale has also been changed, so that both the motor and the tactile maps illustrate data for points taken at two millimeter intervals on the brain. The tactile map is not complete at its lower end, where centers for the tongue are known to lie. Figure 22 may serve as a key to relate Figures 23 and 24 to the brain. Evidence for mirroring of the precentral and postcentral patterns is seen in the face areas.

MOTOR PATHWAYS ARISING IN SI AND SII

It has long been known that electrical stimulation of the parietal lobe can produced skeletal muscle movements similar to those produced by stimula-

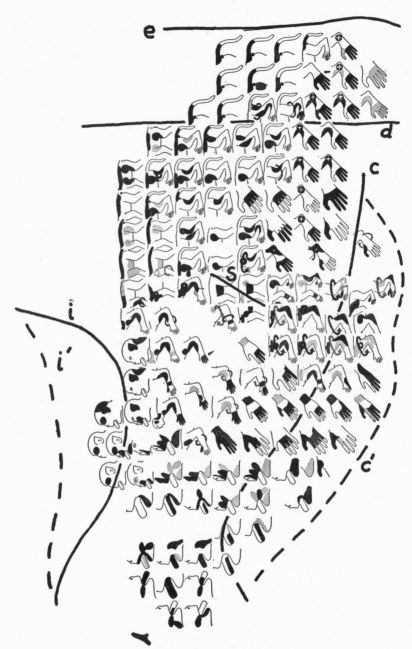

Fig. 23.—Figurine map of the precentral motor area of *Macaca mulatta*. See Fig. 22 for relation of this map to the brain. Labels: c, central sulcus; c′, bottom of central sulcus; d, medial edge of hemisphere; e, sulcus cinguli; i, inferior precentral sulcus; i′, bottom of inferior precentral sulcus; s, superior precentral sulcus.

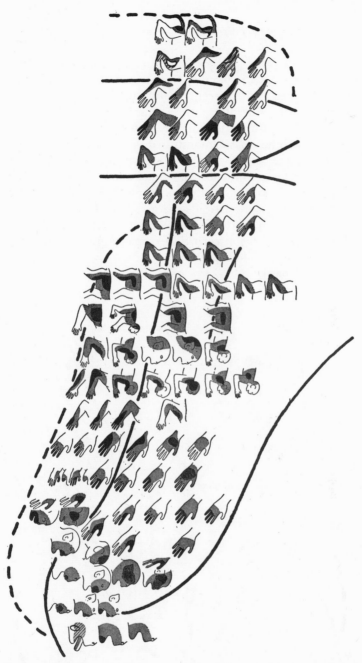

Fig. 24.—Figurine map of the postcentral tactile area of *Macaca mulatta*.

tion of the frontal lobe. Schaefer's (40) map, published in 1900, of the somatic motor zone of the monkey's brain included not only the frontal areas now identified as the precentral and supplementary motor areas but it also included all of the postcentral gyrus. Similar results were reported by the Vogts (51). Stimulation of the cortex of man by Foerster (19), Penfield (32) and others has demonstrated the same thing. However, since the work of Leyton and Sherrington, (27) the preeminence of the precentral gyrus in motor function has dominated teaching and thinking concerning cortical control of the somatic musculature and the motor effects of postcentral stimulation generally have been explained as the result of the spread of excessive stimulating currents to the precentral area, or on the basis of corticocortical connections with this area, or as mediated by extrapyramidal pathways (19).

In 1943, Kennard and McCulloch (22) studied the electrical excit-

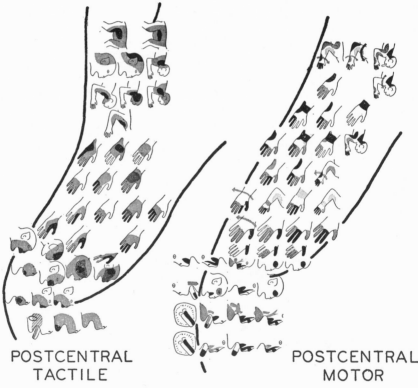

POSTCENTRAL
TACTILE

POSTCENTRAL
MOTOR

Fig. 25.—Comparison of postcentral tactile localization pattern with the postcentral motor localization pattern of *Macaca mulatta.*

ability of the postcentral gyrus sometime after removal of Brodmann's areas 4 and 6 from infant monkeys and found that it was still possible to produce focal movements similar to those elicitable normally from the precentral gyrus. They interpreted their results as indicating a high degree of plasticity on the part of the juvenile, as contrasted with the adult, nervous system. Recently we have stimulated in detail the postcentral gyrus of several large, adult monkeys, from which the precentral and supplementary motor areas were removed months earlier, and have been able to demonstrate the existence of a well-organized postcentral motor outflow after complete degeneration of the motor pathways from both frontal lobes (64).

Figure 25 provides a comparison of the motor and tactile localization patterns of the postcentral gyrus for the face and arm subdivisions and for a part of the trunk area. The tactile pattern on the left is a part of the tactile map shown in Fig. 24. The motor pattern on the right illustrates the results obtained in one of the experiments of Woolsey, Travis, Barnard and Ostenso (64). In spite of the fact that the sensory and the motor maps are not derived from the same animal, they show remarkable similarities in their patterns of somatotopical organization. Points receiving tactile impulses from particular parts of the face, hand or trunk, on stimulation with 60 cycle alternating current, cause movements to occur in closely related parts of the body. Thus stimulation of cortical points (in Figure 25,R) corresponding in position to those receiving afferent impulses from the occiput and neck (Fig. 25,L) causes movements of the dorsal neck musculature. It appears clear, then, that a basic relationship exists between the origin of the input signals to the postcentral gyrus and the destination of motor volleys leaving this area. Since the precentral motor areas (except for the left precentral face area) were absent from both frontal lobes of the animal stimulated, there must exist a well-organized postcentral motor system which can function independently of the frontal motor paths.

In addition to the motor pathway originating in the postcentral gyrus, there is another parietal motor system associated with the second somatic sensory area in the parietal operculum. This was first described by Sugar, Chusid and French (43) and thought by them to lie rostral to the second somatic sensory area. However, studies on the squirrel monkey by Benjamin and Welker (8) and by Welker, Benjamin, Miles and Woolsey (52) indicate that the sensory and the motor patterns are laid down together and coincide somatotopically. A similar relationship of sensory and motor localization patterns in the second somatic area of the cat had already been found in a few experiments (55).

AFFERENT CONNECTIONS TO MI AND MII

When Poliak (35) studied the main afferent systems to the cerebral cortex of the monkey, he described strong projections to both the pre- and the postcentral regions. The total somatic afferent field defined by him coincided satisfactorily with the sensory area of the cortex delimited by Dusser de Barenne with the strychnine method (17). However, the functional significance of these precentral connections has continued an open question in spite of the fact that the thalamic nucleus which projects upon the precentral cortex is known to receive connections from the cerebellum. This is so because the cerebellum is now known to receive many kinds of afferent information (4, 42) in addition to proprioceptive. Thus, it is clear that afferent information to the precentral region need not be limited to any specific sensory modality.

Under pentobarbital anesthesia, mechanical movement of hairs results in essentially monophasic surface positive evoked potentials limited to the postcentral cortex of macaque. Under the same conditions, electrical

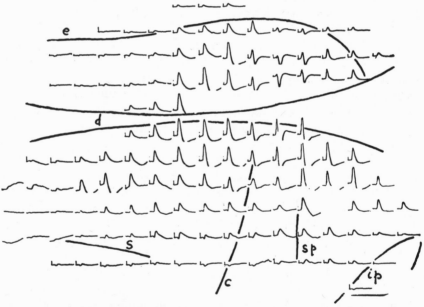

Fig. 26.—Potential changes (positive up) evoked pre- and postcentrally on the dorso-lateral and medial surfaces of the leg region of the cerebral cortex of *Macaca mulatta* by single condensor discharges applied through stimulating electrodes to the right seventh lumbar dorsal root (L 7). From an unpublished experiment by Woolsey, Chang and Bard (59). Labels: sp, superior postcentral sulcus; ip, intraparietal sulcus; for others see legend of Fig. 23.

stimulation of spinal dorsal roots activates not only the postcentral but also the precentral region (57, Fig. 26). Malis, Pribram and Kruger (28) have reported that precentral responses can be evoked by electrical stimulation of cutaneous nerves alone and that the precentral responses still occur after removal of the parietal lobe and after ablation of the cerebellum. This suggests the existence of a direct spinothalamocortical path mediating some form of cutaneous sensibility to the precentral gyrus. It will be important to determine the modality concerned and the detailed pattern of somatotopic organization for this system.

Some evidence for precentral tactile responses in the porcupine (26) and the squirrel monkey (8) has been obtained, but a definitive study of the pattern of organization remains to be done. That the precentral system cannot substitute for the postcentral tactile area in the management of the tactile placing reactions has already been established by Woolsey and Bard (see Bard, 6). The functional contributions of the pre- and postcentral systems, therefore, must differ significantly. Penfield (31) has reported for man that 25% of the points which on electrical stimulation give rise to sensation in conscious patients are precentrally located. The character of the sensation ("numbness, tingling, feeling of electricity") is the same whether the stimulus is applied pre- or postcentrally, except that the desire to move an extremity practically always comes from precentral stimulation. Penfield also states that "sensory responses from the precentral gyrus do not depend upon activation of the postcentral gyrus, for when the postcentral gyrus has been ablated at operation, stimulation of the precentral gyrus still gives occasional sensory responses referable to the arm or leg which corresponds with the portion of postcentral gyrus just removed."

Penfield's (31, 32) observations on the supplementary motor area of man indicate that this area also may be involved in some way in sensory function. Electrical stimulation in conscious patients has been found to produce sensations referred somewhat diffusely to various parts of the body, sometimes to both sides. In addition, Penfield (31) reports some evidence for a somatic sensory representation, posterior to the postcentral foot area on the medial aspect of the parietal lobe. He refers to this as a supplementary sensory area. To date no evidence for a supplementary sensory area has been found in animals, but further study of this question is needed.

Since the evidence indicates that the rolandic region consists of at least four distinguishable, somatotopically organized areas, each of which appears to be concerned with both sensory and motor functions, it may be in order to suggest a nomenclature which is more in keeping with the facts than the terminology which we have used up to this point. We therefore propose the following designations: *somatic sensory-motor area I* (SmI) for the postcentral gyrus and its homologues in non-primate forms; *somatic sensory-motor area II* (SmII) for the "second" sensory area; *somatic motor-sensory area I* (MsI) for the precentral motor area; and *somatic motor-sensory area II* (MsII) for the supplementary motor area. The abbreviations in parentheses indicate, by capitals and lower case letters and by order, the relative dominance of sensory and motor features of each area, as these are revealed under conditions of barbiturate anesthesia. These differences may be obscured under other circumstances, such as the absence of anesthesia, as Dr. Lilly makes clear in his presentation.

ASSOCIATION CORTEX

Comparison of Figures 19, 20, 21, and 22 reveals the striking differences in amount of cortex not devoted to sensory and motor projection systems (39). If we omit consideration of the medial aspect of the hemisphere and the limbic areas in which the mammillothalamocortical path terminates (38), it is evident that very little cortex outside the sensory and motor projection areas exists in the hemispheres of rat and rabbit. The frontal association cortex must be much less extensive in the rat than Krieg's (23) cytoarchitectural study of this animal allots to it, or has been assumed in some behavioral studies. This area is also very small in the rabbit (37). The largest area in these species not now preempted by sensory and motor projection systems lies caudal to the auditory and lateral to the visual areas in the temporal region. It seems clear that many of the identifications of homologues made on cytoarchitectural grounds, such as those of Gerebzoff (21) for rabbit and guinea pig, are invalid. Cortex which could conceivably be classified as "associational" in these two species, therefore, must be of minimal extent.

In the cat considerably more "association" cortex exists. Some studies have been carried out to establish the nature of the connections to the association centers from the primary projection fields, such as that of Amassian (5) for cat parietal cortex, the studies of Clare and Bishop (15) on the visual system of the cat, and that of Ades (1) on the auditory area.

In monkey still larger portions of cortex remain after the sensory and motor projection areas have been defined. However, in this animal, it is still necessary to delimit the second visual area. This presumably includes Brodmann's area 18 and perhaps area 19. In the marmoset (58) the visual response area as defined by gross photic stimulation far exceeds the limits of the striate cortex and actually includes all the cortex designated by Peden and Bonin (30) as areas OC, OB, OA and PFG. These areas extend toward the temporal region as far as the caudal border of the auditory cortex. A part of this visual response area is probably homologous with the third visual response area of Marshall, Talbot and Ades (29) and with the visual association area of Clare and Bishop (15). The findings, when more fully developed, should be of considerable relevance to behavioral studies involving the posterior association areas (14; see also Pribram, this Symposium).

COMMENTS

The results obtained in the field of cortical localization, since the introduction of oscillographic techniques for the study of afferent systems and through the reinvestigation of motor systems, which the sensory studies have stimulated, demonstrate the inadequacies of earlier views and call for a renewed attack on the relations of anatomically and functionally differentiated regions of the cortex to both neurological and behavioral functions. Such studies should not merely refine problems already explored but may be expected to yield qualitatively different results. One need only consider the relative crudeness of even the best surgery and the lack of precise controls in the placement of lesions to appreciate how infrequently tissue removed has actually coincided with any specific anatomical or physiological system. Errors of incomplete or excessive removal have been inevitable. This comment applies both to studies on sensory and motor projection systems and to those involving so-called association areas. A region of particular difficulty in this respect is the parietal-occipital-temporal in the monkey. When in addition we find that sensory and motor projection systems are not simple, single entities but that every system appears to have multiple connections with the cortex, it is not surprising that experiments based on hypotheses visualizing simpler relationships have been disappointing. The papers on the auditory system of Neff *et al.* and of Rose and Woolsey in this Symposium indicate that studies may become more productive when the anatomical and physiological complexities of the systems concerned are more adequately taken into consideration. They imply more complex behavioral mechanisms than present methods of testing are designed to reveal. There is opportunity for much greater control of the placement of lesions and for determination of completeness of lesions involving the sensory systems by application of oscillographic methods at time of surgery and at sacrifice of animal than has yet been achieved. While some (9, 16, 24) have become pessimistic over the possibility of relating cytoarchitectural and functional differentiations, it may well be that this pessimism is premature, since only relatively recently have the electrical methods of recording made possible the type of study through which such correlations may become possible. As yet practically no such studies have been made.

A real need, of basic importance to all studies on the effects of localized cortical lesions, is the determination of the functional capacities of the nervous system after total removal of all cortex. No really adequate study of the learned behavioral capacities of totally decorticated mammals has been carried out to date and yet studies of this kind would seem to be essential before one is justified in drawing conclusions from more limited ablations, especially when partial lesions result in transient and impermanent deficiencies. The experiences of Bromiley (12) on the decorticate dog, of Macht and Bard on decerebrate cats (see Bard, 7) and of Travis and Woolsey (49) on decorticate monkeys suggest that much could be done in the behavioral study of adequately maintained totally decorticated animals, including primates.

REFERENCES

1   Ades, H. W. A secondary acoustic area in the cerebral cortex of the cat. *J. Neurophysiol.*, 1943, *6:* 59–63.
2   Adrian, E. D. Double representation of the feet in the sensory cortex of the cat. *J. Physiol.*, 1940, *98:* 16 P (Abstract).
3   ———. Afferent discharges to the cerebral cortex from peripheral sense organs. *J. Physiol.*, 1941, *100:* 159–91.
4   ———. Afferent areas in the cerebellum connected with the limbs. *Brain,* 1943, *66:* 289–315.
5   Amassian, V. E. Studies on organization of a somesthetic association area, including a single unit analysis. *J. Neurophysiol.*, 1954, *17:* 39–58.
6   Bard, P. Studies on the cortical representation of somatic sensibility. Harvey Lecture, Feb., 1938. *Bull. N. Y. Acad. Med.*, 1938, *14:* 585–607.
7   ———. *Medical physiology.* 10th Ed. St. Louis: C. V. Mosby, 1956.
8   Benjamin, R. M., and W. I. Welker. Somatic receiving areas of cerebral cortex of squirrel monkey *(Saimiri sciureus). J. Neurophysiol.*, 1957, *20:* 286–99.
9   Bonin, G. Von, and P. Bailey. *The neocortex of Macaca mulatta.* Urbana, Ill.: Univer. Illinois Press, 1947.
10 Borge, A. F. *The motor cortex of the cat.* Unpublished master's thesis, Univer. Wisconsin, 1950.
11 Brodmann, K. *Vergleichende Lokalisationslehre der Grosshirnrinde in ihren Prinzipien dargestellt auf Grund des Zellenbaues.* Leipsig, Germany: J. A. Barth, 1909.
12 Bromiley, R. B. Conditioned responses in a dog after removal of neocortex. *J. comp. physiol. Psychol.*, 1948, *41:* 102–10.

13 Campbell, A. W. *Histological studies on the localisation of cerebral function.* Cambridge: Cambridge Univer. Press, 1905.

14 Chow, K. L., and P. J. Hutt. The "association cortex" of *Macaca mulatta.* A review of recent contributions to its anatomy and functions. *Brain,* 1953, *76:* 625–77.

15 Clare, M. H., and G. H. Bishop. Responses from an association area secondarily activated from optic cortex. *J. Neurophysiol.,* 1954, *17:* 271–77.

16 Clark, W. E. LeG. A note on cortical cyto-architectonics. *Brain,* 1952, *75:* 96–104.

17 Dusser de Barenne, J. G. Experimental researches on sensory localization in the cerebral cortex of the monkey (*Macacus*). *Proc. roy. Soc., London,* 1924, 96B: 272–91.

18 Economo, C. Von, and G. N. Koskinas. *Die Cytoarchitectonik der Hirnrinde des erwachsenen Menschen.* Berlin: J. Springer, 1925.

19 Foerster, O. Motorische Felder und Bahnen. Bumke und Foerster, *Handbuch der Neurologie,* Berlin: J. Springer, 1936. Vol. 6, pp. 1–357.

20 Fulton, J. F. *Physiology of the nervous system.* New York: Oxford Univer. Press, 1949.

21 Gerebtzoff, M. A. Recherches sur l'écorce cérébrale et le thalamus du cobaye. I. Étude architectonique. *La Cellule,* 1940, *48:* 337–52.

22 Kennard, M. A., and W. S. McCulloch. Motor responses to stimulation of cerebral cortex in absence of areas 4 and 6 (*Macaca mulatta*). *J. Neurophysiol.,* 1943, *6:* 181–89.

23 Krieg, W. J. S. Connections of the cerebral cortex. I. The albino rat. A. Topography of the cortical areas. *J. comp. Neurol.,* 1946, *84:* 221–75.

24 Lashley, K. S., and G. Clark. The cytoarchitecture of the cerebral cortex of Ateles: A critical examination of architectonic studies. *J. comp. Neurol.,* 1946, *85:* 223–306.

25 LeMessurier, D. H. Auditory and visual areas of the cerebral cortex of the rat. *Fed. Proc.,* 1948, 7: 70–71 (Abstract).

26 Lende, R. A., and C. N. Woolsey. Sensory and motor localization in cerebral cortex of porcupine (*Erethizon dorsatum*). *J. Neurophysiol.,* 1956, *19:* 544–63.

27 Leyton, A. S. F., and C. S. Sherrington. Observations on the excitable cortex of the chimpanzee, orang-utan and gorilla. *Quart. J. exper. Physiol.,* 1917, *11:* 135–222.

28 Malis, L. I., K. H. Pribram, and L. Kruger. Action potentials in motor cortex evoked by peripheral nerve stimulation. *J. Neurophysiol.,* 1953, *16:* 161–67.

29 Marshall, W. H., S. A. Talbot, and H. W. Ades. Cortical response of the anesthetized cat to gross photic and electrical afferent stimulation. *J. Neurophysiol.,* 1943, *6:* 1–15.

30 Peden, J. K., and G. Von Bonin. Neocortex of *Hapale. J. comp. Neurol.,* 1947, *86:* 37–63.

31   Penfield, W., and H. Jasper. *Epilepsy and the functional anatomy of the human brain.* Boston: Little, Brown and Co., 1954.

32   Penfield, W., and T. Rasmussen. *The cerebral cortex of man.* New York: Macmillan Co., 1952.

33   Petit-Dutaillis, D., J. A. Chavany, B. Pertuiset, and G. Lobel. Remarques sur les représentations senisitives corticales, primaire et secondaire à propos d'une aura sensitive. *La Presse med.,* 1953, *61:* 429–31.

34   Pinto Hamuy, T. Retention and performance of "skilled movements" after cortical ablations in monkeys. *Johns Hopk. Hosp. Bull.,* 1956, *98:* 417–44.

35   Poliak, S. *The main afferent fiber systems of the cerebral cortex in primates.* Berkeley: Univer. Calif. Press, 1932. *(Univer. Calif. Publ. Anat.,* 1932, *2).*

36   Rose, J. E. The cellular structure of the auditory region of the cat. *J. comp. Neurol.,* 1949, *91:* 409–39.

37   Rose, J. E., and C. N. Woolsey. The orbitofrontal cortex and its connections with the mediodorsal nucleus in rabbit, sheep and cat. *Res. Publ. Ass. nerv. ment. Dis.,* 1948, *27:* 210–32.

38   ———. Structure and relations of limbic cortex and anterior thalamic nuclei in rabbit and cat. *J. comp. Neurol.,* 1948, *89:* 279–347.

39   ———. Organization of the mammalian thalamus and its relationships to the cerebral cortex. *EEG clin. Neurophysiol.,* 1949, *1:* 391–404.

40   Schaefer, E. A. *Textbook of physiology.* New York: Macmillan Co., 1898–1900. 2 vols.

41   Settlage, P. H., W. G. Bingham, H. M. Suckle, A. F. Borge, and C. N. Woolsey. The pattern of localization in the motor cortex of the rat. *Fed. Proc.,* 1949, *8:* 144 (Abstract).

42   Snider, R. S., and A. Stowell. Receiving areas of the tactile, auditory and visual systems in the cerebellum. *J. Neurophysiol.,* 1944, *7:* 331–58.

43   Sugar, O., J. G. Chusid, and J. D. French. A second motor cortex in the monkey *(Macaca mulatta). J. Neuropath. exper. Neurol.,* 1948, *7:* 182–89.

44   Talbot, S. A. A lateral localization in the cat's visual cortex. *Fed. Proc.,* 1942, *1:* 84 (Abstract).

45   Talbot, S. A., and W. H. Marshall. Physiological studies on neural mechanisms of visual localization and discrimination. *Amer. J. Ophthal.,* 1941, *24:* 1255–64.

46   Thompson, J. M., C. N. Woolsey, and S. A. Talbot. Visual areas I and II of cerebral cortex of rabbit. *J. Neurophysiol.,* 1950, *13:* 277–88.

47   Travis, A. M. Neurological deficiencies after ablation of the precentral motor area in *Macaca mulatta. Brain,* 1955, *78:* 155–73.

48   ———. Neurological deficiencies following supplementary motor area lesions in *Macaca mulatta. Brain,* 1955, *78:* 174–98.

49   Travis, A. M., and C. N. Woolsey. Motor performance of monkeys after bilateral partial and total cerebral decortications. *Amer. J. phys. Med.,* 1956, *35:* 273–310.

50   Ullrich, D. P., and C. N. Woolsey. Trigeminal nerve representation in the

"upper head area" of the postcentral gyrus of *Macaca mulatta. Trans. Amer. neurol. Ass.,* 1954, 23–28 (Abstract).

51 Vogt, C., and O. Vogt. Allegemeinere Ergebnisse unserer Hirnforschung. *J. Psychol. Neurol., Lpz.,* 1919, *25:* 277–462.

52 Welker, W. I., R. M. Benjamin, R. C. Miles, and C. N. Woolsey. Motor effects of cortical stimulation in squirrel monkey *(Saimiri sciureus). J. Neurophysiol.,* 1957, *20:* 347–64.

53 Woolsey, C. N. "Second" somatic receiving areas in the cerebral cortex of cat, dog and monkey. *Fed. Proc.,* 1943, *2:* 55. (Abstract).

54 ———. Additional observations on a "second" somatic receiving area in the cerebral cortex of the monkey. *Fed. Proc.,* 1944, *3:* 43 (Abstract).

55 ———. Patterns of sensory representation in the cerebral cortex. *Fed. Proc.,* 1947, *6:* 437–41.

56 ———. Patterns of localization in sensory and motor areas of the cerebral cortex. Chap. 14 in: Milbank Symposium. *The biology of mental health and disease.* New York: Hoeber, 1952.

57 ———. Somatic sensory areas I and II of the cerebral cortex of the chimpanzee. *19th Internat. Physiol. Congr., Abst. Communications,* 1953, 902–3 (Abstract).

58 Woolsey, C. N., K. Akert, R. M. Benjamin, H. Leibowitz, and W. I. Welker. Visual cortex of the marmoset. *Fed. Proc.,* 1955, *14:* 166 (Abstract).

59 Woolsey, C. N., H.-T. Chang, and P. Bard. Distribution of cortical potentials evoked by electrical stimulation of dorsal roots in *Macaca mulatta. Fed. Proc.,* 1947, *6:* 230 (Abstract).

60 Woolsey, C. N., and D. Fairman. Contralateral, ipsilateral and bilateral representation of cutaneous receptors in somatic areas I and II of the cerebral cortex of pig, sheep and other mammals. *Surgery,* 1946, *19:* 684–702.

61 Woolsey, C. N., and D. H. LeMessurier. The pattern of cutaneous representation in the rat's cerebral cortex. *Fed. Proc.,* 1948, *7:* 137 (Abstract).

62 Woolsey, C. N., W. H. Marshall, and P. Bard. Representation of cutaneous tactile sensibility in the cerebral cortex of the monkey as indicated by evoked potentials. *Johns Hopk. Hosp. Bull.,* 1942, *70:* 399–441.

63 Woolsey, C. N., P. H. Settlage, D. R. Meyer, W. Sencer, T. Pinto Hamuy, and A. M. Travis. Patterns of localization in precentral and "supplementary" motor areas and their relatiton to the concept of a premotor area. Chap. XII, in: *Patterns of organization in the central nervous system. Res. Publ. Ass. nerv. ment. Dis.,* 1951, *30:* 238–64.

64 Woolsey, C. N., A. M. Travis, J. W. Barnard, and R. S. Ostenso. Motor representation in the postcentral gyrus after chronic ablation of precentral and supplementary motor areas. *Fed. Proc.,* 1953, *12:* 160.

65 Woolsey, C. N., and E. M. Walzl. Topical projection of nerve fibers from local regions of the cochlea to the cerebral cortex of the cat. *Johns Hopk. Hosp. Bull.,* 1942, *71:* 315–44.

66 Woolsey, C. N., and G. H. Wang. Somatic areas I and II of the cerebral cortex of the rabbit. *Fed. Proc.,* 1945, *4:* 79.

John C. Lilly

Correlations Between Neurophysiological Activity in the Cortex and Short-Term Behavior in the Monkey

This research has been supported by aid from the E. R. Johnson Foundation, University of Pennsylvania, the Coyle Foundation, the extramural program of the National Institute of Neurological Diseases and Blindness of the National Institutes of Health, Bethesda, Maryland, and is currently being conducted in the National Institute of Mental Health, National Institutes of Health, Bethesda, Maryland. Various individuals have contributed: the author wishes to particularly thank Dr. John R. Hughes, Dr. William W. Chambers, Miss Ruth Cherry, and Mrs. Thelma W. Galkin for their participation and careful analyses of data.

One of the problems posed by this Symposium seems to involve an appalling task—the correlation of neurophysiological activity in the brain, the structure, the total behavior, and, presumably, the subjective activity within each animal. If one takes a very close look at the data obtained in the fields of research dealing separately with these four aspects, one is overwhelmed by the missing parts in each separate picture and impressed by the lack of correlatable data taken with individual animals simultaneously in the four areas. Obviously, subjective reports are available at present only from human subjects. Some limited data are being obtained from the human in a number of clinics (3, 4, 6), but the scientific usefulness of these data is questionable because of the limitations of the methods used (anatomical, for example). In my opinion, theories to bridge the fields and fill the gaps in our data within each field are almost useless: The next collector of data can restore the status of the gaps by merely filling in the edges a little more. Instead of theories, we need more data—taken with methods at hand and with new methods being developed.

The anesthetized central nervous system or the partially ablated central nervous system is, for all practical considerations, the classical preparation of electro-neurophysiology. The intact, boxed up, whole animal is the classical preparation of experimental psychology. In recent years there has been a movement in physiology to use unanesthetized animals and in psychology, to use stimulation with electrode implants in the relatively intact animal. Workers in each field are invading the other field, at least methodologically, and sometimes by coöperative effort. We come from the physiological side and intend penetrating into the psychological territory but with physiological weapons and intentions.

One of the big gaps in our knowledge, not filled by either physiology or by psychology, is an accurate time-space description of central nervous system electrical activity and behavior in the very short time-intervals. Psychologists tend to deal with long cumulative phenomena, the results of many billions of short-term events. The classical learning-motivation-drive studies illustrate the point; even perceptual-discrimination–motor-response experiments involve a long-term, complex spatial-temporal sequence of stimuli of unending variety from one millisecond to the next; such experiments also bring in long chains of multiple, interlocked behavioral continua lasting seconds to minutes, repeated in complex variety over hours and days and weeks. Such studies generate repeatable patterns for each species which can be described and pinned down as "laws" couched in statistical terms.

Physiologists tend to investigate CNS events which occur in intervals of time of microseconds to tens of seconds and of short-term behavior of comparable time-spans (called "movements," "arousal," or "autonomic responses"). If a physiologist wishes to deal with the field of learning or drive, he contemplates the long and laborious task of analyzing a learning sequence. He sees that there are 3,600,000 msec. in every hour and several hundreds of millions of neurons, each of which is significantly active in one way or another at least several times per second; he can fairly easily record the activity of, and influence the action of, parts of groups of fifty thousand or so neurons at a time, and he can seek repeatable patterns lasting tenths of seconds to seconds. It may be that clues to CNS learning mechanisms can be found in such patterns; it may be profitable to hunt during a learning situation, for *changes* in such patterns during the time necessary for learning to take place, in new distributions of such patterns, and in the large field of that which we, in our ignorance, call "spontaneous" activity. Such studies on the detailed mechanisms of learning assume that one can see statistically significant short-term patterns or modulations of patterns in the CNS activity of an *unanesthetized* animal, patterns related to sensory events ("evoked responses"), to movements ("motor responses"), and to integrative events. We have been studying the evoked responses and the elicitable movements in unanesthetized monkey's cerebral cortex; our first problem has been to relate the findings in the unanesthetized brain to those found in the anesthetized one. In brief, on the motor side the patterns are similar with a few important differences; on the sensory side there are distinctive differences, mainly with respect to the much larger cortical areas over which responses can be seen, and in respect to the animal's external environment which is necessary to see any responses at all.

As far as integrative events are concerned, we do not yet have a clear picture of how much of what we traditionally include under "sensory," "motor," or "spontaneous" activities are truly integrative. We suspect that if we can separate out the strictly repeatable and stereotyped activities from the more fluid, plastic, modifiable ones, we can at least distinguish that which the monkey's brain has already acquired (by learning or other processes) from that which it can yet acquire in a new conditioning or learning situation. It is these repeatable patterns that we have been exploring to date; the conditioning experiments will come later, when we understand something of the more or less fixed parts of the CNS patterns; these parts may be modifiable, but we need to know more of how fixed they are under a variety of conditions.

In working with unanesthetized monkeys we found that which is already probably obvious to psychologists: Monkeys are not only distractable, but can be intractable. They are extremely sensitive, affectionate, curious, active, and responsive, and they learn rapidly the limits of restraint. When a monkey is stimulated through implanted electrodes on the cortex, one can see repeatable movements only with the coöperation of the monkey; this procedure takes unending patience—each monkey has its own ways of foiling our aim of repeatibility, and most monkeys become impatient when one part of the body moves again and again in the same way. Despite these difficulties, given weeks of time to work on the same animal, one can obtain a fair picture of evocable short-term motor movements tied to the stimulus parameters and the locus stimulated. A large fraction of the time, a pattern of movement is so tied to the stimulus that even naive visitors can see it superimposed and standing out from the noisy background. This situation is far better than that for observing the electrical activity within the CNS: In this latter case, there are fewer patterns that one can see, much less record, in the background in a noisy environment.

The external conditions under which one can record repeatable CNS patterns is reminiscent of the Pavlovian camera: The animal must be isolated from all distracting stimuli, even very weak ones. The subsonic vibrations in the laboratory because of a streetcar moving two blocks from the building at 3 A.M. have destroyed the reproducibility of responses. There are a few exceptions to this rule: If a voluntary movement is violent enough, one can see related, repeatable patterns in the CNS, but even these require special means for detection. We find that the visualization of the activity of many zones at once, so that one can see the instantaneous *relations* among the activities of these zones, to be the important set of variables if we are to see the patterns related to the movement. We have tried the usual ink-writers and oscilloscopes, but among all the bumps and hollows of the record, one is quickly lost—it is the difference between walking over a terrain and moving above it and looking down on it. The ink-writer carries one through every rise and fall; the instantaneous viewer (bavatron [10]) gives one a look at the relations between neighboring rises and falls, so that one can see the patterns of the surface. Or, to emphasize the point further, it is the difference between viewing the video signal of a television station with a very high-speed ink-writer and viewing a proper receiver with the traces placed in their proper places in sequence; it is not very easy to reconstruct the moving images from the ink-written amplitude record alone.

In order to start on the trek toward the psychological side with unanesthetized animals, in 1949 we started implanting arrays of pickup and stimulating electrodes on the pial surface of the monkey's cortex. The site was chosen because it was thought that the alternative, penetrating electrodes may give a picture contaminated by the activities of damaged cell groups; a "normal" physiological baseline was needed first in order to quantify possible pathological activity caused by penetration. The first arrays contained 25 electrodes; later ones contain 29, 36, and 121 electrodes covering 1 sq. cm. of cortex. Our latest monkey had 610 electrodes implanted over approximately 19 sq. cm. of cortex at about 1.5- to 2-mm. intervals over one hemisphere (30 electrodes/cm²) (Plate 14).

The method of picking up and recording the electrical activity is designed to present and to record through 25 channels in a square array 5 by 5, maintaining the spatial relations on the cortical surface in the final record (10, 13). At present we are limited to simultaneous data from any 25 electrodes in our present array of 610.

The method of restraint of the monkey to prevent self-inflicted damage to the head has been evolving slowly. It started with a table with a hole for the head and a suspended seat, and an additional Lucite sheet was added over the lap; the size was finally doubled as we began to use fully matured monkeys. We are still not satisfied with this method—some movements are impeded too much. Lately we have been trying some new arrangements, none of which are completely satisfactory.

CNS STIMULATION

Electrical stimulation of brain activity has posed several problems: Our aim has been to use stimuli patterned spatially as well as temporally, but many preliminary experiments must be completed before such "spatial" stimulation can be accomplished. In order to do this over long periods of time through many electrodes, it has been thought necessary to find a waveform which excites in a brief time (less than 0.5 msec.) and which does not injure neurons when used for many hours per day for several weeks. The brevity of the excitation period for each pulse is necessary for fine control of neuron populations near each electrode by amplitude and/or frequency modulation of the stimulating pulse trains; as one decreases pulse duration, one finds an increasing range of amplitudes at a given frequency between just-threshold effects and full, violent local afterdischarge patterns, and an increasing change of threshold with changes in frequency of the pulse repetition rate (14, 17). Rectangular unidirectional pulses were used and discarded because they were found to be injurious (14, 18). Symmetrical brief bidirectional pulse-pairs offer a noninjurious stimulus for one solution to the stimulation problem (17); if both pulses are brief enough, they cause minimal artifact and allow simultaneous stimulation and recording in nearby areas.

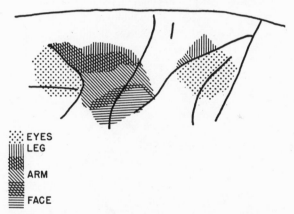

```
:::: EYES
|||| LEG
     ARM
     FACE
```

Fig. 27.—Summary map of six unanesthetized macaques: responses to 60 pp/sec currents. By the usual techniques of adjusting sulci and maps to fit, the data from six macaques with implanted arrays of 25 to 121 electrodes/ sq. cm. were combined in this map. These results show parts of the postcentral somatic motor map, the anterior and posterior eye fields, and the classical precentral motor area. Because of difficulties of correlating the landmarks and the response maps from one monkey to the next, it was decided to do the maximum size of map in one un- anesthetized monkey with a large implanted array (Fig. 28 and 29 and Plate 14).

In order to use spatially patterned stimuli within the brain, it is convenient to know what responses are produced by stimulation through single electrodes when used without the others; such trains of stimuli, introduced through single electrodes, produce test spots of hypersynchronized, more or less controlled activity within the CNS and cause small stereotyped patterns of behavior for short time-intervals; with such stimuli, we see the results of single hypersynchronized fractions of groups of fifty thousand or so cells. To obtain threshold excitation of such cortical spots, more than one pulse-pair is needed; and the threshold is a function of the number of pulse-pairs, the frequency, and the duration of the train. Trains have been found to be necessary for build-up of most motor responses (14, 17). Trains in the region of 60 pulse-pairs per second evoke the classical type of motor map; low-frequency pulses of about 2 per second give the Liddell and Phillips type of map (9).

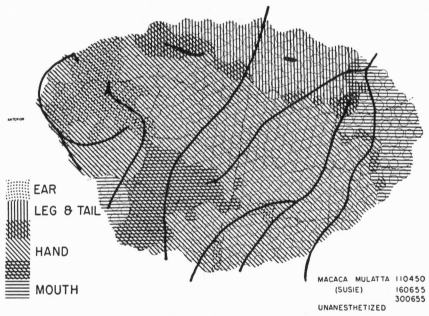

EAR

LEG & TAIL

HAND

MOUTH

ANTERIOR

MACACA MULATTA 110450
(SUSIE)   160655
                      300655
UNANESTHETIZED

Fig. 28.—Motor map at 2 pp/sec (unanesthetized *Macaca mulatta*). At such low frequencies at threshold, one sees only a single response per pulse-pair: There is no build-up of response, either latently or obviously by visual observation. Above threshold, with much larger currents, build-up occurs, and the part responding becomes that seen at higher frequencies (Fig. 29). There is still no satisfactory explanation for the low-frequency responses; for example, the elicitation of lip movements from visual areas makes less sense than the eye-head movements elicited by higher frequencies from the same area.

In *anesthetized* monkeys, extensive areas of cortex have been shown to produce specific movements: Horsley and Schäfer (7) found pre- and postcentral somatic areas; Woolsey, *et al.* (25) showed the detail on the precentral gyrus; W. K. Smith (22) and R. B. Livingston (19) mapped the anterior eye fields; Walker and Weaver (23) demonstrated the existence of some of the posterior eye fields; Bechterew (2) found a temporal ear field.

With implanted arrays in six monkeys, we found that those same areas of cortex produce very similar movements in the *unanesthetized* monkey (Fig. 27) (12).

The maps of the movements elicitable from most of the lateral con-

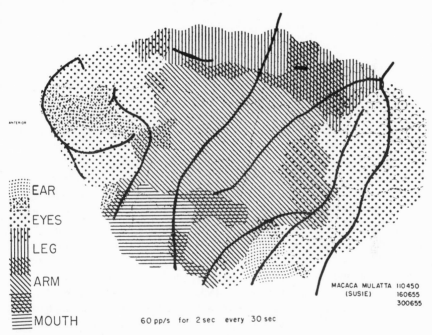

EAR
EYES
LEG
ARM
MOUTH

60 pp/s for 2 sec every 30 sec

MACACA MULATTA 110450
(SUSIE) 160655
300655

ANTERIOR

Fig. 29.—Map of movements elicited at 60 pp/sec at threshold from the cortex of unanesthetized *Macaca mulatta* (610 electrodes). There was no electrode which did not give a movement: no discontinuities in threshold values were found over this large fraction of the hemisphere. (More details about the threshold values are to be published elsewhere.) These results demonstrate that most of the cortex has efferent connections with the periphery. In a given receiving area the movements are appropriate for the sense organ involved, i.e., eyes and head move from stimulation of visual areas, ear for acoustic area, somatic musculature for tactile areas, etc. Apparently cerebral cortex is involved in target-seeking and target-following servomechanisms in mutual feedback with subcortical mechanisms.

vexity of the hemisphere in an unanesthetized monkey with 610 implanted electrodes, have been completed and checked in detail over a period of eight weeks; there are no gaps in the maps over the hemisphere from the lateral to the medial borders and from the frontal pole to the occipital areas. At low frequencies, lip, tongue, leg, tail, and ear are found, but thumb and fingers respond over most of the area (Fig. 28) (9). At higher frequencies (Fig. 29), coördinated eye and head movements occur in extensive frontal, occipital, and temporal regions; arm and hand movements over a very extensive precentral-parietal region; leg, over a more medial region of the precentral-parietal cortex. Face, lips, and tongue are found laterally over precentral-parietal cortex, and ear movements in frontal cortex and over that which we estimate to be near or on temporal acoustic cortex (20).

This map confirms the work of others mentioned above on anesthetized animals. In addition, the anterior eye fields are found to extend to the frontal pole. These results demonstrate that once the variable depth of anesthesia is abolished, most, if not all, cortical areas have motor connections in quite detailed and specific ways. Contrary to the expectations of some workers (25), the maps are stable and easily elicitable in the unanesthetized monkey; by judicious procedures, the level of excitability from animal to animal can be held constant.

The area given to movements of the spinal column also gives bilateral limb movements. The area corresponds closely to that for "back" in the anesthetized animal (25). Stimulation here causes rather surprising activation of the whole monkey: it seems to be very much aroused when we work with this region; in contrast with other regions, the monkey does not doze as long as stimuli enter here. The movements elicited are rather striking; for example, at one electrode, we found a movement we call "shrink," which consists of complete pulling-together of the contralateral pinna and closure of the external auditory meatus, tight closure of the contralateral eye, pulling of the head to the ipsilateral side, and raising and flexing of the contralateral arm—all as if to ward off and "shrink" from a blow to the contralateral side of the head. At an adjacent electrode, we found a pattern called "goose"; this pattern involves the whole body, and the reaction looks as if the monkey had been forcefully mechanically stimulated *per anum*. (Apparently this region corresponds to part of area "4S" and can cause "activation" rather than the "suppression" one might expect from the work of Dusser de Barenne and McCulloch [5].) Some presumptive evidence from electrical responses picked up from this region, evoked by stimulating other regions electrically, suggests that this small area has extensive inputs from the whole large "arm" and "leg" area. The "hyper-arousal" effect suggests it has efferents to the subcortical "arousal" systems (see H. W. Magoun's contribution to this Volume).

Taken as a whole, this "motor cortex" map suggests at least two "motor monkeys" (simiusculi [25]): the anterior one of Woolsey *et al.* (25), facing forward and down with legs up and back, but including eyes anterior to arcuate sulcus, and one posterior with eyes looking aft, whose orientation is still not thoroughly worked out; if its "spine" is not found postcentrally, a major reinterpretation of these simiusculi is then possible.

We have, as yet, no direct evidence as to how such an extensive area as this surface of the hemisphere can connect directly or indirectly with anterior horn cells of the cranial and spinal motor nerves. Theoretically, many main pathways, including the pyramidal one, are activated. It seems rather surprising that we did not obtain more widespread bilateral movements in the absence of anesthesia. We found some around the "spine" region, and, as did Woolsey *et al.* (25), some in the far lateral mouth area; apparently the commissural connections do not have an extensive and important role in cortical efferent activity. Perhaps both hemispheres are more coöperative than slavish in their relations. Of course, "eyes" are a special case.

From the behavior of the monkey, it can be deduced that somatic sensory events may have a lower threshold postcentrally than the motor responses; a few percentage points below the threshold for movement, the monkey may move around uneasily during the train, scratch at the part which moves at higher currents, or carefully inspect the part visually. We call such behavior "reactions to sensory responses" to separate them from the more stereotyped motor responses.

In terms of behavior, it may not be surprising to find such large cortical areas implicated in arm and hand and eye movements in the monkey. It does use eyes and hands extensively in its usual way of life in quite specific, integrated, and complex patterns of behavior. It is probable that the "sensory" inputs and the "motor" outputs are computed here in ways yet to be determined. Since we feel that these results are to be attributed more to the "superb architect" and less to the "sloppy workman" of Huggins and Licklider (8), we have done some preliminary analyses of the areas of these maps and their relationships.

Adrian (1) suggested that the scale of the somatosensory map of a given peripheral area mapped on cortex is closely related to the necessity of detailed information from that part of the periphery used most often in the behavior of the animal. It has long been suspected that the scale of the movement-muscle map is closely related to the frequency of use and the necessity of detailed and multidirectional control of positions and movements of the peripheral part.

The use of one part depends on that of others: the use of the fingers and the hand depends on that of the arm, and the arm on that of the shoulder and spine. On the cortex, "spine" is very small and lies in the large "shoulder" area and between "arm" and "leg"; "shoulder" is small and lies in the larger "arm" area, which, in turn, lies in the larger "hand" area; therefore, we call the hand-arm-shoulder a functional group represented as a unit on the cortex; "spine" is related also to "leg" and, as stated above, is a special region also related to many deep systems. All the large group of body parts thus can be divided, motor-wise, into functional groups: hand-arm-shoulder, eyes-head, spine, foot-leg-hip, tongue-lips-jaw, and ear. (The latter one probably should be "ear-head".) The corresponding cortical areas show extensive, if not complete, overlap of parts within each group. With this division we find, on the available cortical surface, the cortical areas to be those given in Table 1.

TABLE 1

Superficial area on lateral convexity of one hemisphere for movement of given parts

Movement of	Number of electrodes	Estimated area cm.^{2}	Fraction of total area observed
Hand-Arm-Shoulder	294	9.80	0.38
Eyes-Head	267	8.90	0.34
Foot-Leg-Hip	84	2.80	0.11
Tongue-Lips-Jaw	62	2.07	0.08
Ear	50	1.67	0.06
Spine	26	0.87	0.03

The areas found are only minimal values: cortex in sulci, and beyond our array, contributes additional area to at least some of these groups. We estimate that the "eyes-head" area will be sizably increased when we can explore the depths of the lunate sulcus and the rest of the occipital and temporal lobes. We do not expect "hand-arm-shoulder" to be as greatly increased as "eyes-head." A large fraction of this area is already bounded on our present map, and the supplementary and secondary motor areas are relatively small. "Leg" will probably be sizably increased when the medial cortex is explored (25). Allowing for such probable additions for each group, we guess that the order of the areas will be shown to be that of Table 2. Careful quantitative studies of total macaque behavior may

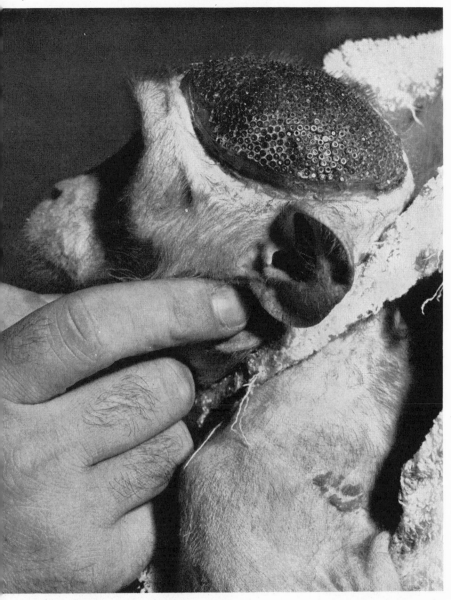

Plate 14.—*Macaca mulatta* with 610 implanted electrodes. The array was fashioned by moulage impression and moulding techniques. The electrodes are type 316 stainless steel (0.040 in. diameter) imbedded in plastic: each one is removable for depth studies. The inner end of each electrode is flush with the moulded plastic which fits the contours of the arachnoid-brain surface. The outer end of each electrode is surrounded by a 3 to 4 mm. length of plastic tubing. This tube is removable to allow a female socket to grasp the outer end of the electrode for attachment of leads. Tantalum gauze imbedded in the edge of the plastic matrix is used for sealing and anchoring the array in place.

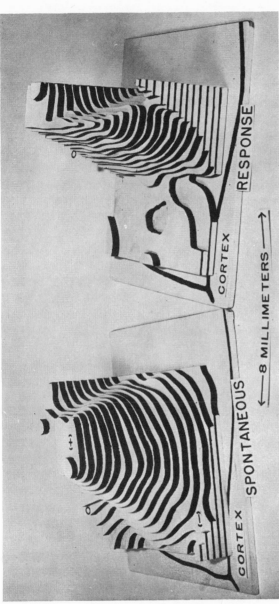

Plate 15.—Three-dimensional models of a spontaneous and an evoked figure in the activity of the cerebral cortex. These are two models of equipotential contour maps taken from records of the electrical activity in the acoustic cortex of a cat under anesthesia by means of an "electro-iconograph" (bavatron [8]). Each model represents one instant in the history of each electrical figure with the same electrodes in the same area (implanted array). The "response" model is one phase in a cortical response to a click stimulus; the "spontaneous" model is a phase in a cortical figure occurring with no introduced stimuli (11, 13, 14). The two figures here show distinctive differences, and at no time during the course of either one is there a sufficient similarity to confuse the one with the other. For prints from original electro-iconograms, see subsequent pictures (Plates 16, 17, 18.)

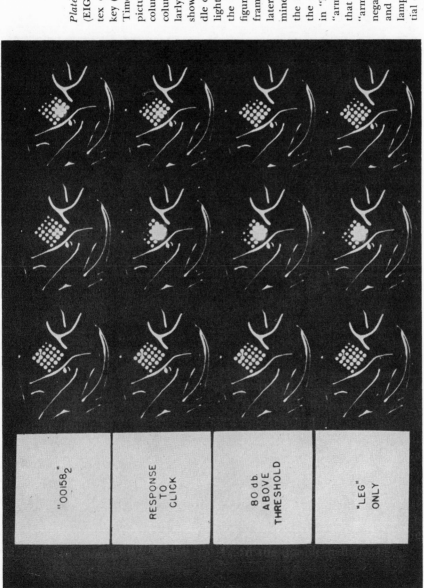

Platé 16.—Electro-iconograms (EIG's) from the precentral cortex of an unanesthetized monkey (130250): response to a click. Time in this and in subsequent pictures moves downward in a column and left to right from column to column. An irregularly shaped signal light is shown just posterior to the middle of central sulcus. When this light went out, frame 3 (col. 1), the click occurred. The large figure of the response begins in frame 5 (col. 2), about 16 msec. later. The motor map determined by passing current into the same electrodes shows that the upper half of this array is in "leg" area, the lower half in "arm" area. It is to be noted that the click response shows "arm" as brightening (relatively negative potential differences) and "leg" as dimming of the lamps (relatively positive potential differences).

Plate 17.—EIG's continued: The spontaneous, slow figures occurring during sleep. In contrast to the evoked response, the sleep figures alternate between brightening "arm" and dimming "leg," and vice versa. This is the level of sleep at which the usual slow waves are at maximal amplitude. These EIG's, illustrate that a boundary between functional cortical areas can be seen with purely spontaneous activity as well as with evoked responses (Plate 16).

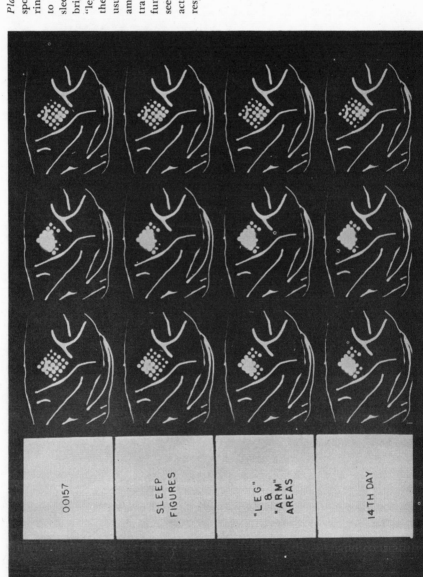

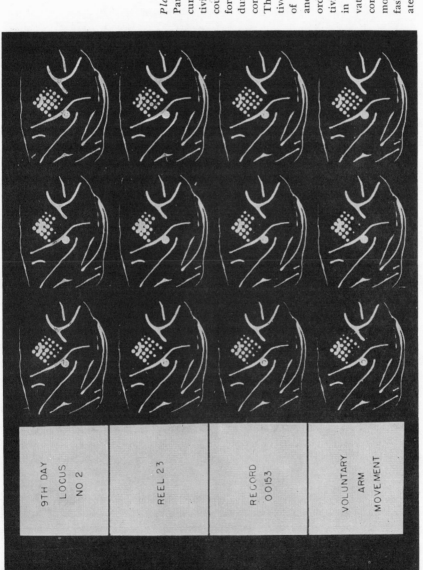

Plate 18.—EIG's continued: Parts of the rapid figures occurring during "voluntary" activity. The monkey was encouraged to strike suddenly and forcibly; this record was taken during such a strike with its contralateral hand and arm. The "arm" area becomes relatively positive in this sequence of events. Striking with its leg and foot leads to a similar record but showing relative positivity in the "leg" area and not in the "arm" area. These observations suggest that the motor cortex is involved in voluntary movement in a very specific fashion yet to be fully delineated.

TABLE 2

Presumed rank of given functional units
by total cortical area

Area rank	Functional unit
1.	Eyes-Head
2.	Hand-Arm-Shoulder
3.	{ Foot-Leg-Hip Tongue-Lips-Jaw
4.	Spine

reveal the exact relations of the use of these groups and these cortical quantities. Naturalistic observations suggest that the behavioral frequency-of-use rank order is very close to this cortical-area rank order. The monkey appears to "lead with its eyes" in most situations, and get busy with its hands almost as frequently—when it is eating, its eyes, hands, and mouth are very busy; when climbing, its hands and feet are very busy.

Overlap of the cortical maps for these groups and the lengths of the boundaries between them, may be related to their necessary behavioral relations: Table 3 gives this rank order from the map. These results neg-

TABLE 3

Relations between cortical representatives of parts

Rank order	Cortical overlap and borders between
1.	"Eyes-Head" and "Hand-Arm-Shoulder"
2.	"Hand-Arm-Shoulder" and "Foot-Leg-Hip"
3.	{ "Eyes-Head" and "Ear-Head" "Hand-Arm-Shoulder" and "Tongue-Lips-Jaw"
4.	"Hand-Arm-Shoulder" and "Spine"
5.	"Eyes-Head" and "Foot-Leg-Hip"

lect buried cortex and cortex outside the array. When other cortex is explored, we estimate that this rank order will not change very much—but we will be able to add the lower-order relations about parts which have only small areas on this lateral convexity of the hemisphere. We eliminated from Table 3 all parts with fewer than ten electrodes on borders or overlaps. Referring again to the naturalistic picture of monkey behavior, eyes-hands relations seem to be dominant and have the finest detail of spatial control in three dimensions: binocular visual fields and target-seeking behavior of eyes and head, and searching, picking, probing, grooming, lifting, and grasping with hands are two interlocked sets of relations presumably needing large areas of cortex and large areas of border and overlap. Feeding and grooming take up some of the hand and mouth relations, etc.

We have been intrigued by the question of what is missing from this movement map—apparently a large amount of basic facial and vocal expression is yet to be found, and may exist in regions outside our present array, deeply, laterally, and/or medially.

In our series of stimulated monkeys, including Susie with the 610 electrodes, we have found that the threshold current for movement, at any one locus, varies with the state of the animal. There are short-term variations, depending on the just-previous stimuli and on voluntary movements and inhibitions of movements by the monkey itself (wherever *it* is in the CNS!); in electromyographic records, we see waxing and waning of the amplitude over periods of 5 to 10 sec. or less (Fig. 30). High-frequency, subthreshold trains of electrical stimuli can decrease, briefly,

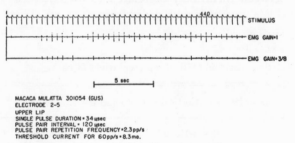

MACACA MULATTA 301054 (GUS)
ELECTRODE 2-5
UPPER LIP
SINGLE PULSE DURATION = 34 μsec
PULSE PAIR INTERVAL = 120 μsec
PULSE PAIR REPETITION FREQUENCY = 2.3 pp/s
THRESHOLD CURRENT FOR 60pp/s = 8.3 ma.

Fig. 30.—Electromyographic changes of responses in unanesthetized *Macaca mulatta*. This record illustrates the short-term variations in the amplitude of response to single pulses found in all unanesthetized monkeys to date. The amplitude variations can be partially correlated with changes of general state and with associated movements. Drastic changes in amplitude occur during concomitant "voluntary" movements (Fig. 31), during dozing and after eating (Fig. 32). However, the changes shown here are not yet understood and may be reflections of changes induced in the central nervous system by a noisy and changing environment. In the absence of violent activity, of startling stimuli, of sleep, and of eating, this amount of variation of response remains fairly constant for hours/day for many weeks.

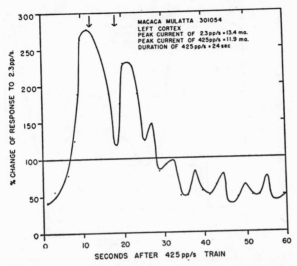

Fig. 31.—Increase of response caused by a subthreshold high-frequency train: effect of a spontaneous movement on the facilitation. This is the same preparation as Fig. 30. The 100 per cent level is the average of all responses occurring in a 60-sec. period before stimulating with the high-frequency train. Subsequent to the train, each successive group of four responses is averaged and plotted as a single point on this graph. A "spontaneous" movement occurred at the time shown on the graph. Other records taken at times free of movement show a smooth rise and fall of averaged amplitude without the "notch" in the falling phase. These results show that the mechanisms of "spontaneous" movement can exert a profound transient inhibition on the prolonged facilitation caused by a high-frequency train applied to cerebral cortex. The subnormal responses following the facilitated ones continued for about 200 sec. beyond the time shown on this graph.

and then increase strongly the amplitude of subsequent responses for up to 30 sec. later (Fig. 31) ("prolonged facilitation" of Larrabee and Bronk; "post-tetanic potentiation" of Lloyd).

Longer-term variations in threshold are seen with dozing, sleeping, and eating. Dozing and sleep raise the threshold 25 to 100 per cent above that of the awake state. About ½ to 1 hr. after eating, there is a small (15 to 25 per cent) fall in threshold (Fig. 32).

I cite these facts as a reminder that the unanesthetized CNS *is* complex and constantly in need of careful and close observation to account for its

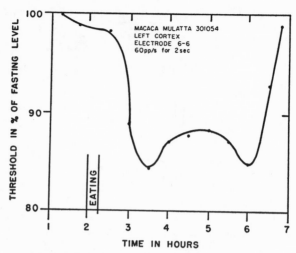

Fig. 32.—An example of the fall of threshold (60 pp/sec) following eating in the unanesthetized monkey. The same preparation was used as in Fig. 30 and 31. The values of threshold current are those averaged over several observations during time intervals free of spontaneous movements, dozing, extreme excitement, etc. The postprandial fall is fairly typical of the usual diet for this monkey (bananas, grapes, bread, etc.); no systematic attempt was made to see what the effects of various components of the diet have on this threshold. The changes apparently occur in a parallel time-course to that of the changes in blood chemistry ("alkaline tide," etc.).

apparent "instability." Instead of being "instable," however, it seems to take facts into account which, as yet, are not fully available to us.

We find, as did James W. Ward (24) in unanesthetized cats, that what the monkey is doing has something to do with the movement elicited by the electric current (but we do not yet agree with his "common final position" interpretation). If we work with a cortical zone that gives progressing "elbow flexion" when the arm is relaxed and extended, and persist long enough, the monkey may get tired of this game and voluntarily flex its elbow strongly enough to stop our efforts. At that point, we see progressing relaxation of the biceps in response to our stimuli. Similarly, if the response is "eyes and head turning to the contralateral side," the monkey may stare at something ipsilateral and raise the apparent threshold; but if it loses interest, the eyes start moving contralaterally. Once in a while we see a "nystagmoid" series of eye movements as the monkey pushes one way and the stimulus pushes the other.

When I say "it pushes" or "it does this," I am taking the "common sense" view of the situation. If one works in close quarters with these beasts for several weeks, one develops the feeling there is someone in the unstimulated majority of that body-brain either aiding or hindering the experiments, a someone whose efforts are not usually seen in a Skinner Box.

CNS ELECTRICAL ACTIVITY

With the method of recording from 25 electrodes at once, the electrical activity can be seen to be traveling waves or "figures" (11, 13, 15, 16). These figures differ from one cortical area to the next and are different for responses to normal inputs (ear, eye, etc.) and for "spontaneous" activity. In the cat's acoustic (AI and AII) cortex and the posterior ectosylvian field (Ep) of Jerzy Rose (21), the differences between evoked figures and spontaneous ones are particularly striking (Plate 15) (15, 16). A figure, evoked by a click, starts in AI and AII and grows with an advancing edge velocity of 1–2 m/sec; at the boundary with Ep, the edge slows to 0.1 m/sec. The retreating edge velocity over the whole area is about 0.1 m/sec.

The spontaneous figures usually arise in Ep just posterior to the AI-Ep boundary or at a locus near the posterior suprasylvian sulcus. The velocity of the advancing and retreating edges of these figures is about 0.1 m/sec. These figures in Ep can excite new ones in AII and in turn can be stimulated by "startling" sounds. This latter result apparently is due to connections of Ep with the reticular formation, and "arousal" reactions involve Ep as well as other cortical areas (16). As opposed to the response figures, the spontaneous ones have a wider range of variability; their histories are expressible in terms of statistical statements (16).

In the unanesthetized monkey cortex, complex figures can be seen, for example, in areas classically called "sensorimotor" in the pre- and postcentral gyri—evoked figures after acoustic stimuli, spontaneous ones during sleep, and "sensorimotor" ones during voluntary motor activity (12).

The evoked figures (Plate 16) are stereotyped for any given state of the animal but vary with the state and with the time after the stimulus. A wide-awake, excited animal has very small, rapid evoked figures, but as it dozes off, the figures become larger, slower, and travel in different apparent paths over the cortex. For example, they start in motor "leg" and go to "arm" when the monkey is lightly dozing; but when it is deeply asleep, they start in "arm" and go to "leg." The early parts of the evoked figures are tied to the stimulus, but the later parts have more variability and finally seem to merge with the "spontaneous" activity. It seems as if the short-latency figures are giving data tied to the stimulus and the state, and the later ones to related data from other regions which may involve habituation and learning. Before we can effectively speculate on these matters, we need more data over wider areas, such as has been done for the motor map found above.

Spontaneous figures during sleep (Plate 17) travel in such a characteristic fashion that with a little practice one can see, for example, the boundaries between the "arm" and the "leg" regions quite easily. As the animal's state varies from an excited one to deep sleep, the variability of the boundaries decreases.

During voluntary movements, characteristic figures can be seen in the cortical areas from which similar movements are elicitable by electric stimuli, and yet no such figures are seen in the surrounding areas. For example, if the arm strikes, figures show in "arm" area but not in "leg" or "face" (Plate 18).

Thus, these figures are sensitive indicators of the states and of the activities of the monkey. It is to be expected that as wider areas of the CNS are covered, we shall begin to find closer ties between these figures and behavior even to the point of seeing progressive changes in some of the figures as the monkey progresses in a learning situation.

One is left, of course, with many facts ultimately to be explained by structural connections, neurophysiological factors, and by extremely careful behavioral records and histories. One of the large difficulties in correlating structure, behavior, and CNS activity is the spatial problem of getting enough electrodes, and small enough electrodes, *in* there with minimal injury. Still another difficulty is the temporal problem of getting enough samples from each electrode per unit of time, over a long enough time, to begin to see what goes on during conditioning or learning, especially when a monkey can learn with *one* exposure to a situation, as we see repeatedly. As for the problem of the investigator's absorbing the data —if he has adequate recording techniques, he has a lot of time to work on a very short recorded part of a given monkey's life.

REFERENCES

1 Adrian, E. D. *The physical background of perception.* Oxford: The Clarendon Press, 1947.
2 Bechterew, W. von. *Die Funktionen der Nervencentra.* Jena: Gustav Fischer, 1908–11. 3 vols.
3 Bickford, R. G., *et al.* Symposium on intracerebral electrography, *Proceedings of the Staff Meetings Mayo Clinic,* 1953, *28:* No. 6, 145–92.

4 Chapman, W. P. Physiological evidence concerning importance of the amygdaloid nuclear region in the integration of circulatory function and emotion in man. *Science,* 1954, *120:* 949–51.

5 Dusser de Barenne, J. G., and W. S. McCulloch. Suppression of motor response upon stimulation of area 4-s of the cerebral cortex. *Amer. J. Physiol.,* 1939, *126:* 482.

6 Heath, G., *et al. Studies in schizophrenia.* Cambridge, Mass.: Harvard Univer. Press, 1954.

7 Horsley, V., and E. A. Schäfer. A record of experiments upon the functions of the cerebral cortex. *Phil. Trans.,* 1888, *179B:* 1–45.

8 Huggins, W. H., and J. C. R. Licklider. Place mechanisms of auditory frequency analysis. *J. Acoust. Soc. Amer.,* 1951, *23:* No. 3, 290–99.

9 Liddell, E. G. T., and C. G. Phillips. Thresholds of cortical representation. *Brain,* 1950, *73:* part 2, 125–40.

10 Lilly, J. C. A method of recording the moving electrical potential gradients in the brain: the 25-channel bavatron and electro-iconograms. Second Annual Joint AIEE-IRE Conf. on Electronics in Nucleonics and Medicine, 1949, New York. *American Institute of Electrical Engineers,* New York, 1950, pp. 37–43.

11 ———. Forms and figures in the electrical activity seen in the surface of the cerebral cortex. Milbank Memorial Fund Symposium, 1950; *The Biology of Mental Health and Disease.* New York: Hoeber, 1952, pp. 206–19.

12 ———. Significance of motor maps of the sensorimotor cortex in the conscious monkey. *Fed. Proc.,* 1953, *12:* 285.

13 ———. Instantaneous relations between the activities of closely spaced zones on the cerebral cortex. *Amer. J. Physiol.,* 1954, *176:* 493–504.

14 Lilly, J. C., G. M. Austin, and W. W. Chambers. Threshold movements produced by excitation of cerebral cortex and efferent fibers with some parametric regions of rectangular current pulses (cats and monkeys). *J. Neurophysiol.,* 1952, *15:* 319–41.

15 Lilly, J. C., and R. B. Cherry. Surface movements of click responses from acoustic cerebral cortex of cat: Leading and trailing edges of a response figure. *J. Neurophysiol.,* 1954, *17:* 521–32.

16 ———. Surface movements of figures in spontaneous activity of anesthetized cerebral cortex: Leading and trailing edges. *J. Neurophysiol.,* 1955, *18:* 18–32.

17 Lilly, J. C., J. R. Hughes, E. C. Alvord, Jr., and T. W. Galkin. Brief, noninjurious electric waveform for stimulation of the brain. *Science,* 1955, *121:* 468–69.

18 ———. Production and avoidance of injury to brain tissue by electrical current at threshold values. *Electroenceph. clin. Neurophysiol.,* 1955, *7:* 458.

19 Livingston, R. B. In J. F. Fulton (Ed.), *Functional localization in the frontal lobes and cerebellum.* Oxford: The Clarendon Press, 1949.

20 Pribram, K. H., B. S. Rosner, and W. A. Rosenblith. Electrical responses

to acoustic clicks in monkey: Extent of neocortex activated. *J. Neurophysiol.*, 1954, *17*: 336–43.

21 Rose, J. E. The cellular structure of the auditory region of the cat. *J. comp. Neurol.*, 1949, *91*: 409–39.

22 Smith, W. K. The frontal eye fields. In *The precentral motor cortex*. P. C. Bucy (Ed.), Urbana: Univer. Illinois Press, 1949.

23 Walker, A., and T. A. Weaver, Jr. Ocular movements from the occipital lobe in the monkey. *J. Neurophysiol.*, 1940, *3*: 353–57.

24 Ward, J. W. Motor phenomena elicited in the unanesthetized animal by electrical stimulatiton of the cerebral cortex. *Ass. Res. Nerv. Ment. Dis. Proc.*, 1952, *30*: 223–37.

25 Woolsey, C. N., P. H. Settlage, D. R. Meyer, W. Sencer, T. Hamuy, and A. M. Travis. Patterns of localization in precentral and "supplementary" motor areas and their relation to the concept of a premotor area. *Res. Publ. Ass. Nerv. Ment. Dis. Proc.*, 1952, *30*: 238–64.

William D. Neff and Irving T. Diamond

The Neural Basis of Auditory Discrimination

This research was supported by the Office of Naval Research under contract N6 ori-20, T. O. XXIV, Project NR 144 608.

In the experimental study of the brain and behavior, the oldest and the most often used method has been that in which behavior of animals has been observed before and after selective ablation of neural structures. Though the method is old, its value has not decreased. On the contrary, it has been enhanced by the development of improved experimental techniques. Comparative and physiological psychology have contributed new procedures and devices for the measurement of behavior. Anatomy and neurophysiology have provided improved methods for tracing neural pathways and mapping or outlining neural centers. Researchers from the several disciplines have devised more exact and better controlled techniques of experimental surgery.

In our application of the ablation method in the study of auditory discrimination, we have made a number of assumptions. We assume that units defined by anatomical and physiological methods have significance for behavior such that if a given unit is ablated, some measurable aspect of behavior will be altered. We start, then, with a given unit or part defined by anatomical and electrophysiological techniques, and we seek to find what attributes of behavior are dependent upon this unit or part.

We do not think of a given unit or part as being the "seat" or locus of some function. We do not expect that there will be necessarily a correspondence between the structural units we are dealing with at the anatomical level and categories of behavior as delimited at the psychological level. For example, we do not expect to find that a given function such as pitch discrimination will necessarily depend upon a specific area of the brain. Rather, we look to see how the behaviors involved in pitch discrimination, loudness discrimination, or other kind of discrimination are changed when a given part of the central nervous system is destroyed or altered.

There is nothing particularly new or unusual about these working assumptions, but we state them explicitly here because, in many past studies involving measurement of behavior changes which result from ablation of structures of the central nervous system, it is apparent that no such assumptions were made. Ablations have been made which invaded several areas without including all of any. This, we think, may be a severe handicap in advancing knowledge of the neural mechanisms underlying behavior. Furthermore, there has been a tendency on the part of many investigators to measure a given kind of discrimination, then to ablate a region of the brain and to test for loss or retention of the particular function measured. More often than not, there is no clear-cut change in the behavior variable as measured. And, unfortunately, the investigator too often goes on to investigate another part of the brain and another function without giving closer attention to the adequacy of his information defining the given region of the brain and without trying other behavioral tests or looking more closely for subtle changes in the behavior under question.

In the series of studies which we shall describe briefly below, our aims have been these:

1. To base our definitions of neural units upon the best information available from anatomical and neurophysiological studies.

2. To include, in the first ablations of any experiment, all of the region defined as a unit.

3. To use a number of tests of behavioral discrimination, not necessarily for each animal, but for different animals with similar lesions.

4. To look for changes in behavior more subtle than failure to retain a learned discrimination or inability to relearn.

5. To use both standard anatomical and electrophysiological techniques in checking the extent of our experimental ablations.

That we have not always been able to realize all these aims will be apparent from our report. The most interesting and most meaningful results have been obtained, we believe, in those experiments which have most nearly fulfilled all five of the desired conditions.

EXPERIMENTAL STUDIES

Localization of Sound in Space

In a first study of the role of the auditory cortex in auditory discrimination (15), a situation was selected in which there was opportunity to observe behavior of the experimental animal in a relatively free, unrestricted situation. It was hoped that if the particular learned response could be made after ablation of auditory cortex, some change in the manner of making the response might appear and that, if such change occurred, it might suggest further tests which could be made to bring out more clearly the behavior deficit. A diagram of the situation selected is shown in Figure 33.

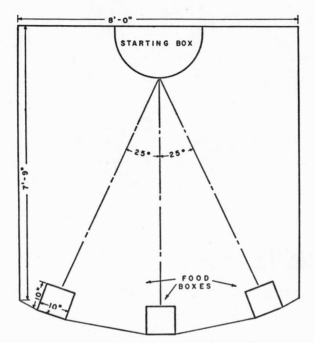

Fig. 33.—Floor plan of three-choice situation for testing localization of sound in space.

A starting box and three food boxes were placed, as shown, in a semi-soundproof room. Cats were trained to approach and open the door of the food box behind which a buzzer was sounded. Food reward was given for correct responses.

During the course of the experiment, the situation was changed: first, by removing the center box, thus making a two-choice situation with an angle of 50 degrees between the two remaining food boxes, and, second, by decreasing the distance between starting box and food boxes and, thus, again widening the angle between the boxes (130 degrees).

Four animals were trained and tested before and after bilateral ablations of auditory areas of the cortex. In all animals, all or most of AI was ablated. In two animals, nearly all of AI, AII, and Ep was ablated; very small remnants of AII may have been left intact.

Figure 34 shows results which are typical of all animals of this series. Preoperative learning was fairly rapid and, if testing was continued after a level of 95 or 100 per cent correct trials in a day's session had been reached, performance remained very stable, with only an occasional in-

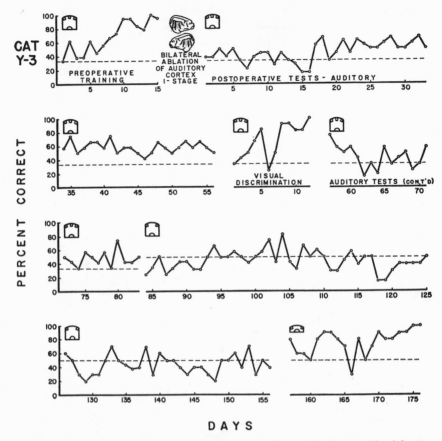

Fig. 34.—Pre- and postoperative performance curves for cat Y-3. Ten to 18 trials were given per day. The small box-shaped figures above the graph show the test situation used, i.e., 3-box, 2-box, or 2-box restricted area. The dotted lines indicate levels of performance which would be reached by chance.

correct response. In postoperative tests, all animals showed slightly better than chance behavior in the three-box and two-box, large-area situations, but performance did not reach the level attained preoperatively and was not stable even at a lower level. Moreover, there was no improvement when training was continued for a period much longer than that required for preoperative learning. For Cat Y-3, the case illustrated, post-operative training was continued for more than two thousand trials given over a period of 155 days.

To discover if the deficit in behavior was specific to auditory discrimination, two animals were tested on a visual discrimination in which the same boxes and general setup were used but in which the auditory cues were replaced by visual cues, a white card positive and black cards negative. This visual discrimination was readily learned, and stable performance obtained at the 95 to 100 per cent level. (See, for example, the curve marked "visual discrimination" in Figure 34.)

The two-box, restricted-area situation was designed in order to maximize the chances that an animal would continue its initial course when it was released from the starting cage. In this situation, all animals performed better than in the two-box or three-box, large-area situations. Performance at the 100 per cent level for a day's trials was reached, but in no case was it maintained. Day-to-day performance fluctuated between chance level and 100 per cent (see last curve of Figure 34).

From this first study, it was apparent that animals with large bilateral ablations of auditory cortex could localize sound in space but that performance in this kind of discrimination was inferior to that of normal animals. It was not clear whether the deficit in performance was due to decrease in ability to localize sound, decrease in ability to maintain attention to a sound cue and to use that cue to guide behavior, or decrease in ability to learn that sound was the signal that food was available; the change in performance of operated animals might be interpreted as a loss in one or several of these different abilities.

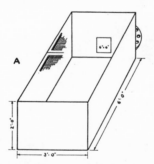

Fig. 35.—Test situation with single door leading to food reward.

To examine the possibility that animals with ablations of auditory cortex are deficient in the ability to learn that food may be obtained whenever a sound signal is presented, several animals with bilateral ablations of auditory areas AI, AII, and Ep were trained and tested by Dr. Rosner (20) in the situation shown in Figure 35.

The learned response in this situation was simply the opening of the

single door when a buzzer or tone was sounded and the inhibition of responses during silent intervals. Learning was measured in terms of decrease in reaction time to the sound signal and decrease in number of
spontaneous responses during the intervals between sound presentations.
Operated animals performed in this situation almost as well as normal
animals; they differed mainly in that they tended to make more spontaneous responses.

To carry this line of investigation further, a new set of experiments
was planned with Dr. Arnott (3, 14), and a new apparatus to test localization of sound in space was constructed (see Fig. 36), making it possible to

Fig. 36.—Semicircular enclosure with starting cage and
two food-reward boxes. This arrangement was used in
testing minimum angles of sound localization. The sound
signal, a buzzer, was placed behind one or the other of the
food boxes.

vary the distance between food boxes (and, likewise, of positions of buzzer)
from 180 degrees to zero degrees. Thus, threshold angles of discrimination
could be measured. The situation was also designed so that animals could
be trained and tested under a variety of conditions, e.g., in complete
darkness, in a dimly lighted room with the doors of the food boxes illumi-

nated, and in the presence of distracting background noise. It was hoped that by altering there different conditions, it would be possible to obtain evidence which would enable us to have a clearer picture of why performance in the localization situation was affected by ablation of auditory cortex. Furthermore, it was the intention, in making experimental lesions of the cortex, to ablate all of areas AI, AII, and Ep.

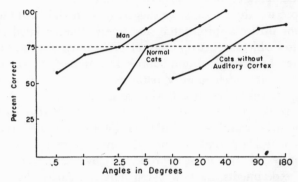

Fig. 37.—Curves showing angles discriminated correctly in sound localization by man, normal cats, and cats with auditory cortex ablated. The dotted line indicates the 75 per cent level.

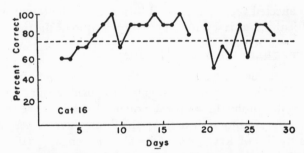

Fig. 38.—Curve showing postoperative performance for cat A-16 in sound localization situation. Angle between food boxes and, thus, between successive positions of buzzer was 180 degrees.

The results of the study are summarized briefly by Figures 37 and 38. As shown in Figure 37, normal animals could discriminate at the 75 per cent level (50 per cent was chance) an angle of 5 degrees. This compares favorably with the performance of man in the same situation. This latter measure is a rough approximation only. Animals with ablation of auditory areas AI, AII, and Ep were able to make discriminations at the 75 per cent level only when the angle between successive positions of the buzzer was 40 degrees or more.

Moreover, as may be seen in Figure 38, a curve for one animal, but typical of the performance curves of all animals in the operated group, again showed the same variability of performance from day to day that had been observed in the earlier experiments.

In interpreting these results, we suggest that animals without auditory cortex cannot utilize appropriately the finely differentiated patterns of nerve impulses which are set up in lower brain centers when the two ears are stimulated by a single sound source, i.e., at the level in the central nervous system at which sensory patterns are translated to motor behavior, the patterns are confused, whereas in the animal with intact cortex they are readily differentiated. We further suggest that animals without auditory cortex cannot maintain attention to sound signals and, therefore, behavior over a period of time (temporal intervals of a few seconds to a few minutes) is not guided appropriately by a sound signal.

Further experiments are now being done to clarify the mechanisms underlying localization of sound in space. Preliminary results obtained in experiments done with Mr. W. Blau and now being continued with Miss G. C. Nauman, indicate that the ability to localize, as measured in the situations described above, is not affected by section of the *corpus callosum,* is affected very little if at all by section of the commissure of the inferior colliculus, but is severely affected by section of the trapezoid body.

FREQUENCY DISCRIMINATION

A series of experiments, distinct from those on localization of sound in space, was begun in order to investigate the possible significance of the tonotopic organization which evoked-potential studies have shown to be a feature of the auditory cortex. At the time these experiments were started, the studies of Kryter and Ades (10), Rosenzweig (19), and Raab and Ades (17) had shown that for the cat, bilateral ablation of areas AI, AII, and Ep does not produce any change in absolute intensity thresholds throughout the frequency range 125 to 8000 cps or in the differential thresholds for intensity. The learned discriminations were, in some cases, affected by the ablations, but relearning was rapid, and discrimination after relearning was as good as before surgery.

Because of the tonotopic organization of the auditory cortex, it is a rather obvious hypothesis that perhaps the cortical projection areas play an important role in the discrimination of changes in frequency. In an experiment designed to test this hypothesis and carried out in collaboration with Dr. Butler (5), cats were trained to respond to a change in frequency of a pulsing tone (on for 1 sec., off for 1 sec.) by crossing from one side to another of a double-grill box in order to avoid shock. When the experimental animals had learned to respond correctly to a large change in frequency, the difference between negative and positive signals was gradually reduced to a near-threshold level. At a difference slightly above threshold, training was then given to establish stable performance. In half the animals (Group A) used in this experiment, cortical areas AI, AII, and Ep were ablated bilaterally; in the other half (Group B), the lesion was extended into somatic area II in addition to AI, AII, and Ep. A summary of results is shown in Table 4.

TABLE 4

Summary results of frequency discrimination tests

Group	Cat	Frequency Change	Percent of CR's Preop.	Percent of CR's Postop.	Mock Trials % R's Postop.	Intensity Trials—% R's Preop.	Intensity Trials—% R's Postop.
A	1	200–210	60	55	10	5	10
	2	2000–2025	70	80	25	20	0
	3	8000–8200	65	70*	14	0	40
B	4	200–210	80	55	10	20	20
	5	2000–2025	95	60	13	5	35
	6	8000–8200	85	80	0	5	0

* Frequency change in postoperative trial of cat 3 was 8000–8300.

In brief, it may be noted that bilateral ablation of AI, AII, and Ep had little or no effect on the ability of the experimental animals to discriminate changes in frequency. Animals which had damage to somatic II in addition to ablation of AI, AII, and Ep performed slightly less well postoperatively but still could make quite fine frequency discriminations. Control tests indicated that responses were not due to spontaneous activity nor to changes in the sound signal other than changes in frequency.

Postoperative retention of the learned habit of frequency discrimination was measured in two ways: by number of correct responses made on unreinforced test trials given before retraining was begun, and by savings in time for retraining to a criterion of three correct responses in four successive trials. Animals of both groups failed to show signs of retention as measured by the test trials, but all except one animal showed marked savings in relearning. The one exception had severe blindness due to damage to optic radiations. Therefore, in its postoperative learning, it was handicapped by an initial period of disorientation in the double-grill box.

Brains of the experimental animals used in the frequency experiment were sectioned and stained, thionin for cells and Weil's stain for tracts. From the sections, the lateral surfaces of the two cerebral hemispheres were reconstructed to show the areas of the cortical lesions, and plots were made of degeneration in the thalamus.

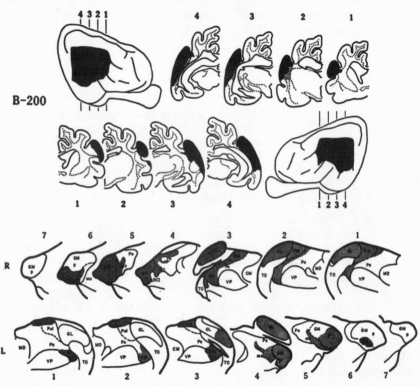

Fig. 39.—Area of cortex ablated and retrograde degeneration in thalamus of cat B-200. Ablated cortex is indicated by blackened area; damaged and probably nonfunctional tissue, by stippling; thalamic degeneration, by diagonal lines. Abbreviations used in Figures 39, 40, 45, 46, and 47 are as follows: *BCI,* brachium of inferior colliculus; *CL, n. centralis lateralis; CM, n. centrum medianum; GL,* lateral geniculate body; *GMmc,* or *mc,* magnocellular division of medial geniculate body; *GMp,* principal division of medial geniculate body; *LD, n. lateralis dorsalis; LP, n. lateralis posterior; MD, medialis dorsalis; Mid,* midbrain; *Po,* posterior group; *Pul, n. pulvinaris; TO,* optic tract; *VP, n. ventralis posterior; VPL, n. ventralis posterolateralis; VPM, ventralis posteromedialis.*

In Group A, the lesions of all three animals included areas AI, AII, and Ep. Reconstructions show that the lesions were bounded anteriorly by the anterior suprasylvian sulcus, dorsally by the medial suprasylvian sulcus, and posteriorly by the posterior suprasylvian sulcus. The extent of the lesion in a ventral direction differed some from animal to animal. The most restricted lesion of this series is shown in Figure 39 (Cat B-200). All of the cortex of AI, AII, and Ep has been removed bilaterally with the possible exception of a remnant in the depths of the anterior ectosylvian sulcus (see frontal section 2, left side). On the right side, the ablated region extends somewhat further ventrally than it does on the left.

In the thalamus (Fig. 39), the posterior part of the principal division of each medial geniculate body is largely intact; the degeneration in the left medial geniculate is less extensive than in the right. There is bilateral degeneration in the posterior group, in the pulvinar, and in the lateral geniculate.*

In animals of Group A, the anterior and middle portions of the principal division of the medial geniculate bodies appear to be completely degenerated in every case. There is some variation in the extent to which the degenerated area penetrates into the posterior tip; more extensive degeneration appears to be related to the amount of cortex removed in the region ventral to AI, AII, and Ep.

We have studied two brains in Group B of the frequency-discrimination cats. The third was lost to histology. The reconstructed cortical lesion and selected cross sections of the thalamus for one animal (Cat B-165) are shown in Figure 40. The lesion on both sides includes, in addition to AI, AII, and Ep, some cortex ventral to AII in the vicinity of the pseudosylvain sulcus and cortex anterior and ventral to the audi-

---

* The principal division of the medial geniculate. (GMp) first appears between the optic tract and *n. ventralis posterior* (VP). Dorsal to GM and VP and lying between the lateral geniculate body (GL) and *n. medialis dorsalis* (MD) is an area conventionally divided into *n. pulvinaris* (Pul) dorsolaterally, and *n. lateralis posterior* (LP) medially. The ventral part of this complex has been called a portion of the posterior group (Po) by Rose and Woolsey. The posterior group includes what some workers have called *n. posterior* and *n. suprageniculatis*. We have adopted Rose's terminology. In a posterior direction, the medial geniculate principal division develops into a curved band of densely packed small cells. Medial to this band is a group of large cells, the magnocellular division of the medial geniculate (GMmc or mc). In places, these two portions are partially separated by the brachium of the inferior colliculus (BCI). Both GMmc and GMp fuse dorsally with Po. The dividing lines are not clear and in some maps of the cat's thalamus, portions of Po are shown as belonging to GMmc or GMp. Still another region where no sharp boundaries can be drawn lies between GMmc, Po, and VP.

B-165

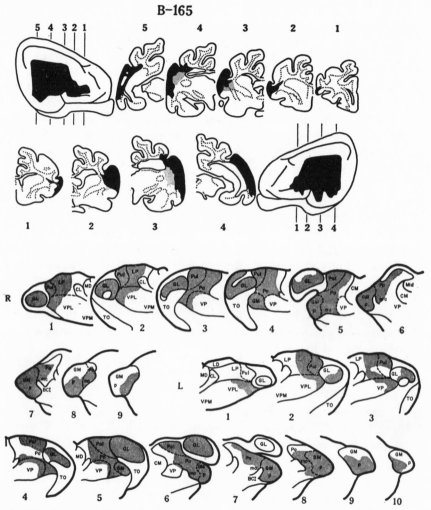

Fig. 40.—Cortical lesion and thalamic degeneration of cat B-165.

tory areas in the anterior ectosylvian gyrus. In the right hemisphere, damage continues parallel to the diagonal sulcus, probably entering the face area of somatic I. The lesion is very superficial in the coronal gyrus (frontal section 1). On the left side, a larger piece of the diagonal sulcus appears anterior to the lesion. Possibly some of the face area of somatic II has been spared; the leg and arm areas appear to have been removed.

Both medial geniculate bodies of Cat B-165 are completely degenerated except for a region in the dorsal half of each posterior tip. In addition, there is massive degeneration bilaterally in the pulvinar, in the *n. lateralis posterior*, in the posterior group, in the lateral geniculate, and in *n. ventralis posterior*.

The cortical lesion of Cat B-159, a second animal with auditory cortex plus somatic II ablation, is less extensive ventrally than that of Cat B-165, but in the anterior direction on both sides it extends to the coronal sulcus. In the thalamus, there is partial degeneration bilaterally of the lateral geniculate, of *n. ventralis posterior*, and of the posterior group as well as of the medial geniculate. Somewhat more of the caudal part of the medial geniculate is preserved than in Cat B-165. The difference between Cats B-159 and B-165 and the cats of Group A is that in the former, degeneration appears in *n. ventralis posterior*. This additional degeneration may have resulted from partial invasion of somatic I or from interrupting thalamic radiations to this cortical sector.

When our results are compared with those reported by Meyer and Woolsey (12), there is agreement that very little, if any, impairment of frequency discrimination occurs after bilateral ablation of AI, AII, and Ep. Findings of the two studies differ, however, in that in Meyer and Woolsey's experiments one animal with ablation of AI, AII, Ep, and somatic II and a second animal with ablation of these areas plus massive ablation of cortex dorsal, posterior, and ventral to the auditory areas, failed to relearn frequency discrimination although both animals did learn an intensity discrimination postoperatively. A third animal with AI, AII, Ep, and somatic II ablated bilaterally performed very poorly postoperatively on the frequency discrimination task. In our experiments, three animals with ablation of AI, AII, Ep, and somatic II relearned frequency discriminations after operation and performed at nearly the preoperative level.

This difference in the results of the two experiments may be due to either of two differences in experimental procedures. One possibility is that the test situations were not the same. In both experiments, avoidance conditioning was used, but Meyer and Woolsey used a rotating cage in which the animal was required to move a few steps forward in response to change in the stimulus, while we used a double-grill box in which the correct response was passage from one compartment to another through an open doorway. From our experience with both the rotating cage and the double-grill box, we feel that the latter is more suitable for use in experiments in which a long period of training trials with repeated reinforcement is necessary. The advantage is that spontaneous responses occur less readily and can be more easily controlled in the double-grill box.

A second possible explanation of the difference between the two experiments may be the extent of the cortical ablations. Very fortunately, this Symposium provides the opportunity for us to compare the results of anatomical examination of brains of our experimental animals with similar results which Dr. Rose and Dr. Woolsey will present for the animals used in the Meyer and Woolsey experiments.

Pattern Discrimination

Although the auditory areas of the cortex are not essential for frequency discrimination, their tonotopic organization and structure in terms of neuronal organization suggest that some notion as to their function may be obtained by exploring more complex discriminations, particularly those involving the integration of temporal patterns of tones. Furthermore, by analogy with the visual system, it would appear as a likely hypothesis that discrimination of patterns of sounds might be affected by cortical ablation.

To examine the role of auditory cortex in pattern discrimination, a situation similar to that of the frequency discrimination study was used (6). Cats were trained in the double-grill box to respond to a change in a temporal pattern of tones. A pattern consisted of three tones, each 0.9 sec. in length with 0.1 sec. between tones. The groups of three tones each

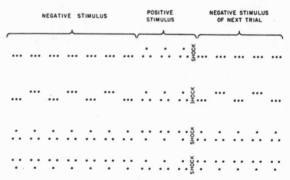

Fig. 41.—Diagram to show sequence of tones in testing discrimination of tonal patterns.

were separated by 2.1 sec. The diagram of Figure 41 shows the different tonal patterns used. It should be noted that in the first sequence only a frequency discrimination is required in order that a correct response can be made to the positive signal, while in the other sequences, the signals have to be perceived as groups or patterns.

Six cats were trained on one or another of the different discriminations shown in Figure 41. After training, they were subjected to bilateral ablation of auditory cortex. In two animals, an attempt was made to ablate AI only; in two others, an attempt was made to ablate AI, AII, and Ep but to do as little damage as possible to cortex outside of these areas. In the remaining two animals, the lesion was made large enough to be certain that all of AI, AII, and Ep was removed.

After completion of postoperative testing and/or retraining, the extent of cortical ablation for some of the animals was evaluated by reexposing the region of the lesion and using the evoked-potential technique to discover if active auditory cortex remained. In this way, it was found that animals with AI ablations had small remnants of AI intact as well as most of AII and Ep. Of the two animals with lesions limited to the auditory areas, one was found to have active auditory cortex remaining in the anterior part of AI. Because of the failure to obtain satisfactory spontaneous responses, the attempt to record evoked responses from the second animal was given up. The ablations of the two animals with the largest lesions clearly extended beyond the boundaries of auditory cortex; therefore, there was no point in attempting to record evoked responses.

With regard to postoperative behavior, the results obtained are illustrated by Figures 42, 43, and 44. In Figure 42, it may be seen that an

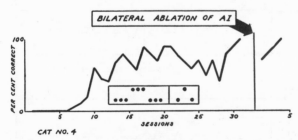

Fig. 42.—Pre- and postoperative performance curves on pattern discrimination for animal with large lesion in AI.

animal with most of AI ablated showed little or no loss of the ability to make a pattern discrimination postoperatively. The other animal with similar ablation behaved in a similar fashion.

Animals with all but a small remnant of auditory cortex ablated behaved as illustrated by the one case whose curves of performance are shown in Figure 43. There was a loss of pattern discrimination after operation, but relearning occurred.

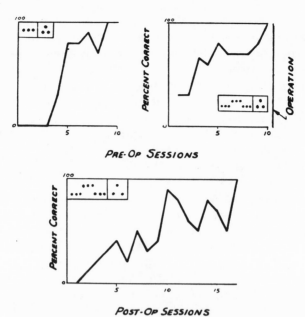

Fig. 43.—Performance curves on pattern discrimination for animal with all but a small remnant of auditory cortex ablated.

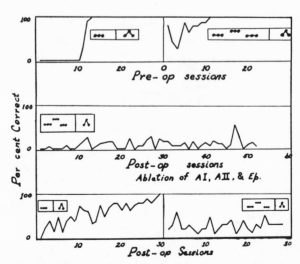

Fig. 44.—Performance curves on pattern discrimination and frequency discrimination for animal with complete ablation of AI, AII, and Ep.

Performance typical of animals with complete ablation of AI, AII, and Ep is illustrated by Figure 44. Postoperatively, frequency discrimination could be learned but pattern discrimination could not.

From the reconstructions of the cortical lesions and the plots of thalamic degeneration, the three groups of animals, as defined by the behavioral tests and by electrophysiological check of cortical damage, differ distinctly both in terms of extent of cortex removed and amount of retrograde degeneration in the thalamus. Anatomical results for a typical animal from each group are shown in Figures 45, 46, and 47.

In the case of Cat D-228, it may be seen that in both cerebral hemispheres, the cortex of most of the region usually called AI is ablated. We know, however, from our electrophysiological examination of the intact cortex surrounding the lesion, that evoked strychnine responses could be obtained from the point marked *a*. This point was maximally sensitive to frequencies in the neighborhood of 500 cps; therefore, it must be part of the low-tone region of AI. Evoked strychnine responses were also

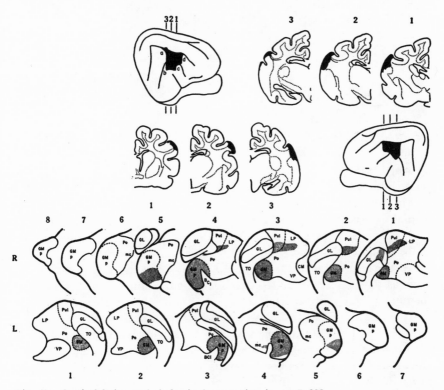

Fig. 45.—Cortical lesion and thalamic degeneration in cat D-228.

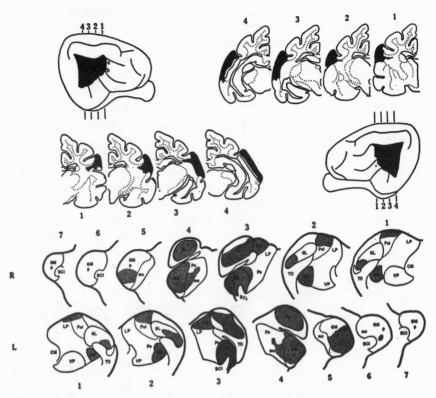

Fig. 46.—Cortical lesion and thalamic degeneration in cat D-218.

obtained from points *b, c,* and *d;* the frequency response curves for these points indicate that they are part of AII.

In the thalamus, the anterior part of the principal division of each medial geniculate body is degenerated; the magnocellular division is intact. There is slight degeneration in the lateral geniculate bodies and in the posterior thalamic group.

In the second cat of the AI group, the cortical lesion is not quite as large as that of Cat D-228. Retrograde degeneration in the thalamus is correspondingly more limited.

In the case of Cat D-218, an animal with cortical ablation of intermediate size, the lesion includes AI and Ep bilaterally. Evoked-potential examination at the time the animal was sacrificed showed that some active auditory cortex remained at points *a* and *b* in the right hemisphere. From the frequency response curves obtained at these points, the intact cortex was identified as belonging to the low-tone region of AII. On the left side, the area surrounding the lesion was not explored by electrical recording methods, but it would appear from the reconstruction that a part of AII in the anterior ectosylvian gyrus is present on this side as well as on the right.

As compared with Cat D-228, degeneration of the principal division of the medial geniculate bodies in Cat D-218 extends further posteriorly; the magnocellular division appears to be normal.

The cortical lesion in the second animal of this group in which the attempt at surgery had been to ablate AI, AII, and Ep but not to go beyond the boundaries of these areas is somewhat larger than that of D-218; the lesion extends further into the anterior ectosylvian gyrus. The extent of degeneration in the principal division of the medial geniculate bodies is similar to that of Cat D-218. In addition, there is some degeneration in the magnocellular division and massive degeneration in the pulvinar and in *n. lateralis posterior*.

Cat D-134 represents a typical animal of the group in which the cor-

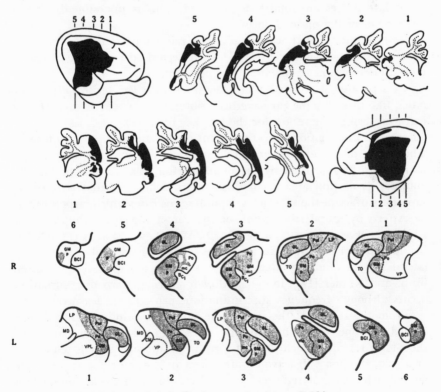

Fig. 47.—Cortical lesion and thalamic degeneration in cat D-134.

tical lesions were enlarged to make certain that all of the auditory areas, AI, AII, and Ep, were ablated. As may be seen from the reconstruction of the lateral surface of the cortex, the cortex of the auditory areas appears to be completely removed. In both hemispheres, the lesion extends ventrally below the tip of the pseudosylvian sulcus. On the left side, in particular, it may be seen that the lesion reaches almost to the rhinal fissure. On both sides, cortex in the anterior ectosylvian gyrus beyond the boundaries of AI and AII is gone, and portions of the upper bank of the suprasylvian sulcus have been removed.

Examination of thalamic sections reveals nearly total degeneration of the principal part of the medial geniculate body on the left side. In a very small dorsal region at the caudal tip, degeneration may not be complete. Slightly more of the caudal tip remains on the right side. Loss of cells and marked gliosis are found in the magnocellular division on both sides. In Cat D-134, there is also massive degeneration of the posterior group, of *n. lateralis posterior,* and of the pulvinar. Both lateral geniculate bodies are totally degenerated. This is undoubtedly due to transection of the optic radiations.

The second animal which failed to relearn pattern discrimination postoperatively is similar to D-134 with regard to extent of cortex removed and amount of thalamic degeneration.

In a parallel study on the monkey done with Dr. Jerison (7), results much like those for the cat have been obtained. It is not as easy, at present, to interpret the results for the monkey because there is less complete anatomical information as to the extent of the auditory projection areas. The results of our experiments indicate, however, that pattern discriminations can be relearned by the monkey after bilateral ablation of the auditory projection area when this area is defined as that part of the superior surface of the superior temporal gyrus from which responses may be evoked by sound stimulation of the ear or electrical stimulation of auditory nerve endings (1, 4, 9, 17, 20). When the lesion is extended to include adjacent cortical tissue in the sylvian fissure and cortex of the lateral surface (auditory areas as recently reported by Pribram, Rosenblith, and Rosner [16]), loss of ability to learn pattern discriminations occurs although frequency discriminations can still be learned.

From the results of the studies on pattern discrimination, it is concluded that one role of the auditory cortex is to provide a mechanism for short-term retention such that, in a group of auditory signals temporally arranged, the first will leave an aftereffect in the central nervous system with which neural activity set up by succeeding signals may interact. As a further test of this hypothesis, experiments have been started in which animals are trained to respond to a change in rhythm, e.g., dot-dash-dot-dot *vs.* dot-dot-dash-dot. Behavioral results are complete for only two animals. In the case of one animal which readily relearned the rhythm discrimination after bilateral ablation of auditory cortex, a small part of AII was found from which evoked responses could be recorded. The second animal failed to relearn after operation. No active cortex could be found in this latter case when evoked-response tests were made at time of sacrifice.

In another series of experiments being done with Mr. Jay Goldberg, very small patches of cortex have been left in AI or AII with all other auditory cortex of these areas and of Ep ablated. The results obtained to date confirm the findings described above, namely, that pattern discrimination can be relearned with a very small amount of cortex remaining in either AI or AII.

FURTHER ANATOMICAL CONSIDERATIONS

The examination of the brains of experimental animals used in studies which have been reviewed above and of selected animals from other experiments which we have not reported here has given us considerable information about the thalamocortical connections of the auditory system of the cat. This information may be summarized briefly as follows:

1. AI of the auditory cortex of the cat receives projections from the principal division of the medial geniculate body. Ablation of all or nearly all of AI without damage to surrounding areas causes retrograde degeneration that is confined to the anterior half (approximately) of the principal division of the ipsilateral medial geniculate body. (See Cat 228, referred to above.) These findings agree with those of earlier investigations (18, 22).

2. As the amount of cortical ablation is extended to include AII and Ep as well as AI, the degeneration in the principal division of the medial geniculate extends somewhat further caudally than with ablation of AI alone. (See Cat B-200, referred to above.)

3. When the area of ablation is increased still further in a ventral direction beyond the line usually considered to be the boundary of AII and Ep, degeneration penetrates into the posterior tip of the medial geniculate. In the case of Cat D-134, for example, only a very small dorsal region is left in the posterior tip, and there is partial degeneration of this region. In view of this finding, we would expect complete degeneration of the medial geniculate with a lesion which includes, in addition to AI, AII, and Ep, a sufficient extent of cortex between the auditory areas and the rhinal fissure. With Dr. Chow, we have made unilateral

ablations restricted to this ventral region in a number of animals in order to study retrograde degeneration in the thalamus. Dr. Chow will comment later on some of the first results which have been obtained from these experiments.

4. In animals with ablations which include considerable cortex ventral to AII and Ep, not only does thalamic degeneration spread to involve most of the principal part of the medial geniculate, but the magnocellular division is also invaded. In Cat D-134, for example, cell loss and marked gliosis is present throughout a large part of the magnocellular division.

5. We have examined two cases (see, e.g., Cat B-165, referred to above) in which all or most of somatic II was ablated in addition to AI, AII, and Ep. In both cases, degeneration occurs in the principal division of the medial geniculate, which is typical of that seen in animals with cortical ablations confined to the auditory areas alone. The additional degeneration which may be seen, we have attributed to damage to subcortical pathways or to partial invasion of somatic I.

Considering the results of our own anatomical and electrophysiological studies and those of other experimenters, we would conclude, at present, that the region to be called auditory cortex may be defined in accordance with at least these three different criteria:

1. As that area in which ablations produce retrograde degeneration in the principal part of the medial geniculate body. By this criterion, the auditory area is that commonly called AI.

2. As that area from which responses may be evoked when the ear is stimulated by tonal pulses or clicks or by electrical stimulation of auditory nerve fibers. By this criterion, the auditory cortex includes AI, AII, and the ventral part of Ep. At present, the evidence is not clear, but it may be necessary to add to the above areas part of somatic II and a region in the anterior suprasylvian gyrus (13, 4).

3. As that area the ablation of which produces complete degeneration of the principal part of the medial geniculate body. By this criterion, the auditory cortex includes AI, AII, Ep, and cortex lying between these regions and the rhinal fissure.

In accordance with the assumptions stated in the introduction of our paper, we would attempt to find changes in behavior which are critically related to ablation of auditory cortex as defined by each of the above criteria. When we say that a behavioral task is critically related to a given cortical area, we mean that the capacity to perform the task sharply distinguishes between animals which have suffered complete ablation of the area in question and animals which have part or all of the area intact.

In our experiments, we have found a test, pattern discrimination, which is critically related to ablation of auditory cortex when the latter is defined according to criterion 2. We cannot say that the ability to localize sound in space is critically related to ablation of auditory cortex as defined by any of the three criteria. We only know at the present time that ablation of all or most of AI or ablation of AI, AII, and Ep results in a deficit in localization ability.

ELECTROPHYSIOLOGICAL STUDIES

Results of two recent studies done in our laboratory by Kiang (9) and by Kennedy, Kiang, and Sutton (8) should be mentioned briefly because they have bearing upon the problem of organization of the auditory cortex in the cat and in the monkey.

Recording from isolated patches of cortex in the auditory subareas, AI, AII, and ventral Ep, Kiang has found that responses can be elicited from a patch in any of these three regions when all other auditory cortex of the same side and all auditory cortex of the opposite hemisphere have been ablated. This finding indicates that AII and ventral Ep as well as AI receive auditory projections from subcortical centers.

Kiang has also confirmed the results, first reported by Ades (1), that an evoked response may be recorded from the ventral part of Ep when strychnine is applied to a small area of AI. Moreover, he has found that this driven response can be obtained when a strychnine patch is placed upon the low-tone portion of AII (the part of AII anterior to the anterior ectosylvian sulcus). The driven response has a longer latency than a smaller response which may be observed in the absence of strychninization of AI or anterior AII. This shorter-latency response is probably the same as that recorded by Woolsey and Walzl (25) from ventral Ep. There are several other interesting characteristics of the driven response of ventral Ep. One, in particular, is that the frequency response curve obtained from a given point in Ep is shifted in accordance with the frequency response curve of the place to which strychnine is applied in AI or anterior AII.

Considered in terms of its response characteristics, both with and without application of strychnine, Kiang suggests that the low-frequency part of AII is more like AI than it is like the part of AII which lies in the pseudosylvian gyrus.

Kennedy, Kiang, and Sutton have mapped the cortex of the rhesus monkey. Tonal pulses were used to stimulate the ear, and the cortex within the sylvian fissure, and on the lateral surface surrounding the sylvian fissure, was explored for evoked responses. With application of strychnine, strychnine spikes could be elicited only from the classical auditory area, a region of the superior surface of the superior temporal gyrus within the sylvian fissure. Tonotopic organization of this area was found. No clear evidence was found for an area corresponding to AII in the cat.

Under Dial anesthesia, a response such as that described by Pribram, Rosner, and Rosenblith (16) was recorded from a widespread area extending over the supratemporal plane into the inferior parts of the post-central and posterior parietal gyri, and over the lateral surface of the superior temporal gyrus. This widespread response could not be obtained under Nembutal anesthesia. On the basis of findings in experiments using depth recording, topical application of drugs, surgical isolation, and thermocoagulation, it was concluded that the responses recorded from the lateral surface are not locally generated.

METHODOLOGY

From our experience in the studies we have described and in other experiments using the ablation method, we have two specific suggestions to make as to methodology.

After completion of postoperative behavioral tests, invaluable information can be obtained by using electrophysiological techniques to explore the region of ablation. In the experiments on pattern discrimination, we were able to discover very small remnants of active auditory cortex. From reconstruction of the cortical lesions and from examination of thalamic degeneration, we could not have given as unequivocal an answer as to the presence of active auditory cortex.

The use of electrical recording techniques under aseptic conditions can also provide an exact way of defining a given neural area or sub-area as a guide to surgery. We have attempted to do this in a few cases and are convinced that with the proper laboratory arrangements, it will be a valuable procedure for future experiments.

REFERENCES

1 Ades, H. W. A secondary acoustic area in the cerebral cortex of the cat. *J. Neurophysiol.*, 1943, *6*: 59–63.
2 Ades, H. W., and R. E. Felder. The acoustic area of the monkey (Macaca mulatta). *J. Neurophysiol.*, 1942, *5*: 49–54.
3 Arnott, G. P., and W. D. Neff. The function of the auditory cortex: The control of learned responses to sound cues. *Amer. Psychologist*, 1950, *5*: 270.
4 Bremer, F. Analyse oscillographique des réponses sensorielles des écorces cérébrale et cérébelleuse. *Rev. Neurol.*, 1952, *87*: 65–92.
5 Butler, R. A., I. T. Diamond, and W. D. Neff. Role of auditory cortex in

discrimination of changes in frequency. *J. Neurophysiol.*, 1957, *20:* 108–20.

6   Diamond, I. T., and W. D. Neff. Ablation of temporal cortex and discrimination of auditory patterns. *J. Neurophysiol.*, 1957, *20:* 300–15.

7   Jerison, H. J., and W. D. Neff. Effect of cortical ablation in the monkey on discrimination of auditory patterns. *Fed. Proc.*, 1953, *12:* 73–74 (Abstract).

8   Kennedy, T., N. Kiang, and S. Sutton. Auditory projection areas of the cortex in monkey (Macaca mulatta). *Amer. J. Physiol.*, 1956, *183:* 634.

9   Kiang, N. Organization of auditory cortex in the cat. *Amer. J. Physiol.*, 1956, *183:* 635.

10   Kryter, K. D., and H. W. Ades. Studies on the function of the higher acoustic nervous centers in the cat. *Amer. J. Psychol.*, 1943, *56:* 501–536.

11   Licklider, J. C. R., and K. D. Kryter. Frequency localization in the auditory cortex of the monkey. *Fed. Proc.*, 1942, *1:* 51 (Abstract).

12   Meyer, D. R., and C. N. Woolsey. Effects of localized cortical destruction on auditory discriminative conditioning in cat. *J. Neurophysiol.*, 1952, *15:* 149–62.

13   Mickle, W. A., and H. W. Ades. Cortical projection of postural impulses. *Fed. Proc.*, 1951, *10:* 92 (Abstract).

14   Neff, W. D., G. P. Arnott, and J. D. Fisher. Function of the auditory cortex: Localization of sound in space. *Amer. J. Physiol.*, 1950, *163:* 738 (Abstract).

15   Neff, W. D., J. F. Fisher, I. T. Diamond, and M. Yela. Role of auditory cortex in discrimination requiring localization of sound in space. *J. Neurophysiol.*, 1956, *19:* 500–12.

16   Pribram, K. H., B. S. Rosner, and W. A. Rosenblith. Electrical responses to acoustic clicks in monkey: Extent of neocortex activated. *J. Neurophysiol.*, 1954, *17:* 336–44.

17   Raab, D. H., and H. W. Ades. Cortical and midbrain mediation of a conditioned discrimination of acoustic intensities. *Amer. J. Psychol.*, 1946, *59:* 59–83.

18   Rose, J. E., and C. N. Woolsey. The relations of thalamic connections, cellular structure and evocable electrical activity in the auditory region of the cat. *J. comp. Neurol.*, 1949, *91:* 441–66.

19   Rosenzweig, M. Discrimination of auditory intensities in the cat. *Amer. J. Psychol.*, 1946, *59:* 127–36.

20   Rosner, B. S., and W. D. Neff. Function of the auditory cortex: Acquisition and retention of an approach response to a sound stimulus. *Amer. Psychol.*, 1949, *4:* 235.

21   Sugar, O., J. D. French, and J. G. Chusid. Corticocortical connections of the superior surface of the temporal operculum in the monkey (Macaca mulatta). *J. Neurophysiol.*, 1948, *11:* 175–84.

22   Waller, W. H. Thalamic degeneration induced by temporal lesions in the cat. *J. Anat., Lond.*, 1939, *74:* 528–36.

23   Walzl, E. M. Representation of the cochlea in the cerebral cortex. *Laryngoscope*, 1947, *57:* 778–87.

24 Woolsey, C. N. Patterns of sensory representation in the cerebral cortex. *Fed. Proc.*, 1947, *6:* 437–41.

25 Woolsey, C. N., and E. M. Walzl. Topical projection of nerve fibers from local regions of the cochlea to the cerebral cortex of the cat. *Johns Hopk. Hosp. Bull.*, 1942, *71:* 315–44.

Cortical Connections and Functional
Organization of the Thalamic Auditory
System of the Cat

This investigation was supported by research grant B-357 to the Johns Hopkins University and by grant B-35 to the University of Wisconsin from the National Institute of Neurological Diseases and Blindness, NIH, U.S. Department of Health, Education and Welfare.

We wish to present some results concerning the problem of localization of function in the auditory cortex of the cat. It is, we believe, proper to present these results in a Symposium at which the significance of the interdisciplinary approach is stressed, first, because the data to be discussed stem from anatomical, electrophysiological, and experimental-psychological investigations, and secondly, because it will be shown that diverse methods applied to the same problem, and whenever practicable to the same material, lead to interpretations which are not at all apparent when any one method alone is relied upon exclusively.

Since in auditory research the use of such diverse methods promises to be fruitful, it is, perhaps, not merely a fortunate coincidence that we have chosen a topic similar to Dr. Neff's. To listen to two expositions on the same subject may tax your patience somewhat. However, we hope that our results are, for the most part, complementary rather than contradictory and that a much needed clarification of certain problems will be the outcome of these presentations.

With the advancement of evoked potential techniques there has been considerable interest in the analysis of the cortical region of the cat which can be activated by sound stimuli. This region is, broadly speaking, bounded by the suprasylvian sulcus and is shown in Figure 48. It consists of the first (AI) and second (AII) auditory areas and the posterior ectosylvian field (Ep). There is a concordance of opinion as to the boundaries of these fields except for the sector which is crosshatched and dotted in the figure. This difference of opinion need not concern us further for there is almost complete agreement among all investigators that these fields together form the auditory region of the cat as far as this region can be determined by the evoked potential method. Below AII and Ep and above the rhinal sulcus lies a region which we shall call the tem-

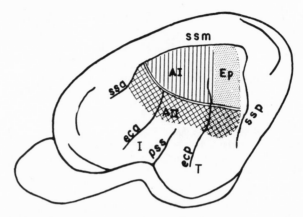

Fig. 48.—Cortical region activated by sound stimuli in deeply anesthetized cat. The double line divides the region into the first (dorsal) and the second (ventral) potential fields as determined by electrical stimulation of cochlear nerve fibers (Woolsey and Walzl, 25). Within the dorsal potential field the hatched area represents the first auditory field (*AI*) as determined cytoarchitecturally. The limits of this field are coextensive with the limits of the essential projection area of the principal division of the medial geniculate body and with the anteroposterior extent of the focal band of electrical activity evoked by localized stimulation of successive groups of cochlear nerve fibers in the spiral osseous lamina. The crosshatched area shows the extent of the oral portion of the second auditory field (*AII*). The upper portion of the posterior ectosylvian area (dotted) is structurally distinct from the first auditory field and gives rise to small potentials on stimulation of cochlear nerve fibers. The dotted and the crosshatched sectors form together the posterior ectosylvian area (*Ep*). The evoked potential studies indicate that the crosshatched-dotted sector is the caudal portion of the second auditory area. Note the location of the temporal region (*T*) and that of the insular region (*I*) in front of the pseudosylvian sulcus (*pss*); *eca*, anterior ectosylvian sulcus; *ecp*, posterior ectosylvian sulcus; *saa, ssm, ssp* are the anterior, middle, and posterior branches of the suprasylvian sulcus, respectively.

poral region of the cat (T), while in front of the pseudosylvian sulcus (pss) there extends the insular region (I).

One might expect that the cortical region which can be activated by sound stimuli would include all the cortex which is directly connected with the thalamic auditory system. That this simple presumption is not correct will be one of the major conclusions to be drawn from our findings. A few years ago Meyer and Woolsey (15) attempted to define the smallest cortical removals which would cause a deficit in the capacity of the animal to discriminate small increments in frequency. They found that bilateral removal of any or all of the then-known auditory fields did not cause any permanent deficit. Such deficit resulted only if in addition to removal of the entire classical auditory region the second somatic cortex was destroyed as well. We shall start with an analysis of these brains in which retrograde degenerations in the thalamus were studied. It will be demonstrated that in addition to the medial geniculate body at least one other thalamic grouping is apparently concerned with auditory activity. Furthermore, we shall show that the thalamic auditory system is directly connected not only with the auditory region as hitherto known but with some other cortical areas as well. We shall consider the nature of these connections and attempt to relate the behavioral and electrophysiological studies to the anatomical data.

Before presenting the anatomical material it is necessary to define some concepts as we shall use them and to give an outline of the normal architectonic composition of the auditory thalamic system. We shall consider that a cortical area receives an *essential projection* from a given thalamic nucleus if destruction of such an area alone causes marked degenerative changes in the nucleus in question. On the other hand, if two cortical areas are considered, and if destruction of neither of them leads to degenerative changes in a thalamic nucleus or to only slight alterations but if a simultaneous destruction of both causes a profound degeneration of this thalamic element, we shall say that both areas receive *sustaining projections* from this nucleus.

It is clear that a very large amount of experimental material is needed to establish with any accuracy the extent of two areas which receive a sustaining projection, and no such material is available at present. However, it is relatively simple to test whether or not a given area receives a sustaining projection from a given thalamic nucleus, and we shall conclude that it does if three conditions are fulfilled: First, removal of such an area alone must cause only minor alterations in the thalamic nucleus in question or no detectable changes at all; secondly, removal of this area jointly with some other area must cause a profound degeneration of this nucleus; thirdly, preservation of this area must assure at least a relative intactness of the nucleus in question after a removal which is less extensive only by the extent of the area investigated than the one which led to a complete degeneration of this nucleus.

Plate 19 will remind you of the normal composition of the medial geniculate body. The principal division (*Mgp*) and medially to it the magnocellular division (*Mgm*) are readily distinguished. Dorsally, the principal and the magnocellular divisions fade into an area which has a cellular composition different from that of either of them. This area represents the posterior nuclear group which adjoins orodorsally the medial geniculate body.

Plate 20 shows the thalamus at the level of the anterior end of the

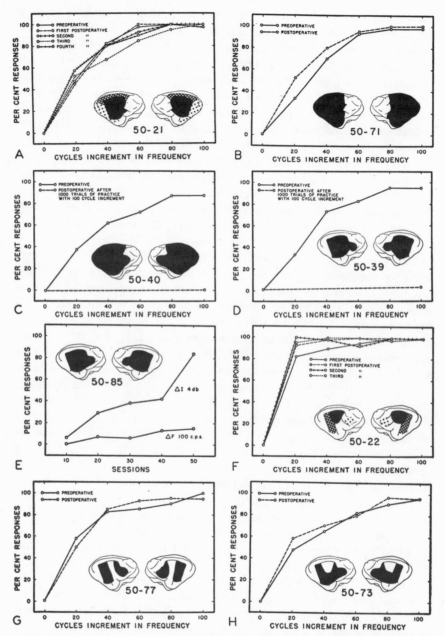

Fig. 49A.—Cat 50–21. Destruction first of auditory areas I and II and posterior ectosylvian gyrus. Subsequent removal of cerebellar *tuber vermis,* suprasylvian gyrus, and temporal cortex, as shown. All operations were without effect. The capacity of the

medial geniculate. The principal division is just appearing. The dorsal lateral geniculate body is in full development. You will notice that the rest of the dorsal thalamus consists of a broad cell-band which is complexly built and difficult to analyze anatomically. It will be convenient to refer to this band by one designation, and we shall call it the pulvinar-posterior system. In the dorsal portion of this band the lateral sector is the pulvinar, while the medial sector is often referred to as *n. lateralis posterior*. Of special interest for further consideration is the ventral portion; we shall refer to it as the posterior group of nuclei. It includes the suprageniculate nucleus and partly at least the region which some workers call the anterior portion of the medial geniculate body itself.

It will be noted that the magnocellular division fuses with the posterior group and in a sense this division can be considered to be a differ-

---

animal to discriminate frequencies was estimated from percentage of responses in 200 critical tests to a 1000 cps tone and tones which were higher by 20, 40, 60, 80, and 100 cycles. For details on the training technique, see Meyer and Woolsey (15), from which all parts of Fig. 49 were taken. The extent of the removals was estimated from gross specimens. In this and in other similar figures these estimates do not differ critically from the extent of the lesions as determined from reconstructions of serial sections.

Fig. 49B.—Cat 50–71. Massive extirpation of posterior portions of cerebral cortex, sparing somatic area II. Capacity for frequency discrimination was retained, but extensive retraining was required about equal to the preoperative learning.

Fig. 49C.—Cat 50–40. Massive removal of the posterior portion of the cerebral cortex including the second somatic area. Postoperatively there was no evidence for frequency discrimination in 50 sessions (1,000 trials), nor for simple conditioning to a pure tone in 40 sessions (800 trials).

Fig. 49D.—Cat 50–39. Removal of auditory areas I and II, posterior ectosylvian gyrus, and somatic area II. Notice the extension of the removal ventrally upon the temporal fields. Postoperative discrimination of frequency is negligible, but simple conditioning to a pure tone was rapidly established and changes in intensity of 6 db. were discriminated.

Fig. 49E.—Cat 50–85. Removal of auditory areas I and II, posterior ectosylvian gyrus, somatic area II, and part of the temporal region. The animal learned preoperatively to discriminate changes both in frequency and intensity. Only postoperative data are plotted. The graph shows percentage of responses as a function of postoperative training sessions. Discrimination of a 100-cycle change lags far behind discrimination of a 4-db. change in intensity as postoperative practice proceeds.

Fig. 49F.—Cat 50–22. Sequential destruction of auditory area I, posterior ectosylvian gyrus, and somatic area II.

Fig. 49G.—Cat 50–77. Removal of somatic area II, posterior ectosylvian gyrus, and all but middle-frequency portion of auditory areas I and II.

Fig. 49H.—Cat 50–73. Removal of auditory area II, posterior ectosylvian gyrus, and somatic area II. None of these operations illustrated in Fig. 49F, G, and H produced changes in capacity for frequency discrimination.

entiated part of the posterior system. Anteriorly, the anterior portion of the posterior group intercalates itself between the medial geniculate and the ventrobasal complex of the thalamus which is the tactile thalamic region. This fact is of special interest since the evidence appears convincing that the posterior group possesses auditory function and since on the other hand it can be shown that the second somatic sensory cortex receives sustaining projection from the anterior portion of this group.

Removal of AI, AII, and Ep was augmented by removal of the suprasylvian gyrus and the posterior portion of the hemisphere and by removal of the cortex ventral to AII and Ep in cat 50–21 (Fig. 49A). This is a figure from the paper of Meyer and Woolsey, and we shall show a similar figure prior to each thalamic series to orient you as to the extent of the cortical removal and the auditory capacity of the animal. The different markings indicate sequential removals which were all without effect on the animal's performance. An additional removal of the *tuber vermis* of the cerebellum was also without effect. Although the cortical lesion largely spares the striate cortex, it is deep and interrupts bilaterally the visual pathways. Consequently the dorsal lateral geniculate body is completely degenerated.

Figure 50 shows outline drawings through the posterior portions of the thalamus of this animal. Areas very severely degenerated are marked in black. The cells of the pulvinar-posterior system and of the geniculates are inked in when not degenerated. Slight or doubtful changes are not marked. These are drawings of frontal preparations cut at 20 μ. They are shown usually 24 sections apart, arranged in orocaudal sequence. The dorsal lateral geniculate is, as mentioned, severely degenerated. In the pulvinar-posterior system there is severe degeneration of the lateral sectors, but the medial portions are in part well preserved. The posterior group is certainly not intact. Since in all animals to be considered the suprasylvian gyrus was either directly removed or undercut, it is not clear to what extent some degenerations in the posterior group may be due to the involvement of this gyrus. However, and this is to be stressed, the anterior division of the posterior group remained quite well preserved. Orally, the principal division is severely degenerated, but the magnocellular division is partly preserved. Proceeding posteriorly the degenerations become less extensive, and in the caudal portions both the principal and the magnocellular divisions are entirely intact. The degenerations in the medial geniculate are more extensive in this animal than they are when only a region consisting of AI, AII, and Ep is destroyed. It will be seen from the next series that this is due not to extension of the ablation medial to the auditory region but results from removal of the cortical region that lies ventral and perhaps posterior to AII and Ep.

Figure 49*B* shows a removal which differs from the ablation shown previously principally by the extension of the lesion to the rhinal sulcus. The visual region which was destroyed in the previous animal, partly directly and partly through subcortical damage, is here completely removed. The posterior limbic region has also been removed, with con-

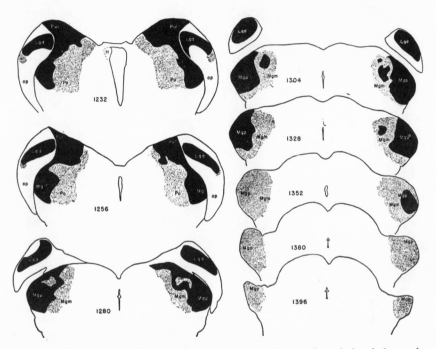

Fig. 50.—Drawings of cross sections through the posterior portion of the thalamus in cat 50–21, showing sites of degenerative changes which resulted from removals illustrated in Fig. 49*A*. Explanations for all similar figures: Black areas indicate areas of severe degeneration. The cells in the preserved portions of the medial geniculate, the pulvinar-posterior system, the lateral geniculate body, and the ventrobasal complex are inked in. The areas in which the cells are inked in but which are enclosed by solid lines indicate regions in which moderate degenerative changes were present. Numbers indicate the serial numbers of sections cut at 20 μ. The lowest number shows the most oral section, the highest the most caudal. Each drawing was prepared from a photomicrograph in which the distinguishable nerve cells were inked in with india ink. The photograph was then bleached and the resulting drawing was rephotographed and reduced for reproduction. *H*, Habenula; *Lgd*, dorsal lateral geniculate body; *Mgm*, magnocellular division of the medial geniculate body; *op*, optic tract; *Po*, posterior group of nuclei; *Pul*, pulvinar; *rf*, retroflex fascicle of Meynert; *Vb*, ventrobasal complex.

sequent degenerations in the thalamus. These degenerations, however, will not be further considered, since they appear immaterial for our problem. It will be noticed that the operation was without lasting effect on frequency discrimination; however, extensive retraining was required (15). We shall return to this fact later.

In the thalamus (Fig. 51) the dorsal lateral geniculate and the pul-

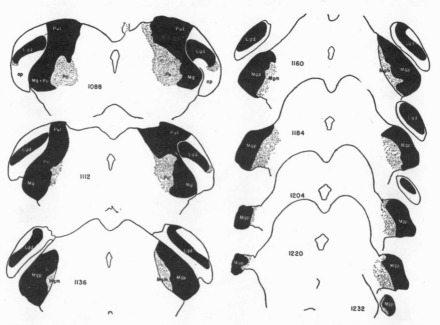

Fig. 51.—Drawings of cross sections through the posterior portion of the thalamus in cat 50–71. Notice that the principal division of the medial geniculate is virtually degenerated throughout. Observe that the posterior group of nuclei is preserved orally.

vinar are degenerated throughout. The changes of the medial geniculate are of great interest. Let us first consider the principal division. This division degenerated most severely throughout its entire extent, indicating that its total projection area must have been removed. The cortex which must be destroyed in addition to AI, AII, and Ep in order to secure such degenerations undoubtedly comprises the homologue of the temporal fields of other mammals, and it may include at least partly some fields of the insular cortex. It is thus necessary to conclude that at least the posterior portion of the principal division entertains connections with this cortex.

A very interesting fact is that this animal with the principal division completely annihilated was capable of normal auditory performance. Since it required an extensive retraining on the problem already mastered before operation, the question arises how well an animal deprived of its entire principal division can learn an auditory task anew. If one assumes that the retraining of this animal took place through the thalamic auditory system, the status of the anatomical groupings around the principal division is of special interest. The magnocellular division is severely affected, particularly orally. The areas in which the cells are inked in but which are enclosed by solid lines all show marked degenerative changes. Posteriorly, some cells are still present in the magnocellular division. Quite anteriorly the anterior portion of the posterior group is quite well preserved. In fact, this is the only grouping in the vicinity of the medial geniculate which is well preserved. It is tempting to believe that the anterior portion of the posterior group has auditory functions and that it was actually responsible for the auditory performance of this animal. That such a premise has merit will be apparent from consideration of the next series.

In Figure 49C the cortical lesion is similar to that in the previous animal, but in addition the second somatic sensory cortical field was removed as well. Actually, apart from the second somatic cortex the removals are not identical, since a thin rim of temporal cortex remained bilaterally, somewhat greater on the left. If the conclusion concerning the projections of the principal division is correct, this should have the consequence that the most caudal tip of the principal division should remain preserved. Postoperatively the animal failed completely to discriminate between 1,000 and 1,100 cps even after 50 training sessions, nor was it possible to condition the animal to the 1,100 cps tone presented by itself. However, it readily responded to the more complex sound of the buzzer when this was presented as a conditioned stimulus.

Figure 52 shows the status of this animal's thalamus. The principal division is severely degenerated throughout except for a tiny caudal tip on the left side. The magnocellular division is also mainly degenerated, but some cells are still left. The most striking difference between this animal and the previous one is that the anterior portion of the posterior group is also severely degenerated. Virtually the entire auditory thalamic system seems to have been eliminated, and impairment of auditory performance also was profound.

These findings offer two interesting conclusions. The first is the inference that the posterior group of nuclei, which, let us remind you, fuses posteriorly with the medial geniculate body itself, indeed possesses auditory functions. The second conclusion is that it is evidently the anterior

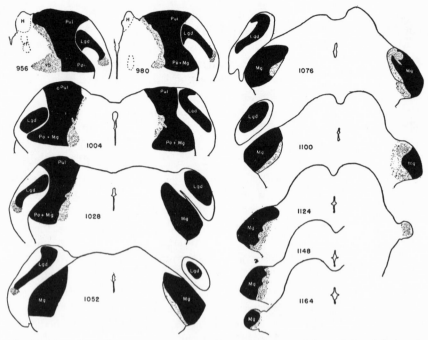

Fig. 52.—Drawings of cross sections through the posterior portion of the thalamus in cat 50–40. Virtually the entire medial geniculate configuration and the posterior nuclei are degenerated throughout.

portion of the posterior group which projects upon the second somatic cortical area.

The latter statement requires some comment. There has been widespread interest, ever since the original discovery of the second somatic area, in the thalamic site which emits projections to this field. We possess several brains in which isolated lesions were placed in this region. The degenerative changes are scanty with such removals. Often, but not invariably, one can see focal degenerations in the posterior sectors of the ventrobasal complex of the thalamus. Since, however, this complex is known to be connected with the first somatic field, a conservative interpretation would imply that such changes could have resulted from subcortical damage to the fibers destined for the first somatic area. In addition, one can observe slight changes in the area just lateral to and behind the ventrobasal complex. A slight gliosis, shrinkage of some cells, perhaps a slight drop in the cell content are all that can be seen, and the conclusion seems justified that the second somatic area cannot be proven to receive any essential projections from the thalamus. However, the marginal changes just mentioned occur in the grouping which is none other than the anterior portion of the posterior group. It follows then that while an isolated removal of the second somatic field is without major effect on this group, the preservation of this field, when the auditory region is removed, assures its relative intactness. If removal of the auditory region is now augmented by removal of the second somatic area, the anterior portion of the posterior group degenerates most severely, indicating that the second somatic field receives sustaining projections from it.

While the animal just described failed postoperatively at all auditory tasks except conditioning to a buzzer, Figure 49D shows a minimal lesion which was effective in impairing frequency discrimination although intensity increments were distinguished. It will be noted that the lesion does not extend to the rhinal sulcus, and consequently some preservation of the caudal end of the medial geniculate is to be expected. Although the ablation spares the visual cortex of the animal, the visual connections have been interrupted by the ablation, with consequent complete degen-

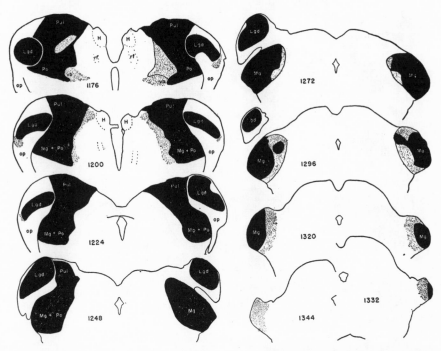

Fig. 53.—Drawings of cross sections through the posterior portion of the thalamus in cat 50–39. Note the bilateral preservation of the caudal tip of the medial geniculate.

eration of the dorsal lateral geniculate and the pulvinar. In the thalamus (Fig. 53) severe degenerations prevail in the posterior group and in the principal and magnocellular divisions, but the very posterior segment of the medial geniculate is preserved.

Figure 49*E* shows another animal with a similar lesion and similar behavioral results. You will again notice that the lesion does not extend to the rhinal sulcus and that while frequency discrimination hardly improves with training, intensity discrimination does. In this animal, as in the previous one, the visual pathways were destroyed subcortically with consequent degenerations in the thalamus, and thus the entire series of animals shown is quite homogeneous in this respect. In the thalamus (Fig. 54) there is again severe degeneration of the posterior group and of the principal and magnocellular divisions. However, a noteworthy sector of the medial geniculate is preserved quite posteriorly, undoubtedly owing to the preservation of neocortex ventral to the ablation.

If one summarizes the maximal degenerative changes which may occur in the thalamic auditory system without any permanent impairment in frequency discrimination and the minimal ones which do result in

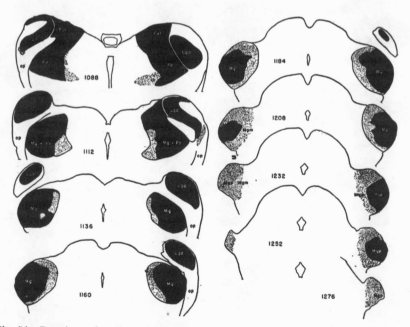

Fig. 54.—Drawings of cross sections through the posterior portion of the thalamus in cat 50–85. Notice that the posterior group is severely degenerated but that substantial segment of the posterior portion of the medial geniculate body was preserved.

such impairment, the following seems to be true. An animal is still capable of learning to discriminate frequencies if severe degenerations occur bilaterally in the entire principal division, in most of the magnocellular division, and in the posterior group of nuclei provided that the anterior portion of the last-mentioned group remains essentially intact. When severe degenerations occur in this portion as well, a lasting impairment seems to result, even if the caudal tip of the medial geniculate remains preserved. It may be argued, however, that cat 50–85, in which the largest amount of medial geniculate was preserved, showed perhaps some sign of relearning.

It will be of great interest to compare the degenerative changes in this material with those in the material of Dr. Neff in order to determine whether some differences between his results and those of Meyer and Woolsey are in fact due to differences in the extent of ablations performed.

Whether or not the anterior portion of the posterior group is uniquely critical for retention of the capacity of the animal to discriminate frequencies cannot be established with certainty with the material at hand. Available evidence, however, suggests that this is not the case.

Figure 49 *F, G,* and *H* shows three lesions of Meyer and Woolsey which were without any effect on frequency discrimination. We shall only show one thalamic series in this group but shall briefly mention some of the pertinent degenerations in the others. In cat 50–22 the removal of AI, Ep, and of SII resulted, as expected, in considerable degeneration of the anterior portion of the posterior group. There is, of course, severe degeneration present in the anterior part of the principal division. However, the posterior portion of the principal division is intact, and the magnocellular division is only a little affected. The findings imply, therefore, that preservation of AII and of the temporal and insular fields assures relative intactness of the magnocellular division, even if AI, Ep, and SII are jointly removed. They further suggest that, if substantial portions of the principal and magnocellular divisions remain preserved, the degenerations in the posterior group are of no consequence for the performance of the animal.

In cat 50–77 the operation aimed to spare a middle portion of the critical region. This was only partly successful because the lesion is deep and the cortical strip between the lesions is partly undermined, infiltrated, or destroyed by anoxic changes. In the thalamus, besides other degenerations, there is severe degeneration of the anterior portion of the posterior group, while the principal and magnocellular divisions are completely destroyed in certain sectors, partly degenerated in others, and well

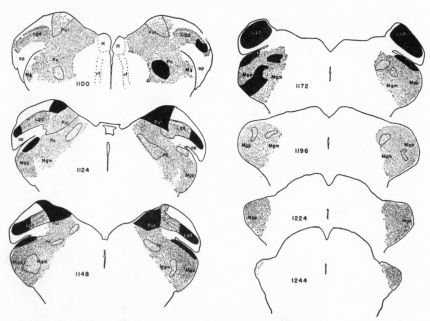

Fig. 55.—Drawings of cross sections through the posterior portion of the thalamus in cat 50–73. Notice that the bulk of the principal and magnocellular divisions of the medial geniculate is preserved. Note also the preservation of the posterior nuclear group. Partial degeneration in the dorsal lateral geniculate body and the pulvinar is almost certainly due to subcortical damage.

preserved in still other sectors. The implication again is that degeneration of the anterior portion of the posterior group is probably inconsequential for frequency discrimination if substantial numbers of cells are preserved in the medical geniculate.

Cat 50–73 is one of the most interesting preparations for testing certain ideas of thalamic connections of the auditory cortex. It is known (21)

Plate 19 (above, facing page).—Normal cat. Frontal section (30 μ thick) through the region of greatest development of the medial geniculate body. Note the principal (*Mgp*) and the magnocellular (*Mgm*) divisions of the medial geniculate. Note also that both these divisions fade dorsally into an area of different architectonic structure (see text). *Lgd* is the dorsal lateral geniculate body.

Plate 20 (below, facing page).—Thalamus at the level of the oral end of the medial geniculate body; same brain as in Plate 17. The principal division of the medial geniculate just appears in the section. Note the development of the magnocellular division. Note further that the magnocellular division fuses dorsally with the region of the posterior nuclear group (*Po*). The posterior nuclear group adjoins the system of the pulvinar (*Pul*) and the lateral group of nuclei. *Lgd*, dorsal lateral geniculate body; *op*, optic tract; *Pt*, pretectal region.

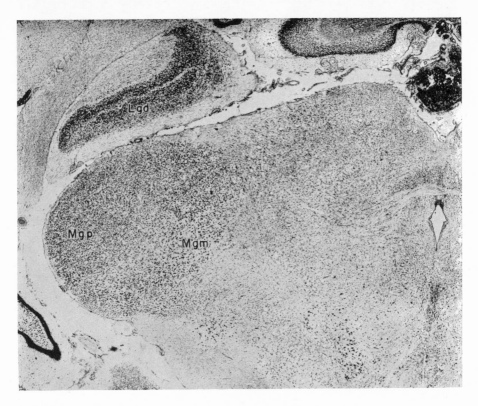

Plate 19 (above) and Plate 20 (below).—See facing page for legends.

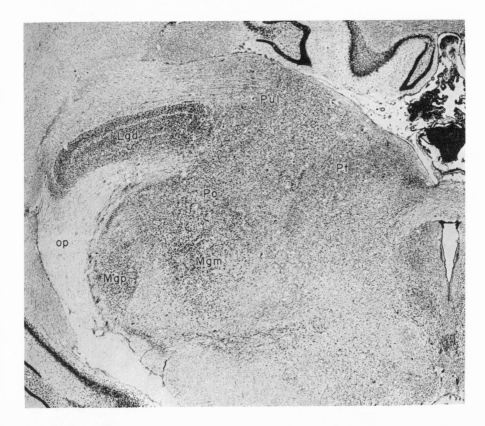

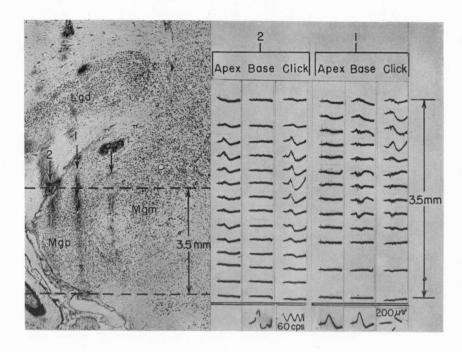

Plate 21 (above) and *Plate 22* (below).—See facing page for legends.

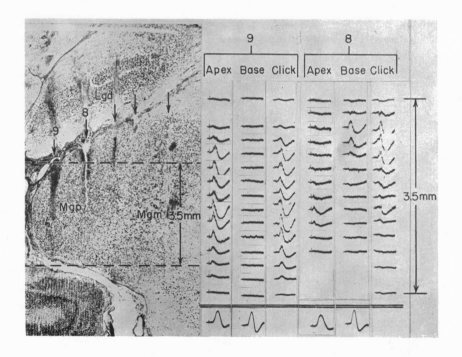

that isolated removals of Ep and AII do not lead to any focal changes in the thalamus. The same was asserted above in respect to SII. The question is whether this is still true if all three are jointly removed.

Figure 55 shows degenerations which resulted in the thalamus of this animal. First, it will be seen that the lesion was deeper than intended and that the visual pathways were partly interrupted with consequent degenerations in the lateral geniculate body and the pulvinar. We believe these changes can be neglected. In regard to the auditory thalamic system it is apparent that it did not remain intact. Thus, there are severe changes present in the posterior group on the left and in the principal division bilaterally in addition to areas of less extensive degeneration indicated by solid lines. However, the fact that a fairly symmetrical cortical removal resulted in a large focal change in the principal division on one side only suggests that this focus probably resulted from subcortical damage. Moreover, the severe focal degenerations in both dorsoanterior sectors are almost certainly due to damage to AI, since severe degeneration in these sectors is known to occur after isolated lesions are placed in the anterior portion of this field. Thus, there is some reason to believe

---

Plate 21 (above, facing page).—On the left: Photomicrograph of a cross section through the anterior sector of the medial geniculate body in cat 53–51. Three electrode tracks are seen. Tracks 1 and 2 both passed exclusively through the principal division. Full length of track 2 is not seen in this section. Distance between dashed lines is 3.5 mm. Evoked potentials recorded along this distance by the electrode in tracks 1 and 2 are shown on expanded scale at the right. Three columns of records are shown for each track. The apex column shows potentials evoked by electrical stimulation of cochlear nerve fibres in the spiral osseous lamina of the apical turn; the base column shows potentials evoked by similar stimulation of the basal turn; click column shows records evoked by clicks delivered to the intact contralateral ear. Strength of the electrical stimulus applied to the spiral osseous lamina was so adjusted as to produce a focal area of responses in the appropriate region of homolateral AI. (A near-threshold stimulation of the basal turn produces a focal response area in the anterodorsal part of AI, while a similar stimulation of the apical turn produces a restricted response area near the dorsal tip of the posterior ectosylvian sulcus.) Records below the double line show responses in the cortical focal areas produced by electrical stimulation of the appropriate cochlear turn with stimuli of the same strength as used for recording activity in the medial geniculate body. Sixty-cps time line and amplification are the same for all records. Note that stimulation of both the apical and the basal turns evokes activity in the principal division, but with different distributions.

Plate 22 (below, facing page).—Medial geniculate body of the cat 53–51, 1 mm. farther caudally. Only records pertaining to tracks 8 and 9 are shown. Observe again that electrical stimulation of the apical and basal turns activates the principal division at this level. Note also here and in Plate 21 that the apical stimulation is effective laterally, that of the base more medially.

that the severe changes at least might have been due to encroachment on, or undercutting of, AI. If this interpretation is correct, it would imply that AI, in addition to the essential projections from a part of the principal division, receives sustaining projections from virtually all auditory thalamic groupings and that this field actually is what is appears to be— the real cortical core of the auditory system. Whether in fact this is true may remain an open question, but in any case it is clear that AI, when preserved, will maintain intact at least a very substantial portion of the auditory thalamic system.

Let us now summarize the degenerative changes which occur in the thalamic auditory system after different cortical removals.

About the *principal division* the following can be stated: First, it is known that the anterior portion of this division degenerates severely after removal of AI alone. Secondly, lesions restricted to AII, Ep, or to certain sectors at least, of the temporal fields will not cause any marked focal changes even though marginal alterations may be detectable. While removal of AII and Ep alone leaves the principal division essentially intact, it is highly probable that removal of AI jointly with AII and Ep will cause more profound and widespread degeneration than will result when AI alone is removed. Thirdly, joint removal of AI, AII, and Ep will still not cause degenerative changes throughout the entire principal division since the posterior sector will remain preserved. If, now, such removals are progressively augmented farther and farther ventralward, devastating degeneration of the principal division will proceed more and more caudalward until, with the removal of the entire neocortex lying ventral to AII and Ep, the entire principal division degenerates most severely.

Thus, it can be concluded that AI receives essential projection from the principal division. While only AI is known to receive such projection—and, curiously enough, only the more anterior portions of the division seem to emit them—there is little doubt that the principal division projects in a sustaining fashion upon a much larger cortical region than AI and that the caudal sectors of the division project upon the temporal and possibly insular fields. The limitations of the material necessitate two qualifications. First, while the projections upon AII and Ep are certainly sustaining, it cannot be stated whether or not all sectors of these fields receive them. On the other hand, while the temporal and possibly insular fields undoubtedly receive projection from the caudal sectors of the division, it is not entirely certain whether this projection is essential or sustaining, even though we know that small lesions placed in certain sectors of the temporal fields do not produce any marked changes. Dr. Mountcastle placed a bitemporal lesion in one animal in connection with another problem and kindly put this material at our disposal. The ablations are very extensive and may have encroached upon AII and Ep. In the principal division there are undoubted changes in both caudal sectors. There is a marked gliosis present, and most caudally there is an appreciable cell loss. However, there is no complete degeneration in any sector, and a great many cells are present even in areas most affected. It would, therefore, appear right to believe that the projection to the temporal fields is sustaining in nature.

In respect to the *magnocellular division* the findings are as follows: No single cortical field is known at present which on destruction causes marked focal changes in this division. Removal of the temporal fields alone or of AI alone is virtually without any effect. Even joint removal of AI, AII, and Ep leaves this division mainly preserved. When the latter removal is augmented by removal of substantial portions of the temporal and insular fields, severe degenerations are observed, even though some caudal sectors of the divisions may still escape destruction. On the other hand, if a removal is made which is smaller only by the extent of AI than an ablation sufficient to cause a severe degeneration in the magnocellular division, the preservation of AI is sufficient to preserve this division substantially unaltered. This implies that the division emits sustaining projectons at least to AI, and probably to AII and Ep as well, but certainly also to the temporal and insular fields. The fact that posterior sectors of the magnocellular division were partly preserved in all animals suggests that these sectors may entertain connections with cortex lying ventral to SII.

It has been implied that apart from the medial geniculate itself the posterior nuclear group forms a part of the thalamic auditory system. Although the material at hand is not critical for determination of the total projection area of this group, there is good reason to believe that the anterior portion of the group sends a sustaining projection to the second somatic cortical field.

The relation of the second somatic field to auditory functions is of special interest. As is known, Tunturi (22) described in the dog in addition to the areas homologous to fields I and II of Woolsey and Walzl (25), a third auditory area which was identified as being within the second somatic field of this animal by Pinto Hamuy, Bromiley, and Woolsey (19). Since the studies of Allen (1) on the dog and of Meyer and Woolsey (15) on the cat are in substantial agreement, it can be concluded that the second somatic area can be shown to possess auditory functions. Actually, with neurophysiological techniques, there is no particular difficulty in registering within the boundaries of SII of the cat potentials evoked by auditory stimuli. Mickle and Ades (16) have demonstrated that within a region which partly includes SII one can record potentials evoked by tactile and auditory stimuli as well as by stimulation of the vestibular nerve. Recently Bremer (2), Bremer, Bonnet, and Terzuolo (3), Perl and Casby (18), and Buser and Heinze (4) reported that potentials evoked by auditory and tactile stimuli in SII or in the cortex adjacent to it can be shown to interact in such a manner that it must be concluded that some auditory potentials in SII indeed originate within this field.

The demonstration that SII receives sustaining projections from the anterior portion of the posterior group is in harmony with all these findings. As stressed before, this portion of the group is intercalated between the ventrobasal complex and the medial geniculate, which makes it an ideal place for tactile and auditory interconnections. The immediate question which arises is whether interaction between discharges provoked by tactile and auditory stimuli takes place already in the thalamus. The posterior group is usually classified as belonging to the intrinsic thalamic system. It is noteworthy, however, that the group is likely to receive some auditory impulses from extrathalamic sources, since it can apparently transmit auditory information even if most of the medial geniculate is destroyed. Furthermore, if the anterior portion of the group is the only thalamic source of SII (but whether or not this is true is not certain), the group would be reached by tactile ipsilateral fibers since SII possesses bilateral representation. Finally, it may be mentioned that, as far as can be determined from his drawings, Knighton (13) was probably activating the second somatic cortex quite often by stimulation of the anterior portion of the posterior group, although he concluded that the thalamic source of SII is exclusively the posterior segment of the ventrobasal complex.

Although the exact extent of the cortical region which is reached directly by fibers from the thalamic auditory system is yet to be determined, there is no doubt that a large number of fields receive such projections. The demonstration, that in addition to AI, AII and Ep also entertain such connections, is actually but an anatomical confirmation of the neurophysiological postulates in this respect (9, 21). However, the fact that SII and the temporal and possibly insular regions as well, also receive direct projections from the thalamic auditory system suggests that the current conception as to what constitutes the auditory region of the cat is in need of drastic revision.

It is of great interest that the evidence for essential and sustaining projections upon the cortex from an extrinsic thalamic nucleus is by no means restricted to the auditory system. The recent work of Le Gros Clark and Powell (6) indicates, in our opinion, that the ventrobasal complex of the thalamus (the tactile region) emits essential projections to area 3 in the monkey while area 2 appears to receive what we have termed here a sustaining projection from this complex.

Only a small fraction of the auditory thalamocortical connections may be considered essential projections, while most of them are sustaining. It is of interest to consider the probable nature of a sustaining projection. If one assumes that a nerve cell will degenerate when all (or most) of its axonic terminations are either directly destroyed or are in contact only with nonviable cells, there could be two somewhat different anatomical arrangements which would result in the same experimental findings. The first would be the collateral type in which the axon of the thalamic cell would simply branch and terminate in two cortical fields. In the other type the axon of a thalamic cell would terminate in one cortical field only, but its collateral would impinge on another thalamic cell, which in turn projects upon a second cortical field. Such a simple arrangement would result in one of these fields being a sustaining area for some thalamic cells, while the other field would function at the same time as an essential projection area for some thalamic cells and as a sustaining area for others. If the thalamic cells were mutually interconnected, only destruction of both cortical fields would be likely to result in any degenerative changes. It is simple to construct a number of other variants of the second type of arrangement. Although the second scheme may be, except for the simplest forms, more complex anatomically than a collateral arrangement the functional results appear to support its existence. It would be quite difficult to understand on the basis of a collateral projection scheme why potentials in AI, AII, and Ep are not evoked with equal ease and why some other characteristics of these potentials may also differ materially.

Regardless of the exact nature of the sustaining projections, it is of interest to point out that their existence may be of significance for an interpretation of the equipotentiality of certain cortical fields (14). If one assumes that a deficit in frequency discrimination will result only if virtually the entire thalamic auditory system is destroyed, it is clear that to achieve this by cortical ablations a certain number of fields must be removed jointly and no other combination will do. This formulation reduces the problem of auditory cortical equipotentiality to more manageable proportions. First, it suggests that by far not all fields are equipotential; at most, only those are equipotential which are directly connected with the thalamic auditory system. Secondly, equipotentiality in these terms need not imply anything more than retention of the capacity of a field to handle auditory signals, even though other relevant fields are destroyed. There is, however, no reason to believe that all fields capable of handling such signals are equivalent in all their functions, and there is even good reason to assume that their auditory connections are not at all identical. If they are not, it is right to expect that some fields may be indispensable for certain auditory tasks while other tasks could be basic enough to be performed by every relevant field.

Results of Butler and Neff (5), Diamond and Neff (8) and Neff, Arnott, and Fisher (17) seem to indicate indeed that certain auditory tasks cannot be performed by animals deprived of a major part of the auditory region, while the results of Allen (1), Meyer and Woolsey (15), and Neff and Tunturi (24) imply that simple frequency discrimination is not beyond the capacity of any field of the system. What the mechanisms underlying this capacity are can be stated only conjecturally at present. There are, however, a few experimental findings which are relevant for this problem.

Thus, Davies, Erulkar, and Rose (7) and Erulkar, Rose, and Davies (10) have recorded responses of single units in the first auditory area of the cat. They studied almost exclusively the posterior sector of AI on the assumption that this portion of the field would prove itself to be a low-frequency region. Most of the units seen were indeed sensitive to low frequencies. Nevertheless, they encountered within this region a unit responding best to a tone of 12 kc., and on occasions units were seen which, while unresponsive to low-frequency sounds, were quite sensitive to natural stimuli which contained high-frequency components. Moreover, somewhat more anteriorly, but still well within the posterior half of AI, on occasions units were seen most sensitive to sounds inaudible to the human ear. The findings imply that, whatever may be the significance of the cortical locus for frequency discrimination, an optimal sensitivity of a single cortical neuron to a given frequency is probably not uniquely dependent upon the cortical sector in which the cell is located. These results are consistent with the findings of Hind (12), if not perhaps with his interpretation, since in the low-frequency region of AI the mean values of his effective frequency bands were not rarely 10 kc. or more.

Another line of evidence bearing on the problem of frequency discrimination stems from experiments on the medial geniculate body which Dr. Lende, Dr. Ullrich, and ourselves undertook some years ago. At that time we knew that AI receives essential projection from the principal division and that the most anterior portion of the division shows degenerative changes after removals of the dorsoanterior portion of the first auditory field. AI has been shown (25) to be activated in a focal manner by successive stimulation of the cochlear fibers in such a way that stimulation of the basal coil activates the anterior portion of AI, while stimulation of the apical coil activates its posterior sector. We expected, therefore, that stimulation of the basal coil would activate exclusively the most anterior portion of the principal division, and stimulation of the apex would be effective more posteriorly.

The experiments were done by opening the cochlea and exposing both the contralateral medial geniculate and the homolateral auditory cortex. Electrical stimuli were then applied to the basal and apical coils, respectively, at such a strength as to evoke focal bands of activity in the appropriate regions of AI. The medial geniculate was then entered with a needle electrode and the responsive region determined in the Horsley-Clarke coördinate system. Records were taken at each responsive point to a homolateral click and to electrical stimulation of the apical and basal turns.

We shall consider here only one finding, namely, that the principal division is not activated as we had anticipated but that stimulation of both the apical and the basal turns evokes activity even in the most anterior portion of the principal division.

Plate 21 shows the anterior portion of the medial geniculate at a level of one experimental plane. You will notice the principal and the magnocellular divisions. Three electrode tracks are visible, but only tracks 1 and 2 will be considered since only those pass exclusively through the principal division. The dashed lines indicate the distance of 3.5 mm. along both electrode tracks, and on the right you see on an expanded scale the records obtained along each of these tracks. Clicks were effective along both tracks. Stimulation of the basal turn was effective only in the track of the more medial electrode. Stimulation of the apical fibers was quite ineffective for the medial track, while tissue along the lateral track responded well to stimulation of fibers just below the apex where the electrode was inadvertently displaced during this particular puncture. The records at the bottom of the columns were taken from the cortex to indicate that stimulation of the fibers at the respective turn was evoking focal activity in the appropriate region of AI.

Plate 22 illustrates the same medial geniculate 1 mm. more caudally. There are several electrode tracks visible, but again only two tracks passed exclusively through the principal division. You will observe again that stimulation of the apex evokes activity along the lateral track, while stimulation at the base activates at least some points along the more medial track. It appears then that stimulation of cochlear fibers from base to apex, respectively, does not activate the principal division in an antero-posterior sequence but probably in a mediolateral succession. While the available evidence is limited and more data are needed before one can draw definite conclusions, the findings as they are do indeed imply that each cross section of the principal division is likely to be connected with all cochlear turns. This interpretation would account for the observation of Galambos (11) that there are units located in the most anterior segment of the medial geniculate which may respond best to low frequencies. Now, you will recall that the principal division projects upon the cortex in such a way that the anterior portion projects upon AI while the most posterior segments project upon the temporal and possibly insular fields. Hence, it appears that any cortical field connected with the principal division is anatomically in a position to receive information from all regions of the cochlea.

The detailed projection pattern of the anterior portion of the principal division upon AI is of special interest. We have previously suggested (21) after an analysis of the results of small lesions in AI that the anterior portion of the principal division projects from its dorsoanterior to its ventroposterior limits to the correspondingly oriented portions of AI. The functional evidence from the medial geniculate implies that if this is so, the sector of the principal division which projects upon the basal portion of AI would receive information not only from the basal coil but also from the apex. The same would be true for the apical region of AI. While such a conclusion does not appear inherently improbable, and, in fact, some observations on single units (10) and the findings of Hind (12) could be interpreted as supporting it, it is nevertheless necessary to stress that the results with large ablations here presented imply that the principal division may actually project from its anterior to its posterior limits in a rather straight dorsoventral sequence upon AI. If this is the case, each cross section of the principal division could be expected to receive information from all cochlear turns, and there would be no anatomical proof that the focal cortical regions receive information from all coils. The available material with small lesions is, we believe, not crucial enough to decide between these alternatives, and thus for the time being it is impossible to assert that the different focal regions in AI can be shown to be anatomically capable of receiving information from all cochlear coils.

It seems useful to consider the problem of frequency discrimination as two independent questions. The first pertains to the number and location of fields which are relevant for such discrimination. The second question is whether a cortical locus within a given field is or is not relevant. The behavioral studies appear conclusive that no single cortical field is indispensable for frequency discrimination, and it appears likely that not only SII, but also the neocortical fields that lie ventral to AII and Ep, may enable the animal to discriminate frequencies in the absence of the classical auditory fields. The answer to the second question is obscure. The findings presented suggest an ablation experiment which perhaps could be helpful in solving this problem. Thus, if one would remove bilaterally AII, SII, Ep, the temporal and insular fields, and preferably AI unilaterally as well, the entire cortical auditory capacity of the animal should depend on the remaining AI. It seems reasonable to expect that such a cat would still discriminate the entire range of frequencies. If now, however, different sectors of AI were removed, a differential loss in the capacity for frequency discrimination should result if cortical locus is indeed essential for such discrimination.

REFERENCES

1 Allen, W. F. Effect of destroying three localized cerebral cortical areas for sound on correct conditioned differential responses of the dog's foreleg. *Amer. J. Physiol.*, 1945, *144:* 415–28.

2 Bremer, F. Analyse oscillographique des réponses sensorielles des écorces cérébrale et cérébelleuse. *Rev. Neurol.*, 1952, *87:* 65–92.

3 Bremer, F., V. Bonnet, and C. Terzuolo. Étude électrophysiologique des aires auditives corticales du chat. *Arch. internat. Physiol.*, 1954, *62:* 390–428.

4 Buser, P., and G. Heinze. Effets d'une association de stimuli périphériques hétérogènes sur l'activité de certaines aires corticales chez le chat. *J. de Physiol.*, 1954, *46:* 284–87.

5 Butler, R., and W. D. Neff. Role of the auditory cortex in the discrimination of changes of frequency. Paper read at Midwest. Psychol. Ass., Chicago, 1950.

6 Clark, W. E. Le G., and T. P. S. Powell. On the thalamocortical connections of the general sensory cortex of *Macaca. Proc. roy. Soc., Ser. B.*, 1953, *141:* 467–87.

7 Davies, P. W., S. D. Erulkar, and J. E. Rose. Single-unit activity in the auditory cortex of the cat. *J. Physiol.*, 1954, *126:* 25P (Abstract).

8 Diamond, I. T., and W. D. Neff. Role of auditory cortex in discrimination of tonal patterns. *Fed. Proc.*, 1953, *12:* 33 (Abstract).

9 Downman, C. B. B., and C. N. Woolsey. Interrelations within the auditory cortex. *J. Physiol.*, 1953, *123:* 43P.

10 Erulkar, S. D., J. E. Rose, and P. W. Davies. Single-unit activity in the auditory cortex of the cat. *Johns Hopk. Hosp. Bull.*, 1956, *99:* 55–86.

11 Galambos, R. Microelectrode studies on medial geniculate body of cat; response to pure tones. *J. Neurophysiol.*, 1952, *15:* 381–400.

12 Hind, J. E. An electrophysiological determination of tonotopic organization in auditory cortex of cat. *J. Neurophysiol.*, 1953, *16:* 475–89.

13 Knighton, R. S. Thalamic relay nucleus for the second sensory receiving area in the cerebral cortex of the cat. *J. comp. Neurol.,* 1950, *92:* 183–91.

14 Lashley, K. S. *Brain mechanisms and intelligence.* Chicago: Univer. Chicago Press, 1929.

15 Meyer, D. R., and C. N. Woolsey. Effects of localized cortical destruction on auditory discriminative conditioning in cat. *J. Neurophysiol.,* 1952, *15:* 149–62.

16 Mickle, W. A., and H. W. Ades. A composite sensory projection area in the cerebral cortex of the cat. *Amer. J. Physiol.,* 1952, *170:* 682–89.

17 Neff, W. D., G. P. Arnott, and J. D. Fisher. Function of auditory cortex: Localization of sound in space. *Amer. J. Physiol.,* 1950, *163:* 738 (Abstract).

18 Perl, E. R., and J. U. Casby. Localization of cerebral electrical activity: The acoustic cortex of cat. *J. Neurophysiol.,* 1954, *17:* 429–42.

19 Pinto Hamuy, T., R. B. Bromiley, and C. N. Woolsey. Somatic afferent areas I and II of dog's cerebral cortex. *J. Neurophysiol.,* 1956, *19:* 485–99.

20 Rose, J. E. The cellular structure of the auditory region of the cat. *J. comp. Neurol.,* 1949, *91:* 409–39.

21 Rose, J. E., and C. N. Woolsey. The relations of thalamic connections, cellular structure and evocable electrical activity in the auditory region of the cat. *J. comp. Neurol.,* 1949, *91:* 441–66.

22 Tunturi, A. R. Further afferent connections to the acoustic cortex of the dog. *Amer. J. Physiol.,* 1945, *144:* 389–94.

23 ———. Physiological determination of the arrangement of the afferent connections to the middle ectosylvian auditory area in the dog. *Amer. J. Physiol.,* 1950, *162:* 489–502.

24 ———. Effects of lesions of the auditory and adjacent cortex on conditioned reflexes. *Amer. J. Physiol.,* 1955, *181:* 225–29.

25 Woolsey, C. N., and E. M. Walzl. Topical projection of nerve fibers from local regions of the cochlea to the cerebral cortex of the cat. *Johns Hopk. Hosp. Bull.,* 1942, *71:* 315–44.

Karl H. Pribram

Neocortical Function in Behavior

This paper was originally presented as an invited address before the March, 1955, meeting of the Eastern Psychological Association.

The important role of neocortical mechanisms in cognitive behavior has been a focus of scientific interest for the past century and a half. In the early 1800's, arguments raged between physiologists (e.g., Flourens [14]) and phrenologists, many of whom were good anatomists (e.g., Gall and Spurzheim [6]), as to whether the cerebral mantle functioned as a unit or whether a mosaic of cerebral suborgans determines complex psychological events. During the intervening period data have been subsumed under one or the other of these two views—almost always with the effect of strengthening one at the expense of the other. In the recent past, the accumulation of data has so markedly accelerated that a re-evaluation of the problem promises to prove fruitful. Specifically, the data obtained by the use of electronic amplifying devices to study neural events has raised questions concerning the validity of concepts generated by neuroanatomical techniques; the adaptation to subhuman primates of measures of choice behavior has stimulated discussion of the validity of concepts derived from clinical neurological material.

PROBLEMS OF NEURAL ORGANIZATION

First, let us take a look at some *neural* data and see how they fit current conceptualizations of cerebral organization. Explicitly or implicitly, most of us tend to think of the brain as being composed of receiving areas (sensory cortex) which function in some fairly simple fashion to transmit receptor events to adjacent areas of "association" cortex. Here, these neural events are "elaborated" and "associated" with other neural events before being transmitted to the motor areas of the brain; these motor areas are said to serve as the principal effector mechanism for all cerebral activity. This model was proposed some fifty years ago by Flechsig (13) on the basis of the then available anatomical information. As we shall see, the neural data available today make it necessary to modify this model considerably.

But, before we can come to grips with a new conception of brain organization, it is necessary to clarify some definitions. Over the years, many of the terms used in neurology have been imbued with multiple designa-

151

tions. "Neocortex" is such a term. Comparative anatomists use this word to describe the dorsolateral portions of the cerebral mantle since these portions show a *differentially* maximum development in microsmatic mammals (such as primates) as compared with macrosmatic mammals (such as cats). In other branches of the neurological sciences (e.g., see Morgan and Stellar [30]), the term neocortex has come to cover *all* the cortical formations which reach maximum development in primates. The definition as used in these sciences subsumes portions of the cortex on the medial and basal surface of the cerebral hemisphere, which, though well developed in macrosmatic mammals, do show *some* additional development in primates. Since this mediobasal limbic cortex has been related (38, 45) to behavior rather different from that which concerns us in this paper, it seems worth while to find an unambiguous term which delimits the dorsolateral cortex. This purpose is served by a definition in consonance with the embryological development of the histological picture of the cerebral cortex. As reviewed in a recent publication (38), the cerebral cortex may be classified according to whether or not it passes through a six-layered embryonic stage. The medial and basal limbic structures do not pass through such a stage and are called "allo-" or "juxtallocortex"; the dorsolateral portions of the cerebral cortex do pass through such a stage and are called "isocortex."

It has been fashionable to subdivide isocortex according to cytoarchitectonic differences; difficulties in classification have been pointed out (3, 24, 35) which question the immediate usefulness of distinctions based solely on the histological picture of the cortex. I should prefer, therefore, to subdivide isocortex on the basis of thalamocortical relationships since these relationships are determined by the most reliable neurohistological technique available to us: namely, retrograde degeneration of neurons in the thalamus following cortical resection. But, if we are to use this criterion of subdivision of cortex because it is a reliable one, we are forced into looking at the organization of the thalamus as the key to the organization of the cortex. Recently, Rose and Woolsey (47) have divided thalamic nuclei into two classes: (1) those receiving large tracts of extrathalamic afferents and (2) those receiving the major portions of their direct afferents from within the thalamus. The former they called extrinsic and the latter, intrinsic nuclei. Thalamocortical connections, demonstrated by retrograde degeneration studies (7, 10, 37, 54), make possible the differentiation of isocortical sectors on the basis of their connections with extrinsic or with intrinsic thalamic nuclei (Figure 56).

It can be seen from Figure 57 that the portions of the cortex labeled as "extrinsic sectors" correspond essentially to those usually referred to

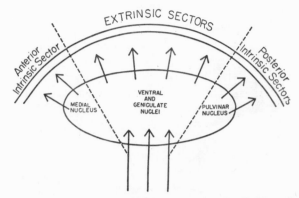

Fig. 56.—Diagrammatic scheme illustrating the division of isocortex into extrinsic and intrinsic sectors on the basis of thalamic afferent connectons. The ventral and geniculate thalamic nuclei which receives major direct afferents from extracerebral structures project to the extrinsic sectors; the medial and pulvinar thalamic nuclei do not receive such afferents and project to the intrinsic sectors.

as "primary projection areas," while those labeled "intrinsic sectors" correspond essentially to those usually referred to as "association areas." However, the terms "association cortex" and "primary projection areas" have their drawbacks: (1) "Association cortex" implies that in these portions of the cortex convergent tracts bring together excitations from the "receiving areas" of the brain. As we shall see, this implication has been unsupported by fact. (2) Electrophysiological experiments (which will be discussed below) have demonstrated a topographical complexity of organization which necessitated labels such as Areas I and II. Should the term "primary projection areas" be used to denote the Areas I only or should it cover such areas as II as well? Additional confusion arises since the intrinsic sectors *do* receive a thalamic projection, so that the term "secondary projection areas" has been suggested for these sectors (49). These considerations have led me to substitute the currently less loaded terms, "extrinsic" and "intrinsic."

Can the subdivision of cerebral isocortex into extrinsic and intrinsic sectors be validated when techniques other than retrograde thalamic degeneration are used? Figure 58 shows the extent of the cortical connections when myelinated fibers are traced by the Marchi (osmic-acid) staining technique from peripheral structures, such as optic tract and dorsal spinal roots, through the thalamus to the cortex. As can be seen by comparing Figures 57 and 58, there are, thus, at least two anatomical techniques

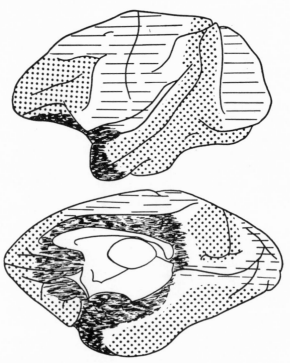

Fig. 57.—Diagrams of the lateral (above) and mediobasal (below) surfaces of the monkey's cerebral hemisphere showing the divisions discussed in the test. Shaded indicates allo-justallocortex; lined indicates extrinsic isocortex; dotted indicates intrinsic isocortex. Boundaries are not sharply delimited; this is, in part, due to minor discrepancies which result when different techniques are used and, in part, to difficulties in classification due to borderline instances and inadequate data (e.g., how should the projections of *n. ventralis anterior* and of *lateralis posterior* be classified?)

which permit approximately the same subdivision of isocortex: one derived from cell body stains; the second, from nerve fiber stains. Further support for the classification comes from electrophysiological data. When receptors are mechanically or electrically stimulated or when peripheral nerves are electrically stimulated, an abrupt change in electrical potential can be recorded from portions of the brain which are connected to these peripheral structures. Under appropriate conditions of anaesthesia, maps may be constructed on the basis of size of the potential changes evoked and the latency which intervenes between the time of stimulation and the recording of the potential change (Fig. 59). As can be seen from the comparison of the maps made by the histological and electrophysiological techniques, there is considerable (though by no means complete) correspondence between various delineations of the extrinsic from the intrinsic sectors of the isocortex.*

Enough of definitions. I am sure you are convinced by now that the cerebral isocortex may usefully be divided according to whether its major input derives, via the thalamus, directly from the periphery or whether that input is largely intracerebral. But, have you noticed that, according to all of the techniques mentioned, input from extracerebral structures reaches the portions of the cortex usually referred to as "mo-

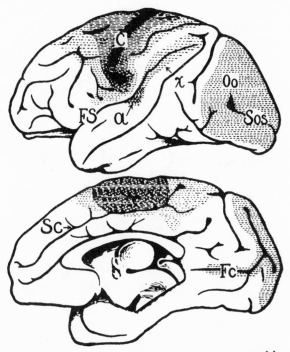

Fig. 58.—From Poliak (33). Extrinsic sectors as mapped by staining degenerating axons following thalamic lesions.

* The most glaring discrepancies between the electrophysiological maps and the anatomical maps are found along the boundaries of the various extrinsic areas. Thus, how are the projection areas of *n. ventralis anterior* and *n. lateralis posterior* (9) to be labeled? And, just where *do* the Areas II and III fit best? These problems are not solved by the proposed classification of isocortex into extrinsic and intrinsic sectors; however, clarification of nomenclature makes possible the posing of relevant questions.

tor" as well as those known as "sensory" areas? Electrophysiological experiments demonstrate that somatic afferents are distributed to both sides of the central fissure of primates. Since the *afferents* reaching the precentral "motor" areas as well as those reaching postcentral "sensory"

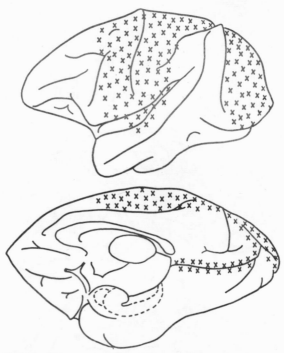

Fig. 59.—Diagrams of the monkey cerebral hemisphere as in Figures 57 and 58. This map of the abrupt electrical changes induced in cortex by peripheral stimulation was compiled from studies (20, 43, and an unpublished study) using animals sufficiently anesthetized with barbiturates to practically abolish the normally present spontaneous rhythms of potential changes recorded from the brain. Those potential changes were counted which were larger than 50 μv. and showed a latency within 3 sec. of the minimum latency of any abrupt potential change evoked in the particular afferent system investigated. These criteria were chosen as the most likely to indicate major direct afferents from periphery to cortex. The correspondences and minor discrepancies between this figure and Figure 58 indicate the approximate range of such similarities when different techniques and brain diagrams are used.

areas originate in both skin and muscle nerves, the critical differences between the input to the precentral and to the postcentral cortex must yet be determined if the differences in effect of resection of the pre- and postcentral cortex on behavior are to be explained in terms of input. What is important for us today is the fact that afferents from the periphery reach "motor" cortex relatively directly through thalamus, a fact which becomes more meaningful on consideration of the efferents leaving the isocortex.

It has been commonly held for the past 20 or 30 years that the pyramidal tract takes origin in the "motor" cortex, especially that portion close to the central fissure. A recent monograph by Lassek (25) documents thoroughly the evidence for a more extensive origin of the pyramidal tract from the entire extent of the precentral as well as from the postcentral cortex of primates: a return to an earlier held anatomical position which had become submerged during the first half of this century. Another conception held during this latter period, the distinction between pyramidal and extrapyramidal, has recently been questioned in the light of these and other data. Woolsey (57) has shown that the differences in movement brought about by electrical stimulation of the various parts of the precentral cortex may be ascribed to differences in somatotopic relationships rather than to differences in the complexity of organization of the movement. Thus, Woolsey finds that stimulations in the more forward portions of the precentral region, which had formerly been called premotor, activate the axial musculature, while those close to the central fissure activate appendicular musculature. Since axial muscles are larger, the movements they produce appear grosser than those produced by such discrete appendicular muscular units as those found in the hand—one need not invoke different orders of coördination or complexity to distinguish between the posterior and anterior portions of the motor cortex. Thus, the distinction between motor and premotor cortex fades and, as a result, makes unnecessary the classical distinction between the locus of origin of the pyramidal and extrapyramidal systems which has already been called into question by anatomical data.

On the other hand, evidence from ablation and stimulation experiments in both man and monkey indicates the continued necessity for differentiating precentral "motor" from postcentral "sensory" mechanisms (20). Certainly the distinction cannot be thought of simply in terms of afferents reaching the postcentral and efferents leaving the precentral cortex. Thus, with these data in mind, a thorough reinvestigation is needed of the organization of the input-output relationships of the extrinsic system related to somatic structures.

The marked overlap of input-output is not limited to the somatic extrinsic system. With respect to vision, eye movements can be elicited from stimulation of practically all the striate cortex (55); these eye movements can be elicited after ablation of the other cortical areas from which eye movements are obtained. With respect to audition, ear movements have been elicited from the auditory extrinsic system (4). From the portion of the cortex implicated in gustation, tongue and chewing movements may be elicited (2, 51); respiratory effects follow stimulation of the olfactory "receiving" areas (18, 38). Thus, an overlap of afferents and efferents is evident not only in the neural mechanisms related to somatic function but also in those related to the special senses. The over-generalization to the brain of the law of (Bell and) Magendie (27), which defines sensory in terms of afferents in the dorsal-spinal and motor in terms of efferents in the ventral-spinal roots, must, therefore, give way to more precise investigation of the differences in internal organization of the afferent-efferent relationship between periphery and cortex in order to explain differences such as those between "sensory" and "motor" mechanisms. As yet, only a few experiments toward this end have been undertaken (1, 11, 46).

The afferent-efferent overlap in the *extrinsic* system suggests the possibility that the intrinsic systems need not be considered as association centers upon which pathways from the extrinsic sensory sectors converge to bring together neural events anticipatory to spewing them out via the motor pathways. Unfortunately, there are few reliable anatomical data concerning the connections of the intrinsic sectors so that our analysis of the organization of these systems relies largely on neuropsychological data. Let us turn, therefore, to experiments which manipulate cerebral isocortex either by stimulation or resection, and observe the effects of such manipulations on behavior.

PROBLEMS OF NEURAL ORGANIZATION IN COGNITIVE BEHAVIOR

For the purposes of this presentation, cognitive processes will be inferred from discriminative and problem-solving behavior since most of the recent relevant data stem from experiments in this area of investigation. The relation of the extrinsic sectors to such behavior has been extensively studied in the past, and I shall not dwell on recent contributions which elaborate usually held notions. It is worth mentioning, however, that, with the exception of the vestibular mechanisms, a different subdivision of the extrinsic sector (or an allocortical counterpart) has been related to each of the special senses (defined as those in which receptors are aggregated in a discrete sense organ), whereas the search for a specific relationship between subdivisions of the extrinsic sectors and submodalities of sensation, such as touch versus cold or pattern versus color, has thus far proved unsuccessful. The problem of the organization of sensory function has hardly been posed in terms of current knowledge of receptor mechanisms and neural organization.

The classic prototype of the experiment relating extrinsic cortex to sensory behavior is that of Klüver (19), which shows that monkey deprived of its occipital lobes reacts visually only to total luminous flux; differential reactions to more complex visual events are absent. Regarding motor behavior, the classical prototype experiment is that of Lashley

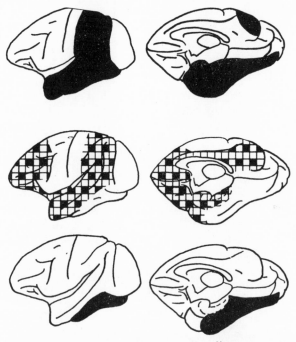

Fig. 60.—From Pribram (35). The upper diagrams represent the sum of the areas of resection of 15 subjects showing a decrement in the performance of a preoperatively learned visual discrimination task. The middle diagrams represent the sum of the areas of resection of 25 subjects showing no such decrement. The lower diagrams represent the intersect of the area shown in black in the upper and that *not* checkerboarded in the middle diagram. This intersect represents the area invariably implicated in visual choice behavior by these experiments.

(21): a monkey deprived of precentral cortex reacts only with grossly organized movements. More discretely organized patterns of movement are disturbed not in terms of the final solution of the problem presented, but rather in terms of increased time taken to complete the solution of the problem because of awkwardness. But, loss of occipital tissue does not completely destroy the organism's differential reaction to light, nor does loss of precentral tissue result in total loss of differentiated movements; rather, the impairment following invasion of the extrinsic cortical sectors may be characterized as a limit placed on the complexity of possible behavior. Interference with peripheral mechanisms imposes the greatest restriction. Interference with extrinsic cerebral mechanisms imposes a lesser, though still devastating restriction. I shall return to this point later.

With this background, let us turn to a large body of neuropsychological experiments made on monkey during the past ten years which delineate the organization of intrinsic cortex in choice behavior. There are two anatomically distinct intrinsic sectors: a posterior or parieto-temporopreoccipital, and an anterior or frontal. There are now several studies which suggest that the posterior sector may be subdivided into areas, each of which serves a separate sense modality. The following figures illustrate this point. Resections of most areas of the cerebral cortex are *not* followed by decrement in a monkey's performance of visual discrimination tasks (Fig. 60). However, when the inferotemporal area of the posterior intrinsic system is invaded, the animal is unable to make a great variety of visual choices even though it had learned to make them preoperatively. That this deficit in choice behavior is limited to the visual modality can be seen from Table 5. In the experiment illustrated here, the monkeys were taught somesthetic as well as visual choice problems. Occipitoparietal resections interfered with performance of the somesthetic problem but not with performance of the visual task; the converse finding

TABLE 5

Further behavioral analysis of the PTO cortex

	P48	P46	P49	T44	T45
Visual 10 (0–70)	0	0	0	(500)	(500)
Somatosensory 60 (0–100)	460	120	350	70	50
New Somatosensory	(1000)	(1000)	(1000)	320	260

was obtained following inferotemporal resections. In taste and olfaction, there is some evidence that the anterior temporal region (including allo-juxtallocortical structures) functions selectively (36): preliminary studies underway show promise of delineating a relationship between a portion of the posterior intrinsic sector and audition (56). Thus, portions of the *posterior intrinsic sector* have been related to discriminative behavior in one or another of the special senses or in somesthesis: Cognitive processes

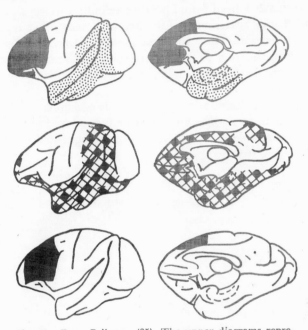

Fig. 61.—From Pribram (35). The upper diagrams represent in black the sum of the areas of resection of 6 subjects that showed a decrement in the performance of delayed reaction preoperatively learned. The middle diagrams represent the sum of the areas of resection of 24 subjects that showed no such decrement. The lower diagrams represent the intersect of the area shown in the upper diagram and that *not* checkerboarded in the middle diagram. This intersect represents the area invariably implicated in delayed-reaction performance in these experiments. (Resection within the area stippled in the upper diagram occasionally results in "deficit"; however, a similar deficit occasionally appears in nonoperate controls. Such aberrant cases are not found when delayed alternation rather than delayed response is used. Alternation may, therefore, be considered a somewhat more reliable measure of frontal lobe deficit.)

are served, therefore, not only by modality-specific extrinsic mechanisms but by modality-specific intrinsic mechanisms as well.

No discussion of cerebral mechanisms in cognitive behavior is complete without reference to the *frontal intrinsic sector.* A series of experiments begun by Carlyle Jacobsen (16) has shown an invariant relationship between lesions of the frontal intrinsic system of monkey and decrements in performance of delayed reaction; no other resection of intrinsic isocortex has been found to alter reliably this class of behavioral events, and frontal resections fail to affect the many other types of choice behavior so far tested. Thus, since *completely separate* behavioral factors have been shown related to the posterior and to the frontal intrinsic sectors, any notion of the frontal lobes as a "higher" integrative mechanism is precluded (Fig. 61).

Further analysis has shown that the effects on choice behavior of frontal lesions extend to a variety of tasks of the delayed-reaction type; for instance, to those tasks in which monkeys are taught to alternately choose

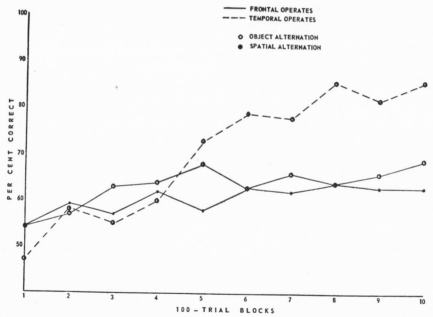

Fig. 62.—From Pribram and Mishkin (41). Performance curves of anterofrontal and control (inferotemporal) operates on spatial and object alternation. Note that anterofrontal operates are equally impaired in the performance of both tasks. On spatial alternation the control operates achieved a 90 per cent level of performance within 250 trials.

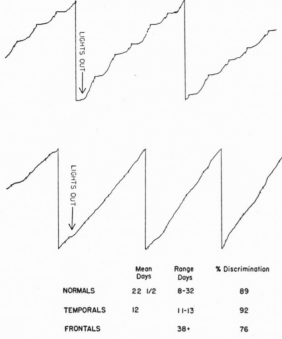

	Mean Days	Range Days	% Discrimination
NORMALS	22 1/2	8-32	89
TEMPORALS	12	11-13	92
FRONTALS		38+	76

Fig. 63.—Examples of the rate of bar-pressing response of monkeys as cumulatively recorded. These curves were generated by an inferotemporal operate (above) and an anterofrontal operate (below) trained to respond differentially to different sequences of reward contingencies administered as a "multiple" schedule of reinforcement. This schedule consisted of a sequential alternation between two conditions, one in which 40 bar presses were rewarded by a peanut (fixed ratio) and the other in which 4 min. elapsed before reward, irrespective of the number of bar presses (fixed interval); initially, the ratio schedule was signaled by a red light, the interval schedule by a green light. During each 1½-hr. testing session the lights were turned off after 20 min. so that correct response rate was contingent solely on the animal's own prior behavior. Note the indiscriminate rate shown after "Lights Out" by the anterofrontal operate (lower curve). The numbers below the curves refer to the mean and range of the number of days taken to reach an 85 per cent criterion of discrimination between the fixed-ratio and the fixed-interval schedule in the absence of the light signal by four unoperated normal monkeys, two inferotemporal operates (Temporals), and two anterofrontal operates (Frontals). The subjects were considered to be making the discrimination whenever they took longer to make the first 40 bar presses while the interval schedule was in force. Note that the inferotemporal operates reached criterion in fewer days than most normals, which suggests that these operates relied more than did normals on nonvisual cues even when the signal was present. Note also that the anterofrontal operates failed to reach criterion.

one of two cups, spatial alternation (17, 42). Figure 62 describes the results of an experiment in which the monkey must choose alternately one of two randomly placed objects (nonspatial, visual object alternation); resection of the frontal intrinsic system impairs performance when spatial cues are replaced by purely visual cues. Figure 63 graphs the results of another "alternation" experiment. In this, the alternation of two patterns of response rate is contingent on two schedules of reinforcement; the animal with a frontal resection is shown deficient when the alternation is made dependent on its own prior behavior rather than on environmental cues. Taken together, these experiments suggest that resections of the frontal intrinsic system impair performance *whenever* a correct choice depends exclusively on transient events not present at the time the choice is made—irrespective of "modality."

As can be seen from these data, the basis for stating that different cortical areas serve different functions applies equally to the intrinsic and the extrinsic sectors; that is, manipulations of certain portions affect certain classes of behavior while manipulations of other portions affect other classes. Such findings have given rise to "mosaic" conceptualizations of brain function in behavior. We must admit that these data are striking.

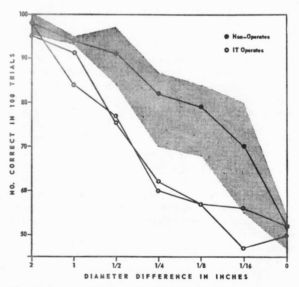

Fig. 64.—From Mishkin and Hall (28). Scores for two operates and four controls on the first run of size discrimination. Shaded area indicates the range of performance of the four nonoperate controls.

It is easy to see, therefore, how the "localizationist" is impressed and how he may be satisfied with the conception that the cerebral isocortex (both intrinsic and extrinsic) can be subdivided further into units, each of which may serve a different function.

But this is not the whole story. A comparison of the effects of resection of the extrinsic and of the intrinsic systems involved in vision poses difficulties for the "mosaic" notion. As we have seen, the inferotemporal area of the posterior intrinsic system and only this portion of the intrinsic system is critically implicated in visual discrimination performance. Since similar and more drastic effects on visual choice behavior follow extensive lesions of the primate occipital lobe, how can we characterize the difference in function between the intrinsic and extrinsic "visual" systems? Two separate classes of visual behavior can be sought: one related to the extrinsic and the other, to the intrinsic system. However, no such separable relationships have been found to exist. Instead, any effect of resection of the intrinsic system may be duplicated by extensive resection of

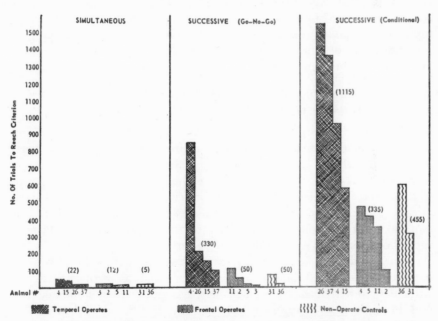

Fig. 65.—From Pribram and Mishkin (40). Comparison of learning scores of three groups of animals (inferotemporal operates, anterofrontal operates, and nonoperate controls) in a simultaneous task and two types of successive tasks in which the *same* cues were used. The increment of impairment of the inferotemporal group, as compared with controls, appears roughly proportional to the increasing difficulty of the task for controls.

the extrinsic systems. Furthermore, the latter produces additional effects (e.g., field defects). Thus, the difference between the effects of resection of the intrinsic and of the extrinsic systems on vision is analogous to that which obtains between the effects of resection of the extrinsic system and of the sense organ: Resection of the intrinsic visual system limits the complexity of the organism's possible visual behavior but not so much as resection of the extrinsic visual system or that of the receptor. So far, independent measures of "complexity" are poor. One such measure has been the relative difficulty which normal animals have in learning visual problems. An analysis of "difficulty" has shown that the variables which must be taken into account include the physical parameters of the cue (Fig. 64), the situation in which cues are imbedded (Fig. 65), and the experience which the animal has had with this or with similar cues (44).

The fact that monkeys with inferotemporal resections show an impairment in visual behavior which is not as extreme as that found after total occipital lesions nor as severe as that which results when the sense organ itself is removed demonstrates that a hierarchical organization of neural systems exists in vision. Thus, functionally separable parts of the isocortex do not *necessarily* serve *different* functions. Do these findings presage the possibility of finding other hierarchical organizations of cerebral events when other categories of behavior are studied?

DISCUSSION: AN ALTERNATIVE TO THE TRANSCORTICAL REFLEX

Models of cerebral organization in cognitive processes have, heretofore, been based to a large extent on clinical neurological data and have been formulated with the "reflex" as prototype. Such models state that input is organized in the extrinsic "sensory," elaborated in the intrinsic "associative," and from there relayed to the extrinsic "motor" sectors. I have already pointed out that the afferent-efferent overlap in the extrinsic system makes such notions of cerebral organization suspect. A series of neuropsychological studies by Lashley (23), Sperry (49, 50), Chow (8), Evarts (12), and Wade (53), in which the extrinsic sectors were surgically crosshatched, circumsected, or isolated by large resections of their surround with little apparent effects on behavior, has cast further doubt on the usefulness of such a "transcortical" model. Additional difficulties are posed by the negative electrophysiological and anatomical findings whenever direct connections are sought between the extrinsic and intrinsic sectors (5, 39). These data focus anew our attention on the problem faced repeatedly by those interested in cerebral functions in cognitive behavior. Experimentalists who followed Flourens in dealing with the hierarchical aspects of cerebral organization—e.g., Munk (31), Monakov (29), Gold-stein (15), Loeb (26), and Lashley (22)—have invariably come to empha-size the importance of the *extrinsic* sectors not only in "sensorimotor" behavior but also in the more complex "cognitive" processes. Each inves-tigator has had a slightly different approach to the functions of the *intrin-sic* sectors, but the viewpoints share the proposition that the intrinsic sec-tors do not function independently of the extrinsic. The common diffi-culty has been the conceptualization of this interdependence between in-trinsic and extrinsic systems in terms other than the transcortical "reflex" model—a model which became less cogent with each new experiment.

Is there an alternative which meets the objections levied against the transcortical "reflex" yet accounts for currently available data? I believe there is. The hierarchical relationship between intrinsic and extrinsic systems can be attributed to convergence of the *output* of the two systems at a subcortical locus rather than to a specific input from the extrinsic cortex to the intrinsic. Some evidence supporting this notion is already available. Data obtained by Whitlock and Nauta (57) using silver staining techniques, show that *both* the intrinsic and the extrinsic sectors impli-cated in vision by neuropsychological experiments are *efferently* con-nected with the superior colliculus. On the other hand, lesions of the in-trinsic thalamic nuclei fail to interfere with discriminative behavior (9, 32). Thus, the specific effects in behavior of the intrinsic systems are ex-plained on the basis of *output* to a subcortically located neural mecha-nism which functions specifically (e.g., superior colliculus in vision). This output, in turn, affects input to the extrinsic systems either directly or through the efferent control of the receptor (e.g., in vision, mechanisms of eye movement, accommodation). According to this conception, the "as-sociative" functions of the central nervous system are to be sought at con-vergence points throughout the central nervous system, especially in the brain stem and spinal axis, and not solely in the intrinsic cerebral sectors.

What are the differences in the experimental approach suggested by these formulations? Let us return to the discussion of the relationship be-tween frontal cortex and delayed reaction. According to the *old* model of the role of "association" cortex in behavior, we could conceive of the defi-cit in delayed-reaction–type behavior as a deficit in intersensory inter-action, a possibility recently suggested by Teuber and Mishkin (52). Search for other intermodality "interactions" would follow. On the other hand, by taking into account the finding that the relationship between frontal and posterior intrinsic sectors to separate classes of behavior is distinct rather than hierarchical, a search would be instituted for a class or classes of variables distinct from those which have been found related to the posterior (modality-specific) intrinsic systems: e.g., for a class "transient events not cotemporaneous with the response which they determine" such as predelay cue and reinforcement variables. Also, on the basis of analogy with the posterior intrinsic systems, we would predict the discovery of some "extrinsic" neural mechanism related to the anterior intrinsic sector. One possibility is that the limbic allo-juxtallocortical structures function in this manner. Experiments designed to discover a hierarchical relationship between the limbic and the anterior intrinsic cortex by neuropsychological experiment have been only partially successful. These experiments have shown that performance of tasks of the delayed-reaction type is *not* affected by limbic lesions (35); on the other hand, conditioned avoidance is affected by both frontal and limbic system ablations (45). Other forebrain structures, such as the neostriatum, must also be considered as possible "extrinsic" mates to the anterior intrinsic system since Rosvold and Delgado (48) were able to interfere with monkeys' performance of spatial alternation by stimulating with electrodes implanted in the caudate nucleus.

These, then, are some examples of the direction which the alternative to the transcortical reflex conception of the neural mechanisms serving cognitive processes can give experimenters. Apparently, the question as to whether a complex cognitive event is determined by the cerebral mantle as a unit or by a mosaic of cerebral suborgans continues to generate interest even when some old controversial issues are replaced by new ones.

SUMMARY

Conceptions concerning neocortical mechanisms in cognitive behavior have been re-evaluated in terms of recently accumulated data. Since the designation "neocortex" has become ambiguous, "isocortex" is substituted; relations to cognitive processes are inferred from discriminative and problem-solving behavior.

Isocortex has been classified according to the input it receives from the thalamus. When a sector of isocortex receives fibers from a thalamic "relay" nucleus which, in turn, receives its major afferents from outside the thalamus, the sector is called extrinsic. When a sector of isocortex receives fibers from a thalamic nucleus which receives no such extra-thalamic afferents, that cortex is classified as intrinsic.

Neurally distinct portions of the *extrinsic* isocortex are known to serve distinct classes of behavior. The distinctions are in part related to differences in input from different peripheral receptor mechanisms (e.g., sense organs). Other distinctions such as between "motor" and "sensory" cortex *cannot* be attributed to such gross anatomical differences (e.g., that only afferents reach "sensory" and efferents leave "motor" cortex). Rather, differences in detail of the organization of the overlapping input to and output from *each* of the extrinsic sectors must be investigated.

Intrinsic isocortex can also be divided according to demonstrated relationships to one or another class of behavior. Discriminative behavior in specific modalities is affected when particular subdivisions of the posterior intrinsic cortex are removed. When the anterior intrinsic cortex is ablated, those discriminations are affected which are based primarily on transient events which are not cotemporaneous with the choice, irrespective of modality.

In several instances intrinsic and extrinsic systems are related to the *same* class of behavior. In these instances, the organism is limited in the possible complexity of cognitive behavior when the intrinsic cortex is resected—a limitation which is, however, not as severe as that resulting from extensive damage to the extrinsic system nor as that resulting from gross interference with receptor mechanisms. The hierarchical relationship described by these data has, heretofore, been attributed to specific afferents originating in subdivisions of extrinsic, and connecting to subdivisions of intrinsic, isocortex. Experiments have been quoted which make it unlikely that such *specific afferents* exist. Instead, the specificity of function of subdivisions of the intrinsic isocortex is, in this analysis, attributed to *convergence* on a common subcortical mechanism of *efferents* from hierarchically related intrinsic and extrinsic systems. The output from the intrinsic systems is, in this manner, conceived to influence the output from (and perhaps, via regulation of the peripheral sensory mechanism, the input to) the extrinsic systems. Thus, the primacy of the function of the extrinsic systems *and* the essential role of the intrinsic systems in cognitive behavior are accounted for without invoking the classical transcortical reflex to support a completely "mosaic" notion of cerebral function and without resorting to a non-localizationistic view of the intrinsic systems.

REFERENCES

1 Amassian, V. E. Interaction in the somatovisceral projection system. *Res. Publ. Ass. nerv. ment. Dis.*, 1952, *30:* 371–402.

2 Bagshaw, M., and K. H. Pribram. Cortical organization in gustation (*Macaca mulatta*). *J. Neurophysiol.*, 1953, *16:* 499–508.

3 Bailey, P., and G. Von Bonin. *The isocortex of man.* Urbana, Ill.: Univer. Illinois Press, 1951.

4 Bechterew, W. Von. *Die Funktionen der Nervencentra.* Vol. 3. Pp. 1859–64. Jena: Gustav Fischer, 1908–11. 3 Vols.

5   Bonin, G. V., H. W. Garol, and W. S. McCulloch. The functional organiza-
    tion of the occipital lobe. *Biol. Symp., 7.*
6   Boring, E. G. *A history of experimental psychology.* (2nd ed.) New York:
    Appleton-Century-Crofts, 1950.
7   Chow, K. L. A retrograde cell degeneration study of the cortical projection
    field of the pulvinar in the monkey. *J. comp. Neurol.,* 1950, *93:* 313–40.
8   ———. Further studies on selective ablation of associative cortex in relation
    to visually mediated behavior. *J. comp. physiol. Psychol.,* 1952, *45:* 109–18.
9   ———. Lack of behavioral effects following destruction of some thalamic
    association nuclei in monkey. *Arch. Neurol. Psychiat., Chicago,* 1954, *71:*
    762–71.
10 Chow, K. L., and K. H. Pribram. Cortical projection of the thalamic ventro-
    lateral nuclear group in monkey. *J. comp. Neurol.,* 1956, *104:* 57–75.
11 Dell, P. Corrélations entre le système végétatif et le système de la vie de
    relation: Mesencèphale diencéphale et cortex cérébral. *J. Physiol. Path.
    Gen.,* 1952, *44:* 471–557.
12 Evarts, E. V. Effect of ablation of prestriate cortex on auditory-visual asso-
    ciation in monkey. *J. Neurophysiol.,* 1952, *15:* 191–200.
13 Flechsig, P. *Die Localisation der geistigen Vorgänge insbesondere der Sin-
    nesempfindungen der Menschen.* Leipsig, 1896.
14 Flourens, P. *Recherches expérimentales sur les propriétés et les fonctions
    du système nerveux dans les animaux vertébrés.* Paris: Crevot, 1924, *26:* 332.
15 Goldstein, K. Die Topik der Grosshirnrinde in ihrer klinischen Bedeutung.
    Dtsch. Z. Nervenheilk., 1923, 77: 7–124.
16 Jacobsen, C. F. Studies of cerebral functions in primates: I. The functions
    of the frontal association areas in monkeys. *Comp. Psychol. Monogr.,* 1936,
    13: No. 3 (Whole No. 63), pp. 3–60.
17 Jacobsen, C. F., and H. W. Nissen. Studies of cerebral functions in primates.
    IV. The effects of frontal lobe lesions on the delayed alternation habit in
    monkeys. *J. comp. Psychol.,* 1937, *23:* 101–12.
18 Kaada, B. R., K. H. Pribram, and J. A. Epstein. Respiratory and vascular
    responses to monkeys from temporal pole, insula, orbital surface and cingu-
    late gyrus: A preliminary report. *J. Neurophysiol.,* 1949, *12:* 347–56.
19 Klüver, H. Visual functions after removal of the occipital lobes. *J. Psychol.,*
    1941, *11:* 23–45.
20 Kruger, L. Observations on the organization of the sensorimotor cerebral
    cortex. Unpublished doctor's dissertation, Yale Univer., 1954.
21 Lashley, K. S. Studies of cerebral function in learning: V. The retention of
    motor habits after destruction of the so-called motor areas in primates.
    Arch. Neurol. Psychiat., Chicago, 1924, *12:* 249–76.
22 ———. *Brain mechanisms and intelligence.* Chicago: Univer. Chicago Press,
    1929.
23 ———. The mechanism of vision: XVIII: Effects of destroying the visual
    "associative areas" of the monkey. *Genet. Psychol. Monogr.,* 1948, *37:* 107–66.
24 Lashley, K. S., and G. Clark. The cytoarchitecture of the cerebral cortex of

Ateles: A critical examination of architectonic studies. *J. comp. Neurol.*, 1946, *85:* 223–305.

25 Lassek, A. M. *The pyramidal tract. Its status in medicine.* Springfield, Ill.: Charles C Thomas, 1954.

26 Loeb, J. *Comparative physiology of the brain and comparative psychology.* London: J. Murray, 1901.

27 Magendie, F. Expériences sur les fonctions des racines des nerfs rachidiens. *J. Physiol. exp.*, 1822, *2:* 276–79.

28 Mishkin, M., and M. Hall. Discrimination along a size continuum following ablation of the inferior temporal convexity in monkeys. *J. comp. physiol. Psychol.*, 1955, *48:* 97–101.

29 Monakov, C. von. *Die Lokalisation im Grosshirn und der Abbau der Funktion durch Korticale Herde.* Wiesbaden: J. F. Bergmann, 1914.

30 Morgan, C. T., and E. Stellar. *Physiological psychology.* (2nd ed.), New York: McGraw-Hill, 1950.

31 Munk, H. *Uber die Funktionen der Grosshirnrinde: gesammelte Mitteilungen aus den Jahren.* Berlin: Hirschwald, 1881.

32 Peters, R. H., and H. E. Rosvold. The effect of thalamic lesions upon spatial delayed alternation performance in the rhesus monkey. Unpublished M. D. thesis, Yale Univer., 1955.

33 Poliak, S. *Main afferent fiber systems of the cerebral cortex in primates.* Berkeley, Calif.: Univer. California Press, 1932.

34 Pribram, H. and J. Barry. Further behavioral analysis of the parieto-temporo-preoccipital cortex. *J. Neurophysiol.*, 1956, *19:* 99–106.

35 Pribram, K. H. Toward a science of neuropsychology (method and data). In R. A. Patton (Ed.), *Current trends in psychology.* Pittsburgh: Univer. Pittsburgh Press, 1955, pp. 115–42.

36 Pribram, K. H., and M. Bagshaw. Further analysis of the temporal lobe syndrome utilizing fronto-temporal ablations. *J. comp. Neurol.*, 1953, *99:* 347–75.

37 Pribram, K. H., K. L. Chow, and J. Semmes. Limit and organization of the cortical projection from the medial thalamic nucleus in monkey. *J. comp. Neurol.*, 1953, *98:* 433–48.

38 Pribram, K. H., and L. Kruger. Functions of the "olfactory brain." *Ann. N. Y. Acad. Sci.*, 1954, *58:* 109–38.

39 Pribram, K. H., and P. D. MacLean. Neuronographic analysis of medial and basal cerebral cortex: II. Monkey. *J. Neurophysiol.*, 1953, *16:* 324–40.

40 Pribram, K. H., and M. Mishkin. Simultaneous and successive visual discrimination by monkeys with inferotemporal lesions. *J. comp. physiol. Psychol.*, 1955, *48:* 198–202.

41 ———. Analysis of the effects of frontal lesions in monkey: III. Object alternation. *J. comp. physiol. Psychol.*, 1956, *49:* 41–45.

42 Pribram, K. H., M. Mishkin, H. E. Rosvold, and S. J. Kaplan. Effects on delayed-response performance of lesions of dorsolateral and ventromedial frontal cortex of baboons. *J. comp. physiol. Psychol.*, 1952, *45:* 565–75.

43   Pribram, K. H., B. S. Rosner, and W. A. Rosenblith. Electrical responses to acoustic clicks in monkey: Extent of neocortex activated. *J. Neurophysiol.,* 1954, *17:* 336–44.

44   Pribram, K. H., and M. Varley. Further analysis of the effect of variations of delayed reaction on the performance of monkeys with frontal lesions. See Pribram, K. H. The intrinsic systems of the forebrain: an alternative to the concept of cortical association areas, Fig. 14 in *Handbook of Physiology.* New York: McGraw-Hill, in press.

45   Pribram, K. H., and L. Weiskrantz. Comparison of the effects of medial and lateral cerebral resections on conditioned avoidance behavior of monkeys. *J. comp. physiol. Psychol.,* 1957, *50:* 74–80.

46   Rose, J. E., and V. B. Mountcastle. Activity of single neurons in the tactile thalamic region of the cat in response to a transient peripheral stimulus. *Johns Hopk. Hosp. Bull.,* 1954, *94:* 238–82.

47   Rose, J. E., and C. N. Woolsey. Organization of the mammalian thalamus and its relationships to the cerebral cortex. *Electroencyph. clin. Neurophysiol.,* 1949, *1:* 391–404.

48   Rosvold, H. E., and J. M. R. Delgado. The effect on the behavior of monkeys of electrically stimulating or destroying small areas within the frontal lobes. *Amer. Psychologist,* 1953, *8:* 425–26.

49   Sperry, R. W. Cerebral regulation of motor coordination in monkeys following multiple transection of sensorimotor cortex. *J. Neurophysiol.,* 1947, *10:* 275–94.

50   Sperry, R. W., N. Miner, and R. E. Meyers. Visual pattern perception following subpial slicing and tantalum wire implantations in the visual cortex. *J. Comp. physiol. Psychol.,* 1955, *48:* 50–58.

51   Sugar, O., J. G. Chusid, and J. D. French. A second motor cortex in the monkey (Macaca mulatta). *J. Neuropath.,* 1948, *7:* 182–89.

52   Teuber, H. L., and M. Mishkin. Judgment of visual and postural vertical after brain injury. *J. Psychol.,* 1954, *38:* 161–75.

53   Wade, M. Behavioral effects of prefrontal lobectomy, lobotomy and circumsection in the monkey (Macaca mulatta). *J. comp. Neurol.,* 1952, *96:* 179–207.

54   Walker, A. E. *The primate thalamus.* Chicago: Univer. Chicago Press, 1938.

55   Walker, A. E., and T. A. Weaver, Jr. Ocular movements from the occipital lobe in the monkey. *J. Neurophysiol.,* 1940, *3:* 353–57.

56   Weiskrantz, L., and M. Mishkin. Effect of various cortical lesions on auditory discrimination in the rhesus monkey. In preparation.

57   Whitlock, D. G., and W. J. H. Nauta. Subcortical projections from the temporal neocortex in Macaca Mulatta. *J. comp. Neurol.,* 1956, *106:* 185–212.

58   Woolsey, C. N., P. H. Settlage, D. R. Meyer, W. Spencer, T. Hamuy, and A. M. Travis. Patterns of localization in precentral and "supplementary" motor areas and their relation to the concept of a premotor area. *Res. Publ. Ass. nerv. ment. Dis.,* 1952, *30:* 238–64.

Donald R. Meyer

Some Psychological Determinants of Sparing and Loss Following Damage to the Brain

The investigations described in this report were supported in part from funds granted to The Ohio State University by the Research Foundation for aid in Fundamental Research, in part by funds provided by the Wisconsin Alumni Research Foundation, and in part by grant B-732 from the National Institute of Neurological Diseases and Blindness, NIH, USPHS. The monkey experiment was performed during the author's tenure as a research associate at the University of Wisconsin in 1953–54, and he wishes to express his thanks for the hospitality extended to him by the Departments of Psychology and Physiology.

This Symposium is concerned with the problem of communication between the various approaches to the study of the central nervous system, and, it is to be hoped that it also may show us ways in which we can extend the scope of our investigations.

Those of us who are mostly psychologists often find, in fact, that we communicate more readily with colleagues across the campus than with the man down the hall, the molar behaviorist, who is likely to regard our research as interesting but hardly relevant, and who is able to raise the most embarrassing queries with regard to its significance for prediction of behavior. He is the purist who is not at all averse to our aims but doubts the accuracy of our timing. He is the champion of the point of view that biology is best served by independent progress to degrees of scientific development which should make the problem of correlation an ultimately simple one.

While this argument is hardly cogent for such well-developed areas as hearing and vision, it is quite defensible in other instances. The molar behaviorist is at his best in studies and theories of learning, and it is in this area that psychophysiology is weakest. Those of us who study learning and retention in brain-damaged animals often find it particularly difficult to show a molar theorist a result that implies some change from, or confirmation of, his thinking, and we rarely do studies that have their genesis in contemporary molar analysis. What we have borrowed from the study of behavior is the method and the basic faith. Most of our concepts come from other sources, and through them are we interested in problems that are quite remote from psychological discourse.

One such question, and a very important one indeed, is that of functional localization. Psychological procedures have been used with great effect in this realm, but it must be admitted that our localizations are much more precise than our concepts of the functions localized. The outcome is that our results may bear directly on problems of anatomy, where our only question may be whether or not two regions differ in any respect, and yet fail to have any contemporary psychological meaning. It is thus not surprising that the molar behaviorist regards such findings to be outside his immediate domain, and thinks that we would all have been much better off to have waited until our instruments had been refined.

Such an argument is very hard to refute, and about the only answer that we have is that we are doing our best. We could use help that is not now available to us because, on one hand, we spend time that might have been devoted to such questions, in learning technical skills which we cannot hope to master, and on the other, we rarely conduct investigations that will stimulate the interest of the men who perform such analyses exclusively.

The mandate, I think, is quite clear. Some of us, at least, must work to maintain our contacts with molar theorists, even if in doing so we sacrifice our technical growth as anatomists or physiologists. I think it is our business to know the results that are developed in this field and to integrate them with our own. But this is very different from trying to do this work ourselves. We must face the fact that a mastery of technical neurology and neurophysiology is completely incompatible with a mastery of psychology.

This would seem to dictate the team approach to research in this field, and many workers already regard this as our only alternative. With this position I cannot agree. I think that it is possible to do experiments with and without coöperation, depending upon the kinds of questions that we ask. And I think that brain damage can be a useful tool for the molar analyst provided that investigations are designed to yield psychological as well as neurological consequences.

Such investigations are somewhat out of fashion at the moment, for they tend to be performed in eras of doubts about the question of localization. Quite a number have faded from the picture because they lacked structural checks, and we have made such a shibboleth of reconstruction that we often overlook the fact that such procedures may not be crucially important. We tend, in this day of anatomical ascendance, to applaud the serial section as a key to the prime, if not the only, source of variations in our results. This, I believe, is not a very accurate representation of the facts. There are ways and ways of proceeding, and one can do experiments in which the information thus developed is quite frankly not worth the bother.

I want to illustrate this point of view by describing two experiments. The first is a free-lance investigation, the second the product of a team. Both involve the use of brain-damaged animals, but neither fits the customary pattern of fixing the test and varying the lesion. Instead, we fix the lesion and manipulate the training. The brain damage, in studies of this kind, is a dispositional variable analogous to deprivation or some similar constant condition. We prepare an animal with properties of interest, and then manipulate the environmental situation until we can determine some of the relevant conditions of the property. The philosophy of this approach stems from the assumption that some results are more directly affected by an animal's experience outside a surgery than what happens to him within it.

The first experiment is one that I performed in coöperation with Dr. Walter Isaac, now of the University of Washington, and Dr. Brendan Maher, currently a member of the faculty of The Ohio State University. The problem to which we addressed ourselves is a classic question in both physiology and psychology. Does an organism have, as an intrinsic property, the capacity for rapid, spontaneous reorganization of behavior when subjected to changes which disrupt its characteristic modes of action? We are all familiar, I am sure, with Sperry's painstaking approach to this general query. In a series of brilliant papers he was able to show that systematic alterations of central and peripheral relationships lead, in many animals, to highly persistent maladaptive responses. It was his conclusion that the central nervous system is not nearly so plastic as it was purported to be, and that such recoveries as are observed in elementary coördinations require a great deal of practice.

When we turn to learned responses, however, the picture is considerably different. I have in mind, particularly, an experiment of Stewart and Ades (10) on retention of a simple auditory habit by monkeys. These investigators found that their animals lost this response if both superior temporal gyri were destroyed simultaneously or in succession provided that the interval between removals of the two sides was six days or less. Seriatim removal of the two superior temporal gyri with an interoperative interval of seven days or more resulted in retention. This was interpreted as indicating spontaneous reorganization, and so it would seem if we mean by "spontaneous" that no special training needs to be given the monkeys for the sparing to occur.

We undertook, in our experiment, to explore this result a little further. A brief consideration made it abundantly clear that a procedurally similar experiment was out of the question. In the first place, it seemed improbable that we would be able to obtain the coöperation of a neuro-anatomist. To control variations in surgery, then, we would need to employ a statistical approach—the psychologist's well-worn answer to any problem of inference involving uncontrolled individual differences. In other words, instead of trying for absolute consistency of outcome—which no one obtains anyway—we decided to aim for trends instead.

Such a program requires a large number of subjects, and hence it was necessary for us to consider carefully the choice of animal. Monkeys were out of the question; we had half a dozen, but the study promised to require at least half a hundred animals. At times like this, we turn to rats. In view of the fact that this species will learn simple habits as quickly as a monkey, the choice is not an inconvenient one.

The decision, however, broached another problem to be solved only by altering another aspect of the Stewart and Ades experiment. The man who works with rats in auditory studies is plagued in two ways. First, it is relatively difficult to produce a soundproof chamber, and rats have a tendency to make their own noises even if a good one can be had. Secondly, many are afflicted with middle-ear disease, and this is difficult to diagnose until it is well advanced. Since complete control of some form of stimulation was deemed necessary—both at home and in the training situation—we decided to work on visual problems instead. Thus, our experiment finally resembled its primary instigator only in conceptual features.

It turned out that the study was to be a close relation to Lashley's investigation of the effects of brain damage on brightness discrimination. You will recall that he found that rats with lesions in the striate areas lose a habit based on brightness differences, but relearn it at a rate comparable to that observed in normal animals. Actually, the present study differs with regard to the method of training; in place of the old discrimination box, we employed an avoidance-conditioning situation. What we did, essentially, was to place our subject in a square compartment with an electric grid for a floor. Within this compartment, at the center, was a light bulb enclosed in a plastic container of the sort used for storing foods in a refrigerator. The top was covered over by glass so that the experimenter could observe the responses of the animals. The rats were trained to perform a jumping response to the light, thus escaping shock to the feet. Our measure was the number of trials required for each animal to reach a criterion of 9 responses in a block of 10 presentations. Time relations were such that shock, which was paired with a buzzer, occurred 2 sec. after the onset of the light.

Our surgical problem was to find an ablation which would lead to the loss of our conditioned avoidance habit. Actually, it was by no means clear that such a loss could be produced at all in animals trained by this method. We could be reasonably certain, however, that effective lesions would doubtlessly involve the posterior regions of the cerebral cortex. We decided to make them generous in size, to err in the direction of too much rather than too little. The intent is summarized in Figure 66, which shows the ablation we attempted to produce in relation to the visual field as determined electrically by Woolsey and Lemessurier. We used the aspiration method, and exposed only those parts of the cortex which were subsequently removed. Placement of the lesions was guided by bony criteria, extending anteriorly to the frontoparietal suture and laterally to the vertical tangent of the skull. Cortex lying below and posterior to the transverse sinus was excavated to the extreme posterior margin.

Fig. 66.—This drawing shows the extent of the intended ablation in black, and the border of the electrically defined visual area in white.

As a first venture we trained a group of four rats, performed simultaneous bilateral ablations on them, and retrained them 18 days later. The rats stayed in their home cages during the latter interval. All four subsequently showed a loss of the habit; in fact, they all took longer to relearn it than to learn it. Although this was not too rigorous a validation of our surgical procedure, we decided not to extend this inquiry. It was felt that were it necessary to enlarge the group, we could do so later. Actually, the outcome of the experiment proper bore out this decision very nicely.

In the major experimental groups, our concern was not with variations on the theme of what is to be removed. Before their final tests, all operated animals had suffered cortical ablations which were as like as we were able to make them. The operations were, however, performed sequentially, first on one side and then on the other. It was our plan to see, first of all, if reorganization would take place, and if it did, to see whether or not such reoganization is dependent upon visual stimulation. The plan of the study and its results are outlined in Figure 67. At the top of this chart we have a resumé of the pilot study with the four animals. As it shows, the rats were trained on day zero and were operated upon on day 1. After surgery, all were returned to their cages, where

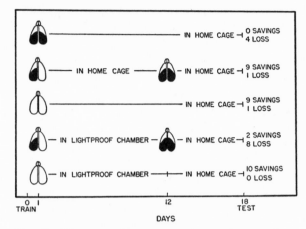

Fig. 67.—Diagrammatic summary of procedures and results. Savings and losses are determined by comparisons of learning and relearning to an arbitrary criterion of performance.

they remained until they were tested for retention by relearning on day 18. The fact that all animals completely lost the habit is recorded in the figure at the right.

In the next line, we have the results for the first major group. As before, these animals were trained on day zero. The following day they were subjected to removals of the posterior regions of one hemisphere. Then they were placed in their home cages for a 12-day rest, and on day 12 the contralateral area was destroyed. Once again the animals were returned to their cages, and on day 18 they were tested. Here we note that although these animals have suffered the same destruction as had the first four rats, nine of the ten show a measurable amount of retention. From the next line we learn that this is what is expected from normal animals that are merely trained and then tested for retention after 18 days. Thus we confirm the general finding of Stewart and Ades. Reorganization has been observed, and our remaining question is whether such reoganization is in fact spontaneous.

In our third major group, we return to seriatim destruction. These animals, however, were confined to a lightproof chamber for the time between their first and second operations. This chamber was designed to accommodate the type of cage used on our regular racks, and it was ventilated by means of a series of small fans which forced air through lightproof louvers. The animals recovered from anesthesia in darkness, and were exposed to light only long enough for checks on their survival and for the maneuvers necessary for preparing them for their second operation. After that, they were returned to their home cages in the light for 6 days, and then were tested in the same fashion as the others. Their results are quite different, as we see; now eight animals out of ten show a loss. This result, if we test it with Fisher's (3) exact treatment for a two-by-two contingency table, is highly significant from a statistical standpoint. That this reversal is not due simply to confinement in the dark is clear from behavior of normal rats kept in the lightproof chamber for 12 days, and then in their home cage for 6 days, before the retest. All ten animals treated in this fashion, our last major group, showed excellent retention of the habit. Thus, we are forced to conclude that the reorganization observed in our first major group is not spontaneous, but is dependent upon stimulation of the visual mechanism.

The most significant fact is that such stimulation is not practiced as we usually conceive it. Once trained, the animals were never placed in the test situation until all these procedures were complete. We are thus reminded of the dictum of the therapist who, in dealing with aphasic disorders, maintains that stimulation with words is necessary but that recovery may well be noticed which has no relation to specific practice (12). We may question whether learning in its usual sense is responsible for the sparing that is frequently noted in cases of slow and progressive destruction of the cerebral cortex. The results are reminiscent of the diaschisis doctrine as developed by von Monakow (8), for it seems quite clear that traces that otherwise would not have been detected have been activated by exposure to the normal cage environment. It is equally clear, however, that recovery is not spontaneous. What we find to be the case is a compromise between the views of those who emphasize central autonomous processes and those who implicate the periphery.

We must recognize that all our conclusions are without benefit of reconstruction. Could it be that the deviations we have observed within these groups are due to differences in surgery? Let me emphasize that we know not and care not; no attempt is made to parcel out such errors from others that we might describe as random stomach-aches or just plain individual cussedness. Nor is such a parceling necessary in view of the fact that we are not concerned with anatomical questions. The study has a limited objective, but I think a most important one for molar psychological analysis.

I do not maintain that a lack of reconstruction is a virtue, but that the use of such procedures when they are unnecessary is a vice. Situations do arise in which verification is both necessary and practical. Such were the conditions under which the second experiment I wish to describe was performed. It began when I was graced with an opportunity to work with Clinton Woolsey and Konrad Akert. Our mutual interests prompted a study of the functions of the temporal lobes of the monkey. To the surgeon, such excisions are a challenge if they are to be done properly; to the anatomist, the reconstructions provide evidence on points above and beyond those raised by the psychological results.

From the latter standpoint, we are once again primarily concerned with training variables. The study was largely instigated by a recent work of Riopelle, Alper, Strong, and Ades (9) concerned with the effects of temporal lobectomy upon the acquisition of what is known as the "discrimination learning set." Such sets are inferred from the transfer of training that we observe if a monkey is confronted with a series of equivalent visual discrimination problems. The problem stemmed from the classical experiments of Harlow (4). If monkeys are called upon to learn which one of two objects conceals a small piece of food, and then to do the same thing with other objects, they soon learn to solve the individual problems in a single trial. Gradually, it seems, the monkeys are changed in some fashion so that they are freed from the gradual trial-and-error process that we see in the naive animal. My own analyses (6, 7) have suggested that the learning set is something apart from the process that leads to mastery of the single problem; thus, for example, we can show that learning sets can be established and extinguished without such variations introducing any marked alteration of the intraproblem process. Specific learning, the mopping-up process, is apparently associated with entirely different mechanisms from those involved in learning sets. In support of this, we have the fact that learning-set formation rates may be markedly different in species which vary little in their capacity to learn single problems.

Now, what the group at Emory seemed to show is this: If one subjects monkeys to extensive temporal ablation and then trains them on a series of object-discrimination problems of the sort just described, they are very similar to normal monkeys at first. Gradually, however, the normal monkeys pull away from the temporals. To the temporal monkeys, apparently, each new problem was a fresh experience—they never formed a learning set. This, I submit, is an exciting result. It tends to confirm the conclusions that we drew from our study of normal monkeys by showing that surgical intervention can dissociate the intraproblem and interproblem processes. Also, it makes good evolutionary sense in that the brain region destroyed is well developed only in those animals that also form learning sets readily. Here, certainly, is one instance of a study that gives as much back to molar behavior theory as it took when it employed the tests made meaningful by molar behavior analysis. The crucial lesion for this effect has not as yet been determined, for Riopelle and Ades do not inform us as to exactly what was lost and what was spared. But this is not the tragedy that some would make of it; the study is important in that it shows that there exists a lesion which will accomplish the dissociation. It is similar, in this regard, to the study of Klüver and Bucy (5), a fairly famous temporal experiment that raised more questions than it answered.

A second experiment in this general area has been recently reported by Chow (2). In his investigation the question was asked of retention rather than of acquisition. Chow first trained his animals and then operating, directing his attention to the temporal neocortex. Afterward he found that one of three monkeys retained its learning set for objects, while two that lost the set relearned it after limited practice.

The meaning of this difference is far from clear at present. Chow prefers the possibility of an anatomical solution, but the studies are dissimilar in other respects as well. We have further evidence for the compatibility of excellent performance levels and extensive posterior removals in a study by Warren and Harlow (11), whose monkeys were even more experienced than Chow's prior to the completion of extensive bilateral temporal, parietal, and prestriate lesions. What is needed, then is a single study of both learning and retention, with simplified, consistent training methods and proper anatomical controls. Such is the type of task which justifies a team experiment.

We began with eight rhesus monkeys and set about extracting the maximal amount of behavioral information. In the rat study the single subject mattered little; here, it is very important. A monkey must be strictly budgeted, and not because of the high initial cost alone. Every investment is multiplied, from the time we spend in taming to the time in surgery, which in this experiment typically took 6 hr. Our aim must therefore be to suppress variability. An atypical rat is merely a nuisance to be discounted by the weight of evidence. An atypical monkey, when we work with such small samples, is a frank catastrophe.

It was decided that all the animals would be subjected to ablation; there would be no normal control group. We began by splitting the group in two so that animals might be given differential experience prior to their operations. The latter, as in the experiment with rats, were to be as similar from animal to animal as twenty years of surgical experience could make them. It was deemed important, too, that all animals be given identical experience with the testing situation; we are concerned not so much with training as with differences in *kind* of training.

The behavioral procedures were carried out in the Primate Laboratory of the University of Wisconsin. The preliminary steps followed the patterns that have long been standard here. The animals were tamed and adapted to the Wisconsin General Test Apparatus. After the animals would readily enter the apparatus and would eat from the experimenter's hand, all were trained to displace a single neutral object.

The differential procedures were then introduced. Four animals were placed on a training program designed to develop a discrimination learning set for objects. Successive pairs of dissimilar objects were presented to them; their task was to learn which of the two concealed a peanut or raisin. We used the noncorrection procedure and presented each pair of objects for a total of 6 trials, which is defined as a problem. Each animal was given 7 problems a day, a total of 42 trials, and worked five days per week for four weeks. Each subject thus encountered 140 problems in all, which is sufficient, as shown in Figure 68, for marked but incomplete development of the learning set.

While this group was occupied along these lines, we busied the other four monkeys with the learning of a single visual discrimination. Their task was to pick a blue object in preference to a green, where these colors are defined in the Munsell notation as 10B 6/6 and 10G 6/6. This we do not represent to be a hue discrimination, though hue is the most obvious difference. The colors were presented on wooden wedges with a surface 3 in. square.

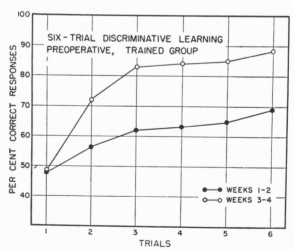

Fig. 68.—Discrimination learning set curves for the monkeys of the trained group.

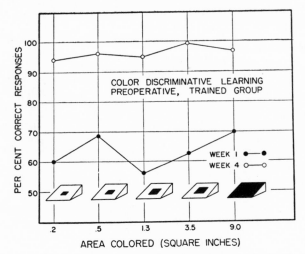

Fig. 69.—Color learning as a function of extent of colored area by monkeys upon the single habit.

The blue-green problem was varied to a certain extent. We made up five varieties, as shown in Figure 69. The colors presented on the two wedges either covered the surface entirely, or were surrounded by borders of white. The amount of colored area varied from 9 sq. in. down to .2 sq. in. in a logarithmic series. Regardless of such variations, of course, one color was always reinforced and the other not. The colored areas were always the same for any given pair of test objects. As we see, reducing the area does not substantially increase the difficulty of the problem for the normal monkey. All in all, this second group was tested for 14 trials per size, three sizes per day, five days a week for four weeks. When they were finished, they had had 840 practice trials on this color problem, the same total number of trials as had been given to the other four monkeys on their problems.

All eight animals were readied for surgery at approximately the same time, and were operated on in rapid succession. This was calculated to contribute to consistency. Every effort was made to restrict the lesion to the cortex and to the area shown in Figure 70. The operations were essentially uneventful, and all the animals recovered. Afterward, they rested for a period of roughly one month, but we made observations of their behavior in their cages and gradually adapted them once more to the testing apparatus. The most striking immediate result was the appearance, in all animals, of marked Klüver-Bucy syndrome. The animals were tested informally with bits of food mixed with small hardware, which was picked up more or less indiscriminately. The monkeys, however, did re-fuse meat. Rubber snakes which terrified the normal animals did not con-cern them in the least; one even succeeded in getting the model away from me and biting off its head. The laboratory triumvirate of negative objects—nets, water hoses, and brooms—failed to arouse them at all. Ac-tual restraint was the only means discovered for evoking withdrawal and attack. The animals were with one exception notably mute as well. We did not observe any clear-cut alteration of sexual behavior patterns, but this may well be due to the fact that the monkeys were all juveniles.

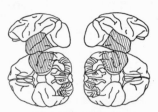

Fig. 70.—Operator's estimate of size of lesions at the time of surgery; *xxx* indicates area of maximal doubt.

Just at the time that formal testing was to recommence, one monkey from the color group died of a gastrointestinal disorder. After some vacil-lation, for time was running out, we initiated a crash program to train a substitute. This animal, number 263, was given an adaptation with the rigor of total-push psychotherapy, and was then given two training ses-sions daily, one in the early morning and the other in late afternoon. Nothing in its training performances, however, gave us any clue to the fact that it would turn out to be atypical.

Upon postoperative resumption of formal training, all the monkeys were tested on the green-blue discrimination problem. It was our intent that subsequent recall was not to be affected by such variables as forget-ting of responses unrelated to the learning set per se; or in ordinary lan-guage, we wished to keep the animals from going stale while they were healing. We chose this problem for the two groups because what evidence we have indicates that learning sets are little affected by training on sin-gle problems, even when training is continued for fairly long periods of time.

Although the color problem is ancillary to the main question, we do get a certain amount of free information. It is happily free, for at first glance at least it is by no means consistent. As Figure 71 shows, there is

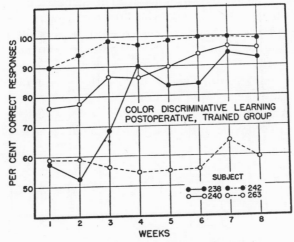

Fig. 71.—Postoperative color learning curves of monkeys trained preoperatively. These animals had not been given training in the learning set.

excellent retention of the habit in two of the animals. A third monkey has lost the habit, but is performing at a reasonable level by the end of the fourth week. Number 263, our crash-program subject, does very poorly indeed, and is still at the level of 60 per cent correct responses in the eighth week of practice. For comparison, the individual practice curves

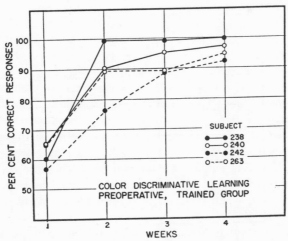

Fig. 72.—Color learning curves for comparison with those of Fig. 70, showing the performances of the same subjects prior to operation.

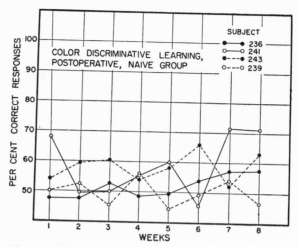

Fig. 73.—Individual color learning curves for monkeys with no prior practice. These animals had been given training in the learning set.

for these monkeys prior to operation are illustrated in Figure 72. There is nothing in the preoperative behavior to suggest the differences observed, and hence we must look forward to an explanation from the anatomical side.

This lack of decisiveness is missing, however, from the picture for

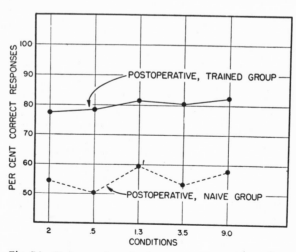

Fig. 74.—Postoperative color learning as a function of extent of colored area.

the animals for which the color discrimination is a new and different task. As we see in Figure 73, all four monkeys performed very badly throughout the eight-week period. The best level reached by any of them, despite 1680 trials, is about 70 per cent correct responses. It is apparent from this that the naive monkey is enormously handicapped by decortication of the temporal regions, even though sophisticated animals may show little or no deficit. The size variable has no differential effects upon either the trained or the untrained animals; this is clear from Figure 74.

Turning next to the data which are of the most concern to us, we find essentially the same analytical situation as before. The groups, of course, are reversed with regard to naïveté and sophistication. Animals pretrained in the learning set problem are now being tested for retention after a period of some three months during which time they were occupied with what we regard to be irrelevant problems. The monkeys trained on the single habit are now being asked to learn a set for the first time. What would seem to be missing from this design is some meas-

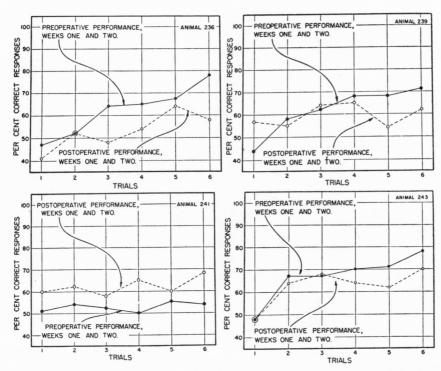

Fig. 75.—Individual comparisons of preoperative and postoperative discrimination learning curves, weeks 1 and 2.

ure of learning set retention in the group trained prior to operation; this was not included because such sets have been retained with little deficit for periods up to a year. We can thus be reasonably sure that changes are not the result of forgetting.

Let us first examine the results obtained with the trained group. There are some individual differences, and hence it is perhaps worth while to call the roll. In the first series of curves, we show the performances of trained animals in the first two weeks of pre- and postoperative practice. We can see from these charts in Figure 75 that retention of the set is very poor. The only monkey that does better in its second testing is animal 241, which is perhaps related to the fact that its preoperative performance was far from distinguished. If we wish to say that performances that average 60 per cent correct responses are significant retention, then that is what we have.

The lack of immediate retention is not the only deficit observed; rates of recovery are sharply attenuated as well. This we can illustrate in one

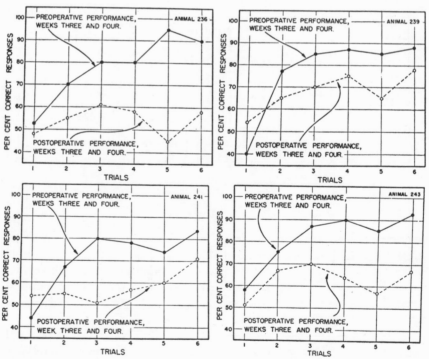

Fig. 76.—Individual comparisons of preoperative and postoperative discrimination learning curves, weeks 3 and 4.

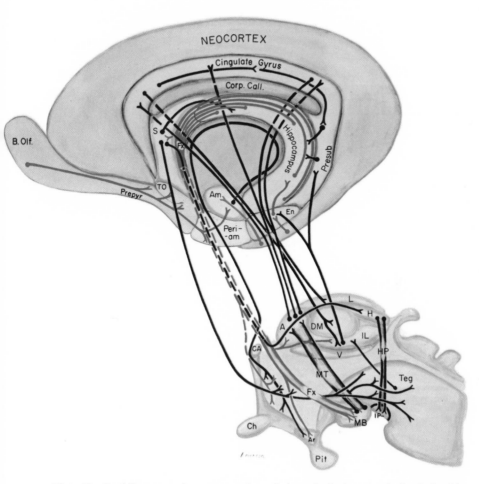

Plate 23.—Semidiagrammatic representation of the principal anatomical relationships between the paleocortex (in red), the juxtallocortex (in green), and the several sub-cortical structures (in yellow) considered in the present treatment of the limbic system. The brain stem portions of the system have been schematically displaced from the hilus of the hemisphere and represented in the lower half of the figure to facilitate visualization of the numerous anatomical interconnections involving these structures. Abbreviations: *A,* anterior nucleus of the thalamus; *Am,* amygdaloid complex; *Ar,* arcuate nucleus; *B. Olf.,* olfactory bulb; *CA,* anterior commissure; *Ch,* optic chiasm; *Corp. Call.,* corpus callosum; *DM,* dorsomedial nucleus of the thalamus; *En,* entorhinal area; *Fx,* Fornix; *H,* habenular complex; *HP,* habenulointerpeduncular tract; *IL,* intralaminar thalamic nuclei; *IP,* interpeduncular nucleus; *L,* lateral thalamic nucleus; *MB,* mammillary bodies; *MT,* mammillothalamic tract; *Periam,* periamygdaloidcortex; *Pit,* pituitary; *Prepyr,* prepyriform; *Presub,* presubiculum; *S,* septal region; *Teg,* midbrain tegmentum; *TO,* olfactory tubercle; *V,* ventral nucleus of the thalamus.

way by calling the role again, this time comparing performances in the third and fourth weeks both preoperatively and postoperatively. Such curves, which appear in Figure 76, show that relearning does not progress as rapidly as learning; if it did, such curves would be essentially coincident. It is apparent from this that training does not completely protect an animal from the devastating effects of a temporal decortication. The observed impairment is much more serious than that reported by Chow (2), and the reasons for this are not completely clear.

How far and how fast the animals progress beyond this level is largely an individual matter. We show this by citing the performances of different subjects during their third month of training; by this time, all have had postoperative experience with 280 problems. We find, in Figure 77, that

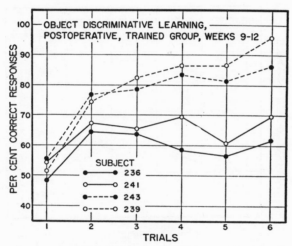

Fig. 77.—Performances of the set-trained monkeys in the final weeks of postoperative learning.

monkeys 236 and 241 are still below the level of 70 per cent correct responses. The others, however, are performing very creditably. It is probable that differences existing prior to surgery account for such results; in preoperative learning, 236 and 241 were also the poorest subjects. From this we presume that anatomical studies will not reveal particularly striking variations in this group.

Among the animals that had not received preoperative experience with the learning set problem, the picture is somewhat more severe. The third-month performances of three of the monkeys, numbers 238, 240, and 263, shown in Figure 78, contain no indication of learning set formation. Progressive curves from which these graphs were summarized also seemed to indicate that these levels are the ceiling. Such performances would lead us to believe that the Emory workers were correct, and that their results can be duplicated by much less extensive operations than they indicated verbally. This conclusion, however, must be tentative until we find some very good reason why the last monkey, number 242, performs better than the best of the trained animals. We have gone as far as we can go with our behavioral methods, and here the case must rest with reconstruction. Our suspicion that some marbles remain in the ring is enhanced to some extent by the fact that animal 242 was the slowest of its group in the learning of color discriminations preoperatively, but the best in the same performance postoperatively.

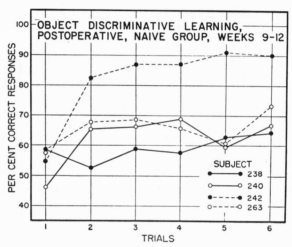

Fig. 78.—Performances of the set-naive group in the final weeks of postoperative learning.

To briefly recapitulate the spirit of the psychological program in these two studies, the following summation is made. First, the emphasis in each is upon environmental factors governing the sparing or loss of the performances evaluated. It is my belief that many of the so-called discrepancies between experiments in this field are the result of procedural differences rather than of anatomical variations.

These remarks, I hope, will not be interpreted as meaning that I am no longer concerned with differential effects of various kinds of brain damage. Actually, such information can be derived from the monkey study, for which we have the reconstructions. I refer in particular to our finding that the monkeys showed many of the characteristics noted by Klüver and Bucy. Without wishing to anticipate the anatomical report any more than is necessary, it should be pointed out that our lesions were almost entirely restricted to the temporal neocortex. I am informed that there is some entorhinal involvement, but that the amygdala is spared. The observed correlation has been intimated to a certain extent by Chow (1), who performed a fairly comparable though less extensive extirpation of the temporal neocortex in one monkey. This animal was said to show the initial confusions between small pieces of food and inedible objects, but Chow does not inform us whether this more or less transitory phenomenon was accompanied by the essentially permanent change in responsiveness to fear-provoking objects. Nor does Chow mention any such effect in another study (2) of monkeys with temporal lesions that are said to have spared most deep temporal structures. Since the syndrome is hard to overlook, we may assume that it was not observed. This may be due to a difference in the sizes of the lesions, for smaller ones characteristically are not sufficient. Our eight monkeys show very plainly that many features of the syndrome can be produced without removal of the amygdala. Thus there are at least two ways of doing this anatomically.

In summary, I would like to say again that I cannot accept the current philosophy that all research must conform to the pattern of test, operate, retest, and reconstruct. However important this procedure may be for solving anatomical questions, or for controlling variations in studies that utilize small numbers of subjects, there are many kinds of problems for which accession to this demand makes research completely impractical. If all manipulations are to be done properly, we need a specialist for each. This would imply that such research must be restricted to a limited number of institutions where, by happy chance, all these are both available and eager for commitment to the interests of the group at large. Happily, however, there is much that a man can do by himself, so long as he does not attempt to do *all* by himself.

I have no objection to the team approach as such, but it does have its disadvantages. When the time of several people is at stake on a single outcome, we tend to restrict our studies to the probable and seldom take a flyer. In a sense, the team is analogous to a bureau in the government—for some kinds of work it is very efficient, but it is a damper on others. Relatively few spectacular advances have come from team research, although it almost universally produces at a steady pace. The realization and acceptance of the fact that there are ways of studying problems other than the way that might happen to suit us personally fosters a tolerance essential to the exploration that opens, rather than closes a field.

REFERENCES

1 Chow, K. L. Further studies of selective ablation of associative cortex in relation to visually mediated behavior. *J. comp. physiol. Psychol.*, 1952, *45:* 109–18.

2 ———. Effects of temporal neocortical ablation on visual discrimination learning sets in monkeys. *J. comp. physiol. Psychol.*, 1954, 47: 194–98.

3 Fisher, R. A. *Statistical methods for research workers.* (10th Ed.) London: Oliver and Boyd, 1946.

4 Harlow, H. F. The formation of learning sets. *Psychol. Rev.*, 1949, *56:* 51–65.

5 Klüver, H., and P. C. Bucy. An analysis of certain effects of bilateral temporal lobectomy in the rhesus monkey, with special reference to "psychic blindness." *J. Psychol.*, 1938, *5:* 33–54.

6 Meyer, D. R. Food deprivation and discrimination reversal learning by monkeys. *J. exp. Psychol.*, 1951, *41:* 10–16.

7 ———. Intraproblem-interproblem relationships in learning by monkeys. *J. comp. physiol. Psychol.*, 1951, *44:* 162–67.

8 Monakow, C. von. *Die Lokalisation im Grosshirn und der Abbau der Funktion Korticale Herde.* Wiesbaden: J. F. Bergmann, 1914.

9 Riopelle, A. J., R. G. Alper, P. N. Strong, and H. W. Ades. Multiple discrimination and patterned string performance of normal and temporal-lobectomized monkeys. *J. comp. physiol. Psychol.*, 1953, *46:* 145–49.

10 Stewart, J. W., and H. W. Ades. The time factor in reintegration of a learned habit lost after temporal lobe lesions in the monkey (*Macaca mulatta*). *J. comp. physiol. Psychol.*, 1951, *44:* 479–86.

11 Warren, J. M., and H. F. Harlow. Learned discrimination performance by monkeys after prolonged postoperative recovery from large cortical lesions. *J. comp. physiol. Psychol.*, 1952, *45:* 119–26.

12 Wepman, J. M. *Recovery from aphasia.* New York: Ronald Press, 1951.

Joseph V. Brady

The Paleocortex and Behavioral Motivation

It has been some time since the first truly interdisciplinary investigations of the brain-behavior problem (75) focused attention upon the relationship between the paleocortex and behavioral motivation. In their now classical presentation before the 1937 meetings of the American Physiological Society, Klüver and Bucy reported dramatic behavioral alterations produced by rather extensive temporal neocortical and paleocortical lesions in the rhesus monkey. A few months later, Papez's speculative paper (100) on "A Proposed Mechanism of Emotion" appeared with its emphasis upon prominent paleocortical components, and since that time numerous anatomical, neurophysiological, and behavioral studies in this area have testified to the interdisciplinary character of the problem which provides the title for this paper.

Indeed, a report as early as 1888 by Brown and Schafer in the Philosophical Tranactions (30) had noted the marked taming effects of temporal lobe lesions involving paleocortical structures upon the behavior of preoperatively intractable monkeys. And of course, the pioneering efforts of men like Goltz (54), Sherrington (139), Cannon (32), Dusser de Barenne (38), and Bard (6, 11) during the first three decades of this century, elaborating the role of forebrain mechanisms in motivated or, in particular, "emotional" behavior, can now be seen to have effectively set the stage for the more specific emphasis upon the behavioral aspects of paleocortical function. As the first systematic attempt at an experimental analysis of this relationship, however, the work of psychologist Klüver and neurosurgeon Bucy stands as somewhat of a landmark among the traditionally interdisciplinary approaches to the brain-behavior problem.

The strong dependence upon the interdisciplinary application of what have now come to be highly developed specialized skills to further our understanding of behavior and its more broadly defined "neural correlates" is perhaps nowhere more clearly evident than in the analysis of the paleocortex and behavioral motivation. Until very recently, progress has been slow in the development of both physiological and psychological techniques appropriate for investigating the specific relationships of most interest in this particular area. Anatomically, not only have the functional relationsthips beween important structures been only poorly understood, but there has been somewhat less than unanimous agreement as to just which morphological entities are to be identified as "paleocortex." Behaviorally, "motivation," and more specifically, "emotion," which has been of most central concern in this area, have continued to pose vexing problems for the psychologist. Although considerable success has been achieved in the behavioral assessment of motor skills, sensory capacities, and even higher intellectual processes, valid and reliable techniques for the evaluation of motivation or, in particular, emotional behavior, have been slow to develop. Within the past few years, however, the refinement of histologic staining techniques (94, 49) and renewed interest in neural substrata of emotional behavior (105, 74) have combined to produce an ever increasing body of information on the anatomy of the paleocortex (130, 4, 93). In addition, the last five or six years have seen important advances in the development of behavioral control techniques (121, 39). The more recent application of such methodological skills to the experimental analysis of affective behavior (17, 18, 19) has already begun to yield information relevant to the differential effects of various physiological and psychological conditions upon which the organization of emotional behavior depends. It is this very emphasis upon the application of highly specialized and rapidly developing skills and techniques *within* the related disciplines of anatomy, physiology, and psychology which makes our dependence upon collaborative efforts *between* these disciplines so complete.

Within the framework of this interdisciplinary emphasis, then, the following discussion of the paleocortex and motivated behavior will be concerned primarily with three general topics. First, some anatomical characteristics of the paleocortex and related structures will be considered, with particular emphasis upon their morphological and functional properties. Secondly, some attention will be devoted to a review of the behavioral observations following paleocortical injury which have suggested a relationship between these structures and the more broadly defined aspects of motivation and emotion. Finally, an account will be given of some more recent work in this area concerned specifically with emotional behavior and its neural correlates, including some interdisciplinary efforts from our own laboratories at the Walter Reed Army Institute of Research.

SOME ANATOMICAL CONSIDERATIONS *

In the recent literature on emotional behavior and its more broadly defined "neural correlates" (74, 84, 105), several terms, presumed to be roughly

* The author wishes to express his profound gratitude to Dr. Walle J. H. Nauta of the Neuroanatomical Laboratory, Walter Reed Army Institute of Research, without whose guidance and assistance over the past three years, this section could not have been written. Credit for the conception and preliminary art work on the schematic diagram presented in Plate 23 must also be given in large part to Dr. Nauta.

synonymous, have been used to refer to groups or systems of functionally related forebrain structures believed to be associated with affective expression. "Rhinencephalon," "visceral brain," "limbic system," and "paleocortex" are but a few of the labels which have been used to identify these anatomical entities. Definitions of which morphological formations are to be subsumed under these terms differ widely, however, and some brief consideration of the anatomy of most central concern in this discussion would seem indicated.

In the interest of both morphological and functional clarity, it has seemed expedient, if somewhat arbitrary, to consider those forebrain structures of primary interest in this paper within three general anatomical classes or groups, as illustrated schematically in Plate 23.

First, "paleocortex" or "allocortex" will be strictly defined so as to include only those surface structures which meet the criteria for "cortex" suggested by Rose and Woolsey (110)—a composition of at least three layers with the superficial layer constituting a fiber layer—and which also have clear phylogenetic primacy. By this rather strict definition, the structures which are to be regarded as paleocortex are represented in red on the figure and include only the hippocampus (Ammon's horn and the dentate gyrus), the pyriform lobe (prepyriform cortex, periamygdaloid cortex, and entorhinal area), and the olfactory bulb and tubercle.

Secondly, "juxtallocortex" will be used to refer only to that group of cortical regions which are intermediate in position between the phylogenetically old paleocortex and the phylogenetically young neocortex, and most of which have demonstrable anatomical connections with paleocortical structures. Such juxtallocortical regions are represented in green on the schema and would include the cingulate gyrus or "limbic cortex" (24, 122), the presubiculum, and the "frontotemporal" cortex as recently defined by Pribram and Kruger (105).

Finally, a third group of "subcortical structures" (not meeting the criteria for "cortex") which have been shown to be intimately related, both anatomically and functionally, to the paleocortex and juxtallocortex, must be considered. These are represented in yellow on the figure and would include the amygdaloid complex, the septal region (septal nuclei and the nucleus of the diagonal band), certain thalamic and hypothalamic nuclei, and possibly even the caudate nucleus and midbrain reticular formation.

It should be pointed out that most of the structures included in the above classification were formerly believed to be involved in mechanisms of olfaction and have been consequently regarded as the "olfactory brain" (105). This view, which tends to be perpetuated by the broad usage of the term "rhinencephalon" (74), would presently appear to be untenable since recent studies (35, 40) have clearly demonstrated a much more restricted distribution of primary olfactory afferents, i.e., of fibers originating from the olfactory bulb. On the basis of this evidence, the term "rhinencephalon" will be used to refer only to those structures subserving olfactory functions, including the olfactory bulb and tubercle, prepyriform and periamygdaloid cortex, some of the nuclei of the amygdaloid complex, and the bed nucleus of the *stria terminalis.*

Although restrictions imposed by limitations of both space and time prohibit a complete analysis of the structural interconnections between the numerous cell formations subsumed under each of the above three groups, some brief review of the more prominent anatomical relationships discernible throughout this system may help to clarify some of the semantic confusion and lay the groundwork for a more meaningful synthesis in this area. It should be emphasized that this review makes no pretense to a comprehensive coverage of all the anatomical and physiological relationships described in the voluminous literature on this subject (69, 74, 105) but will be restricted in large part to a summary of those neuroanatomical connections more recently verified with reliable histological techniques (50, 52, 49, 93, 94). Plate 23 illustrates, in schematic form, some of the more important structural relationships between prominent areas within the three anatomical groupings.

Paleocortex

Let us start with the more strictly defined "paleocortical structures." The *olfactory bulb* is found to project directly to the olfactory tubercle, prepyriform cortex, periamygdaloid cortex, and the corticomedial nuclei of the amygdaloid complex (35). In addition, direct olfactory bulb projections appear to enter the medial forebrain bundle via the medial olfactory tract, although their distribution beyond this point is not presently known. The *olfactory tubercle,* too, sends fibers of as yet unknown destination into the medial forebrain bundle (82) and in addition is seen also to project directly to the septal region (25). Both the *prepyriform* and *periamygdaloid cortex,* in addition to the input from the olfactory bulb, are known to receive fibers from the "nonspecific" intralaminar thalamic nuclei (95). But again, the ultimate destination of direct projections from these two portions of the pyriform lobe into the medial forebrain bundle are as yet unknown. The *entorhinal* area, on the other hand, while known also to receive fibers from the nonspecific intralaminar thalamic nuclei and temporal neocortex, has to date been reliably credited with only one strong projection system into both Ammon's horn and the dentate gyrus of the hippocampus (31, 83).

The final structure to be considered within this first group of paleocortical structures is the *hippocampus*, which would seem to enjoy a most important and central position, both functionally and anatomically, in any consideration of the structural integrity of those forebrain systems presumably related to motivational-emotional aspects of behavior. There are but three anatomically known sources of input directly to the hippocampus, although speculation about numerous other inflow systems, both direct and indirect, has been all too confusingly frequent. In addition to the efferent system from the entorhinal area indicated above, fibers enter both Ammon's horn and the dentate gyrus directly from the presubiculum (31), and also from the medial nuclei of the septal region via the fornix (36). It is now quite clear, however, that the direct hippocampal outflow via the fornix is considerably less restricted than more traditional views involving the septal region and mammillary bodies as the primary end-station of such projections would seem to indicate (31). Nauta (93) has recently verified that fibers from both Ammon's horn and the dentate gyrus project, in addition, directly to the nucleus of the diagonal band, the preoptic region, the dorsal hypothalamic area, the anterior nucleus and the mid-line regions of the thalamus, the supramammillary region, and the rostral extreme of the central gray substance of the midbrain. In addition, the caudal one-third of the hippocampus projects directly to the periventricular zone of the hypothalamus, and particularly to the arcuate (tuberoinfundibular) nucleus (93). Clearly, this extensive influence exercised by the hippocampus more than justifies the potentially critical role attributed to this morphological entity in the organization and control of behavioral motivation.

Juxtallocortex

Among the *juxtallocortical cell groups* to be considered within this second class of structures, the *presubiculum* would seem to be most intimately related to what we have now seen to be the virtual hub of the system, the hippocampus. Receiving large contributions from the cingulate gyrus via the cingulum (1, 31), and from the supracallosal striae, probably originating in the septal region (31), along with some fibers from the nonspecific intralaminar thalamic cell groups (95), the presubiculum, as we have seen, discharges its only known direct projections into the hippocampus. Consideration of the *cingulate gyrus* reveals that, in spite of the central position it has come to occupy in contemporary theorizing about the neural correlates of emotional behavior, little is actually known about the source of influences which might impinge upon it. Indeed, the more traditional fiber pathways from the anterior thalamic nuclei (34, 110), along with the more recently demonstrated projections from the nonspecific intralaminar thalamic cell groups (95), constitute the sum total of the known input to the cingulate gyrus. Again, however, numerous direct projections have been demonstrated from the cingulate gyrus to the presubiculum (1, 31), the anterior thalamic nuclei (97), the dorsomedial (97) and lateral (92) nuclei of the thalamus, the nonspecific intralaminar thalamic cell groups, as well as to the superior colliculus and midbrain tegmentum (92). Finally, the structural interconnections of that junctional band of cortex between the pyriform lobe and orbito-frontal and polar temporal neocortex which Pribram and Kruger (105) have called the "frontotemporal cortex" (orbito-insulo-temporal cortex), are at present only poorly understood. The periamygdaloid cortex is believed to send fibers to at least some portions of this frontotemporal complex, however, while some direct projections from this area are thought to terminate in the ventromedial nucleus of the hypothalamus and the head of the caudate nucleus (45).

Subcortical Structures

In considering the third group of subcortical structures with demonstrably important paleocortical and juxtallocortical interconnections, it is apparent that a number of recent physiological and behavioral studies have focused attention upon the *amygdaloid complex*. As has been indicated above, fibers coming directly from the olfactory bulb are known to terminate in the *corticomedial* cell groups of the amygdala (35), while the basal portions of the temporal neocortex have now been shown to project directly to the *basolateral* amygdaloid nuclei (138). On the efferent side, direct projections from both the corticomedial and basolateral amygdaloid nuclei to the septal region and the hypothalamus (preoptic nuclei and infundibular region) via the *stria terminalis* have long been known to exist (69). In addition, fibers from the amygdala have been observed to course in the anterior commissure to the amygdaloid complex of the opposite side, while there is also reason to believe that some amygdala fibers project directly to the caudate nucleus. Consideration of the *septal region* reveals that anatomical descriptions of afferent fibers directly to this area from the hippocampus via the precommissural fornix (46) and the amygdala via the *stria terminalis* (69) have been available for some time. On the efferent side, fibers can be traced from the septal region directly to the habenular complex of the thalamus, the area of the diagonal band, the lateral nuclei of the preoptic region and hypothalamus, the hippocampus, the mammillary bodies, and to paramedian regions of the pons, midbrain, and pontine tegmentum (93).

Among the *thalamic cell groups* which must now be considered within this third group of subcortical structures on the basis of their intimate relationships with paleocortical and juxtallocortical regions, the *anterior nucleus of the thalamus,* as we have seen, receives at least a few direct afferent influences from the cingulate gyrus (97) which reciprocate the above-mentioned projection of these nuclei to the cingulate cortex (34, 110). The main afferent influx to the anterior nucleus, however, would seem to originate in the hippocampus and the mammillary bodies. Only the cingulate gyrus, however, is known to receive direct efferent fibers from the anterior thalamic nucleus (34, 110). While the structural interconnections of the *intralaminar thalamic nuclei* are somewhat more complex, recent studies have elaborated important relationships between these nonspecific thalamic cell groups and both paleocortical and juxtallocortical structures. Important afferent influences of telencephalic origin impinge upon the intralaminar nuclei directly from the hippocampus and septal region (93, 132), the cingulate cortex (92), motor neocortex (92), and reticular nuclei of the midbrain tegmentum (68). In addition, some of the more classical sensory pathways, including the medial lemniscus and *brachium conjunctivum,* probably contain fibers which terminate directly in these nonspecific thalamic nuclei. Although the direct efferent end-stations of the numerous fibers from the intralaminar nuclei have been a source of considerable controversy, it is now quite clear that widespread influences from these nuclei project directly to virtually all the more specific thalamic nuclei, with the possible exception of the geniculate bodies (89). In addition, fibers from these nonspecific thalamic nuclei are now known to project directly to the basal ganglia (caudate nucleus, putamen, and *globus pallidus*), juxtallocortex (cingulate gyrus and presubiculum), and paleocortex, especially the prepyriform cortex and entorhinal area (95). It may be significant that this last-mentioned projection from the intralaminar nuclei is the only known afferent input to the entorhinal area with the possible exception of a few scarce fibers from the basal portions of the temporal neocortex. Finally, the *habenular complex* represents the last of the thalamic nuclei with important known paleocortical and juxtallocortical interconnections. Via the *stria medullaris,* the habenula receives massive afferent influences from the septal region and apparently also from the region of the lateral hypothalamus. On the efferent side, the functional significance of the only known projection from the habenula to the interpeduncular nucleus via the *fasciculus retroflexus* of Meynert is at present only poorly understood.

Virtually all portions of the *hypothalamus* are known to have important structural relationships with the several aspects of paleocortical and juxtallocortical anatomy under consideration in this paper. Starting with the *mammillary bodies,* we have seen that important efferent projections from the hippocampus and septal region terminate in this area (31, 93). In addition, ascending fibers from as yet unidentified regions of the midbrain tegmentum also course to the mammillary bodies via the mammillary peduncle (99). Of course, the efferent projections of the mammillary bodies to the anterior nuclei of the thalamus in the bundle of Vicq D'Azyr are well known, while the descending projection of fibers originating from this hypothalamic structure to the midbrain tegmentum in the mammillo-tegmental tract provides for important reciprocal relationships with these lower brain centers. The *infundibular region* of the hypothalamus including the ventromedial, dorsomedial, arcuate, and diffuse supraoptic nuclei again receives direct projections from the hippocampus and septal region via the fornix (93) and also from the amygdaloid complex through the *stria terminalis* (93). In addition, it is quite possible that massive projections reach this region of the hypothalamus via the medial forebrain bundle from the head of the caudate nucleus, the olfactory tubercle, and related basal forebrain structures (*substantia innominata* of Reichert, and the like). Certain reports also mention afferent connections from the prefrontal cortex to the infundibular region (13). Althought the efferent connections of the infundibulum are only poorly understood at present, important influences, both neural and vascular, are known to impinge directly upon the pituitary apparatus (57, 58), thus providing a possible link between these hypothalamic regions and critical endocrine functions of the anterior hypophyseal lobe (53). Although too little is presently known to speculate further on the efferent influences of the infundibular region, it would seem safe to say that there may also be direct infundibular fibers coursing through the periventricular system of Schutz and the medial forebrain bundle to terminate in the reticular formation of the lower brain stem.

Moving on to a consideration of the *lateral hypothalamus* (including the lateral preoptic and hypothalamic nuclei), we find that afferent fibers from the hippocampus and especially the septal region contribute significantly to this area (93). In addition, fibers from numerous basal forebrain structures presumably related to the medial forebrain bundle (*substantia innominata,* olfactory tubercle, head of the caudate nucleus, prepyriform and periamygdaloid cortex) also terminate in the lateral hypothalamus (82) along with ascending influences from the midbrain tegmentum (68). On the efferent side, a reciprocal relationship with the midbrain tegmentum is again completed by fibers projecting directly from the lateral hypothalamus and probably continuing into the lower

brain stem and spinal cord to possibly influence the regulation of autonomic activity. There are also some indications that fibers from the lateral
hypothalamus ascend directly to the septal region (and thence, perhaps,
on to the hippocampus), while fibers from this region also course in the
stria medularis to the habenula. Then, too, it has recently been observed
that fibers from the caudal portion of the lateral hypothalamus project
directly to the nonspecific intralaminar nuclei of the thalamus.* The
preoptic area of the hypothalamus also receives direct projections from
the hippocampus and septal region (93), as well as from the amygdala
via the *stria terminalis* (93) and possibly from some basal forebrain structures related to the medial forebrain bundle (head of the caudate nucleus,
among others). In addition, ascending fibers from the midbrain reticular
formation are know to terminate in this region (91). The efferent projections of the preoptic area are all but unknown except that fibers coursing to adjacent hypothalamic nuclei (lateral hypothalamus) are thought
to link indirectly the preoptic area with the midbrain tegmentum. It
probably should be mentioned that detailed consideration of the *magnocellular hypothalamic nuclei* has been omitted here since they seem to be
functionally related primarily to the posterior lobe of the pituitary on
the efferent side, and their specific afferent supply is virtually unknown.
It is conceivable, of course, that these magnocellular portions of the hypothalamus also bear important, but as yet unidentified, structural relationships to the paleocortical anatomy here under consideration.

Although the *caudate nucleus* is usually not regarded as bearing either
a very close anatomical or functional relationship to paleocortical structures, some recent findings would seem to necessitate a more careful consideration of the role played by this portion of the striatum in the organization and control of motivational-emotional aspects of behavior. On
the afferent side, it has been generally assumed that the caudate nucleus
would receive most of its incoming fibers from the neocortex (31). Recent
anatomical and physiological studies, however, fail to substantiate such
afferent relationships of the caudate with the neocortex; rather, these
studies seem to suggest that efferent fibers *from* the caudate project *to*
at least some parts of the frontal neocortex (64, 86). Indeed, afferent connections of the caudate nucleus seem to originate in the cingulate gyrus
(92) and, like those of many other portions of this system, in the intralaminar cell groups of the thalamus (95). Additional fibers are now also
known to project from large portions of the temporal neocortex to the
caudate nucleus (138), and it would appear likely that some fibers from
the general region of the amygdaloid complex also project to this portion

* Whitlock, D. G., and Nauta, W. J. H. Personal communication.

of the striatum. Known efferents from the caudate are also generally believed to project to the lentiform nucleus (including the *globus pallidus*) and would seem to implicate the caudate in extrapyramidal motor functions.

The inclusion of the *reticular formation of the brain stem* in a paper concerned with the paleocortex and behavioral motivation might at first appear somewhat presumptious, but it is clear from even the most cursory review of paleocortical anatomy that these nonspecific lower brain stem cell groups must now be considered among our third group of subcortical structures intimately related to the more strictly defined paleocortex and juxtallocortex. Indeed, it has already become apparent that many efferent projections from paleocortex and juxtallocortex (hippocampus, cingulate cortex) converge upon the midbrain reticular formation, which, in turn, conceivably reciprocates with fibers going back to many of these same structures. For example, the midbrain reticular formation is known to project to the nonspecific intralaminar nuclei of the thalamus (68), which, in turn, have recently been demonstrated to bear intimate reciprocal anatomical relationships with numerous portions of the paleocortex and related structures, including the hippocampus, septal region, and cingulate cortex, among others (93, 92). More significantly, perhaps, the midbrain reticular formation has recently been identified as the source of important ascending pathways to the neocortex (90), thus constituting a possible subcortical link between the paleocortex and neocortex. Of course, a further possible source of paleocortical influence upon the neocortex is to be found in the direct paleocortical connections with the intralaminar thalamic cell groups now known to have important anatomical and functional connections with widespread areas of the neocortex (89). It should be realized, moreover, that in addition to these corticipetal projections, the midbrain reticular formation is known to project massively to lower brain stem and spinal cord structures (108), thus providing a possible mechanism for paleocortical influence on widespread sources of visceral innervation. Finally, it should be mentioned that although some specification of the anatomical and physiological significance of *efferent* connections of the midbrain reticular formation with more rostral forebrain structures would now seem to be possible (e.g., the cortical activation phenomenon [90]), the distribution and function of *afferent* connections to the midbrain reticular formation from the neocortex and paleocortex are at present only poorly understood.

It should by this time be clear why a need has arisen for some convenient descriptive term ("visceral brain," "rhinencephalon," and the like) to refer to this complex of interrelated structures presumed to have some common functional properties. Indeed, this very anatomical complexity, along with the numerous functional interpretations of which it permits, now makes it quite obvious that few of the terms currently in use, including even "paleocortex" as we have defined it, avoid the restrictiveness necessarily implied by their more traditional connotations. Perhaps Broca's (24) early reference to the "limbic lobe" based upon the gross morphologic characteristics of the ringlike formation around the hilus of the hemisphere constituted by many of the structures we have been here considering, offers the least functionally restrictive possibility for a convenient descriptive label. Indeed, support for such a structural grouping has come not only from cytoarchitectural comparisons based on Nissl techniques, but also from the studies of Cajal (31) and Lorente de Nó (83) comparing, in silver stains, the minute fibroarchitecture of these limbic portions of the cerebral mantle with some of the lateral cortex. More recently Fulton (43) has made use of a related but somewhat less restrictive reference to the "limbic system" which would seem to permit inclusion of the numerous cell groups covered in this brief, and doubtless incomplete, anatomical review. Future references to this group of interrelated structures in the following sections concerned with behavioral relationships will make use of this somewhat neutral but inclusive term, "limbic system."

In considering the anatomy of this limbic system, a deliberate attempt has been made to avoid, insofar as possible, any arbitrary *functional* classification of the numerous structural entities which constitute this complex. Currently available data relevant to such functional interrelationships are, at best, both contradictory and bewildering. Indeed, this state of affairs with respect to the limbic system is clearly discernible even in two of the more recent and valiant efforts by McLean (84) and by Pribram and Kruger (105) to derive some order from this chaos. Certainly, the following review and analysis of the behavioral data relevant to this problem will make this even more apparent, although it should at least be possible to indicate why various components of the limbic system have come to be associated with the organization and control of motivational-emotional aspects of behavior.

BEHAVIOR RELATIONSHIPS

Even before the work of Klüver and Bucy, a number of important physiological studies had begun to yield observations implicating portions of the limbic system in the mediation of motivational-emotional behavior patterns. The early work of Goltz (54) and Sherrington (139) with decerebrate preparations involving transection of the brain stem at the intercollicular level demonstrates quite clearly that at least some primitive, "pseudoaffective" behavioral reactions within the "motivational-emotional" sphere can be readily elicited at this midbrain level in the absence of all other forebrain (limbic system) structures. Section of the brain stem below this level, however, abolishes such behavior completely (7) and strongly suggests involvement of the midbrain reticular formation in the mediation of these rather fundamental aspects of emotional expression. During the half century or more since these early experiments, several authors have confirmed and elaborated these basic observations on decerebrate preparations, and considerable attention has been drawn to reticular influences in behavioral motivation (10, 12, 41, 70, 71, 81, 113, 114). Within the past few years, Lindsley (80) has even proposed an "activation theory of emotion" which assigns a most critical executive role to the reticular formation of the brain stem, and most recently, fundamental aspects of consciousness have been intimately related to these nonspecific brain stem nuclei (37).

Of course, the early experiments of Dusser de Barenne (38) and Cannon and Britton (32) with decorticate preparations and the now famous "sham rage" phenomena characteristic of such animals, must also be considered as important precursors of more recent efforts to delimit specific functional properties of the limbic system. By comparison with the more drastic Sherringtonian decerebrates, these decorticate preparations can be observed to respond even more readily and in a somewhat more intense, better organized fashion to ordinary handling and care, although the behavior remains poorly directed and short-lived. Of particular interest, moreover, was the subsequent demonstration by Bard and Rioch (7, 11) that this sham rage response can still be elicited after removal of all cerebral tissue rostral, dorsal, and lateral to the hypothalamus including virtually all of the paleocortex, juxtallocortex, and major portions of the related subcortical structures. This vigorously patterned activity fails to develop, however, following truncation of the brain stem at any level below the caudal hypothalamus. Clearly, these experiments reveal the striking facilitory influence exerted by the addition of limited, but obviously critical, portions of the limbic system (hypothalamus) to the more primitive reticular activating mechanisms.

To be sure, numerous subsequent experiments have provided convincing corroboration of the central, if somewhat complicated, role played by hypothalamic portions of the limbic system in mediating critical aspects of behavioral motivation. Within a few years, Ranson and his collaborators (67, 107) had demonstrated the emotionally exciting effects ("fear" and "rage" responses with multiple sympathetic manifestations) of direct

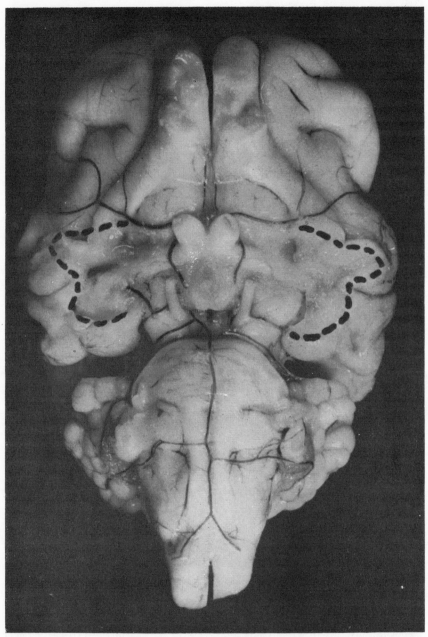

Plate 24.—Ventral view of the brain of a cat with a typical rhinencephalic lesion. The lateral extent of each lesion is indicated by broken lines. (From Brady *et al.*, ref. 22.)

hypothalamic stimulation in intact cats and monkeys, while lesions in the posterior hypothalamus and mammillary bodies, occasionally encroaching upon the rostral midbrain, were seen to result in complete loss of emotional responsiveness (masklike faces, stolidity), and sometimes in patterns of somnolence and sleep. That the hypothalamic role in the mediation of affective behavior was not to be regarded as unitary and uncomplicated, however, was soon to be demonstrated by Wheatley (137), who studied the effects of experimental diencephalic lesions upon the behavior of cats. Involving a rather large series of animals and good anatomical controls, these experiments showed that localized destruction of the ventromedial nuclei of the hypothalamus can produce extremely ill-tempered cats, in rather sharp contrast with the neutral or even antithetical effects produced by lesions placed more caudally, rostrally, or laterally. In addition to such gross emotional factors associated with hypothalamic function, moreover, it is now quite clear that other important aspects of behavioral motivation also bear critical relationships to this portion of the limbic system. During the last two decades, numerous experiments have shown that restricted bilateral hypothalamic lesions can produce profound effects upon such basic biological motivations as hunger (23, 28, 27), thirst (131), sleep (91, 107, 109), sex (8, 26, 27), and activity (63). More recently, Stellar (126) has presented a physiological theory of motivated behavior which places a heavy explanatory burden upon hypothalamic excitation in accounting for a wide range of motivational behavior patterns.

Clearly, then, the weight of presently available evidence would seem to indicate that at least some primitively organized, relatively undifferentiated patterns of motivated or emotional behavior may be elaborated within limited reticular and hypothalamic levels of the limbic system. The functional limitations of such gross reaction patterns contrast sharply, however, with the more delicately balanced and restrained discriminative behavior of which the normal animal is seen to be capable, and this necessarily implies that important influences from more advanced forebrain levels of integration contribute significantly to the elaboration and refinement of complexly organized and finely differentiated motivational-emotional response repertoires. The specific role played by various paleocortical, juxtallocortical, and more extensive subcortical portions of the limbic system in this integrative process may, indeed, provide the common thread which could conceivably tie together numerous studies which have occupied so much of the time of anatomists, physiologists, and psychologists during the past two decades.

There can be little doubt but that the early interdisciplinary efforts of Klüver and Bucy provided the first and most striking demonstration of extensive limbic system influence in the balancing, integration, and elaboration of critically profound motivational behavior patterns. These now classical experiments (75, 76, 77) defining dramatic behavioral changes in monkeys following temporal neocortical and paleocortical lesions involving the frontotemporal cortex, pryriform lobe, amygdaloid complex, presubiculum, and hippocampus are too well known to require detailed review. Suffice it to recall that profound alterations involving critical motivational systems, including increased oral tendencies, loss of dietary discriminations, increased sexual activity, and decreased emotional reactivity, were found to be associated with injury to these limbic structures although no such changes were found when temporal neocortical lesions failed to involve the limbic system or when the lesions were unilaterally restricted. The obvious relationship between these findings and the independently derived speculation of Papez (100) concerned with an anatomical "emotion circuit" (hippocampus→fornix→mammillary body→ anterior thalamic nuclei→cingulate gyrus→cingulum→hippocampus), served to focus attention even more sharply upon the limbic system and its functional properties. A number of subsequent studies have been concerned with a more detailed analysis of the Klüver-Bucy syndrome and the structural localization of its various elements. In addition, however, many interdisciplinary efforts have continued to broaden the base for a more thorough understanding of extensive limbic system components involved in the mediation of behavioral motivation.

Indeed, the experiments reported by Spiegel, Miller, and Oppenheimer (125) demonstrated quite clearly that more rostral portions of the limbic system, including olfactory tubercle and septal region, participate rather dramatically in complicated motivational-emotional behavior patterns. Although somewhat complicating the picture of limbic system involvement in affective expression, sham rage reactions were observed by these authors following bilateral lesions confined to these areas in both cats and dogs, while similar effects resulted from injury to the anterior amygdaloid nuclei, parts of the hippocampus, and the fornix. As a matter of fact, a report by Fulton and Ingram (44) as early as 1929 described similar rage reactions in cats following bilateral prechiasmal lesions at the base of the brain, and several more recent reports by Brady and Nauta (20, 21), Harrison and Lyon (59), and King (72) confirm these findings in the rat. Some conflicting, if incompletely reported, findings have appeared recently, however, in a publication by Heath *et al.* (61) concerned with the effects of lesions in the cat involving principally the septal region, caudate nucleus, and olfactory tubercle. The fact that these authors observed placidity and emotional unresponsiveness (no "fear" or "rage" reactions even to strongly provoking stimuli) in such preparations serves to illustrate only one of many such contradictory findings in this area and should provide some indication of the ignorance which continues to obscure our understanding of specific neural-behavioral relationships.

Probably the single most extensive and systematic approach delineating the role of forebrain mechanisms in the mediation of motivational-emotional behavior patterns to follow the work of Klüver and Bucy is to be found in another noteworthy interdisciplinary program initiated by Bard and Mountcastle (9, 10). Concerned primarily with the role of paleocortical, juxtallocortical, and related subcortical structures in the management of emotional behavior, their initial experiments with cats showed that removal of all neocortex, while sparing these limbic structures, produced a markedly placid and emotionally unresponsive animal. Clearly, these results would seem to indicate that portions of the limbic system, either singly or in concert, can exert a restraining influence upon lower brain stem mechanisms demonstrated to be prepotent in the mediation of gross affective expression. And, indeed, subsequent experiments in this same series strongly suggest that the amygdaloid complex and/or cingulate gyrus might well be specifically involved in the mediation of this restraining influence in the absence of neocortex, since rather striking increases in emotional reactivity follow removal of these structures in the previously neodecorticated preparation. More recently, Rothfield and Harman (112) have confirmed the placidity and emotional unresponsiveness resulting from neocortical ablation sparing the limbic system in cats, and have further demonstrated that the fornix (distributing important hippocampal fibers to the septal region, diencephalon, and rostral midbrain) figures prominently in the mediation of such restraining influences. Interruption of the fornix in these neodecorticate preparations resulted in a significant lowering of the rage threshold.

Continuing their efforts to delimit the functional properties of specific limbic components, Bard and Mountcastle (9) proceeded to analyze the effects of relatively discrete paleocortical, juxtallocortical, and related subcortical lesions in otherwise intact cats. Although bilateral removal of the hippocampus and presubiculum produced little demonstrable change in affective expression with the possible exception of mild increases in pleasurable reactions, bilateral removal of the pyriform lobe and amygdaloid complex, while sparing other limbic structures, resulted in dramatic, if somewhat delayed, behavioral changes. Contrary to the earlier findings of Klüver and Bucy (75, 76, 77) in the monkey, these cats were observed to develop a markedly lowered rage threshold, posing another of the limbic system dilemmas which the voluminous literature developed on this subject over the past five years or more has, as yet, failed to resolve. This same series of experiments, however, also called attention to the somewhat complicated role of the cingulate gyrus in such complex motivational-emotional behavior patterns. Although removal of this juxtallocortical structure in neodecorticate preparations was observed to *lower* the rage threshold in their earlier experiments, Bard and Mountcastle (9) found that cingulate ablation in otherwise intact cats tended to *raise* this threshold and produce emotionally less responsive animals. Indeed, several previous reports (51, 123, 134) refer to similar consequences of cingulectomy ("loss of fear," "social indifference"), and although Pribram and Fulton (104) have recently emphasized the rather limited extent and duration of such changes, their findings generally confirm the character and direction of these effects.

Of course, the anterior nuclei of the thalamus have also attracted some recent attention as a consequence of the intimate relationship of these subcortical structures to broadly defined limbic "circuits" and, more specifically, to the cingulate gyrus. Significantly, Baird *et al.* (5) have reported that extensive lesions in this region of the thalamus produce marked reductions in the emotional responsiveness of cats to ordinarily noxious stimuli. More recently, these effects of anterior thalamic lesions in the cat have been confirmed by Schreiner *et al.* (118), although most striking changes in the opposite direction—increased irritability and lowered rage threshold—were observed following destruction of the dorsomedial thalamic nuclei. It is also interesting to note that this same report describes effects following destruction of the intralaminar thalamic nuclei similar to, if somewhat less severe than, the effects produced by lesions involving the midbrain reticular formation (transient lethargy, somnolence, and reduced reactivity to noxious stimuli) (41, 80). Finally, Chow (33) has most recently reported the lack of any significant behavioral changes in monkeys following thalamic lesions involving the pulvinar nucleus, even though some of these same animals also sustained damage to the dorsomedial thalamic nuclei.

Clearly, however, the most popular interdisciplinary pastime of the last few years in this area has been the analysis and delimitation of what has now become quite well known as the "temporal lobe syndrome." Following the early work of Klüver and Bucy (75, 76, 77) and the brilliant experimental analysis of Bard and Mountcastle (9, 10), numerous recent experiments have been concerned with delineating the specific role of various limbic components in the mediation of these rather dramatic behavioral phenomena. Fulton *et al.* (45), reporting their findings before the American Neurological Association in 1949, showed that bilateral ablation of the frontotemporal cortex in monkeys produces alterations in behavioral motivation similar to, but apparently not as extensive as, those found by Klüver and Bucy (75, 76, 77) with widespread temporal neocortical and paleocortical lesions. Much of the compulsive oral behavior and apparent lack of emotional responsiveness to aversive stimuli appear to have been present, although no mention is made of the change in sexual behavior reported in the earlier work. The motivational-emotional character of such changes would appear to be even more limited when the lesions are restricted to the lateral surface of the temporal lobe and the preoccipital cortex, although Blum, Chow, and Pribram (14) do report some alterations in monkeys following such lesions which they feel are at least somewhat related to behavioral motivation (deficits in complex visual tasks, conditioned behavior, etc.).

On the other hand, Smith (124) showed that when experimental lesions are restricted only to the pyriform lobe, amygdaloid complex, and hippocampus in the monkey, sparing neocortical regions for the most part, very striking portions of the Klüver-Bucy syndrome do indeed appear (loss of "fear" and "anger" responses, docility, compulsive oral behavior) without gross motor or sensory deficits (the changes in visual behavior associated with the Klüver-Bucy syndrome). As a matter of fact, this author further reports that the docility and loss of fear can be produced in such animals without the compulsive oral behavior by selectively ablating specific components of this pyriform-amygdaloid-hippocampal complex, although he does not further delimit the particular structures involved. Thompson and Walker (128, 133), reporting on monkeys with bilateral lesions of the medial surface of the temporal lobe, further confirm the "taming" effects of such lesions presumably restricted to the amygdaloid complex and hippocampus, although they emphasize the temporary character of such changes (four to five months' duration) and indicate that lesions in other parts of the inferior temporal cortex do not produce such effects. Aside from this increased docility and reduction in fear responsiveness (all these animals could still express anger and rage to an appropriate stimulus), these authors report none of the other changes characteristic of the Klüver-Bucy syndrome except to note that their animals showed a *decrease* in sexual activity, at least during the first two postoperative weeks. Anatomical analysis of their data, with one exception, supports the implication that the amygdala is primarily involved in the changes resulting from such lesions. Poirer (101) also found fragments of the Klüver-Bucy syndrome in monkeys with somewhat more restricted lesions of the temporal pole, but this author seemed more impressed with the apathy and drowsiness exhibited by these animals and made little mention of other behavioral changes.

Continuing attempts to analyze the specific relationships to be found in this temporal lobe–amygdala–hippocampus syndrome have led recent investigators to a wide variety of different species in their quest for some basic understanding of the neurological correlates involved in this complex motivational-emotional phenomenon. Pribram and Bagshaw (103), for example, have been concerned with the effects of lesions involving the frontotemporal cortex, temporal pole, and amygdaloid complex upon the behavior of both baboons and monkeys. Disturbances in oral behavior and avoidance of noxious stimulation similar to those previously described appeared to be positively correlated with the extent of involvement of the frontotemporal cortex and amygdaloid complex. Fuller, Rosvold, and Pribram (42) also studied the effects of bilateral lesions of the amygdaloid complex, pyriform lobe, and hippocampus upon the behavior of highly inbred dogs (cocker spaniels), reporting changes in the direction of greater docility such as submissiveness, lack of initiative, and higher threshold to emotion-provoking stimuli and increased oral activity. When sufficiently provoked, however, these animals did appear to retain the ability to express marked anger and rage. Mishkin and Pribram (87, 88), working with both baboons and monkeys in an attempt to produce isolated ablations of the temporal lobe and also of the anteromedial temporal tip, conclude that the rostral part of the temporal lobe, including the amygdala, pyriform lobe, and rostral portions of the hippocampus, can produce, in these animals, disturbances in behavioral motivation similar in kind, although somewhat reduced in degree, to those reported by Pribram *et al.* (106) for baboons with more extensive frontotemporal and amygdala lesions. More recently, Schreiner and Kling (115) have reported behavioral changes associated with lesions of the amygdaloid complex and pyriform lobe in cats, agoutis, and lynx. In the cat preparations, which were most extensively studied, they found changes in the direction of greater docility, including refractoriness to rage- or anger-producing stimuli, exaggerated oral and vocal behavior, and marked hypersexuality. Gastaut (47) has also reported similar behavioral effects of amygdala lesions in the cat. The most striking finding in the notably wild and intractable agoutis and lynx was a dramatic conversion to virtually complete (if somewhat temporary, in the case of the lynx) docility following bilateral lesions in the amygdala and pyriform lobe. Schreiner and Kling (116) have also recently reported that the state of hypersexuality found in cats following amygdalectomy can be abolished by castration and restored with substitution therapy, thus pointing up important neuroendocrine relationships involving the limbic system. Furthermore, these authors have reported that the placid cat produced by amygdalectomy can be readily converted into a "vicious," "rageful" animal by an additional lesion in the ventromedial nucleus of the hypothalamus (115).

Even the social behavior of monkeys has now been shown to be markedly influenced by lesions involving the limbic system and, more specifically, the amygdaloid complex. Rosvold, Mirsky, and Pribram (111) have recently made important observations on both the individual- and group-cage behavior of eight, male rhesus monkeys before and after amygdalectomy, and report increased aggressiveness in the individual-cage situation after amygdalectomy but a change from dominant to submissive positions in the group hierarchy. These authors seem to feel that the differences between animals are more likely to be attributable to the social environment confronting each animal returning to the group after surgery and to the length of time the preoperative relationships had existed rather than to any differences in the extent or location of the lesions.

Despite the fact that even this more recent accumulation of experimental observations could hardly be said to yield a well-integrated picture of the role played by the limbic system in behavioral motivation, there has never been any shortage of speculative efforts assigning specific functional significance to the various components of this anatomical complex. Although representatives of many disciplines have tried their hand at such theorizing, a significant thread of similarity is discernible throughout these many neurological hypotheses. A few decades ago, for example, Herrick (62), on a comparative anatomical basis, proposed that the limbic system may serve as a "nonspecific" activator for all cortical activities, acting upon "the internal apparatus of general bodily attitude, disposition, and affective tone." Even Kleist (73), speculating about the limbic system, "inner brain" in his terminology, expressed the view that these structures were not only basic for emotional behavior, attitudes, and drives, but were also instrumental in correlating "visceral receptions" from the oral, anal, and genital regions and the intestines, thus subserving functions related to the search for food and sexual objects. Within the past decade, Grunthal (56) has concluded from the study of human patients with limbic system lesions that the hippocampus represents a "catalytic activator" which, although not necessarily participating in specialized functions itself, is nevertheless basic for the proper functioning of affective and neocortical activity. More recently, MacLean (84) has reviewed and elaborated the Papez (100) theory of emotions, suggesting that the limbic system ("visceral brain") is of basic importance not only for emotional behavior, but also for correlating "oral (smell, taste, mouth) and visceral sensations" as well as "impressions from the sex organs, body wall, eye, and ear." Even Pribram and Kruger (105) in their current review of the "olfactory brain" have speculatively assigned olfactory-gustatory, metabolic, and socio-emotional functions to the various limbic components comprising their three "systems." Insofar as possible, however, the present treatment of this limbic system subject matter has been and will attempt to remain at a descriptive-behavioral level, since progress in understanding the relationships between neural structure and behavioral function would seem to depend less upon theorizing than upon the interdisciplinary experimental analysis of critical behavioral, anatomical, physiological, and biochemical factors and their interactions. The experiments concerned with this problem which have occupied our time at the Walter Reed Army Institute of Research these past years were conceived within this more empirical framework and represent the combined efforts of virtually all these disciplines freely contributing their multiple skills.

SOME RECENT EXPERIMENTS

Several years ago when the neuropsychiatric laboratories at the Walter Reed Army Institute of Research were first conceived, the broad outlines of an interdisciplinary approach to problems in this area were vaguely discernible, although few of us could be said to have felt very strongly committed to such collaborative efforts. Indeed, there did appear to be some common elements among the several specific problems of primary interest to the few people in the laboratories at that time, but the character of our activities in those early days could hardly have been described as interdisciplinary. Dr. Robert Galambos and Dr. Leon Schreiner (117) were rather deeply engrossed in the application of their combined neurophysiological and neurosurgical skills to an investigation of the more broadly defined physiological consequences of limbic system ablations involving the amygdaloid complex, pyriform lobe, hippocampus, and various diencephalic nuclei in cats. Dr. Walle J. H. Nauta (94) was devotedly exploring the neuroanatomical intricacies of the fornix system in the rat with his newly developed silver stain, assiduously analyzing the degenerative consequences of discrete lesions in the septal region, hippocampus, and related limbic structures. And in the behavior laboratory, we were frankly concerned with the problem of conditioning emotional responses in cats and rats, analyzing the properties of these learned reaction patterns, and exploring the conditions under which durable changes in such behavior could be effected (17). Fortunately, both laboratory space and the scope of our professional contracts were severely limited during these first months, with the result that it became virtually impossible to avoid some familiarity with the several different approaches represented by as many different disciplines. Before long, it was clear that each had something to offer the other, and it is not surprising that the focus of much of our collaborative effort during the past three or four years should have centered upon the very problem which provides the title for this paper.

At that time, for example, a rather large number of cats had been prepared at the laboratory with lesions of the amygdaloid complex and overlying pyriform lobe, as illustrated in Plate 24, in an attempt to delineate further some of the limbic system relationships previously suggested by the Klüver-Bucy and Bard-Mountcastle work. The gross behavioral changes observed in these animals were strikingly obvious (115), but the lack of a common yardstick made it difficult to compare these motivational-emotional patterns with presumably similar, but in some instances notably contradictory, alterations described in earlier reports (9, 10, 74, 76, 77). At least a potential solution to this problem of defining, in more specific terms, the character of the "emotional" changes apparent in such preparations seemed to be suggested by the possible application of some of the more quantitative conditioning techniques with which the behavior laboratory was attemping a systematic evaluation of certain aspects of motivational-emotional behavior repertoires. Specifically, it was decided to investigate the acquisition and retention of a conditioned avoidance response in these amygdalectomized cats, comparing their behavior in this respect with both normals and animals with lesions involving other brain structures. And, indeed, the outcome of this initial interdisciplinary effort demonstrated quite clearly the way in which such collaborative experiments can be expected to contribute significantly at both a behavioral and a neurological level (22).

Briefly, the avoidance technique employed in this experiment consisted of the animal's passage through an open doorway separating the two compartments of a conventional "double-grill" box in response to the presentation of a 30-sec. conditioned clicker stimulus, thus terminating the clicker and preventing the shock which followed the failure to respond within the 30-sec. interval. *Acquisition* of such an avoidance response was found to be significantly slower (require more trials to reach a 90 per cent conditioned avoidance criterion) in a group of ten bilaterally amygdalectomized cats than in either a normal control group or an operated control group with hippocampal or cingulate lesions. Interestingly enough, however, virtually identical bilateral lesions of the amygdaloid nuclei sustained by three cats *following* acquisition of the avoidance response produced no apparent decrement in postoperative *retention* of the response. This finding not only begins to provide some insight into the differential functional properties of the more specific amygdaloid portions of the limbic system in the mediation of motivational-emotional behavior patterns involving avoidance, but also suggests interesting implications for systematic formulations of avoidance behavior within the framework of "anxiety" or "fear-reduction" hypotheses (22). It would also appear noteworthy that since the initiation of these more or less quantitative attempts to approach the "temporal lobe problem" some years ago, similar efforts with primates have been reported by Weiskrantz and Pribram (135, 136), who find correspondingly significant decrements in conditioned avoidance behavior following bilateral lesions involving not only the amygdaloid complex, but other portions of the "limbic system" as well (frontotemporal cortex, cingulate gyrus). At least the beginnings of rigorous control and systematic analysis of the motivational-emotional behavior changes associated with involvement of specific limbic components appear to be emerging as a consequence of these more recent interdisciplinary efforts.

Even less well formalized were the beginnings of our experiments on the septal region and the evaluation of behavioral changes associated with involvement of this and related portions of the limbic system (20, 21). Early in the course of Dr. Nauta's experimental investigation of the limbic system neuroanatomy, it became apparent, mostly as a consequence of the complaints of unsuspecting animal caretakers, that in rats with reasonably discrete septal lesions, illustrated diagrammatically in Figure 79, rather gross behavioral changes ("wildness," "savageness") frequently developed during the seven- to ten-day postoperative "degeneration" period before sacrifice and histologic preparation. Indeed, similar observations had previously been made by Fulton and Ingram (44), Krieg (78), and Spiegel, Miller, and Oppenheimer (125), but again, rigorous control and systematic analysis could hardly be said to have characterized the behavioral descriptions found in these earlier reports. Clearly, another important aspect of behavioral motivation and the representation of its neural correlates within apparently limited portions of the limbic system seemed available to critical interdisciplinary analysis, and the collaborative application of behavioral, neurosurgical, and neuroanatomical skills could be expected to yield valuable information. Again, the question of how best to assess and define the behavioral changes associated with such septal lesions was of central concern, and several comprehensive, if somewhat selective and quantifiable, aspects of the rat's conditioned and uncondi-

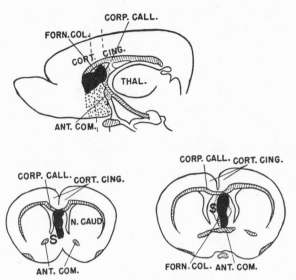

Fig. 79.—Semidiagrammatic representation of the rat fore-brain illustrating reconstruction of a typical septal lesion. Upper figure: medial aspect with the septal region stippled. Lower figures: two frontal sections at levels indicated by broken lines through stippled area of upper figure. The location and extent of the lesion is indicated in black on the reconstruction. Abbreviations: *ANT. COM.,* anterior commissure; *CORP. CALL.,* corpus callosum; *CORT. CING.,* cingulate cortex; *FORN. COL.,* fornix columns; *N. CAUD.,* caudate nucleus; *S.,* septal region; *THAL.,* thalamus.

tioned emotional behavioral repertoire were subjected to experimental analysis. Specifically, the effects of septal lesions and lesions of other limbic structures upon the acquisition and retention of a conditioned emotional response of the "anxiety" or "fear" type, upon the magnitude of the startle response to an explosive auditory stimulus, and upon general emotional reactivity as reflected in a seven-item rating scale, were investigated.

The conditioned "fear" response used in these studies represents a technique exploited for several years in connection with a general program related to the experimental analysis of emotional behavior (17, 18, 19) and will be seen to play a rather prominent role in much of the work to be reported in the following pages. In brief, the response represents the animal's learned anticipation of an unavoidable painful event, and is superimposed upon a simple but stable lever-pressing habit in order to provide a quantitative indicator of the emotionally disturbing effects. Figure 80 illustrates the basic conditioning procedure and the typical appearance of the "fear" response in the lever-pressing curve. After the lever-pressing habit for a water reward has been established, thirsty animals, working for water in this way, receive successive pairings of a conditioned auditory stimulus (a clicking noise which lasts for 3 min.) and a painful electric shock to the feet contiguous with termination of the

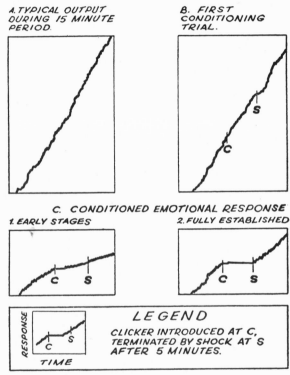

Fig. 80.—The conditioned emotional response as it appears typically in the cumulative response curve. From Hunt and Brady, (66).

clicker. The "fear" response appears after a few such pairings as a suppression of the lever-pressing rate accompanied by crouching and defecation in response to presentation of the clicker. Comparison of the number of lever responses emitted during presentation of the conditioned fear stimulus with the number emitted in similar periods without the stimulus, provides a means of quantifying certain aspects of the animal's motivational-emotional behavior repertoire.

Large cortical lesions and lesions of the cingulate gyrus in rats were found to have little or no effect upon the acquisition, retention, or extinction of such a conditioned emotional response, but involvement of other limbic system components produces significant changes. In experiments reported on the septal region, for example (20, 21), *retention* of such an anxiety response has been found to be markedly impaired when the lesions involve extensive interruption of the fornix system. Three or 4 days following surgery such preparations fail to respond to the conditioned fear stimulus, as they had preoperatively, with suppression of lever-pressing, crouching, and defecation, although tests conducted some 30 days later without intervening conditioning trials or level-pressing runs reveal that the anxiety response reappears in a manner similar to that previously reported following the attenuating effects of electroconvulsive shock (15, 66). Animals with similar septal lesions involving the fornix system or with lesions of the habenular complex of the thalamus (one of the main receiving stations for direct septal projections via the *stria medularis*) but without preoperative emotional conditioning show no apparent decrement in *acquisition* of such a "fear" response. Further, although such preparations with habenular lesions show no impairment in *immediate retention* of a preoperatively conditioned "anxiety" response, they do show a significantly more rapid rate of *extinction* of the emotional response as compared with normal controls and other operated groups, including the septal animals, when the conditioned clicker stimulus is presented alone without shock during 11 successive postoperative trials. Most recently, we have found that lesions of the hippocampus in the rat can virtually eliminate the conditioned emotional response and make it difficult, if not impossible, to recondition. In a group of animals conditioned preoperatively, rather extensive hippocampal lesions, surgically produced, resulted in virtually complete loss of the conditioned suppression, crouching, and defecation, without spontaneous recovery or reconditioning being demonstrable after more than a 30-day postoperative period. These latter findings must be viewed with some caution, however, since histological examination of these brains is not as yet complete, and some damage to the neocortex is an inevitable consequence of such surgical intervention, although cortical lesions alone do not produce these effects.

In order to provide some quantitative method of evaluating certain other specific, if somewhat limited, aspects of the rather gross behavioral changes readily observable in some of our early septal preparations, a technique was adapted from an earlier report (29) on the measurement of the startle response in rats. One of the first observations noted to be characteristic of these animals with septal lesions was a somewhat explosive reaction to auditory as well as tactile stimulation, and the possibility of getting some measure of this, utilizing some sort of stabilimeter-type apparatus, appeared promising. The method involved the modification of a simple 5-lb. postage stamp scale so that the movements of a small cage surmounted on the platform could be transmitted by means of a thread to an ink-writing muscle lever whose deflections were recorded on a moving tape. With this technique, it was possible to obtain measures of the magnitude of the rat's startle response to an explosive auditory stimulus provided by the discharge of a 22-caliber blank pistol 2 ft. from the animal. In a rather straightforward "before-and-after" experiment, a significant increase in the magnitude of the startle response was demonstrable following the septal lesions, although neither the habenular preparations nor the more recently studied rats with hippocampal lesions showed any significant postoperative changes on this measure. It is interesting to note, however, that even in the septal animals these increases in startle response magnitude were relatively transient and disappeared upon repeated testing 15, 30, 45, and 60 days postoperatively.

Finally, in an attempt to approximate some quantitative definition of the numerous broader aspects of the organism's "emotional" repertoire undergoing alteration as a result of limbic system damage, a rating scale similar to scales investigated by Stone (127) and Tryon *et al.* (129), was devised to evaluate seven behavior components prominently observed in such preparations. Ratings were made independently by three observers of the rats' preoperative and postoperative behavior with respect to (*a*) resistance to capture in the home cage; (*b*) resistance to handling, (*c*) muscular tension, (*d*) squealing and vocalization, (*e*) urination and defecation, (*f*) aggressive reaction to presentation of forceps close to snout, and (*g*) aggressive reaction to prodding with forceps. A zero- to four-point scale was used for each item, with the zero point fixed by the behavior of tame albino rats conventionally employed in laboratory experiments, and the sum of the ratings on each item on any one day represented a given animal's "emotional reactivity score." The ratings were found to be highly reliable, yielding correlation coefficients of better than .90 between the judgments of the three raters, and the scales proved to be sufficiently sensitive to differentiate effectively and quantitatively the postoperative behavior of animals with septal lesions from both their own preoperative behavior and the behavior of operated and unoperated controls. As we have previously reported in some detail (20, 21), significant increases in "emotional reactivity" measured in this fashion were found to be an immediate consequence of septal lesions in the rat, although, again, such changes appear to be of limited duration. When such animals are handled for daily postoperative ratings, this hyperactivity disappears within a two-week period, but even without extensive intervening handling, such animals have been found to return to "normal" within a 60-day period. No such increases in "emotional reactivity" have been observed in any of our other operated preparations, including the rats with lesions of the neocortex, cingulate gyrus, habenula, or hippocampus. Indeed, several of these latter hippocampal preparations have been observed to show poorly directed aggressive reactions to noxious stimuli such as forceps applied to the tail, but the threshold of the response appears to be neither lower nor higher than that found in unoperated controls.

It should be noted that recently, Professor Clifford T. Morgan and Mr. Fred King, one of his students at the Johns Hopkins University Department of Psychology, have been following up these findings on the effects of limbic system lesions in both albino and hooded rats. King (72) has found, for example, that both the magnitude and the duration of such gross increases in emotional reactivity following septal lesions are a function of the "normal" preoperative "emotional level" of the animals, hooded septal rats displaying significantly more intense reactions than albino rats with similar septal lesions. Even more important from the standpoint of our present interests, however, is a personal communication from this same laboratory that, with at least two hooded rats, such gross increases in emotional reactivity following septal lesions have been dramatically eliminated by the superimposition of an amygdala lesion. Of course, determination of the extent and location of these lesions awaits histological verification, and a number of necessary control observations remain to be accomplished, but a somewhat similar finding has also been reported by Anand and Brobeck (3), who reported that a rat made vicious as a consequence of a lesion in the ventromedial hypothalamus could be similarly converted to a relatively docile animal by superimposing an amygdala lesion. A careful definition of such reciprocal relationships will doubtless contribute significantly to the clarification of the somewhat confusing and contradictory reports presently available on the functional properties of various limbic components, and the application of ever more refined techniques for behavioral analysis within this affective sphere should provide a broader understanding of integrated limbic system function.

Probably the one finding which has had the most extensive influence upon our recent interdisciplinary work on the limbic system at the Walter Reed Army Institute of Research laboratories was the report by Olds and

Milner (98) from Professor Hebb's laboratory at McGill University demonstrating the reinforcing characteristics of limbic system electrical stimulation. Although for several years prior to this report there had been an abiding interest in the possibilities offered by chronically implanted electrodes in laboratory animals, and both electrophysiologists and neurosurgeons had begun to approach various phases of this problem, the novel introduction of self-stimulation contingencies clearly opened up extensive new vistas in the behavioral analysis of limbic system function. In large part, our efforts have been concentrated upon refining the behavioral, electrophysiological, and neuroanatomical techniques essential to the application of such an approach to neural-behavioral correlations, but with many of these problems now behind us, it has been possible to elaborate, at least on a preliminary basis, some apparently important relationships. With both cats and rats, for example, we have found it possible to sustain rather stable rates of lever pressing for such electrical stimulation reward on both periodic and ratio schedules. With indwelling electrodes placed in the septal region of the rat (Plate 25), and in the caudate

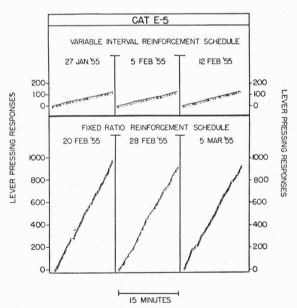

Fig. 81.—Sample cumulative response curves showing stable lever-pressing rates for variable-interval (mean of 16 sec.) and fixed-ratio (7 to 1) intracranial electrical stimulation reward. Oblique "pips" indicate reinforcements. From Sidman, *et al.*, (120).

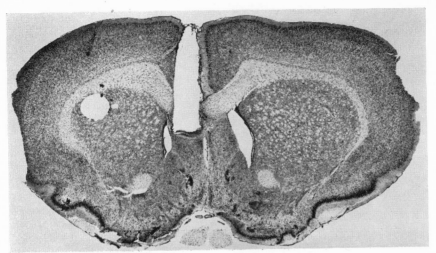

Plate 25.—Low-power photomicrograph of a rat brain section showing electrode tract coursing through the cingulate cortex and corpus callosum with stimulating tip in the septal region.

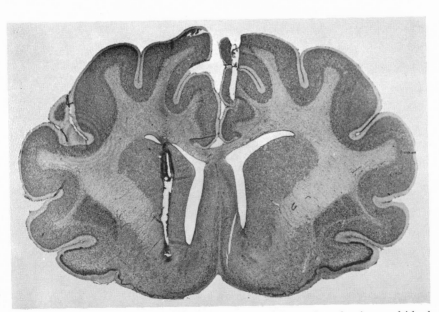

Plate 26.—Low-power photomicrograph of a cat brain section showing multi-lead electrode tract coursing through the head of the caudate nucleus with ventral tip in the anterior limb of the anterior commissure.

nucleus of the cat (Plate 26), a bar-pressing response which is reinforced only at irregular intervals (aperiodic schedule) or only every-so-many responses (fixed-ratio schedule) by electrical stimulation through such electrodes, develops stable and durable properties, illustrated in Figure 81, characteristically similar to bar-pressing rates generated by the use of more conventional extrinsic rewards such as food and water (120). We have found it possible, by utilizing such a reward, to reproduce stable lever-pressing rates from one session to the next over periods of several months in both cats and rats by standardizing the conditions of our experiment (including the use of an electrical stimulator recently described by Lilly *et al.* [79]), thus making it possible to study systematically the operation of such variables as the stimulus parameter, reinforcement contingencies, physiological status, and emotional disturbance.

It is now quite clear, for example, that a variety of motivational-emotional factors bear rather important relationships to the reinforcing properties of such intracranial self-stimulation. By varying the average interval between electrical stimulation rewards when the animal is performing on an aperiodic or variable-interval reinforcement schedule, it is possible to show that the rate of responding is negatively correlated with the duration of the interval between electrical stimulations (120). Furthermore, it is also apparent from Figure 82 that the characteristically high lever-pressing rates which can be produced by arranging the electrical

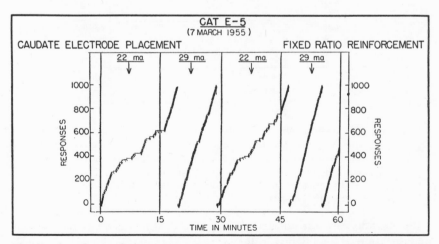

Fig. 82.—Sample cumulative response curve showing a 60-min. lever-pressing session for fixed-ratio (8 to 1) intracranial stimulation reinforcement. The intensity of the electrical reward stimulus was varied as indicated during alternate 15-min. periods. Oblique "pips" indicate reinforcements. From Sidman, *et al.*, (120).

stimulation reward contingencies on a fixed-ratio schedule (i.e., ten lever responses required to produce one electrical stimulation reward) are remarkably sensitive to changes in intracranial electrical stimulus intensity ("amount of reward") (120). Interesting interactions have also been found between the reinforcing properties of such intracranial self-stimulation and other basic biological motivations (16). Investigation of the effects of food deprivation upon lever pressing for electrical stimulation has revealed that reliably higher rates of responding for stimulation reward can be obtained under conditions of extended food deprivation than under conditions of satiation. Both cats and rats on 48-hr. food deprivation have been found to produce higher, more stable rates of bar pressing for an aperiodic electrical stimulation reward than these same animals do after only 1-hr. deprivation. Measures obtained following 4- and 24-hr. food deprivation, as indicated in Figure 83, illustrate this same positive correlation between

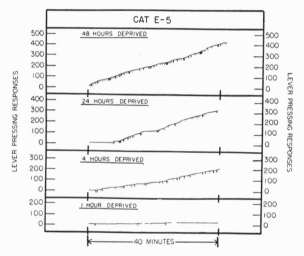

Fig. 83.—Sample cumulative response curves showing lever-pressing rates for variable-interval (mean of 16 sec.) intracranial electrical stimulation reward during four separate 40-min. experimental sessions following 1, 4, 24, and 48 hr. of deprivation, respectively. Oblique "pips" indicate reinforcements.

lever-pressing rate for intracranial electrical stimulation reinforcement and duration of food deprivation.

Probably the most exciting finding to date involving this intracranial self-stimulation technique has to do with interaction effects involving the "anxiety" or "fear" reaction (conditioned emotional response) mentioned above in connection with our limbic system ablation studies. Utilizing animals with a rather long history of lever pressing for intracranial shock stimulation, we attempted to evaluate the effects of emotional disturbance or "fear" of this type upon a stable output of electrical-stimulation–rewarded lever responses. Accordingly, the animals were first taken off intracranial stimulation and placed on lever pressing for an aperiodic water reward until a stable rate was obtained. Then, the conditioned anxiety response was superimposed upon the stable habit of lever pressing for water, as illustrated in Figure 80 above, appearing as suppression of the response rate, accompanied by crouching and defecation, during presentation of the conditioned clicker stimulus which had been previously paired with the painful electric shock to the feet. When the animals were then returned to lever pressing for an aperiodic intracranial electrical stimulation reward, however, presentation of the clicker failed to elicit the fear response. The animals did not stop pressing the lever when working for electrical stimulation and did not crouch or defecate, although all these behavioral indices of the anxiety response did appear when the animals were again run on an aperiodic water-reward schedule. Figure 84 shows a cumulative response curve obtained from one rat with an electrode in

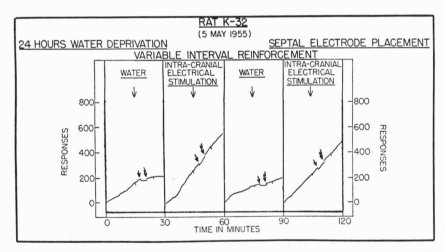

Fig. 84.—Sample cumulative response curve showing the differential effect of the conditioned "anxiety" procedure during a 2-hr. experimental session with alternate 30-min. periods of variable-interval (mean of 16 sec.) water and intracranial electrical stimulation reward. The oblique solid arrows indicate the onset of the conditioned auditory stimulus, and the oblique broken arrows indicate the termination of the conditioned stimulus contiguously with the brief unconditioned grid-shock stimulus to the feet during each of the alternate 30-min. periods.

the septal region during a 2-hr. lever-pressing session with alternating 30-min. periods for water reward and for intracranial electrical stimulation reward. Although presentation of the clicker, which is indicated by the first arrow in each segment of the curve, clearly suppresses the lever-pressing rate (and also produces crouching and defecation) during the water-reward periods, no such effect is apparent during the periods of electrical stimulation reward *even though* termination of the clicker is accompanied on each occasion by shock to the feet, indicated by the second arrow in each segment of the curve. Furthermore, it is now quite clear that a remarkable resistance to acquisition of the conditioned anxiety response can be observed when the animal is concurrently provided with the opportunity for intracranial self-stimulation of at least these rather restricted portions of the limbic system. Figure 85 shows several cumula-

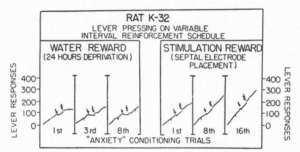

Fig. 85.—Sample cumulative response curves showing acquisition trials for the conditioned "anxiety" response superimposed upon lever pressing for variable-interval (mean of 16 sec.) water and intracranial electrical stimulation reward. The oblique solid arrows indicate the onset of the conditioned auditory stimulus, and the oblique broken arrows indicate the termination of the conditioned stimulus contiguously with the brief unconditioned grid-shock stimulus to the feet during each trial.

tive response curves for this same rat, first during superimposition of the anxiety response upon lever pressing for water reward, and then upon lever pressing for electrical stimulation reward. By the third conditioning trial, presentation of the clicker during the water-reward lever-pressing sessions produces the characteristic rate suppression, crouching, and defecation, although no such "anxiety" indicators appear after as many as 16 pairings of clicker and grid shock during lever-pressing sessions for electrical stimulation reward. Again, the small arrows indicate onset of the clicker and its termination with grid shock during each lever-pressing session.

Before concluding, I would just like to mention briefly two related areas of investigation on the limbic system and its electrophysiological and neuroendocrinological correlates which have developed in our laboratories more or less as a consequence of refinements in this indwelling-electrode technique. One of these recent developments in the able hands of Dr. Robert Galambos and Dr. Guy Sheatz has been concerned with the recording of electrical responses to auditory stimulation from these same animals with implanted limbic system electrodes. Trains of click stimuli have been found to elicit rather clearly defined electrical responses from various limbic components such as the hippocampus and possibly even the amygdaloid complex, caudate nucleus, and septal area. Indeed, somewhat similar findings have been previously reported for at least some of these areas (48, 55), but the present experiments (119) have afforded an opportunity for the careful analysis of the functional properties of such phenomena in the unanesthetized preparation. It is now clear, for example, that the magnitude of the electrical response to virtually all clicks in a given series (usually ten) *except* the first click, tends to diminish with repeated presentations of the series and as a function of the repetition rate. That is, although the response to the first click in a train is usually large, responses to subsequent clicks diminish faster on repeated presentation when they are spaced 1 sec. apart than when they are spaced as long as 3 sec. apart.

Most interesting, however, is the fact that these electrical responses of the limbic system can be "conditioned" by means of a technique quite similar to that described in previous portions of this paper dealing with the conditioned anxiety response. After a rather extensive adaptation period, for example, during which virtually all responses to later clicks in a series have dropped out, a series of "conditioning" trials have been administered in which the previously inocuous presentation of the ten-click train was followed by a painful electric shock through the cat's harness contiguous with the final click. Within a few trials, presentation of the click train alone now elicits electrical responses to *each* click in the series comparing favorably in magnitude and duration with the response to the first click. Further, the conditioned electrical response of certain limbic system components can be shown to behave in accordance with known learning principles, since repeated presentations of the click train alone without shock (experimental extinction) results in gradual diminution of the magnitude of the electrical responses to subsequent clicks in the train. And, of course, reconditioning is readily accomplished by appropriate introduction of the shock again. As a matter of fact, there is even some indication that somewhat more complex discriminative learning may be demonstrated using this technique under conditions where two different levels of illumination indicate whether shock will follow a given series of clicks or not.

Of course, there are numerous problems associated with these experiments including histological verification of the electrode location, controls for various behavioral and electrical artifacts, and the like, but at least some information has already been obtained relative to such questions. Recent experiments have shown, for example, that the conditioned electrical responses can be established and extinguished with the animal curarized, suggesting that muscle responses probably do not contribute significantly to the phenomenon.

Most recently, Dr. John Mason, who heads our neuroendocrinology labortory, has been conducting some experiments investigating central nervous system regulation of endocrine function, and has begun to elaborate some important relationships between the limbic system and pituitary-adrenal activity. Utilizing a technique originally developed by Nelson and Samuels (96) for the direct measurement of 17-hydroxy-cortico-steroids in peripheral blood, it has been possible to obtain a relatively specific index of adrenal-cortical activity (ACTH release in certain unanesthetized laboratory animals as well as in man) (60). One of the applications of this technique to the study of direct limbic system stimulation effects appears quite promising and has already begun to elucidate certain critical neural-endocrine relationships.

First, it has been consistently and reliably demonstrated that direct electrical stimulation of the tubero-infundibular portions of the hypothalamus through chronically implanted electrodes in monkeys can produce significant and dramatic increases in blood steroid levels. These findings tend to confirm previous reports, utilizing less direct assay techniques (eosinophil or lymphocyte counts, adrenal ascorbic acid, etc.), of similar changes in pituitary-adrenal activity following hypothalamic stimulation (58, 65, 85, 102). It has been possible in the present studies, however, to explore systematically the effects of direct electrical stimulation of other limbic components known to contribute anatomical influences to the tubero-infundibular region and to demonstrate selective changes in 17-hydroxy-cortico-steroid levels. Recent findings indicate, for example, that stimulation of the amygdala complex can also produce significant elevations in blood steroid levels, although no such changes occur as a consequence of stimulation involving adjacent neural structures (putamen, anterior thalamus). In an obviously related group of studies, we have been attempting to evaluate the effects on blood steroid levels of gross behavioral changes associated with emotional disturbance. Preliminary findings with monkeys, in a study utilizing the conditioned "fear" technique superimposed upon a stable lever-pressing habit for a reward of sugared orange juice indicate that, again, significant rises in 17-hydroxy-cortico-steroid levels can be shown to accompany behavioral indications of reasonably well specified emotional disturbance indicated by suppression of lever pressing, crouching, defecation, and urination. No such elevations occur, however, as a consequence of other obviously disturbing situations including extinction of the bar-pressing response by nonreinforcement or drastic changes in ratio of reward schedules.

Of course, it must again be emphasized that all these latter studies are still very much in the preliminary stages with respect to histological verification of electrode placements, behavioral controls, and the like, but some enthusiastic prospecting would seem justified on the basis of even the most cautious interpretation of this limited number of rather specific and unequivocal observations. That much work remains to be accomplished if we are to improve our understanding of behavioral motivation and its neural correlates, seems almost too obvious to require further comment. But that the interdisciplinary framework, within which such studies can seemingly now only be accomplished, affords the best opportunity for making such progress, would seem to be most brilliantly demonstrated by the very contributions of this Symposium.

REFERENCES

1 Adey, W. R. An Experimental study of the hippocampal connexions of the cingulate cortex in the rabbit. *Brain,* 1951, *74:* 223–47.

2 Anand, B. K., and J. R. Brobeck. Hypothalamic control of food intake in rats and cats. *Yale J. Biol. Med.,* 1951, *24:* 132–40.

3 ———. Food intake and spontaneous activity of rats with lesions in the amygdaloid nuclei. *J. Neurophysiol.,* 1952, *15:* 421–30.

4 Bailey, P. Betrachtungen über die chirurgische Behandlung der psychomotorischen Epilepsie. *Z. Neurochir.,* 1954, *14:* 195–206.

5 Baird, H., B. Guidetti, V. Reyes, H. T. Wycis, and E. A. Spiegel. Stimulation and elimination of anterior thalamic nuclei in man and cat. *Fed. Proc.,* 1951, *10:* 8–9.

6 Bard, P. A diencephalic mechanism for the expression of rage with special reference to the sympathetic nervous system. *Amer. J. Physiol.,* 1928, *84:* 490–515.

7 ———. On emotional expression after decortication with some remarks on certain theoretical views. Parts I and II. *Psychol. Rev.,* 1934, *41:* 309–329, 424–49.

8 ———. The hypothalamus and sexual behavior. *Res. Publ., Ass. nerv. ment. Dis.,* 1940, *20:* 551–79.

9 ———. Central nervous mechanisms for the expression of anger in animals. In M. L. Reymert (Ed.), *Feelings and emotions: The Moosehart Symposium.* New York: McGraw-Hill, 1950, pp. 211–37.

10 Bard, P., and V. B. Mountcastle. Some forebrain mechanisms involved in expression of rage with special reference to suppression of angry behavior. *Res. Publ. Ass. nerv. ment. Dis.,* 1948, *27:* 362–404.

11 Bard, P., and D. M. Rioch. A study of four cats deprived of neocortex and additional portions of the forebrain. *Johns Hopk. Hosp. Bull.,* 1937, *60:* 73–147.

12 Bazett, H. C., and W. G. Penfield. A study of the Sherrington decerebrate animal in the chronic as well as the acute condition. *Brain,* 1922, *45:* 185–265.

13 Beck, E., A. Meyer, and J. Le Beau. Efferent connexions of the human prefrontal region with reference to fronto-hypothalamic pathways. *J. Neurol. Psychiat.,* 1951, *14:* 295–302.

14 Blum, J. S., K. L. Chow, and K. H. Pribram. A behavioral analysis of the organization of the parieto-temporo-preoccipital cortex. *J. comp. Neurol.,* 1950, *93:* 53–100.

15 Brady, J. V. The effect of electro-convulsive shock on a conditioned emotional response: The permanence of the effect. *J. comp. physiol. Psychol.,* 1951, *44:* 507–11.

16 ———. Motivational-emotional factors and intra-cranial self-stimulation. *Amer. Psychologist,* 1955, *10:* 396 (Abstract).

17 ———. Experimental analysis of emotional behavior. *Proc. Fourteenth int. Congr. of Psychol.* Amsterdam: North-Holland, 1955, 148–49.

18 ———. A comparative approach to the experimental analysis of emotional behavior. In P. Hoch and J. Zubin (Eds.), *Experimental psychopathology.* New York: Grune and Stratton, 1957.

19 Brady, J. V., and H. F. Hunt. An experimental approach to the analysis of emotional behavior. *J. Psychol.,* 1955, *40:* 313–24.

20 Brady, J. V., and W. J. H. Nauta. Subcortical mechanisms in emotional behavior: Affective changes following septal forebrain lesions in the albino rat. *J. comp. physiol. Psychol.,* 1953, *46:* 339–46.

21 ———. Subcortical mechanisms in emotional behavior: The duration of affective changes following septal and habenular lesions in the albino rat. *J. comp. physiol. Psychol.,* 1955, *48:* 412–20.

22 Brady, J. V., L. Schreiner, I. Geller, and A. Kling. Subcortical mechanisms in emotional behavior: The effect of rhinencephalic injury upon the acquisition and retention of a conditioned avoidance response in cats. *J. comp. physiol. Psychol.,* 1954, *47:* 179–86.

23 Brobeck, J. R., J. Tepperman, and C. N. Long. Experimental hypothalamic hyperphagia in the albino rat. *Yale J. Biol. Med.,* 1943, *15:* 831–53.

24 Broca, P. Localisations cerebrales: Recherches sur les centres olfactifs. *Rev. anthrop.* 1879, *2:* 385.

25 Brodal, A. The origin of the fibers of the anterior commissure in the rat. Experimental studies. *J. comp. Neurol.*, 1948, *88:* 157–207.

26 Brookhart, J. M., and F. L. Dey. Reduction of sexual behavior in male guinea pigs by hypothalamic lesions. *Amer. J. Physiol.*, 1941. *133:* 551–54.

27 Brookhart, J. M., F. L. Dey, and S. W. Ranson. The abolition of mating behavior by hypothalamic lesions in guinea pigs. *Endocrinology*, 1941, *28:* 561–65.

28 Brooks, C. M. Appetite and obesity. *N. Z. med. J.*, 1947, *46:* 243–54.

29 Brown, J. S., H. I. Kalish, and I. E. Farber. Conditioned fear as revealed by magnitude of startle response to an auditory stimulus. *J. exp. Psychol.*, 1951, *41:* 317–28.

30 Brown, S., and E. A. Schäfer. An investigation into the functions of the occipital and temporal lobes of the monkey's brain. *Phil. Trans. Ser. B.*, 1888, *179:* 303–27.

31 Cajal, S. R. *Histologie du système nerveux de l'homme et des vertébrés.* (Tr. from the Spanish by L. Azouley.) Paris: A. Maloine, 1909. 2 vols.

32 Cannon, W. B., and S. W. Britton. Studies on the conditions of activity in endocrine glands XV. Pseudaffective medulliadrenal secretion. *Amer. J. Physiol.*, 1925, *72:* 283–94.

33 Chow, K. L. Lack of behavioral effects following destruction of some thalamic association nuclei in monkey. *Arch. Neurol. Psychiat., Chicago*, 1954, *71:* 762–71.

34 Clark, W. E. Leg., and R. H. Boggon. On the connexions of the anterior nucleus of the thalamus. *J. Anat., Lond.*, 1933, *67:* 215–26.

35 Clark, W. E. Leg., and M. Meyer. The terminal connexions of the olfactory tract in the rabbit. *Brain*, 1947, *70:* 304–28.

36 Daitz, H. M., and T. P. Powell. Studies of the connexions of the fornix system. *J. Neurol. Psychiat.*, 1954, *17:* 75–82.

37 Delafresnaye, J. F. (Ed.) *Brain mechanisms and consciousness.* Oxford: Blackwell, 1954.

38 Dusser de Barenne, J. G. Recherches expérimentales sur les functions du système nerveux central, faites en particulier sur deux chat cont le néopallium avait été enlevé. *Arch. néerl. Physiol.*, 1920, *4:* 31–123.

39 Ferster, C. B. The use of the free operant in the analysis of behavior. *Psychol. Bull.*, 1953, *50:* 263–74.

40 Fox, C. A., W. A. McKinley, and H. W. Magoun. An oscillographic study of olfactory system in cats. *J. Neurophysiol.*, 1944, *7:* 1–16.

41 French, J. D., and H. W. Magoun. Effects of chronic lesions in central cephalic brain stem of monkeys. *Arch. Neurol. Psychiat., Chicago*, 1952, *68:* 591–604.

42 Fuller, J. L., H. E. Rosvold, and K. H. Pribram. The effect on affective and cognitive behavior in the dog of lesions of the pryriform-amygdala-hippocampal complex. *J. comp. physiol. Psychol.*, 1957, *50:* 89–96.

43 Fulton, J. F. The limbic system: A study of the visceral brain in primates and man. *Yale J. Biol. Med.*, 1953, *26:* 107–18.

44   Fulton, J. F., and F. D. Ingraham. Emotional disturbances following experimental lesions of the base of the brain. *J. Physiol.*, 1929, *67:* xxvii–xxviii.

45   Fulton, J. F., K. H. Pribram, J. A. Stevenson, and P. D. Wall. Interrelations between orbital gyrus, insula, temporal tip, and anterior cingulate. *Trans. Amer. neurol. Ass.*, 1949, *74:* 175–79.

46   Ganser, S. Vergleichend-anatomische Studien über das Gehirn des Maulwirfs. *Morph. Jb.*, 1882, *7:* 591–725.

47   Gastaut, H. Corrélations entre le système nerveux végétatif et le système de la vie de relation dans le rhinencéphale. *J. Physiol. Path. gén.*, 1952, *44:* 431–70.

48   Gerard, R. W., W. H. Marshall, and L. J. Saul. Electrical activity of the cat's brain. *Arch. Neurol. Psychiat., Chicago*, 1936, *36:* 675–738.

49   Glees, P. Terminal degeneration within the central nervous system as studied by a new silver method. *J. Neuropath.*, 1946, *5:* 54–59.

50   ———. The time factor in central fiber degeneration. *Acta anat.*, 1948, *6:* 447–50.

51   Glees, P., J. Cole, C. W. M. Whitty, and H. Cairns. The effects of lesions in the cingular gyrus and adjacent areas in monkeys. *J. Neurol. Psychiat.*, 1950, *13:* 178–90.

52   Glees, P., and W. J. H. Nauta. A critical review of studies on axonal and terminal degeneration. *Mschr. Psychiat. Neurol.*, 1955, *129:* 74–91.

53   Gloor, P. Telencephalic influences upon the hypothalamus. In Fields, W. S., *et al.* (Eds.). *Hypothalamic Hypophysiol. Interrelationships.* Springfield, Ill.: Charles C Thomas, 1956.

54   Goltz, F. Der Hund ohne Grosshirn. *Pflüg. Arch. ges. Physiol.*, 1892, *51:* 570–614.

55   Green, J. D., and A. A. Arduini. Hippocampal electrical activity in arousal. *J. Neurophysiol.*, 1954, *17:* 533–57.

56   Grünthal, E. Uber das klinische bild nach umschriebenem beiderseitigem ausfall der ammonshornrinde. Ein beitrag zur kenntnis der funktion des Ammonshorns. *Mschr. Psychiat. Neurol.*, 1947, *113:* 1, 219–27.

57   Harris, G. W. Neural control of the pituitary gland. I. Neurohypophysis. *Brit. med. J.*, 1951: 2, 559–64.

58   ———. Neural control of the pituitary gland. II. Adenohypophysis with special reference to the secretion of A.C.T.H. *Brit. med. J.*, 1951, *2:* 627–34.

59   Harrison, J. M., and M. Lyon. The role of the septal nuclei and components of the fornix in the behavior of the rat. *J. Comp. Neurol.*, 1957, *108:* 1, 121–38.

60   Harwood, C. T., and J. W. Mason. A systematic evaluation of the Nelson-Samuels 17-hydroxy-corticosteroid method. *J. Clin. Endocrinol. and Metab.*, 1956, *16:* 790–96.

61   Heath, R. G. Behavioral changes following destructive lesions in the subcortical structure of the forebrain in cats. In R. G. Heath, *et al., Studies*

in schizophrenia. Cambridge, Mass.: Harvard University Press, 1954. Pp. 83–84.

62 Herrick, C. J. The functions of the olfactory parts of the cerebral cortex. *Proc. nat. Acad. Sci.,* 1933, *19:* 7–14.

63 Hetherington, A. W., and S. W. Ranson. The spontaneous activity and food intake of rats with hypothalamic lesions. *Amer. J. Physiol.,* 1942, *136:* 609–17.

64 Hovde, C. A., and F. A. Mettler. Distant electrical potentials evoked by stimulation of the putamen. *Anat. Rec.,* 1953, *115:* 324–25. (Abstract).

65 Hume, D. M., and G. J. Wittenstein. The relationship of the hypothalamus to pituitary-adrenocortical function. In J. R. Mote (Ed.), *Proceedings of the first ACTH Conference.* Philadelphia: Blakison, 1950, pp. 134–47.

66 Hunt, H. F., and J. V. Brady. Some effects of electro-convulsive shock on a conditioned emotional response ("anxiety"). *J. comp. physiol. Psychol.,* 1951, *44:* 88–98.

67 Ingram, W. R., R. W. Barris, and S. W. Ranson. Catalepsy: An experimental study. *Arch. Neurol. Psychiat., Chicago,* 1936, *35:* 1175–197.

68 Johnson, F. H. Neuro-anatomical tracts considered as correlates of the ascending reticular activating system in the cat. *Anat. Rec.,* 1953, *115:* 327–28 (Abstract).

69 Kappers, C. U., G. C. Huber, and E. C. Crosby. *The comparative anatomy of the nervous system of vertebrates, including man.* New York: Macmillan, 1936. 2 vols.

70 Keller, A. D. Autonomic discharges elicited by psychological stimuli in mid-brain preparations. *Amer. J. Physiol.,* 1932, *100:* 576–86.

71 Kelly, A. H., L. E. Beaton, and H. W. Magoun. A midbrain mechanism for facio-vocal activity. *J. Neurophysiol.,* 1946, *9:* 181–89.

72 King, F. A. Effects of septal and amygdaloid lesions on emotional behavior and conditioned avoidance responses in the rat. *J. Nerv. Ment. Dis.,* 1958, *126:* 1, 57–63.

73 Kleist, K. *Gehirn-Pathologie vornehmlich auf Grund der Kreigeserfahrungen. Aus Handbuch der ärzlichen Erfahrungen im Weltkreig.* Vol. 4. Leipsig: Barth, 1934, pp. 343–1408.

74 Klüver, H. Brain mechanisms and behavior with special reference to the rhinencephalon. *J. Lancet,* 1952, *72:* 567–74.

75 Klüver, H., and P. C. Bucy. "Psychic blindness" and other symptoms following bilateral temporal lobectomy in rhesus monkeys. *Amer. J. Physiol.,* 1937, *119:* 352–53.

76 ———. An analysis of certain effects of bilateral temporal lobectomy in the rhesus monkey, with special reference to "psychic blindness." *J. Psychol.,* 1938, *5:* 33–54.

77 ———. Preliminary analysis of functions of the temporal lobes in monkeys. *Arch. Neurol. Psychiat., Chicago,* 1939, *42:* 979–1000.

78 Krieg, W. J. Personal communication to W. E. LeG. Clark. In W. E. LeG.

Clark, J. Beattie, G. Riddoch, and N. M. Dott, *The hypothalamus*. London: Oliver and Boyd, 1938.

79 Lilly, J. C., J. R. Hughes, E. C. Alvord, Jr., and T. W. Galkin. Brief non-injurious electric waveform for stimulation of the brain. *Science*, 1955, *121:* 468–69.

80 Lindsley, D. B. Emotion. In S. S. Stevens (Ed.), *Handbook of experimental psychology*. New York: Wiley, 1951, pp. 473–516.

81 Lindsley, D. B., L. H. Schreiner, W. B. Knowles, and H. W. Magoun. Behavioral and EEG changes following chronic brain stem lesions in the cat. *Electroenceph. clin. Neurophysiol.*, 1950, *2:* 483–98.

82 Loo, Y. T. The forebrain of the opossum, Didelphis virginiana. II. Histology. *J. comp. Neurol.*, 1931, *52:* 1–148.

83 Lorente de Nó, R. Studies on the structure of the cerebral cortex. II. Continuation of the study of the ammonic system. *J. Psychol. Neurol., Lpz.*, 1934, *46:* 113–77.

84 MacLean, P. D. Psychosomatic disease and the "visceral brain": Recent developments bearing on the Papez theory of emotion. *Psychosom. Med.*, 1949, *11:* 338–53.

85 McCann, S. M. Effect of hypothalamic lesions on the adrenal cortical response to stress in the rat. *Amer. J. Physiol.*, 1953, *175:* 13–20.

86 Mettler, F. A., H. Grundfest, and C. A. Hovde. Distant electrical potentials evoked by stimulation of the caudate nucleus. *Anat. Rec.*, 1952, *112:* 359 (Abstract).

87 Mishkin, M. Visual discrimination performance following partial ablations of the temporal lobe: II. Ventral surface vs. hippocampus. *J. comp. physiol. Psychol.*, 1954, *47:* 187–93.

88 Mishkin, M., and K. H. Pribram. Visual discrimination performance following partial ablations of the temporal lobe: I. Ventral vs. lateral. *J. comp. physiol. Psychol.*, 1954, *47:* 14–20.

89 Morison, R. S., and E. W. Dempsey. A study of thalamo-cortical relations. *Amer. J. Physiol.*, 1942, *135:* 281–92.

90 Moruzzi, G., and H. W. Magoun. Brain stem reticular formation and activation of the EEG. *Electroenceph. clin. Neurophysiol.*, 1949, *1:* 455–73.

91 Nauta, W. J. H. Hypothalamic regulation of sleep in rats: An experimental study. *J. Neurophysiol.*, 1946, *9:* 285–316.

92 ———. Some projections of the medial wall of the hemisphere in the rat's brain (cortical areas 32 and 25, 24, and 29). *Anat. Rec.*, 1953, *115:* 352.

93 ———. An experimental study of the fornix system in the rat. *J. comp. Neurol.*, 1956, *104:* 247–71.

94 Nauta, W. J. H., and P. A. Gygax. Silver impregnation of degenerating axons in the central nervous system: A modified technique. *Stain Tech.*, 1954, *29:* 91–93.

95 Nauta, W. J. H., and D. G. Whitlock. An anatomical analysis of the non-specific thalamic projection system. In· J. F. Delafresnaye (Ed.), *Brain mechanisms and consciousness*. Oxford: Blackwell, 1954, pp. 81–116.

96 Nelson, D. H., and L. T. Samuels. A method for the determination of 17-hydroxycorticosteroids in blood: 17-hydroxycorticosterone in the peripheral circulation. *J. clin. Endocrin.*, 1952, *12*: 519–26.

97 Niemer, W. T., and J. Jimenez-Castellanos. Cortico-thalamic connections in the cat as revealed by "physiological neuronography." *J. comp. Neurol.*, 1950, *93*: 101–24.

98 Olds, J., and P. Milner. Positive reinforcement produced by electrical stimulation of septal area and other regions of rat brain. *J. comp. physiol. Psychol.*, 1954, *47*: 419–27.

99 Papez, J. W. The mammillary peduncle Marchi method. *Anat. Rec.*, 1923, *25*: 146 (Abstract).

100 Papez, J. W. A proposed mechanism of emotion. *Arch. Neurol. Psychiat.*, Chicago, 1937, *38*: 725–43.

101 Poirier, L. J. Anatomical and experimental studies on the temporal pole of the macaque. *J. comp. Neurol.*, 1952, *96*: 209–48.

102 Porter, R. W. Hypothalamic involvement in the pituitary-adreno-cortical response to stress stimuli. *Amer. J. Physiol.*, 1953, *172*: 515–19.

103 Pribram, K. H., and M. Bagshaw. Further analysis of the temporal lobe syndrome utilizing frontotemporal ablations. *J. comp. Neurol.*, 1953, *99*: 347–75.

104 Pribram, K. H., and J. F. Fulton. An experimental critique of the effects of anterior cingulate ablations in monkey. *Brain*, 1954, *77*: 34–44.

105 Pribram, K. H., and L. Kruger. Functions of the "olfactory brain." *Ann. N. Y. Acad. Sci.*, 1954, *58*: 109–38.

106 Pribram, K. H., M. Mishkin, H. E. Rosvold, and S. J. Kaplan. Effects on delayed-response performance of lesions of dorsolateral and ventromedial frontal cortex of baboons. *J. comp. physiol. Psychol.*, 1952, *45*: 565–75.

107 Ranson, S. W. Somnolence caused by hypothalamic lesions in the monkey. *Arch. Neurol. Psychiat.*, Chicago, 1939, *41*: 1–23.

108 Ranson, S. W., and H. W. Magoun. The hypothalamus. *Ergebn. Physiol.*, 1939, *41*: 56–163.

109 Ranström, S. *The hypothalamus and sleep regulation.* Kopenhagen: E. Munksgaard, 1947.

110 Rose, J. E., and C. N. Woolsey. Structure and relations of limbic cortex and anterior thalamic nuclei in rabbit and cat. *J. comp. Neurol.*, 1948, *89*: 279–347.

111 Rosvold, H. E., A. F. Mirsky, and K. H. Pribram. Influence of amygdalectomy on social behavior in monkeys. *J. comp. physiol. Psychol.*, 1954, *47*: 173–78.

112 Rothfield, L., and P. Harman. On the relation of the hippocampal-fornix system to the control of rage responses in cats. *J. comp. Neurol.*, 1954, *101*: 265–82.

113 Rothmann, H. Zusammenfassender Bericht über den Rothmannschen grosshirnlosen Hund nach klinischer und anatomischer Untersuchung. *Z. ges. Neurol. Psychiat.*, 1923, *87*: 247–313.

114 Schaltenbrand, G., and S. Cobb. Clinical and anatomical studies on two cats without neocortex. *Brain*, 1930, *53:* 449–88.

115 Schreiner, L., and A. Kling. Behavioral changes following rhinencephalic injury in cat. *J. Neurophysiol.*, 1953, *16:* 643–59.

116 ———. Effects of castration on hypersexual behavior induced by rhinencephalic injury in cat. *Arch. Neurol. Psychiat., Chicago,* 1954, *72:* 180–86.

117 Schreiner, L., A. Kling, and R. Galambos. Central nervous system lesions and aggressive behavior in cats. *Fed. Proc.*, 1952, *11:* 142 (Abstract).

118 Schreiner, L., D. M. Rioch, C. Pechtel, and J. H. Masserman. Behavioral changes following thalamic injury in cat. *J. Neurophysiol.*, 1953, *16:* 234–46.

119 Sheatz, G. C., V. G. Vernier, and R. Galambos. An EEG study of conditioning. *Amer. J. Physiol.*, 1955, *183:* 660.

120 Sidman, M., J. V. Brady, J. J. Boren, and D. G. Conrad. Reward schedules and behavior maintained by intra-cranial self-stimulation. *Science*, 1955, *122:* 830–31.

121 Skinner, B. F. Some contributions of an experimental analysis of behavior to psychology as a whole. *Amer. Psychologist*, 1953, *8:* 69–78.

122 Smith, G. E. Morphology of the true "limbic lobe," corpus callosum, septum pellucidum and fornix. *J. Anat., Lond.*, 1896, *30:* 185–205.

123 Smith, W. K. The results of ablation of the cingular region of the cerebral cortex. *Fed. Proc.*, 1944, *3:* 42–43.

124 ———. Non-olfactory functions of the pyriform-amygdaloid-hippocampal complex. *Fed. Proc.*, 1950, *9:* 118.

125 Spiegel, E. A., H. R. Miller, and M. J. Oppenheimer. Forebrain and rage reactions. *J. Neurophysiol.*, 1940, *3:* 538–48.

126 Stellar, E. The physiology of motivation. *Psychol. Rev.*, 1954, *61:* 5–22.

127 Stone, C. P. Wildness and savageness in rats of different strains. In K. Lashley (Ed.), *Studies in the dynamics of behavior.* Chicago: Univer. Chicago Press, 1932, 3–55.

128 Thompson, A. F., and A. E. Walker. Behavioral alterations following lesions of the medial surface of the temporal lobe. *Arch. Neurol. Psychiat., Chicago,* 1951, *65:* 251–52.

129 Tryon, R. C., C. M. Tryon, and G. Kuznets. Studies in individual differences in maze ability. X. Ratings and other measures of initial emotional responses of rats to novel inanimate objects. *J. comp. Psychol.* 1941, *32:* 447–73.

130 Ule, G. Uber das Ammonshorn. *Fortschr. Neur. Psychiat.*, 1954, *22:* 510–30.

131 Verney, E. B. The antidiuretic hormone and the factors which determine its release. *Proc. roy. Soc., Ser. B.*, 1947, *135:* 25–106.

132 Vogt, O. Sur un faisceau septo-thalmaigue. *C. R. Soc. Biol., Paris*, 1898, *50:* 206–7.

133 Walker, A. E., A. F. Thomson, and J. D. McQueen. Behavior and the temporal rhinencephalon in the monkey. *Johns Hopk. Hosp. Bull.*, 1953, *93:* 65–93.

134 Ward, A. A., Jr. The cingular gyrus: Area 24. *J. Neurophysiol.*, 1948, *11:* 13–23.

135 Weiskrantz, L. Behavioral changes associated with ablation of the amygdala. *Amer. Psychologist,* 1953, *8:* 452 (Abstract).

136 Weiskrantz, L., and K. H. Pribram. Comparison of the effects of resections of rhinencephalic with those of lateral cortex on conditioned avoidance of monkeys. *J. comp. physiol. Psychol.,* 1956, *49:* 4, 381–91.

137 Wheatley, M. D. The hypothalamus and affective behavior in cats: A study of the effects of experimental lesions, with anatomic correlations. *Arch. Neurol. Psychiat., Chicago,* 1944, *52:* 296–316.

138 Whitlock, D. G., and W. J. H. Nauta. Subcortical projections from the temporal neocortex in Macaca mulatta *J. comp. Neurol.,* 1956, *106:* 183–212.

139 Woodworth, R. S., and C. S. Sherrington. A pseudoaffective reflex and its spinal path. *J. Physiol.,* 1904, *31:* 234–43.

James Olds

Adaptive Functions of Paleocortical and Related Structures

By adaptive behavior we mean some change which makes the organism more fitted for survival in a given environment. The change may be a rigidly determined, automatic response to a need, as when energy demands are met by increase in blood pressure, or oxygen demands by increase in respiratory movement. The change may, however, be less rigid, as when the demands of a new environment are met by alteration in behavior repertory. In both cases the main causal antecedent of the change is a motivational requirement, and the outcome is a better adjustment of the animal to its environment.

We have some tendency to think of the automatic precautionary measures as autonomic, and to think of the learned behaviors as somatic or skeletal. The latter are sometimes called "voluntary," which means mainly, I believe, that they tend to be selected on the basis of the law of effect—reward and punishment. The autonomic-somatic distinction does not hold up under careful scrutiny, for often autonomic and central nervous system control are inextricably intermeshed, as in breathing, where somatic muscles and voluntary control are effective in an essentially vegetative and involuntary process. But it is perhaps possible to think in terms of a rigidity continuum for adaptive behavior and to use the term "autonomic behavior" to specify roughly the rigid (unlearned) end of the continuum.

At the other extreme we might best use the term "instrumental behavior," referring by this to behavior which survives in the repertory on the basis of its effect rather than merely on the basis of eliciting conditions.

The problem of instrumental behavior itself, however, is graded all the way from the seeming automatic stamping-in of correct responses, which occurs in a Skinner box, to the performance of long response sequences based on memory recordings of environments seen only once.

The present paper is to analyze mainly electrophysiological studies of rhinencephalic and related structures with a view to answering the following questions: (1) Is there evidence that the rhinencephalon is involved in the elicitation of automatic adaptive processes: autonomic behaviors? (2) Is there evidence that the rhinencephalon affects the selection of instrumental behaviors? (3) Is there evidence that the rhinencephalon affects the process of environmental recording or memory which is the prerequisite of complex learned adaptation?

While this analysis will be based mainly on stimulation studies, ablation work not already handled in the paper presented by Joseph Brady at this Symposium will be mentioned when it is particularly relevant.

In answering these questions, the author has the good fortune of two extremely recent, clear, and comprehensive reviews of the literature involved. These are the work of Pribram and Kruger (43) and of Gloor (12). Two other recent works of Gloor will also be referred to liberally, one providing new electrographic data on the integration of the structures under consideration (10, 11), and the other providing in English a summary review of the classical work of Hess (15) on electrical stimulation of the hypothalamus in cats (9). As it would be impossible to better the work of these recent reviewers at so early a date, the present paper is free to discuss mainly the findings and the relations among these that are brought to attention by the new data that will make up the main body of this paper.

ELECTROGRAPHIC ANATOMY

Pribram and Kruger (43) have defined three systems within the rhinencephalic formations which concern us.

The major interrelationships among the three systems may be described as follows: Beginning at the olfactory bulb, fibers can be traced to a primary olfactory system consisting of olfactory tubercle, olfactory trigone, the prepyriform cortex, and the corticomedial nucleus of the amygdaloid complex. The primary system of each hemisphere is connected to that of the opposite hemisphere by the rostral fibers of the anterior commissure. This system is connected with the subcallosal and frontotemporal cortex and through the medial and lateral striae with the septal nuclei, nuclei of the diagonal band, and the basolateral part of the amygdaloid complex. These structures make up the second system interconnected through the anterior commissure and *stria terminalis*. As noted, some comparative studies and electrographic data suggest that parts of the striatum might profitably be included in this system. Efferents from the septal nuclei and amygdaloid complex reach the epithalamus and anterior hypothalamus; in turn, the latter connects with the mid-line and intralaminar nuclei of the dorsal thalamus. These nuclei apparently project to the juxtallocortex. Ammon's formation receives fibers from the cingulate, restrosplenial, and entorhinal part of this cortex, thus making up the third system. This system, in addition to the circuit involving *anterior* hypothalamus via the fornix and the septal nuclei, is also related to the *posterior* hypothalamus (mammillary bodies) via the fornix. The mammillothalamic tract, and the projections from the anterior thalamic nuclei to the cingulate juxtallocortex, and the fibers to Ammon's formation from the cingulate cortex complete the circuit.

Using this as the definition of the anatomical systems to be discussed, the present paper will concentrate mainly on the second system. Under this heading will be grouped material on the amygdaloid complex, the septal-subcallosal region, the basomedial boundary between tel- and diencephalon, the anterior and ventromedial hypothalamus, and extensions of this system into the midbrain.

Of secondary concern will be the third system. Under this heading material on the cingulate cortex, the hippocampus, the posterior hypothalamus, and the anterior thalamus will be brought together.

Recent electrographic work by Gloor (10, 11) based on amygdaloid stimulation discloses a projection field for the amygdala which encompasses all the major areas which will be discussed under the second-system heading.

The following structures make up the amygdaloid projection field: (a) the septum and the base of the head of the caudate nucleus, (b) the preoptic area, (c) the hypothalamus, especially the ventromedial nucleus, (d) the subthalamus, (e) the entopeduncular nucleus, (f) some nuclei of the diffuse projection system of the thalamus, (g) certain lateral parts of the midbrain reticular formation at about the level of the red nucleus. In the cortex, projections appear to go to the neocortex of the anterior temporal and insular region; and also there appear to be multisynaptic chains via paleocortex of the pyriform lobe to the hippocampus (Ammon's formation), the latter giving a very large response to amygdaloid stimulation, but a response with extremely long latency.

The subcortical areas are divided by Gloor into primary and secondary projection fields on the basis of latency. The primary amygdaloid field involves the lower septal area, the basal part of the "telencephalon-medium" and the adjacent rostrobasal pole of the diencephalon. From here, it appears that responses are relayed to the remainder of the projection area—the secondary field—through short multisynaptic neuronal links. At the ventromedial nucleus of the hypothalamus, there is an extremely large response to basolateral amygdaloid stimulation; however, the latency is too long to suggest monosynaptic transmission. Finally, there is a part of the lateral reticular formation in the tegmentum which gives short-latency responses suggesting some monosynaptic pathway from the amygdala which bypasses the hypothalamus. The corticomedial nucleus of the amygdala has approximately the same projection as the basolateral except that the former projects a little more into the posterior hypothalamus but apparently does not have the tegmental projections in the lateral reticular formation.

Discussing the characteristics of the responses involved, Gloor has the following comments: the way the amygdala acts on its projection field is not predetermined and rigid. The rate of firing will condition the mode of transmission of impulses. Certain synapses act as barriers under some conditions of excitability and may be opened up under others. Particularly interesting is the fact that repeated pulses often cause recruitment of responses in the hippocampus but occlusion of responses in the ventromedial hypothalamus. However, the same repeated pulses seem to cause potentiation in both areas.

AUTONOMIC AND RELATED SOMATIC EFFECTS

For the telencephalic portions of the limbic system, the following generalizations about autonomic function are formulated by Gloor (12) on the basis of a wide variety of data. The generalizations apply mainly to structures of the second system, except in cases where they are specifically broadened to include structures of the third system.

1. Respiration is ordinarily inhibited by electrical stimulation in the amygdala, the septal area, and the postorbital region when experiments are performed under anesthesia. In the anterior cingulate, there is some evidence that the posterior part produces acceleration of breathing, but the more anterior part, inhibition. Finally, one study (16) from Hess's laboratory suggests that in *unanesthetized* animals the orbital and cingulate gyri give accleration; but inhibition is reported in the same study for anesthetized animals (4, 7, 16, 17, 18, 19, 20, 22, 25, 26, 32, 33, 34, 41, 45, 46, 47, 48, 49, 50).

2. Blood pressure can be either raised or lowered by stimulation in these areas. Also, sometimes the same point of stimulation will do both at different times. No topological difference is found between points producing rise and those producing fall. The level of anesthesia seems important: Sometimes a rise is produced under light anesthesia, a decline under deeper anesthesia. Reversals also occur on the basis of the frequency or form of the stimulus (4, 7, 20, 27, 45, 46, 47, 48, 50).

3. Activity in the stomach can be started or stopped by stimulating various points (2, 5, 20, 27). Kaada (20) showed that the same point might start activity in the nonactive stomach, and stop activity in the active stomach.

4. As for pupillary dilatation and contraction, dilatation is the ordinary response from amygdaloid stimulation. But the anterior limbic cortex and the area around the genu of the corpus callosum produce contraction (7, 17, 18, 20, 28, 45, 47, 50).

5. Defecation, micturition, activation of uterine tonus and contraction, piloerection, and salivation have also been shown to ensue on stimulation of various limbic points (7, 14, 20, 30, 32, 47, 50).

6. Koikegami, Yamada, and Usui (32) have shown that amygdaloid stimulation

produces ovulation in the female rabbit. The response is almost invariable during estrus, and also may often be obtained in the absence of estrus.

7. Heath (13) mentions some evidence suggesting the release of ACTH from the pituitary on stimulation of the septum.

The following effects on related somatic movements are shown in the same material reviewed by Gloor (12).

1. Inhibition of spontaneous movement is the rule from most parts of the second limbic system. In lightly anesthetized preparations, this is combined with inhibition of muscle tone and inhibition of the motor components of electrically produced seizures (20).

2. In unanesthetized animals with implanted electrodes, there is again arrest of spontaneous movement, but here it goes together with *increase* in muscle tone (7).

3. In anesthetized animals, the effects of stimulation on cortically induced and reflex movements is different from the effect indicated above on spontaneous movement. For the reflex and cortically induced movements, there is facilitation, or inhibition, or facilitation reversing to inhibition. Possibly facilitation is the more frequent response. However, there is topological overlap of the three types of response; and facilitation reversing to inhibition, or inhibition alone, predominates in what Kaada (20) considers to be the primary respiratory-inhibitory centers in the subcallosal and orbitotemporal regions.

4. Specific overt responses usually involving masticatory and facial movements are elicited mainly from the orbitotemporal region including the amygdala (7, 20, 34).

5. Vocalization is obtained in some monkeys from the anterior cingulate and the anterior hippocampal gyrus (20, 47).

6. Complex behaviors are reported in unanesthetized animals from electrical stimulation mainly in the second limbic system. The general pattern is (*a*) attentive behavior giving way to (*b*) anxiety and fear, or (*c*) rage, with rising intensity of stimulation (7, 20, 21, 22, 34).

It may be wise to indicate again that except for places where specific mention was made of the hippocampus and posterior cingulate cortex, the autonomic and behavioral effects reported above are largely confined to the structures of the second limbic system, i.e., the septal-amygdaloid system. From the hippocampus, stimulation has been reported by some (1) to produce no overt effects even to the extent of leaving unaffected normal reactivity to environmental stimulation. Others have reported merely an attentive pose to ensue on hippocampal stimulation (21).

In regard to the hypothalamus, the classical chronic-stimulation work of Hess (15) as reviewed by Gloor (9) forms the basis for the following discussion. Hess divides hypothalamic responses into two types. "Ergotropic" ones are of a sympathetic nature but include somatic behaviors. They are considered to enable muscular effort as in defense, attack, or flight. Among them are pupillary dilatation, rise in blood pressure, increase in pulse rate, activation of respiration, increase in motor excitability, and general excitement of the animal.

These are contrasted with "trophotropic" activities of a parasympathetic type. The latter release tension by diminishing the capacity of the organism to produce physical effort. They provide rest and restitution after strain. They include slowing of respiration, drop in blood pressure, micturition and defecation, salivation, pupillary contraction, and loss of muscular tone.

By electrical stimulation in chronic preparations, Hess has produced ergotropic responses in a broad strip of posterior sub- and hypothalamus and anterior midbrain. Generally it is an area above the mammillary bodies. In lateral sections, however, it shoots forward in a narrow strip along, and parallel to, the fornix, almost to the preoptic area. The mammillary bodies themselves appear to be unresponsive. All the ergotropic responses tend to go together so that a point which gives one of these effects ordinarily produces all of them.

Trophotropic or parasympathetic effects are dispersed over the septum, the preoptic area, and all the parts of the sub- and hypothalamus anterior to the ergotropic region. They do not show as much tendency to go together as is seen in the ergotropic responses. Micturition, defecation, slowing of respiration, and decline in blood pressure are seen on stimulation of parts of the septal area and all through the anterior hypothalamus back almost as far as the ventromedial nucleus, except for the narrow area around the fornix, which gives sympathetic responses (or mixed sympathetic and parasympathetic). The lateral part of this anterior hypothalamic field also produces the other trophotropic responses, salivation, pupillary constriction, and loss of muscular tone.

The latter response, called "adynamia" by Hess, involves the animal's sinking down like an inert mass, without any of the normal adjustments involved in lying down. The eyes are left open, and the state is quite different from "sleep," which Hess seems to produce by stimulating the region of the thalamic intralaminar nuclei.

Finally, an area producing only pupillary contraction and arrest of breathing extends up into the lower and anterior quarter of the thalamus.

The only one of the trophotropic effects found over the whole anterior region seems to be arrest of breathing, which occurs, as we have said, on stimulation of septum, all parts of the anterior hypothalamus and preoptic area, and in the lower front quarter of the thalamus.

There are four points to be emphasized from these studies of the hypo-thalamus: (*a*) the more or less sharp division of anterior and posterior hypothalamus into parasympathetic and sympathetic sections, respectively; (*b*) the tendency of sympathetic effects to extend forward into parasympathetic territory along the fornix; (*c*) the tendency for sympathetic effects to go together whereas the parasympathetic ones function independently (*d*) the absence of active points in the mammillary bodies.

A preliminary formulation based on the electrographic anatomy and the functional mapping reviewed in the preceding sections is that the amygdala, the septal area, the posterior part of the mediobasal forebrain, and related cortical regions form one system connected mainly to the non-mammillary portions of the hypothalamus with a focal point at the ventro-medial nucleus and projecting backward up over the mammillary bodies to a higher position in the lateral portions of the tegmental reticular substance above the red nucleus.

This system approximates the second system of Pribram and Kruger (43). It is rich in autonomic effects and seems to be shaded in the parasympathetic direction, although there is much overlap with sympathetic effects, particularly at the cortical level. Also, it produces both facilitation and inhibition of behavior; again it seems shaded in the inhibitory direction so far as spontaneous movement is concerned.

On the other hand, the hippocampus and the cingulate cortex together with the mammillary bodies and some other tegmental reticular areas form a different system. As far as this system is concerned, we are at a loss for definitive data on adaptive effects, although there is electrographic evidence that the hypothalamic and tegmental portions of this system are implicated in diffuse activation of the whole cortex (35). Also ablation work (31) indicates these same subcortical elements are prerequisites to the waking conscious state.

As indicated, it appears that the amygdala projects primarily to the parasympathetic regions of the hypothalamus and the tegmentum. No similar paleocortical projections have been demonstrated to my knowledge to the sympathetic fields of the hypothalamus. The cingulate hippo-campal system seems to project mainly to the mammillary bodies, which are, so far as I can see, unresponsive autonomically on the basis of the Hess data. Thus, there are two intriguing puzzles: first, the curious lack of evidence on effects of stimulating the hippocampal-mammillary system; and second, the absence of evidence for a strong paleocortical afferent to the sympathetic fields of the hypothalamus. In my mind these two puzzles are connected with the almost complete absence of points which produce punishment or negative reinforcement upon electrical stimulation of paleocortical structures. But this takes us to the problem of reinforcement and the next section.

REWARDING EFFECTS

We now turn to self-stimulation studies which have led to the discovery of primary-rewarding effects produced by electrical stimulation of limbic structures of the rat brain (36, 38).

In these studies, electrical stimulation of the brain is carried out by means of chronically implanted electrodes which do not interefere with the health or free behavior of subjects to any appreciable extent.

The electrode is built like a floor lamp, with the two wires which penetrate the brain coming out of the base, and the shaft penetrating the skin. Base and shaft are one solid piece of plastic. Wires are rigidly fixed in the plastic except for their downward extension, which penetrates the brain. The base is screwed to the skull with jewelers' screws. There are thus no movable wires to break under the skin; in fact, there are no movable wires at all. And the only skills required to implant are those of drilling holes and inserting screws. The operation takes about 20 to 30 min., and this together with large-scale production of electrodes permits a major mapping enterprise.

In self-stimulation studies, subjects are tested in Skinner boxes which deliver alternating current to the brain so long as a lever is depressed. The current is delivered over a loose lead, suspended from the ceiling, which connects the stimulator to the rat's electrode.

The testing apparatus consists of a large-levered Skinner box 11 in. long, 5 in. wide, and 12 in. high. The top is open to allow passage for the stimulating lead. The lever actuates a microswitch in the stimulating circuit so that when it is depressed, the rat receives electrical stimulation. The current is obtained from the 60-cycle power line through a step-down transformer and is adjusted between 0 and 10 v. r.m.s. by means of a variable potentiometer. The stimulation may continue as long as the lever is pressed, but ordinarily a time-delay switch is used which cuts the current off after a predetermined interval if the rat continues to hold the lever down. To get more stimulation, the rat must release the lever and press again. Responses are recorded automatically on paper strip.

The scores to be used in the following discussion denote the percentage of time the animal spends responding regularly during acquisition, that is, while the responses are reinforced with electrical stimulation. For computing the score, periods of 30 sec. or longer without a response are counted as periods of "no responding." The rest of the time is counted as "response time." Response time was divided by total acquisition time to get the percentage score.

With no reinforcement at all, rats produce scores ranging from 4 to 10 per cent. Therefore, when a rat spends 20 per cent or more of its time bar-pressing for electrical stimulation, this is well above the operant level, and we may speak of the point of stimulation in the brain as a rewarding placement. Scores of 0 and 1 per cent are definitely below the operant level, and we may speak of avoidance or negative reinforcement.

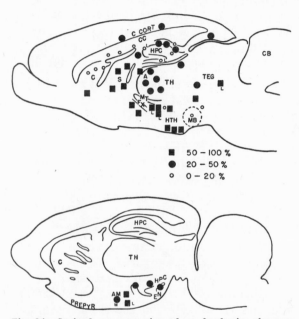

Fig. 86.—Sagittal reconstruction of rat forebrain; the upper is near the mid-line; the lower is 2 to 3 mm. more lateral. Electrode placements are projected on these as squares, filled circles, and open circles. The letter *L* or *M* near a point indicates that the point in question is more than a millimeter lateral or medial to the plane indicated. The percentage score ascribed to a point indicates that electrical stimulation applied to the point produced continuous bar-pressing for the indicated percentage of a 6-hr. test period. Low-scoring placements of 0 to 20 per cent are indicated only for limbic or neighboring structures. All the high-scoring placements uncovered by a random exploration of the brain are shown.

On Figure 86, black squares indicate places in the brain where electrical stimulation produced very high response scores (50 to 100 per cent). Black circles indicate places where moderately high scores were produced (20 to 50 per cent). Open circles indicate some of the places where low scores were produced (0 to 12 per cent). For clarity, many of the low scores falling outside the limbic system have been omitted.

I will review first the very high scores produced in the second system outlined by Pribram and Kruger (43). These are the black squares.

Septal Area

1. High scores are first found anterior to the septal area in the medial cortex and olfactory tract. These are in the first limbic system. They tend to fall between 60 and 70 per cent; they are somewhat below the 80 and 90 per cent scores found generally in the second limbic system. Maze and runway data to be discussed later bear out the assertion that these anterior placements are somewhat less reinforcing than scores farther back.

2. In the middle septal area, very high scores are the rule in both dorsal and ventral portions, although the maze data to be discussed make it appear that positive reinforcement from ventrally placed electrodes (around the Islands of Calleja) surpasses that from dorsal ones.

3. Still farther back in the septal area, the dorsal part shades into the anterior hippocampal commissure, while the ventral part blends with the preoptic area of the hypothalamus. At this point the dorsal scores decline sharply to medium and low percentages. The basal scores, however, do not decline.

Amygdaloid Complex

One electrode in the basolateral area gives a very high score (82 per cent). One anterior to it in the corticomedial region gives a medium score (47 per cent). In between and slightly above these two, again in the basolateral portion, is another high score (65 per cent). Higher, intersecting the white matter, is another medium score (23 per cent). Farther back, between the hippocampus and entorhinal cortex, there is a medium score of 41 per cent.

As the two highest scores are in or near the basolateral region, it appears to be the second-system portion of the amygdaloid complex that gives the highest scores. In the first system (corticomedial region) and third system (hippocampal and entorhinal points) scores decline. It will be remembered that scores declined also at the hippocampal boundaries of the septal region.

Hypothalamus

In the extreme anterior there are two electrodes which give high scores. The more ventral of the two produced a score of 81 per cent; dorsomedial to it, in or just below the fornix, there is a score of 71.

Farther back at the level of the front end of the ventromedial nucleus, two lateral electrodes score 75 and 64. An electrode near the reuniens scores 62. But an electrode near the mammillothalamic tract above the fornix has a score of 1 (which denotes avoidance of the stimulus). A neighboring electrode, again very near the mammillothalamic tract, scores 71 per cent. This reversal by two neighboring electrodes is interesting because it occurs in the part of the hypothalamus where Hess has interlocking sympathetic and parasympathetic fields.

A deep electrode in the anterolateral part of the ventromedial nucleus scores 70 per cent. And two electrodes deep in the heart of the ventromedial nucleus give very high scores (81 and 88 per cent). These are just in front of the mammillary body and just barely dorsolateral to the arcuate.

Back at the mammillary level, the medial mammillary nucleus gives a score of 4 per cent. But up above the mammillary body is a score of 64 per cent; and still higher in or near the habenulo-interpeduncular tract there is a score of 28.

Finally, in the supramammillary decussation there is a score of 9 per cent (neutrality), but in the lateral reticular formation above the red nucleus there is a score of 77 per cent.

Thus, it seems that in the anterior hypothalamus high scores are numerous. High scores in ventral regions continue to the ventromedial nucleus, where scores are consistently high. Then the path of the high scores rises abruptly over the mammillary bodies to a position in the mesial tegmentum above the red nucleus.

In the pattern of high scores there appears an interesting relationship to the data of Hess. First, if we take the whole plot of Hess's trophotropic and ergotropic points, we find it starts high in the septum, dips down into the hypothalamus, and rises sharply in front of the mammillary bodies to the mesial tegmentum. Our high scores behave in much the same way.

Second, there is some tendency for the best scores to correspond to the anterior hypothalamic trophotropic field of Hess. The chief exceptions to this rule are two rewarding medial placements above the mammillary bodies. However, Hess shows a thin band of micturition and defecation (trophotropic) points similarly placed within the ergotropic field. Also, high in the mesial tegmentum, Hess has similar points perhaps corresponding to the area of the high-scoring electrode above the red nucleus.

Third, the only place where seemingly adjacent electrodes gave conflicting evidence between the fornix and the mammillothalamic tract, Hess shows overlapping of the parasympathetic and sympathetic fields.

I should point out in passing that I would not, on the basis of my present data, feel secure in pressing this correlation of rewarding placements with parasympathetically active points. It is one of those things that is no sooner said than proved wrong.

In connection with Gloor's subcortical amygdaloid projection field, there is again a tempting correlation. First, the highest scores are in the base of the septum and the adjoining preoptic region which forms the primary amygdaloid projection field. Second, high scores again appear in the strong point of his secondary field, the ventromedial nucleus of the hypothalamus. Third, and finally, the high score in the tegmentum may well correspond to the area of short-latency tegmental responses.

We take up next the lower but still rewarding placements in the third limbic system. This includes mainly hippocampus, cingulate cortex, mammillary bodies, and the anterior nucleus of the thalamus. These scores are the black circles in Figure 86.

Cingulate Cortex

There are three electrodes, one above the septal area, one above the thalamus, and one above the superior colliculus. The first two give scores of about 36 per cent: and the one above the colliculus scores 24 per cent.

Hippocampus

We may start in the anterior hippocampal commissure, which is contiguous with the septal area. An extremely lateral electrode here scores 14 per cent. Next, two electrodes score 39 and 49 per cent, both in what appears to be the same lobe of the anterior hippocampus. At the same level, an electrode in the fimbria gives a score of 1 per cent; this is the sole instance of negative reinforcement in or near paleocortical structures. At the next level, three electrodes score 11, 37, and 13; the electrode scoring 37 appears to be in the same lobe as the scores of 39 and 49 previously mentioned. An electrode which apparently pierces through the hippocampus into the lateral geniculate produces a score of 34 per cent; this is the only one of some 30 to 40 electrodes clearly outside the limbic system to give a positive score. This inclines one to suppose that there is current leaking in the hippocampus. Finally, an electrode back near the junction with entorhinal cortex scores 32 per cent. We have already mentioned an electrode between entorhinal cortex and hippocampus which produces a score of 41.

It appears on the basis of this material that the hippocampus has an extreme range of scores. At one extreme, four electrodes in the hippocampus produce scores of 30 per cent or more, which are high above the operant level and definitely indicative of reward. In between are three electrodes at very close to operant level. At the other extreme is one electrode in the fimbria which produces negative reinforcement—responding below the operant level. The neutral and negative-reinforcement scores appear to fall in the lateral and borderline parts of the anteromedial part of the hippocampus. However, there is a mesial lobe of the anterior part which seems to give positive reinforcement quite consistently. (The anteromedial portion of the rat hippocampus is not homologous to the anterior hippocampus of the temporal lobe in primates.)

Anterior Thalamus

There are four electrodes with scores of 34, 37, 45, and 65 per cent. It appears that the smaller scores in this group are in the more ventromedial parts of the anterior group. The 45 and 65 per cent scores are dorsal, just below the ventricle. Here we may also mention an electrode in or near the *stria terminalis* scoring 23 per cent, and one just below the ventral thalamic nucleus (near the mammillothalamic tract) scoring 22 per cent.

Fornix and Mammillary Body

We have already mentioned that scores around the fornix and mammillothalamic tract have great variability; and the only score in the mammillary body indicates neutrality (4 per cent).

In summary of the third-system scores: The ordinary score in the third system falls between 20 and 50 per cent. However, there are two negative scores (that is, scores denoting negative reinforcement), and about four neutral scores which seem attributable mainly to structures and fibers around the anterior border regions of the hippocampus, and to the fornix and the mammillary bodies.

Discussion of Placements

There are consistently high scores obtained from all electrodes definitely affecting structures designated by Pribram and Kruger (43) as members of the second system. These structures have been shown by Gloor (10) to project mainly to parasympathetic (anterior) portions of the hypothalamus and to parts of the anterior tegmentum. In harmony with these data we note a tendency for our high scores to follow through the hypothalamus and tegmentum projection field of the second system.

But there are less consistent middle-range positive reinforcement scores obtained from electrodes in structures designated by Pribram and Kruger as members of the third system. The general rule for the third system is scores of from 20 to 50 per cent, which is high above the operant level. But there are several operant-level (neutral) scores eminating from this system.

Finally, there are two scores indicative of negative reinforcement which seem to be attributable to fibers connecting third-system structures.

We may point out again that so far as the paleocortex proper is concerned, there is almost a complete absence of points producing negative reinforcement; and generally, there are suprisingly few points of negative reinforcement in the hypothalamus. Electrodes in the medial lemniscus and the bordering *zona incerta* have produced negative reinforcement quite consistently. But still, it is surprising that there are no negative points in the limbic system, which is supposed by many to control fight and flight responses. This puzzle, as we said earlier, seems somehow related to the fact that the third system has not been found to project to autonomically active areas of the hypothalamus. Rather, it projects to the mammillary bodies, which are quite unreactive according to Hess. One almost has the feeling that a change in the parameters or type of stimulation might produce both negative reinforcement and projection to the sympathetic fields; but this is pure speculation.

High positive reinforcement scores seem to be correlated at cortical and subcortical levels mainly with inhibition of respiration and inhibition of spontaneous movement. However, from the same points, there is both facilitation and inhibition of cortically induced and spinal reflexes when the animal is under anesthesia; facilitation seems to predominate. As for autonomic responses other than respiration, there is a correlation of high scores with structures which yield both parasympathetic and sympathetic responses; and we note the possibility that there is parasympathetic dominance in the highly rewarding areas, particularly at the hypothalamic level. In passing, it should be indicated that these so-called correlations are cross-species. Most of the autonomic work has been done on cats, whereas our work is done on rats.

Effects on Maze Learning

Thus far we have shown that paleocortical and related structures are involved on the one hand in the elicitation of autonomic adaptive processes and on the other in the selection of discrete instrumental responses when electrical stimulation is used as reinforcement in the Skinner box.

So long as our only reported measure of the reinforcing effect is Skinner-box responding, the possibility remains that stimulation has some special effect on bar-pressing without having the general effect of positive reinforcement.

A particularly important question in this connection has to do with the "obsessive" nature of certain seeming reward phenomena. If this is an obsession, the implication is that the animal would not show day-to-day improvement in long-run behavior chains aimed at this reward.

If we show that different and more complex behavior chains are reinforced as though by food, then we have validation for the notion that this is truly reinforcement in the traditional sense. The experiments to be reported now were undertaken to test systematically for learning curves generated in a runway and a maze, using electrical stimulation in the basomedial septal region as the reinforcing stimulus. They will serve to make a transition between the problem of simple instrumental learning and the more complex problem of longer-term memory.

Early experiments indicated that septal animals with electrodes high in the septal area could not learn a maze if this involved running out of a narrow starting alley, across a wide open field, and into a goal box. Running first for food under these conditions, the animal performs satisfactorily. Running later for electrical stimulation, it no longer runs satisfactorily, but seems to be extinguishing. Further exploratory work led to two important changes: (*a*) electrodes were implanted progressively lower in the septal region, until present placements in maze experiments are practically at the base of the brain; (*b*) maze and runway experiments were designed which would eliminate the crossing of an open field.

These two changes taken together have produced excellent learning curves. However, it is still a problem for further experimental analysis to show how much of the variance in maze and runway performance is taken care of by the kind of maze and how much by the placement of the electrode within and below the septal area.

All told, 22 animals have been run in maze and runway after modification of the maze and shift to deeper electrode placements. I shall not review all of these as the data will be available elsewhere (37). I will, however, take up a group of 8 experimental animals run for stimulation and seven operated controls run for food to show how stimulation and food compare in reinforcing maze and runway performance. The over-all procedure takes the following course. On the first day, the electrode is implanted and a 24-hr. feeding schedule is started at the same time. All running is done under 18 to 24 hr. of food deprivation. Three days are allowed for recovery. Then on sucessive days come (*a*) Skinner-box tests, (*b*) 15 pre-training trials from an open field into a goal box for stimulation, (*c*) 15 similar trials in a 9-ft. square runway, (*d*) three days of 15 trials each running a more complicated maze for stimulation, (*e*) 15 trials of extinction in the maze. Controls follow the same sequence, but they are run for food instead of stimulation. After the experiment, brains are sectioned and stained to determine the locus of the point of stimulation in the brain.

Electrical stimulation was carried out again with 60-cycle alternating current; in all cases the rat administered it to itself by depressing a lever. The voltage, the stimulus duration, and the number of rewards were varied by the experimenter on successive runs if the behavior appeared to be extinguishing. The attempt was to keep these parameters at a level to sustain maximum performance.

All eight animals in the stimulation group produced learning curves in both runway and maze. Because all animals showed extreme improvement, there is no need to test the significance of the result. The mean drop in time to traverse the runway was from 28 to 2.5 sec. In the maze it was from 102 to 7.3 sec. During extinction, running time in the maze slowed from a mean of 12 to a mean of 41 sec. in 15 trials.

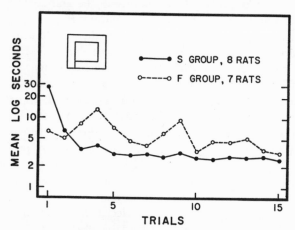

Fig. 87.—Runway results. Log plot with seconds along the ordinate and trials along the abscissa showing improvement in running time for group reinforced by food (dotted line) and for group reinforced by electrical stimulation in basomedial forebrain (solid line).

Figure 87 gives the results obtained from the 15 trials in the runway for stimulation and food groups. Time is measured from crossing a start line to crossing a finish line. Mean scores for the stimulation group are given in the heavy black line; means for the food group, in the dotted line. The time is plotted on a log scale so that the difference between the curves can be clearly seen. Mean running time is plotted for each trial. The stimulation group is ahead of the food group at all points after the third trial. If we define the asymptote for each rat as the score achieved or bettered four times, we may test the difference between the two asymptotes. The mean of the asymptotes for the stimulation group is 2.4 sec.; the mean for the food group is 3.2 sec. This difference is not quite significant, the t being 2.0 as against 2.16 required for a two-tailed test. However, the data are certainly consistent with the theorem that the stimulation group is not worse than the food group. This indicates that stimulation is a strong reinforcement in the runway, for here we have two groups of animals both running under 18 to 24 hr. of food deprivation. One group is appropriately rewarded with food. The other is rewarded only by electrical stimulation in the basomedial septal region of the brain. The stimulation group gives a better average performance than the food group.

The maze results are shown in Figure 88. Here the food group learns more rapidly than the stimulation group. If we use five good runs of 10 sec. or faster as a criterion of learning, the stimulation group takes an average of 34 trials to learn the maze, the food group takes an average of only 18 trials. This difference also misses significance by a narrow margin; the t is 2.14 as against 2.16 required.

But now we have suggestive evidence indicating first that the stimula-

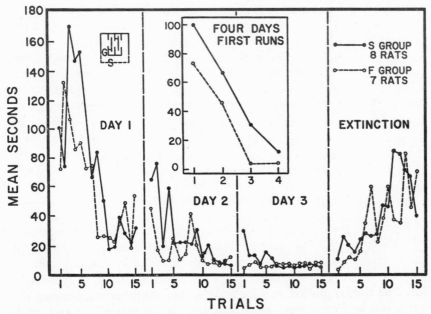

Fig. 88.—Maze results. Graph with seconds along the ordinate and trials along the abscissa showing improvement in running time for three days in maze, and decrement in performance during one day of extinction.

tion group is better than the food group in runway performance, whereas the food group betters the stimulation group in maze learning.

If we measure maze asymptotes defined again as the score achieved or bettered four times, the food group still has a slight edge on the stimulation group. The mean of the food-group asymptotes is 5.3 sec. The mean of the stimulation-group asymptotes is 5.6 sec. This difference is so small as to be considered identity.

Finally, the question arises whether or not the improvement shown by the stimulation group is maintained from day to day. This pertains to the obsessive or nonobsessive nature of the responding involved. If we can show (*a*) that long-run purposive behavior (of maze type) is undertaken in pursuit of electrical stimulation, and (*b*) that the tendency to pursue it survives and increases from day to day, then we will have some indication that this is not mere, momentary, obsessive behavior but, rather, behavior of a more genuinely purposive type.

The insert in Figure 88 shows that the improvement clearly is maintained from day to day. Mean running scores for the first run of the day on four successive days are given for both stimulation and food groups. The stimulation group improves from about 100 sec. for the first run of the first day to 12 sec. on the first run of the fourth day. All animals show the improvement, so no statistical test of the decline is necessary. The food group improves from about 73 sec. on the first day to about 5 sec. on the fourth day. There is some indication that improvement in food scores has leveled off whereas the stimulation group is still improving.

In passing I may indicate that there is always an overnight decrement in stimulation-group performance but an overnight improvement in the food group. This would seem to indicate some memory or motivational deficit prior to the first reward in the stimulation group; however, the extreme day-to-day first-run improvement indicated above makes it clear that retention far outweighs the deficit. It should also be mentioned that the picture is roughly the same if we plot errors instead of running time (37).

Altogether, 22 rats have been run for both food and stimulation under a regimen similar to that described above. Of these, 15 rats had the whole cycle of pretraining, runway, and maze for stimulation first and food second. Seven rats had the cycle for food first and stimulation second. The findings for the whole group may be summarized as follows: In the runway, 15 rats had better asymptotes for stimulation than food; there was 1 tie; 6 rats had better asymptotes for food. In the maze, 9 rats had better asymptotes for stimulation; there were 4 ties; 8 rats had better asymptotes for food; 1 rat missed this test.

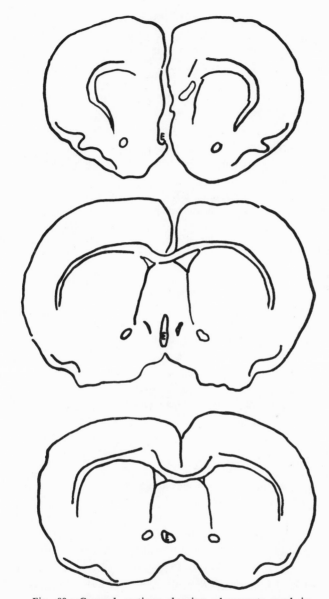

Fig. 89.—Coronal sections showing placements used in runway and maze experiments. The top section shows the anterior boundary of the region studies; the bottom section shows the posterior boundary. *E* marks the lower tip of the electrode track, which is taken to be the point of stimulation. On the middle section, the two dark patches which flank the electrode track are the Islands of Calleja.

As for the location of the electrodes, Figure 89 shows three brain sections with electrodes marked *E*. The sections are *A*, anterior; *M*, middle; and *P*, posterior, in the region of the brain implicated in the present study. If we divide all 22 animals into three groups on the basis of electrode placement in the anterior, middle, or posterior part of the basomedial septal region, we find that the middle group (where the Islands of Calleja are high and pronounced) scores higher than the anterior and posterior group on all counts, scoring consistently better for stimulation than for food in maze and runway tests, and producing Skinner-box scores of 90 per cent or higher. The posterior group was not quite this good, but it did almost as well.

Three of the 22 rats had electrodes in the extreme anterior region, more than a millimeter in front of the optimal placement. All these animals failed to give satisfactory performance on the maze or the runway, although all produced Skinner-box scores of 67 or more.

Finally, the *arresting* effects of reinforcing stimulation on maze performance should be mentioned briefly. When the electrical stimulus is given in the middle of the maze while the rat is running, invariably it produces an abrupt pause which usually lasts for only a second or so even if the stimulus is of indefinite duration. It was originally thought that the duration of the arrest might be correlated with rewarding effects of stimulation. However, the results indicate that, if anything, the correlation is inverse. Only two animals showed extremely long periods of arrest during the period of an indefinite stimulus. Both these animals were poor performers of the extreme anterior group. All the other animals showed extremely brief periods of arrest, ordinarily of about 1 sec., but ranging from $\frac{1}{2}$ to 2 sec.

Discussion of Maze Results

Electrical stimulation in the basomedial portion of the brain below the septal area (particularly around the Islands of Calleja) produces sufficiently strong reward to bring about and maintain runway performance at a level better than that for food under 18 to 24 hr. of hunger. Stimulation in the same area also produces learning in a more complicated maze; while maze learning seems slower for stimulation than food, the groups running for stimulation and food seem to be approaching the same asymptote. In the long run the stimulation group might even run better. Finally, stimulation in this area produces a short period of arrest, lasting for about a second even if the stimulus duration is indefinite, if it is applied in the middle of a maze run.

Electrical stimulation higher in the septal area failed to produce maze learning when the animals were supposed to run from a safe starting alley across an open field into a goal box. It has not yet been determined whether such stimulation would produce learning in present maze and runway experiments, or whether the placements in the mediobasal region would produce satisfactory running from the safe alley across the open field.

However, from the early experimentation, the distinct impression was left that the aftereffects of dorsal septal area stimulation (which also produced very long periods of arrest) produced an extreme fear of novel stimulation. During the electrical stimulus, the animal would be extremely unresponsive even to noxious stimulation, and all behavior would be arrested; but for a long period after termination of the stimulus, the animal was overresponsive and seemed afraid of objects which would normally be approached out of curiosity.

In conclusion, the maze experiments provide good evidence that there are placements within the second limbic system which are, by some reinforcement mechanism, involved in the selection of longer-run behavior chains such as those required in runway and maze performance.

EFFECTS ON PERCEPTION AND MEMORY

We have now progressed through autonomic behavior, instrumental behavior of simple and more complex varieties, and we are come to the question of what is known of the effects of paleocortical structures on the more complex adaptive processes of perception and memory.

Quite slowly, information is beginning to accumulate which implicates parts of the second and third systems in certain cognitive functions. The general outlines of the story may be given as follows:

1. Stimulation in the amygdala is shown by Feindel and Penfield (6) to cause momentary amnesia in conscious human patients during operation for temporal lobe seizures. Stimulation of the hippocampus, however, is reported by Penfield and Jasper (39) to be without any conscious effects on the human patient.

2. In humans also, Penfield and Milner (40) report that bitemporal removals which strongly implicate the hippocampus have an extraordinarily detrimental effect on recent incidental memories, causing forgetting of details which the normal (and preoperative) person would retain. This is not a perceptual or immediate-recall deficit; patients can do about as well as normals in repeating seven-digit numbers forward and backward. But there seems an extreme inability to retain things which are more than five or ten minutes past. There is inability to remember phone numbers, and plans for a day's work, and so forth. It is even reported that

five minutes after his head had been bandaged (even with the bandage there to remind him) one patient had completely forgotten that the bandaging had just been done. The authors compare the effect produced by bilateral hippocampal removals with the forgetfulness in Korsakov's syndrome when mammillary bodies are implicated.

3. These facts may be compared with information from Pribram and Weiskrantz (44) indicating that with removals confined to the second or third system, there is extremely rapid extinction of avoidance behavior learned before operation. Animals with amygdaloid or hippocampal lesions, or lesions in the cingulate cortex, showed almost complete "forgetting" of a preoperative avoidance response; they behaved in a shock-box just as though they had never been shocked there. This also recalls earlier work of Klüver and Bucy (24), Pribram and Bagshaw (42), Glees, Cole, Whitty, and Cairns (8), Kennard (23), and others indicating loss of response to danger signals (but not loss of response to actual pain) after lesions in and near various second- and third-system structures. Also, it may be compared with the somewhat different effects reported by Brady and his collaborators (3) where there was detriment to the learning of an avoidance response after amygdalectomy, but not detriment to retention. Finally, the involvement of the third system recalls the work of Kaada, Jansen, and Andersen (21), who report an attentive response upon stimulation of the hippocampus in unanesthetized cats.

CONCLUDING STATEMENTS

1. Paleocortical structures of the second system and related hypothalamic structures are clearly implicated in the elicitation of autonomic, adaptive behavior of both parasympathetic and sympathetic varieties. In parasympathetic areas, more or less specific autonomic effects go together with general inhibition and facilitation of spontaneous and reflex movements.

2. That these same structures are also involved in the selection of learned behaviors on the basis of effects is indicated by the extremely large number of places within them where electrical stimulation can serve as positive reinforcement to increase the frequency of Skinner-box responses and complicated maze-behavior chains. This electrical reinforcement appears to compete extremely well with food as reinforcement in the hungry animal.

3. There is some indication that paleocortical structures of the second and third system (with perhaps the emphasis on the third system) have an important effect on complex perception and memory. The mechanisms of memory deficits produced by hippocampal lesions, however,

are poorly understood. There is some temptation to believe that they are somehow secondary consequences of attentional or motivational deficit. However, this temptation derives mainly from other work of Magoun and his collaborators (31, 35) implicating the mammillary bodies in the reticular activating system.

4. Finally, our material on reinforcing effects of electrical stimulation seems to validate the assertion of Pribram and Kruger (43) that the second limbic system is a distinct entity; for always here and only here do we find scores exceeding the 75 per cent mark in the Skinner box.

If I were asked to guess how these facts will eventually fit together to form some sort of pattern, I would be tempted to make the following statements: There are areas of the brain which are differentially affected by certain needs of the organism. Under the influence of a need, a given area will elicit an automatic adaptive response of the autonomic variety which will repair the immediate need as quickly as possible. The prototype here would be the release of bodily stores of the needed substance. Under the same influence, the same area will also exercise an influence over learned responses, selecting those appropriate to replenishing the stores in the current environment.

As for innate connections, if the above description were true, the area in question would need to be more or less specifically connected to the particular autonomic behavior which would satisfy the need, but more or less generally connected to skeletal behavior so that it could under different exigencies select *any* behavior that might be appropriate to replenishment of stores in a particular environment.

The finding that general somatic effects of inhibition and facilitation do tend to go together with more or less specific autonomic effects (particularly in the parasympathetic centers) does seem to satisfy the requirement laid down in the preceding paragraph. And further, it does seem that roughly these areas have the general capacity to reward (select) any behavior providing only that electrical stimulation of the area shall follow the behavior chain in question.

As to how a general capacity of these areas to facilitate or inhibit spontaneous movement might be translated into reinforcement of specific response chains, the problem is extremely interesting and quite unsolved. The possibility which most intrigues me at present is that neural traces of whole behavior sequences are laid down in the central nervous system by the mere occurrence of the behavior chain. At the end of some sequences reward is given; and the behavior trace in question is thereby given some afferent control over neural elements implicated in the reward. Later some adequate re-presentation of the environmental stimuli which preceded the behavior will tend to reorganize the whole trace; but the reorganized trace will not be able to elicit its correlated behavior unless it has afferent control of neural elements which provide for the release of organized traces into overt behavior. These would be the neural elements implicated in reward, perhaps located in the areas of the second system and the hypothalamus, which we have discussed.

REFERENCES

1 Akert, K., and O. Andy. Experimental studies on the Ammon's formation in cats and monkeys. *Trans. Amer. neurol. Ass.,* 1953, *78:* 194–97.

2 Bailey, P., and W. H. Sweet. Effects on respiration, blood pressure and gastric motility of stimulation of orbital surface of frontal lobe. *J. Neurophysiol.,* 1940, *3:* 276–81.

3 Brady, J. V., L. Schreiner, I. Geller, and A. Kling. Subcortical mechanisms in emotional behavior: The effect of rhinencephalic injury upon the acquisition and retention of a conditioned avoidance response in cats. *J. comp. physiol. Psychol.,* 1954, *47:* 179–86.

4 Delgado, J. M. R., and R. B. Livingston. Some respiratory, vascular and thermal responses to stimulation of orbital surface of frontal lobe. *J. Neurophysiol.,* 1948, *11:* 39–55.

5 Eliasson, S. Cerebral influence on gastric motility in the cat. *Acta physiol. scand.,* 1952, *26:* Suppl. 95.

6 Feindel, W., and W. Penfield. Localization of discharge in temporal lobe automatism. *Arch. Neurol. Psychiat., Chicago,* 1954, *72:* 605–30.

7 Gastaut, H. Corrélations entre le système nerveux végétatif et le systéme de la vie de relation dans le rhinencéphale. *J. Physiol. Path. gén.,* 1952, *44:* 431–70.

8 Glees, P., J. Cole, C. W. M. Whitty, and H. Cairns. The effects of lesions in the cingular gyrus and adjacent areas in monkeys. *J. Neurol. Psychiat.,* 1950, *13:* 178–90.

9 Gloor, P. Autonomic functions of the diencephalon. *Arch. Neurol. Psychiat., Chicago,* 1954, *71:* 773–90.

10 ———. Electrophysiological studies on the connections of the amygdaloid nucleus in the cat. I: The neuronal organization of the amygdaloid projection system. *Electroenceph. clin. Neurophysiol.,* 1955, *7:* 223–42.

11 ———. Eectrophysiological studies on the connections of the amygdaloid nucleus in the cat. II: The electrophysiological properties of the amygdaloid projection system. *Electroenceph. clin. Neurophysiol.,* 1955, *7:* 243–64.

12 ———. Telencephalic influences upon the hypothalamus. In: Fields, W. S., *et al.* Eds. *Hypothalamic Hypophysiol. Interrelationships.* Springfield, Ill.: Charles C Thomas, 1956.

13 Heath, R. G., *et al. Studies in schizophenia.* Cambridge, Mass.: Harvard Univer. Press, 1954.

14 Henneman, E. The central control of the bladder. *Trans. Amer. neurol. Ass.,* 1948: 150–53.

15 Hess, W. R. *Das Zwischenhirn.* Basel: Benno Schwabe, 1949.

16 Hess, W. R., K. Akert, and D. A. McDonald. The functions of the orbital gyri in cats. *Brain,* 1952, *75:* 244–58.

17 Hodes, R., and H. W. Magoun. Autonomic responses to electrical stimulation of the forebrain and midbrain with special reference to the pupil. *J. comp. Neurol.,* 1942, *76:* 169–90.

18 ———. Pupillary and other responses from stimulation of the frontal cortex and basal telencephalon of the cat. *J. comp. Neurol.,* 1942, *76:* 461–73.

19 Kaada, B. R. Somato-motor, autonomic and electrocorticographic responses to electrical stimulation of "skinencephalic" and other structures in primates, cat, and dog. *Acta physiol. scand.,* 1951, *24:* Suppl. 83.

20 Kaada, B. R., P. Andersen, and J. Jansen, Jr. Stimulation of the amygdaloid nuclear complex in unanesthetized cats. *Neurology,* 1954, *4:* 48–64.

21 Kaada, B. R., J. Jansen Jr., and P. Andersen. Stimulation of the hippocampus and medial cortical areas in unanesthetized cats. *Neurology,* 1953, *3:* 844–57.

22 Kaada, B. R., K. H. Pribram, and J. A Epstein. Respiratory and vascular responses in monkeys from temporal pole, insula, orbital surface and cingulate gyrus: A preliminary report. *J. Neurophysiol.,* 1949, *12:* 347–56.

23 Kennard, M. A. Effects of bilateral ablation of cingulate area on behaviour of cats. *J. Neurophysiol.,* 1955, *18:* 159–69.

24 Klüver, H., and P. C. Bucy. Preliminary analysis of functions of the temporal lobes in monkeys. *Arch. Neurol. Psychiat., Chicago,* 1939, *42:* 979–1000.

25 Koikegami, H., and S. Fuse. Studies on the functions and fiber connections of the amygdaloid nuclei and periamygdaloid cortex. Experiment on the respiratory movements. I. *Folia. psychiat. neur. jap.,* 1952, *5:* 188–97.

26 ———. Studies on the functions and fiber connections of the amygdaloid nuclei and periamygdaloid cortex. Experiment on the respiratory movements. II. *Folia. psychiat. neur. jap.,* 1952, *6:* 94–103.

27 Koikegami, H., A. Kimoto, and C. Kido. Studies on the amygdaloid nuclei and periamygdaloid cortex: Experiments on the influence of their stimulation upon motility of small intestine and blood pressure. *Folia. psychiat. neur. jap.,* 1953, *7:* 87–108.

28 Koikegami, H., T. Yamada, and K. Usui. Stimulation of amygdaloid nuclei and periamygdaloid cortex with special reference to its effect on uterine movements and ovulation. *Folia. psychiat. neur. jap.,* 1954, *8:* 7–31.

29 Koikegami, H., and K. Yoshida. Pupillary dilatation induced by stimulation of amygdaloid nuclei. *Folia. psychiat. neur. jap.,* 1953, *7:* 109–26.

30 Kremer, W. F. Autonomic and somatic reactions induced by stimulation of cingular gyrus in dogs. *J. Neurophysiol.,* 1947, *10:* 371–79.

31 Lindsley, D. B., L. H. Schreiner, W. B. Knowles, and H. W. Magoun. Behavioral and EEG changes following chronic brain stem lesions in the cat. *Electroenceph. clin. Neurophysiol.,* 1950, *2:* 483–98.

32 Livingston, R. B., W. P. Chapman, K. E. Livingston, and L. Kraintz. Stimu-

lation of orbital surface of man prior to frontal lobotomy. *Res. Publ. Ass. nerv. ment. Dis.,* 1948, *27:* 421–32.

33 Livingston, R. B., J. F. Fulton, J. M. R. Delgado, E. Sachs, Jr., S. J. Brend-ler, and G. D. Davis. Stimulation and regional ablation of orbital surface of frontal lobe. *Res. Publ. Ass. nerv. ment. Dis.,* 1948, *27:* 405–20.

34 Maclean, P. D., and J. M. R. Delgado. Electrical and chemical stimulation of frontotemporal portion of limbic system in the waking animal. *Electro-enceph. clin. Neurophysiol.,* 1953, *5:* 91–100.

35 Moruzzi, G., and H. W. Magoun. Brain stem reticular formation and ac-tivation of the EEG. *Electroenceph. clin. Neurophysiol.,* 1949, *1:* 455–73.

36 Olds, J., and P. Milner. Positive reinforcement produced by electrical stimu-lation of septal area and other regions of rat brain. *J. comp. physiol. Psy-chol.,* 1954, *47:* 419–27.

37 Olds, J. A preliminary mapping of electrical reinforcing effects in the rat brain. *J. comp. physiol. Psychol.,* 1956, *49:* 281–85.

38 ———. Runway and maze behavior controlled by basomedial forebrain stimulation in the rat. *J. comp. physiol. Psychol.,* 1956, *49:* 507–12.

39 Akert, K. and O. Andy. Experimental studies on the Ammon's formation in cats and monkeys. *Trans. Amer. neurol. Ass.,* 1953, *78:* 194–97.

40 Penfield, W., and B. Milner. Paper on the effects of bilateral hippocampal lesions in man given in Chicago in June, 1956, at Association for Re-search in Nervous Disease.

41 Pool, J. L., and J. Ransohoff. Autonomic effects on stimulating rostral por-tion of cingulate gyri in man. *J. Neurophysiol.,* 1949, *12:* 385–92.

42 Pribram, K. H., and M. H. Bagshaw. Further analysis of the temporal lobe syndrome utilizing frontotemporal ablations in monkeys. *J. comp. Neurol.,* 1953, *99:* 347–75.

43 Pribram, K. H., and L. Kruger. Functions of the "olfactory brain." *Ann. N. Y. Acad. Sci.,* 1954, *58:* 109–38.

44 Pribram, K. H., and L. Weiskrantz. Paper read at Eastern Psychol. Ass., Philadelphia, April, 1955.

45 Sachs, E., Jr., S. J. Brendler, and J. F. Fulton. The orbital gyri. *Brain,* 1949, *72:* 227–40.

46 Smith, W. K. The representation of respiratory movements in the cerebral cortex. *J. Neurophysiol.,* 1938, *1:* 55–68.

47 ———. The functional significance of the rostral cingular cortex as revealed by its responses to electrical excitation. *J. Neurophysiol.,* 1945, *8:* 241–55.

48 Speakman, T. J., and B. P. Babkin. Effect of cortical stimulation on respira-tory rate. *Amer. J. Physiol.,* 1949, *159:* 239–46.

49 Sugar, O., J. G. Chusid, and J. D. French. A second motor cortex in the monkey (Macaca mulatta). *J. Neuropath.,* 1948, *7:* 182–89.

50 Ward, A. A., Jr. The cingular gyrus: Area 24. *J. Neurophysiol.,* 1948, *11:* 13–23.

Neural and Chemical Regulation of Behavior

The first aim of this chapter is to survey interdisciplinary research dealing with the neural and chemical regulators of behavior. Such a survey, of course, cannot be complete. Recent progress in the development of biochemical techniques and increases in our knowledge of neurophysiological function have produced a remarkable advance in the understanding of the neurochemical bases for behavior. In this area of interdisciplinary research a major break-through in the near future seems almost inevitable.

A second objective of the present discussion is to present a detailed analysis of one type of behavior in terms of its neural and chemical correlates. My purpose is to illustrate the interdisciplinary nature of current research; to show how the neural, chemical, and experiential influences which regulate behavior are being studied; and to examine the way in which all three act together to control one particular type of response.

Longitudinal or epigenetic studies of physiological mechanisms controlling behavior have proven their worth time and again. Relationships between a particular physical system and the organism's behavior are often most clearly seen at the time that the relationship develops. Study of the way such relationships evolve often throws light upon their nature in adult forms. Accordingly, various types of physiology-behavior correlations will be considered here from two points of view: the developmental aspect and the aspect of their nature in the adult organism.

RELATIONSHIPS BETWEEN BEHAVIOR AND THE NERVOUS SYSTEM

Developmental Schedules

The intimate and fundamental nature of relationships between the nervous system and behavior is strikingly revealed by correlations between the appearance of new forms of behavior and the completion of growth changes in associated neural structures. This was convincingly demonstrated by Coghill in his classic studies of swimming behavior in amphibian larva (23). Coghill was able to analyze the development of this complex form of behavior into a sequence of reflexive responses, beginning with lateral flexion of the anterior end of the embryo and resulting eventually in the rapid, undulating movements necessary to true swimming.

At the same time, he showed that the progression from one behavioral stage to the next is closely related to the laying-down of new pathways in the central nervous system. Coghill's work provided a sound basis for the theory that reflexogenic development in embryonic and neonatal organisms depends heavily upon maturational changes within the nervous system.

This generalization also applies to the human fetus, as shown by the investigations of Hooker (33) and Humphrey (34). These workers report that the earliest reflexogenic response of the human infant occurs at approximately seven and one-half weeks of menstrual age. Stimulation of the nose-mouth area evokes contralateral axial flexion which is limited to the cervical region. The appearance of this response to external stimulation is closely correlated with the penetration of the first cervical segments by the descending root of V.

It has long been known that some reflexes which are present in the newborn infant change at a predictable time after birth, and such maturational changes in reflexive response are related to concomitant developments in the nervous system. For example, the waning of the Babinski reflex is usually regarded as a product of maturational changes in the pyramidal tract. Hines's meticulous studies of postural reflexes and progression in the young macaque provide convincing proof that the gradual maturation of locomotory behavior in primates depends upon growth changes within the nervous system (32).

That changes in various bodily adjustments of anthropoid apes and human beings reflect parallel changes in the nervous system is also indicated by the existence of regular "timetables of development." This has been amply demonstrated by Gesell's work on human children (28) and by the more recent studies of Riesen and Kinder on the young chimpanzee (44).

As individuals grow older it becomes more difficult to discern relationships between further developmental changes in physiological systems and behavioral maturation. Nevertheless, it is exceedingly likely that some of the changes which occur in humans during adolescence are related to changes in brain function, such as those that affect the EEG.

Behavior during Maturity

To summarize the evidence concerning relations between the nervous system and adult behavior would be a monumental task and quite out of place in the present discussion. The results of clinical medicine, human brain surgery, and experimental studies of infrahuman animals place beyond question the conclusion that complex behavior and brain function are closely interrelated. Longitudinal studies suggest that the brain may undergo deteriorative changes with advancing age, and there are many psychological investigations which suggest a parallel alteration in certain intellectual capacities and perhaps in emotional behavior as well.

RELATIONS BETWEEN BODY CHEMISTRY AND BEHAVIOR

Developmental Aspects

Chemical factors in neural maturation.—From the ontogenetic point of view one of the first and most important aspects of the relationship between body chemistry and behavior pertains to biochemical factors which control the laying down of basic neural circuits during embryonic development. This evidence has been reviewed by Sperry (49), whose own experimental work brilliantly illustrates the importance to psychology of such interdisciplinary attacks upon central problems.

During the development of the visual system fibers arising in the ganglion layer of the retina extend their axones through the optic stalk to terminate eventually in the optic tectum. The final establishment of midbrain connections is not a chance affair. Instead, axones associated with a particular quadrant of the retina invariably establish contact with cells in a particular tectal region. It is hypothesized that this "homing behavior" of the growing axone depends upon biochemical affinities between different separate parts of the retina and corresponding areas in the optic tectum. Experimental interference with the establishment of normal connections between the visual end-organ and its central projection area results in permanent disturbance of visually directed behavior.

Enzyme systems and behavioral maturation.—Another example of biochemical factors influencing behavioral growth has been revealed by investigations of the development of enzyme systems in amphibian embryos. Following the original studies of Coghill, Sawyer (46) measured the concentrations of acetylcholine and cholinesterase in salamander embryos at different stages of development. His principal finding was that cholinesterase, which is thought to be essential for the rapid transmission of nerve impulses, is present in relatively small amounts in the very young embryo and increases in concentration as the organism develops. Most significant is the fact that a sudden rise in cholinesterase level is closely correlated with the appearance of the fully developed swimming reaction.

The findings of Coghill and Sawyer underscore the fact that the development of swimming behavior depends upon maturational changes in both the nervous system and the enzymes which influence neural function. That neural maturation alone is not sufficient to produce the behavior was demonstrated by Sawyer when he raised salamanders in a solution of esserin, which does not interfere with neural growth but does inactivate cholinesterase. The experimental larvae grew normally, but they showed no swimming activity. Individuals that had been kept in esserin well past the time at which swimming would have appeared were transferred to pure water, and within a very short time, as the esserin effects wore off, fully developed swimming behavior appeared.

Hormonal factors in ontogenesis.—Many changes take place in the endocrine system in the course of development, and some of these are closely associated with changes in behavior. Some of the relationships, although correlated in time, are obviously remote as far as mediating effects are concerned. For example, amphibian behavior changes in several ways as a result of metamorphosis, and the metamorphic change is known to depend upon secretion of thyroxin. The behavioral alterations are thus an indirect product of endocrine activity.

In a few instances fairly direct relationships have been discovered. One example is revealed by Kollros' study of the development of the eye blink reflex in the tadpole (40). Appearance of this response awaits the attainment of a functional condition in certain crucial centers in the midbrain. Kollros implanted minute fragments of agar impregnated with thyroxin in the locality of this reflex center. In this fashion he was able to stimulate precocious appearance of the ocular response well in advance of the expected metamorphic modifications of the total organism.

The striking changes which occur in many species at the time of puberty can often be traced directly to the secretion of hormones by the reproductive glands. Morphologic changes such as growth of the copulatory organ in the male rat or of the comb in the rooster are known to depend upon testicular secretions; and in the absence of these chemical stimulators the normal structural changes do not occur. In addition the testis hormone appears to affect the central nervous system. Thus the young chick injected with testosterone propionate not only grows a large comb but also is stimulated to crow in the fashion of an adult cock. Similarly, androgen treatment of prepuberal male rats produces growth and secretory activity in the seminal vesicles and at the same time induces fully developed copulatory reactions.

Biochemical Factors in Adulthood

Hormones.—Secretions of several endocrine glands affect behavior throughout adult life. More detailed evidence on this point will be presented later, but at the present juncture it is pertinent to note that endocrine pathology is often reflected in abnormal behavior. For example, extreme hypothyroidism has a lasting effect upon behavior, as does hypogonadism, or deterioration of the adrenal cortex, or malfunction of the pituitary.

Roughly speaking, hormonal influences upon behavior can be divided into two categories. There are those effects which are exerted through the central nervous system directly, and those which involve nonnervous structures. The testis hormone influences sexual behavior of some male animals in part by virtue of its capacity to modify the epithelium of the glans penis in such a way as to increase its sensitivity to tactile stimulation (14). Similarly, part of the effect of ovarian hormones upon feminine sexual behavior undoubtedly is due to estrin-induced local changes in the vagina and associated structures.

The parental feeding responses of the ring dove and other members of the pigeon family are stimulated by treatment with prolactin. This hypophyseal secretion undoubtedly has many effects upon the bird, but its influence upon this particular response has been traced to changes which it produces in the crop sac. The engorged crop serves as a source of local stimulation which is important if not essential to the initial feeding responses directed by inexperienced parents toward their first squabs (41).

Of course, it would be a mistake to conclude that all hormonal effects upon behavior must involve changes in receptor or effector structures. It is, for example, quite clear that the sexual responsiveness of male rats remains high despite experimental interference with genital sensation (11). Furthermore, there are some kinds of hormonally conditioned behavior which do not appear to depend upon peripheral changes. For example, the aggressive behavior of the female hamster toward the male is eliminated or greatly reduced by the presence of ovarian hormones, and this appears to be primarily, if not exclusively, a central nervous change (38).

The ingenious experiments of Richter (43) have shown very clearly that the food preferences of some animals are affected by endocrinological factors. In the presence of various hormonal insufficiencies homeostatic shifts in food intake often occur spontaneously. Although it was at one time supposed that changes in peripheral receptors might be responsible, more recent experiments implicate the central nervous system (3).

Other endogenous chemical factors.—Biochemical factors affecting behavior in adulthood involve many effects of enzyme systems. In particular, cholinesterase and acetylcholine appear to play an important role in the functioning of the nervous system. Rosenzweig and Krech, whose work is described in this volume, have measured the relative concentration of these enzymes in different parts of the cerebral cortex of the rat.

They find differences in the cholinesterase activity of different brain regions, and some of these differences are in turn correlated with behavior. The pattern of enzyme activity in the brains of rats whose behavior is dominated by visual cues is different from that found in animals that react primarily to spatial stimuli.

Clinical medicine provides us with numerous examples of behavioral abnormalities which are associated with defects in body chemistry. Thus, the intellectual deficit associated with phenylketonuria is correlated with an abnormally high level of phenylpyruvic acid resulting from inability to metabolize phenylalanine, although the relationship probably is not a direct one (35). The hallucinations and delusions which often accompany pellagra have been shown to be results of the primary vitamin deficiency (50).

COACTION OF NEURAL, HORMONAL, AND EXPERIMENTAL FACTORS IN THE REGULATION OF SEXUAL BEHAVIOR

To shift now from a discussion of generalities to the consideration of more detailed findings, I propose to examine the ways in which neural and hormonal factors function in the regulation of sexual behavior.

Neural Components

A few scattered experiments have dealt with the neural factors involved in mating behavior of fish, amphibia, reptiles, and birds, but most of the available evidence comes from studies on mammals.

Contribution of noncortical mechanisms.—These investigations suggest first of all that many of the simpler, reflexive responses which are normally incorporated into the total sexual pattern are mediated by centers situated below the cortex and even in the spinal cord. For instance, male mammals are capable of genital erection and ejaculation after complete section of the spinal cord in the lumbar region (1). Decerebrate female cats and guinea pigs display the postural reflexes of coition (1). A series of experiments by Bard and others (2, 24) indicate that the fundamental mating reactions of infraprimate females are mediated by thalamic mechanisms. Other studies implicate the hypothalamus as well (26).

Investigations of subcortical function in masculine sexual performance are not numerous. According to Clark (21), hypothalamic injury involving the medial half of the anterior hypothalamus reduces sexual performance in the male rat. A more extensive and systematic investigation by Rogers (45) showed that male rats sustaining damage to the ventromedial premammillary areas eventually cease mating but can be restored to normal sexual performance by the administration of androgen. Apparently the loss of potency in such cases reflects decrease in androgen output by the testis, which in turn is due to interference with pituitary gonadotropic function. In a different category are those rats with complete or nearly complete destruction of the tuberal regions. Animals in this category rarely mate after operation and are unresponsive to androgen therapy. In this instance crucial neural circuits appear to have been disrupted.

It appears that the amygdala and perhaps the pyriform and temporal cortex may contribute to masculine sexual behavior. In any event, Klüver and Bucy (39) reported "hypersexuality" in male monkeys following temporal injury. More recently, Schreiner and Kling (47) have described changes in the sexual behavior of male cats following destruction of the pyriform cortex and extensive invasion of the amygdala. These changes consisted of the appearance of copulatory attempts directed toward a variety of biologically inadequate stimulus partners including chickens, dogs, monkeys, and other male cats.

An unpublished exploratory study conducted in my laboratory suggests that lesions to the amygdala produce a temporary rise in the sexual responsiveness of male dogs, but this change is reversible, and the increased reactivity disappears within a few months. Removal of a large part of the limbic cortex in males of this species is followed by a reduction in sexual activity, but this change also is dissipated several months after operation.

Contribution of the neocortex in male mammals.—The neocortex plays an important role in the mediation of copulatory behavior in males of several species and is less important in others. According to Stone (51), extensive invasion of the neopallium does not eliminate copulatory activity in male rabbits. Brooks (20) found that complete decortication does not abolish the sexual act in males of this species provided the olfactory bulbs are intact. Subsequent loss of the bulbs eliminates coital performance in decorticated males.

Male rats may continue to copulate after loss of large portions of the neocortex, but complete decortication eliminates all responsiveness to the receptive female (4). Furthermore, partial operations which fail to eliminate sexual behavior have nevertheless been shown to reduce the male's susceptibility to sexual arousal.

Partially decorticated males that continue to copulate do so in normal fashion. Apparently at this level of the evolutionary scale the cortex is not essential for coördination of the separate reactions involved in pursuit of the female and execution of the coital response. However, cortical tissue is not without sexual function. Its primary contribution has to do with maintaining the male's sexual excitability at such a level that lower executive centers are stimulated and thrown into action in response to the appropriate external cues.

More recent investigations of cortical function in the sexual activity of male cats tell a different story (17, 18, 54). It is clear that the carnivore cortex is more intimately involved than that of the rodent in the management of mating responses. In the cat, as in the male rat, total decortication abolishes all responses to the estrous female. However, removal of a sufficient amount of cortex from the occipital lobe can interfere with mating without producing any recognizable decrease in the male's sexual excitability. Cats suffering this type of brain injury will copulate normally if they are placed in contact with the receptive female. Cortical blindness prevents their locating the distant female and approaching her, and hence indirectly interferes with sexual activity. It does not reduce sexual excitability or interfere with the ability to execute the coital pattern.

Males of this species which have been deprived of the frontal lobes show no decline in sexual responsiveness. They follow the receptive female continuously and repeatedly attempt to mate with her. However, because of motor abnormalities produced by the frontal lesion, such cats are almost totally incapable of completing the mating. They grip the female, mount her (usually in an abnormal position), and execute copulatory attempts; but they are unable to carry the pattern through to its normal end point.

Comparison of rodents and carnivores makes it apparent that evolutionary changes resulting in the increased corticalization of sensorimotor control over all complex behavior has had its effects upon sexual activity. By virtue of its assumption of a greater degree of authority over a wide variety of behavioral responses, the neopallium in the cat has become more heavily involved in the male's mating performance. It is possible that the neocortex plays a dual role, contributing not only to the organization of the reproductive performance, but also to the general level of excitability of the male.

Contribution of the neocortex in female mammals.—The neural mediators of sexual behavior in female mammals differ from those in males. To begin with, the cerebral cortex seems to be much less heavily involved in feminine sexuality. Decorticated female rabbits (20), guinea pigs (24), and rats (7) continue to show sexually receptive behavior under the appropriate forms of hormonal stimulation. Furthermore, decerebrate female cats (1) and dogs (29) are said to mate with sexually active males. Careful observations of the mating pattern in decorticated rats reveal that it is somewhat disorganized, but the response is sufficiently integrated to permit fertile copulation by a normal male.

It is of considerable interest to note that the differential effects of neocortical injury upon masculine and feminine sexual behavior in the rat can be demonstrated in one and the same individual. Female rats of many different strains will show masculine sexual behavior when placed with a second female that is in estrous. It has been demonstrated that this type of response is totally eliminated by complete decortication despite the fact that the same females continue to show receptive behavior when they are treated with the necessary ovarian hormones and tested with active males (7).

These sex differences are of particular significance because they can be meaningfully related to other differences which will be considered in detail later. The latter pertain to the differential effects of previous experience in males and females and to the degree to which gonadal hormones are essential for mating performance in the two sexes.

With the exception of the study by Klüver and Bucy, there is no evidence concerning the neural control of sexual behavior in primates. If we extrapolate from the studies of rodents and carnivores, it seems reasonable to assume that the mating behavior of primates would be even more seriously affected by extensive cortical injury, since in the higher mammals the brain has become increasingly important as an arbiter of all kinds of voluntary activity.

Hormonal Components

A few experiments have been concerned with the effects of hormones on the sexual behavior of submammalian vertebrates, but most of the evidence pertains to mammals and it is with this class that the following summary deals.

Several endocrine glands including the anterior pituitary, the thyroid, and the adrenals play a role in the maintenance of normal sexual behavior. However, the most direct effects upon sexuality are exerted by the reproductive glands.

Gonadal hormones in female mammals.—In females of most lower mammalian species sexual behavior is heavily dependent upon ovarian hormones. For some animals estrin is the only hormone involved in mating, but for others both estrin and progesterone are important. In either case, sexual behavior is typically exhibited only when the related hormone or hormones are present in sufficient concentration. Mating responses are lacking in prepuberal individuals, and the first display of sexually receptive behavior usually coincides with the first full estrous cycle.

The sudden appearance of adult mating reactions is a direct result of increased secretory activity by the ovaries. Identical behavior can be produced precociously by treating prepuberal females with the appropriate ovarian substances (6). It is clear, therefore, that the neural and muscular components of the sexual response are integrated and capable of action before they are normally thrown into play by the sensitizing effects of ovarian hormone.

Adult infraprimate females normally display sexual activity only at those times when the ovaries are producing relatively large amounts of estrin. This is, of course, the time that the female is fertile and capable of conception as a result of copulation. For most mammals the breeding period is annual or semiannual and lasts a relatively short time. In the case of some domesticated species the female is polyestrous and exhibits a regular cycle of alternating phases of receptivity and nonreceptivity. This cycle is timed by the secretory cycle of the reproductive glands. When a female is not physiologically in estrus, she is not exciting to the male and will not permit coitus. During the estrous period the female appears to be a very stimulating partner and readily permits coition.

In species of this type removal of the ovaries in adulthood produces prompt and permanent loss of the female's sexual receptivity. Replacement therapy involving administration of estrogen or estrogen plus progesterone occasions a temporary resurgence of erotic responsiveness and mating behavior (8).

One point omitted in the foregoing generalizations is of primary importance. This is that they do not apply to every female in every species. There are some females that never come into behavioral estrus. Although the ovaries produce mature follicles which are obviously secreting estrin, and although they show signs of vaginal response to ovarian hormones, there are always a few individuals who fail to display the expected behavioral change. Animals of this type can sometimes be brought into heat after ovariectomy if they are treated with very large amounts of estrogen and progesterone. Less marked differences in sensitivity to hormonal stimulation are found even among females that regularly come into heat. Some can be simulated to show sexual behavior with minimal amounts of the appropriate hormones, whereas others react positively only after two or three times as much hormone has been injected (53).

Like infraprimate mammals, female primates are also clearly influenced by hormonal secretions of the reproductive glands. Immature female monkeys and apes rarely if ever exhibit the complete coital pattern although they sometimes engage in sex play with young males. In adulthood female monkeys and chimpanzees display cycles of sexual responsiveness which are closely correlated with the menstrual cycle, and maximal receptivity occurs during that time when the estrogen level is high and ovulation is imminent. During the rest of the cycle the female is not easily aroused sexually and appears to offer little erotic attraction for the male. It is nonetheless noteworthy that some females will permit copulation when the ovaries are relatively quiescent and when estrogen concentrations are low. This is practically never seen in infraprimate animals and probably marks a significant evolutionary change.

The effects of ovariectomy and replacement therapy on the sexual behavior of female primates are about what might be expected from the foregoing description. The majority of females become sexually inactive after ovariectomy and remain so indefinitely. A few individuals occasionally engage in sporadic sexual contacts, but their behavior is sluggish and is not marked by the characteristic signs of excitement which are shown by the estrous female. Treatment of ovariectomized monkeys or apes with estrogen is followed by the physical signs of estrus, such as swelling of the sex skin, and usually by the appearance of marked behavioral receptivity to the male.

Individual differences in the response to ovarian hormones are more marked than among lower mammals. Some intact primate females are totally unreceptive at all times regardless of the ovarian condition. As suggested earlier, other individuals may be partially receptive despite the complete absence of ovarian secretions. Reactions to the male are affected, not only by the physiological condition of the female, but also by more subtle psychological factors, with the result that distinct individual preferences exist, so that a given female may mate readily with one male and at the same time completely refuse the sexual attentions of a second potential partner.

Gonadal hormones in male mammals.—Turning now to a consideration of the hormonal components of masculine sexual behavior, we may first consider males of the lower mammalian species.

Whereas female rodents, carnivores, and ungulates practically never exhibit the adult mating pattern prior to the first physiological estrus, young males frequently display various portions of the masculine sexual response well before the onset of puberty. They frequently pursue other individuals, and sometimes such pursuit ends with one animal mounting the other, clasping him or her in the sexual position, and executing a few weak pelvic movements. This adumbrated display of masculine coition by prepuberal male mammals is not dependent upon the small amounts of androgen which are known to be secreted by the prepuberal testis, because the prepuberal sexual play of male rats is not prevented by castration on the day of birth (11). Apparently some slight degree of sexual responsiveness is possible without the support of gonadal hormones. In this respect males and females are dissimilar.

That testicular hormones are exceedingly important for masculine sexual performance has been shown in experiments involving injection of androgen into prepuberal males. Immature males treated in this fashion begin to display complete mating reactions including erection and ejaculation (6). Thus, in the male as in the female, the neuromuscular components of copulatory behavior are organized and capable of adult functioning before they are normally called into action.

In the normal course of development the sexual activity of young male rodents undergoes a striking change when the testes start to secrete adult levels of testosterone. It is at this point that mating responses become more frequent, vigorous, and complete and that the terminal reaction of ejaculation puts in its appearance.

Males of many mammalian species are similar to females in that they are inactive sexually save during the annual or semiannual breeding season. Such species are represented by the common ground squirrel, the Alaskan fur seal, and various species of American and Old World deer. In contrast, males of other species remain constantly active throughout the year. The gonads of seasonally breeding males regress and are quiescent except during the time of rut. The testes of constantly breeding species produce sperm throughout the year, and the interstitial tissue secretes androgen at a fairly steady rate.

The sexual inactivity of males out of breeding season is directly related to the absence of gonadal secretions. This has been demonstrated by administering exogenous androgen to animals of this type. Such treatment evokes the prompt appearance of mating responses out of season. The same result can be obtained by stimulating the quiescent testis to secretory activity through appropriate gonadotrophic stimulation (9).

The role of testosterone in males of the constantly breeding type is revealed by the results of castration. Castration of male rodents and lagomorphs is followed by fairly rapid decline in potency. There are differences among species and among individuals within the same species, but in the main, sexual activity declines to a prepuberal level within a few weeks after operation. This is true for the male rabbit (52), guinea pig (9), hamster (15), mouse (9), and domestic rat (12). In every species which has been investigated, the post-castrational loss of sexual responsiveness and ability can be reversed by the administration of androgenic hormone. It is clear that in these animals the susceptibility to sexual arousal and the capacity to mate are heavily dependent upon secretory activity of the reproductive glands. At the same time it should be remembered that individual differences exist and that they have some theoretical significance.

The rate of decline in sexual responsiveness varies from one castrated rat to another, and the amount of hormone necessary to restore preoperational vigor is subject to similar interindividual differences (12). Male guinea pigs also vary in the intensity of their sexual drive. Following castration, males fall off to approximately the same low level of sexual responsiveness. But when such castrates are treated with a constant amount of testosterone propionate, they react differentially. Those males that showed high sexual drive prior to castration return to this level under the influence of the exogenous hormone. Other individuals which had been low-drive males preoperatively respond to the same amount of androgen with the exhibition of mating activity at a low drive level (30). Apparently the precastrational differences in sexual drive are due, not to differences in the amount of hormone secreted by the testis, but to individual differences in the sensitivity of the target tissues which react to testicular secretions.

In mammals above the level of a rodent or lagomorph, the effects of castration are somewhat different. Male dogs and cats that have had sexual experience tend to retain potency and responsiveness for some time after castration. Here, again, individual differences are apparent. Some males exhibit a partial loss of responsiveness within a few months after operation while others show no such change for more than two years postoperatively (48).

Those males that decline in sexual capacity following castration can be restored to normal levels of responsiveness by androgen administration. Apparently the phylogenetic differences between carnivores and rodents include a partial reduction in the degree to which masculine sexual behavior depends upon testicular hormone. This may be indirectly related to a fact mentioned earlier, namely, that concomitant changes appear to have taken place in the neural control of such behavior.

It will be recalled that female primates are somewhat less dependent upon ovarian hormones than are females of infraprimate mammalian types. This difference is accentuated in the male. The perpuberal sexual play of young monkeys and apes is more frequent and varied than that of immature males of lower mammalian species. Erection, masturbation, and attempts at copulation have been observed in prepubescent primates (19). Castration does not eliminate sexual activity in adult males (37), nor does it prevent the development of copulatory patterns when the operation is performed before puberty (22). The only element in the sexual repertoire which seems to necessitate androgenic support is the ejaculatory reflex.

This is not to say that the sexual capacity of castrated primates is equal to that of normal animals. Sexual excitability may remain high for an indefinite period, and copulation may continue, but mating performance is often perfunctory and lethargic, and administration of androgen usually produces recognizable increases in erotic responsiveness and coital capacity.

Experiential Components

The sexual behavior of animals or human beings cannot be understood exclusively in terms of the hormonal condition of the individual or the species organization of the nervous system. A third important factor in sexuality is the individual's previous experience. This component presumably reflects functional changes produced in the nervous system by experience, but present knowledge does not permit us to deal with experiential effects in physiological terms. For the time being, therefore, the behavioral factors must be considered separately.

Effects of experience in the male.—There is ample evidence to support the conclusion that the sexual performance of male mammals can be altered by individual experience. Male rats which have been reared in individual cages and exposed to receptive females periodically during prepuberal life, when complete copulation is impossible, are less likely to show normal copulatory behavior in adulthood than are control males that have never had this type of infant conditioning (36). On the other hand, adult males of this species which have been reared in isolation from the age of weaning are capable of completely normal coital reactions the first time they are placed with a receptive female (5). This is also true of some dogs and cats. In other words, for these animals the achievement of normal sexual goals does not depend upon practice and learning although it may be affected by certain types of experience.

It is clear that experience can exert pronounced effects upon the sexual behavior of males of many mammalian species (27). There are numerous observations to the effect that males tend to become sexually inhibited if their contact with receptive females is rendered painful or frightening. One experiment carried out in my laboratory showed that male rats which were subjected to a punishing electric shock each time they attempted to copulate eventually ceased responding to receptive females. The experimentally induced sexual inhibition persisted for two weeks to a month after the last punishment and was then dissipated in most individuals. A few males remained permanently unresponsive to the female after having been inhibited by electric shock. These individuals were restored to normal sexual performance by a series of electrically induced convulsions (10).

The converse of inhibition has also been demonstrated. Stimuli which are initially neutral become sexually exciting if they have been repeatedly associated with complete sexual expression. An environment in which copulation has occurred tends to evoke premonitory signs of sexual arousal as soon as the male enters it. Male cats and dogs which appear reluctant to mate under laboratory conditions can be induced to do so by appropriate conditioning procedures (16). When this has been effected, the inhibition of sexual responsiveness disappears, and in subsequent contacts with the receptive female the males mate promptly and frequently.

In harmony with the observation that the sexual excitability of male mammals is "conditionable," is the additional evidence that sexual reward can be used to produce the learning of instrumental responses. For example, male rats will learn to turn a wheel when the reward is opportunity for copulation with the receptive female (25). In a comparable study it has been shown that the speed with which male rats will traverse a straight alley to reach a receptive female is directly related to the degree of sexual excitement and intensity of behavior displayed when contact with the female is established. Castration produces a decrease in running speed, and subsequent androgen therapy occasions a gradual increase in alley performance and re-establishment of normal sexual functions (13). It is significant that copulatory behavior and running speed covary even when hormonal conditions are constant. Castrates occasionally show sexual behavior despite the absence of hormone, and upon such occasions they traverse the alley at high speed. Other castrates, having a similar hormonal condition but failing to copulate with the female do not run as rapidly in the alley.

Effects of experience in the female.—In the case of lower mammals the experiential component seems to be less important to the female than to the male. There is no indication that the conditions under which female rats, cats, or dogs are reared have any effect upon their sexual receptivity in adulthood. The first time that a female comes into heat she is normally receptive, and when placed with an experienced male, she will promptly mate. Her initial performance is indistinguishable from that of females that have mated many times.

Preliminary results obtained in the Yale laboratories indicate that receptive females will traverse a straight alley when the goal box contains a male rat. However, the female's speed in the alley is unrelated to her sexual behavior. For animals in one group the goal box contained a sexually active male that copulated promptly as soon as the female emerged from the end of the alley. For a second group the goal box contained a sexually inactive male that never copulated. Opportunity to copulate with the male did not produce faster running to the goal box. In fact, females that received the inactive male as an incentive object tended to show faster running in the alley than did those females with which the male copulated in the goal box. These results are distinctly different from those obtained with male rats. The male's running speed is positively related to sexual reinforcement (13).

I noted earlier that some male cats and dogs fail to copulate when they are first tested under laboratory conditions, although they can be induced to do so and may eventually become very active sexually. Comparable inhibition of sexual performance has never been noted in females of either species. The first time that a female dog or cat is brought into heat and put with a male under laboratory conditions, she exhibits completely normal sexual receptivity and will mate without delay.

The apparent difference in the importance of experience for sexual behavior in male and female rodents and carnivores may be directly related to another sex difference mentioned earlier, namely, the difference in the degree to which the cerebral cortex is involved in masculine and feminine behavior. It will be recalled that decortication eliminates sexual responsiveness in male rats, dogs, and cats but does not have this effect upon females of the same species. Also to be considered in this connection is the difference in the degree to which sexual behavior is dependent upon gonadal hormones. The female's performance seems to be somewhat more rigidly controlled by such secretions than does that of the male.

Phylogenetic differences.—The importance of experience in shaping the individual's sexual habits is much more pronounced in primates than in lower mammals. Nissen's findings suggest that male and female chimpanzees are incapable of successful coitus until they have learned to copulate by trial-and-error experimentation or have been sexually trained by an experienced partner (42). To this observation should be added the facts that autoeroticism and homosexual behavior are much more frequent in primates than in lower mammals (31).

It is reasonable to assume that the evolutionary increase in experiential control of sexual activities is on outcome of the increasing importance of the neocortex as a mediating agent. In addition, the partial relaxation of hormonal dominance over sexual responsiveness makes possible greater latitude in individual sexual adjustments.

Evolutionary shifts in the physiological control of sexuality are most evident in our own species. Here one sees the greatest degree of diversity.

Exclusive homosexuality, complete reversal of sex roles, sexual responsiveness to immature individuals, to animals, or even to inanimate objects, total sublimation of sex drive—these and many other uniquely human manifestations are possible only because the experiential component plays a dominant role in shaping human sexual behavior. The primary importance of individual experience is in turn due to reduced reliance upon gonadal hormones and increased intervention of the cerebral cortex.

THEORETICAL ANALYSIS

The factors involved in sexual behavior include neural mechanisms which mediate erotic arousal, other mechanisms responsible for execution of the coital act, gonadal hormones, and special forms of external stimulation resulting in arousal.

Mechanisms for arousal.—The arousal mechanism (AM) appears to be organized and functional in sexually inexperienced animals. Male and female rats, cats, or chimpanzees demonstrate signs of sexual excitement when stimulated by an active partner of the opposite sex even though they have never copulated.

The reactivity of the AM varies from individual to individual in the absence of previous sexual experience. The majority of naive male rats can be induced to copulate only if they are stimulated by a female in full heat. But there are a few inexperienced males which attempt to copulate with nonreceptive females or with other males. These are individuals in which the AM is very easily stimulated. The differences must be attributed to some inherent quality of the neural mechanism. It cannot be interpreted as a consequence of hormonal variations because similar individual differences are seen in males which have been castrated on the day of birth.

In sexually inexperienced males the AM is primarily reactive to stimuli associated with a biologically appropriate partner, i.e., a receptive female of the same species. However, the reactivity of the AM may be altered by experience. Stimuli which were originally ineffective may later become sexually exciting as a result of their association with biologically adequate sexual stimuli. The AM, in other words, can be "conditioned" to a variety of nonsexual external cues. Such conditioning need not be of a positive nature. Animals and human beings may learn not to respond sexually to stimulus objects which originally were effective evokers of the copulatory reaction.

The susceptibility of the AM to modification by experience varies with the sex and the species of the individual. In male rats, cats, and dogs sexual arousal can be conditioned to new cues, but there is no evidence that females are similarly affected by experience. The sexual responsiveness of male primates is more labile and modifiable than that of male rodents and carnivores, and female primates differ from the females of lower species in that the AM probably can be affected by experience.

Mechanisms for copulation.—When sexual arousal reaches a threshold level, the executive or consummatory mechanism (CM) is thrown into action. The functional organization of the CM is probably complete in inexperienced male and female rats, rabbits, dogs, and cats. The motor pattern of copulation is stereotyped and invariable and is not materially altered by experience.

In contrast, organization of the CM is incomplete in male and female chimpanzees. The separate elements in the copulatory pattern can be elicited, but the naive primate cannot execute them in the proper sequence with the requisite degree of precision to effect successful copulation. Integration of the various responses into a smooth-flowing pattern depends upon practice. Because learning is involved, individual differences in the method of copulation are discernible in this species.

Neural components of the AM and CM.—We cannot as yet describe these mechanisms in precise neurological terms, but it is possible to indicate something about their composition. The CM in males and females of all mammalian species includes spinal components which regulate genital reflexes and some of the gross postural adjustments involved in coitus. The CM of primates embraces centers and systems extending all the way to the neocortex. The cortex and various subcortical tracts and nuclei are also involved in the CM of male carnivores, but this is not true of females. The highest essential centers in the CM of the female carnivore lie in the diencephalon.

It is clear that the CM of female rodents is like that of female carnivores, and it is probable that the same is true of the male. Male rats cease copulating after extensive cortical injury, but this need not reflect interference with the CM. The fact that some brain-operated males can be induced to copulate after administration of large amounts of androgen suggests that the original loss was due to lowered activity of the AM.

As far as the AM is concerned, it appears that this mechanism does not depend upon the cortex in female rodents or carnivores, for decorticated rats, cats, and dogs display full sexual receptivity. Crucial portions of the AM seem to be located within the diencephalon. Males of these same species exhibit a reduction in sexual excitability following extensive cortical injury, hence the masculine AM must include cortical elements. The AM of male and female primates almost certainly involves a large cortical component.

Relations to experience and hormone effects.—Sexual behavior is dependent upon or affected by learning and experience to the extent that the neocortex participates in the functions of the AM or CM.

The neocortex is not involved in the CM of the male or female rat; hence, the coital act can be performed by both sexes without practice. It is involved in the AM of the male but not of the female; therefore, the male's susceptibility to arousal is modifiable by experience, and that of the female is not. The neocortex is involved in both the AM and the CM of male and female primates with the result that they must learn to copulate, and their sexual excitability is modifiable as a result of experience.

The influence of gonadal hormones upon sexual behavior is probably restricted to the subcortical level and lower portions of the brain and cord. The nature of the effect is a reduction in the threshold to stimulation. Cortical portions of the AM serve to supplement or augment the action of sex hormones upon lower centers. In certain instances the cortical component of the AM may assume so dominant a role over the entire arousal mechanism that gonadal hormones are not necessary for the occurrence of sexual behavior. For example, the persistence of copulatory behavior in male dogs and cats castrated after a great deal of sexual experience may be due to the effects of that experience upon the cortical portion of the AM.

If the cortical component is lacking, sexual behavior will not occur in the absence of the appropriate gonadal hormones. This is why female mammals below the level of primates are asexual when not in estrus. A relatively small cortical factor, as in the male rodent, permits modification of arousal through experience but cannot support normal copulatory behavior in the absence of sex hormones.

It is clear that in males of many species the CM does not depend upon androgen. Castrated carnivores and primates can copulate provided the requisite degree of arousal is attained. Whether the same is true of female mammals has not yet been determined.

REFERENCES

1 Bard, P. Central nervous mechanisms for emotional behavior patterns in animals. *Res. Publ. Ass. nerv. ment. Dis.*, 1939, *19*: 190–218.

2 Bard, P., and D. McK. Rioch. A study of four cats deprived of neocortex and additional portions of the forebrain. *Johns Hopk. Hosp. Bull.*, 1937, *60*: 73–147.

3 Bare, J. K. The specific hunger for sodium chloride in normal and adrenalectomized white rats. *J. comp. physiol. Psychol.*, 1949, *42*: 242–53.

4 Beach, F. A. Effects of cortical lesions upon copulatory behavior of male rats. *J. comp. Psychol.*, 1940, *29*: 193–244.

5 ———. Analysis of the stimuli adequate to elicit mating behavior in the sexually inexperienced male rat. *J. comp. Psychol.*, 1942, *33:* 163–207.

6 ———. Sexual behavior of prepuberal male and female rats treated with gonadal hormones. *J. comp. Psychol.*, 1942, *34:* 285–92.

7 ———. Effects of injury to the cerebral cortex upon the display of masculine and feminine mating behavior by female rats. *J. comp. Psychol.*, 1943, *36:* 169–98.

8 ———. A review of physiological and psychological studies of sexual behavior in mammals. *Physiol. Rev.*, 1947, *27:* 240–307.

9 ———. *Hormones and behavior.* New York: Hoeber, 1948.

10 Beach, F. A., M. W. Conovitz, F. Steinberg, and A. C. Goldstein. Experimental inhibition and restoration of mating behavior in male rats. *J. genet. Psychol.*, 1956, *89:* 165–81.

11 Beach, F. A., and A. M. Holz. Mating behavior in male rats castrated at various ages and injected with androgen. *J. exp. Zool.*, 1946, *101:* 91–142.

12 ———. Effects of different concentrations of androgen upon sexual behavior in castrated male rats. *J. comp. physiol. Psychol.*, 1949, *42:* 433–53.

13 Beach, F. A., and L. Jordan. Effects of sexual reinforcement upon the performance of male rats in a straight runway. *J. comp. physiol. Psychol.*, 1956, *49:* 105–10.

14 Beach, F. A., and G. Levinson. Effects of androgen on the glans penis and mating behavior of castrated male rats. *J. exp. Zool.*, 1950, *114:* 159–71.

15 Beach, F. A., and R. S. Fauker. Effects of castration and subsequent androgen administration upon mating behavior in the male hamster (Cricetus auratus). *Endocrinology*, 1949, *45:* 211–21.

16 Beach, F. A., and A. Zitrin. Induction of mating activity in male cats. *Ann. N. Y. acad. Sci.*, 1945, *46:* 42–44.

17 Beach, F. A., A. Zitrin, and J. Jaynes. Neural mediation of mating in male cats. II. Contributions of the frontal cortex. *J. exp. Zool.*, 1955, *130:* 381–401.

18 ———. Neural mediation of mating in male cats. I. Effects of unilateral and bilateral removal of the neocortex. *J. comp. physiol. Psychol.*, 1956, *49:* 321–27.

19 Bingham, H. C. Sex development in apes. *Comp. Psychol. Monogr.*, 1928, *5:* No. 1 (Whole No. 23).

20 Brooks, C. McC. The rôle of the cerebral cortex and of various sense organs in the excitation and execution of mating activity in the rabbit. *Amer. J. Physiol.*, 1937, *120:* 544–53.

21 Clark, G. Sexual behavior in rats with lesions in the anterior hypothalamus. *Amer. J. Physiol.*, 1942, *137:* 746–49.

22 ———. Prepubertal castration in the male chimpanzee, with some effects of replacement therapy. *Growth*, 1945, *9:* 327–39.

23 Coghill, G. E. *Anatomy and the problem of behaviour.* New York: Macmillan, 1929.

24 Dempsey, E. W., and D. McK. Rioch. The localization in the brain stem of

the oestrous responses of the female guinea pig. *J. Neurophysiol.*, 1939, *2:* 9–18.

25 Denniston, R. H., II. Quantification and comparison of sex drives under various conditions in terms of a learned response. *J. comp. physiol. Psychol.*, 1954, *47:* 437–40.

26 Fisher, C., H. W. Magoun, and S. W. Ranson. Dystocia in diabetes insipidus: The relation of pituitary oxytocin to parturition. *Amer. J. Obstet. Gynec.*, 1938, *36:* 1–9.

27 Ford, C. S., and F. A. Beach. *Patterns of sexual behavior.* New York: Harper, 1951.

28 Gesell, A. Behavior patterns of fetal-infant and child. *Proc. Ass. Res. nerv. Dis.*, 1954, *33:* 114–26.

29 Goltz, F. Der Hund ohne Grosshirn. *Pflüg. Arch. ges. Physiol.*, 1892, *51:* 570–614.

30 Grunt, J. A., and W. C. Young. Consistency of sexual behavior patterns in individual male guinea pigs following castration and androgen therapy. *J. comp. physiol. Psychol.*, 1953, *46:* 138–44.

31 Hamilton, G. V. A study of sexual tendencies in monkeys and baboons. *J. Anim. Behav.*, 1914, *4:* 295–318.

32 Hines, M. The development and regression of reflexes, postures, and progression in the young macaque. *Contr. Embryol. Carneg. Instn.*, 1942, *30:* 153–210 (Whole No. 196).

33 Hooker, D. Early human fetal behavior, with a preliminary note on double simultaneous fetal stimulation. *Proc. Ass. Res. nerv. Dis.*, 1954, *33:* 98–113.

34 Humphrey, T. The trigeminal nerve in relation to early human fetal activity. *Proc. Ass. Res. nerv. Dis.*, 1954, *33:* 127–54.

35 Jervis, G. A. The genetics of phenylpyruvic oligophrenia. *J. ment. Sci.*, 1939, *85:* 719–62.

36 Kagan, J., and F. A. Beach. Effects of early experience on mating behavior in male rats. *J. comp. physiol. Psychol.*, 1953, *46:* 204–8.

37 Kempf, E. J. The social and sexual behavior of infrahuman primates with some comparable facts in human behavior. *Psychoanal. Rev.*, 1917, *4:* 127–54.

38 Kislak, J. W., and F. A. Beach. Inhibition of aggressiveness by ovarian hormones. *Endocrinology*, 1955, *56:* 684–92.

39 Klüver, H., and P. C. Bucy. Preliminary analysis of functions of the temporal lobes in monkeys. *Arch. Neurol. Psychiat., Chicago*, 1939, *42:* 979–1000.

40 Kollros, J. J. Localized maturation of lid-closure reflex mechanism by thyroid implants in tadpole hindbrain. *Proc. Soc. exp. Biol., N. Y.*, 1942, *49:* 204–6.

41 Lehrman, D. S. The physiological basis of parental feeding behavior in the ring dove. *Behaviour*, 1955, *7:* 241–86.

42 Nissen, H. Instinct as seen by a psychologist. In W. C. Allee, H. W. Nissen, and M. F. Nimkoff, A re-examination of the concept of instinct. *Psychol. Rev.*, 1953, *60:* 287–97.

43 Richter, C. P. Biology of drives. *J. comp. physiol. Psychol.*, 1947, *40:* 129–34.
44 Riesen, A. H., and E. F. Kinder. *Postural development of infant chimpanzees.* New Haven: Yale Univer. Press, 1952.
45 Rogers, C. M. Hypothalamic mediation of sex behavior in the male rat. Unpublished doctor's dissertation, Yale Univer., 1954.
46 Sawyer, C. H. Cholinesterase and the behavior problem in Amblystoma. *J. exp. Zool.*, 1943, *92:* 1–29.
47 Schreiner, L., and A. Kling. Behavioral changes following rhinencephalic injury in cat. *J. Neurophysiol.*, 1953, *16:* 643–59.
48 Schwartz, M., and F. A. Beach. Effects of adrenalectomy upon mating behavior in castrated male dogs. *Amer. Psychologist*, 1954, *9:* 467–8.
49 Sperry, R. W. Mechanisms of neural maturation. In S. S. Stevens (Ed.), *Handbook of experimental psychology.* New York: Wiley, 1951, pp. 236–80.
50 Spies, T. D., C. D. Aring, J. Gelperin, and W. B. Bean. The mental symptoms of pellagra: Their relief with nicotinic acid. *Amer. J. med. Sci.*, 1938, *196:* 461–75.
51 Stone, C. P. The effects of cerebral destruction on the sexual behavior of male rabbits. III. The frontal, parietal and occipital regions. *J. comp. Psychol.*, 1926, *6:* 435–48.
52 ———. The retention of copulatory ability in male rabbits following castration. *J. genet. Psychol.*, 1932, *40:* 296–305.
53 Young, W. C., E. W. Dempsey, H. I. Myers, and C. W. Hagquist. The ovarian condition and sexual behavior in the female guinea pig. *Amer. J. Anat.*, 1938, *63:* 457–87.
54 Zitrin, A., J. Jaynes, and F. A. Beach. Neural mediation of mating in male cats. III. Contributions of occipital, parietal and temporal cortex. *J. comp. Neurol.*, 1956, *105:* 111–26.

Donald B. Tower

The Neurochemical Substrates of Cerebral Function and Activity

It is now being recognized that many of the disorders or alterations in function of the nervous system appear to be basically biochemical in nature. The necessity for acquisition of fuller understanding of the chemistry of nervous tissue and neurons in health and in disease has established neurochemistry as a special branch of biochemistry and cellular physiology which can serve to fill in the many gaps in our knowledge on these subjects. Neurochemistry has consequently become an integral component of neurological research. There are sufficient leads to suggest that a neurochemical approach to the elucidation of behavioral mechanisms may be fruitful. This paper is intended to serve as a survey of important aspects of neurochemistry and to consider abnormalities and diseases which illustrate certain concepts relating to behavior in its broader sense. Both the psychologist and the neurochemist are on unfamiliar ground at the juncture of the two fields. It is important that each appreciates the values and the limitations inherent in the other's discipline. It is with this concept that the present paper is basically concerned.

The Chemical Anatomy of the Central Nervous System

Water and solutes.—Water comprises 70 to 85 per cent of the total mass of the central nervous system. The major portion of water is situated in the intracellular compartment with only about 15 per cent being in the combined interstitial and cerebrospinal fluid extracellular compartments. Most of the water is apparently freely and rapidly diffusible, and it serves as the solvent or transport vehicle for essential nutrients and metabolites as well as an important component of the osmotic and hydraulic regulatory systems of the central nervous system compartment.

Solutes form a very small proportion of the total mass. In cerebrospinal fluid, typifying the extracellular fluid, the total concentration of solids averages about 1 per cent (56). In the intracellular compartment the solids total more, but that fraction attributable to solutes comprises only about 2 per cent of the total mass (114). Thus, these essential and important substances, such as glucose, electrolytes, amino acids, and the like, contribute little to the mass of the central nervous system and are

285

not stored there to any degree. The composition of the more important solutes in brain and cerebrospinal fluid are given in Table 6.

Lipids.—Most of the 15 to 30 per cent solids present in central nervous tissue is lipid in nature. The cerebral lipids comprise 40 to 65 per cent of the total solids (Fig. 90), a fact which has long interested biochemists. The

TABLE 6

Composition of brain electrolytes and solutes

Component	Units	Gray	"Brain"	White	CSF*
Water	%	84.0	76	71.0	99.0
Total solids	%	16.0†	24	29.0†	1.0
Sodium	mAtoms/kg	60	57	60	141
Potassium	mAtoms/kg	95	95.6	95	3.3
Calcium‡	mAtoms/kg	. . . .	1.0	. . . . .	1.25
Magnesium‡	mAtoms/kg	. . . .	5.7	. . . . .	1.2
Chloride	mAtoms/kg	45	36.7	36	124
Total phosphate	mAtoms P/kg	77	. . . . .	132 ⎫	
Inorganic phosphate	mAtoms P/kg	15	. . . . .	12 ⎬	0.5
Sulfate	mAtoms S/kg	21	. . . . .	37 ⎭	. . . . . .
Bicarbonate	mEq/kg	. . . .	. . . . .	. . . . .	21
Lactate	mEq/kg	. . . .	. . . . .	. . . . .	1.7
Total base	mEq/kg	. . . .	210	. . . . .	155
Glucose	mM/kg	. . . .	. . . . .	. . . . .	3.4
Glycogen	mM/kg	. . . .	6.8	. . . . .	. . . . . .
Non-protein nitrogen	g N/kg	2.2	. . . . .	3.3	0.2

* Expressed per liter of CSF.
† Percentage of ash about 2.1 for both gray and white.
‡ Values for gray and white in doubt. Calcium is about equal in each; magnesium considerably higher in white than in gray.

Data derived from Rossiter (114), Manery (80), Holmes and Tower (56), Klein and Olsen (70), and Tower and Peters (unpublished).

early neurochemist, J. L. W. Thudichum (137), devoted his investigations almost exclusively to the elucidation of their nature, and much of the present knowledge of cerebral lipids is derived directly from his work of more than fifty years ago. The lipids of the central nervous system are highly complex and to a great extent different from lipids elsewhere in the body. Because of the formidable problems inherent in lipid chemistry, much remains to be learned of the nature and function of the cerebral lipids.

Most of the simple constituent units of nervous tissue lipids are now known. The currently accepted classification is given in Table 7. Neutral

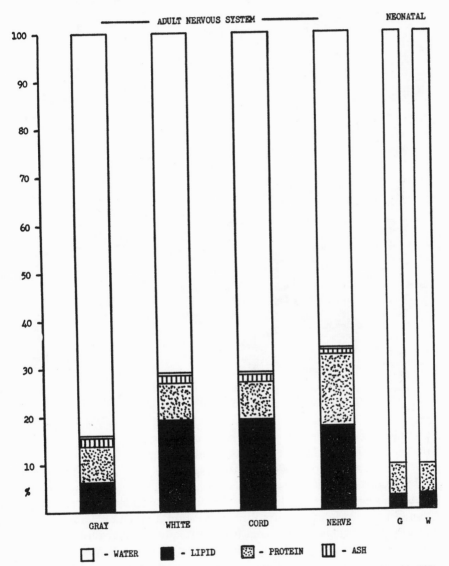

Fig. 90.—Chemical constitution of nervous tissues (approximate). The fraction of solids not specified in the graphs represents primarily NPN (60, 114).

fats (tri-glycerides) and cholesterol esters, which are common to most body tissues, do not normally occur in central nervous tissue. With the exception of free cholesterol, which has a steroid configuration, the basic structures of central nervous system lipids are simple units built upon glycerol, sphingosine, or inositol (Fig. 91) to which are added phosphate or hexose (usually galactose) groups plus fatty acids and often amino com-

TABLE 7

Classification of lipids*

I STEROLS
  A. *Cholesterol*
    1. *Free*
    2. Esters†
  B. Dicholesteryl Ethers
II PHOSPHATIDES (Phospholipids = Fatty acid + P)
  A. *Phosphoglycerides*
    1. Phosphatidyl Choline = *Lecithin*
    2. Phosphatidyl Ethanolamine ⎫
    3. Phosphatidyl Serine ⎬ *Cephalins* (monoamino phospholipids)
    4. Acetal Phosphatides (Plasmalogens) ⎭
  B. Phosphoinositides
    1. *Diphosphoinositide*
  C. Phosphosphingosides
    1. *Sphingomyelin*
III GLYCOLIPIDS (Hexose + sphingosine + fatty acid)
  A. Glycosphingosides = *Cerebrosides*   Sphingolipids
  B. *Gangliosides*
  C. Related Compounds
    1. Strandin
    2. Sulfatides
IV NEUTRAL FAT (Triglycerides)†

* From Folch-Pi and Sperry (40) and Rossiter (114).
(† Not normally present in C.N.S.)

pounds. Concentrations of the major lipid compounds in gray and white matter are given in Table 8.

There is an obvious difference in composition between these two gross subdivisions of central nervous tissue, the white matter containing appreciably more cholesterol, sphingomyelin, and cerebrosides. That these compounds are associated with myelin, which sheaths much of the fiber tracts in white matter, may be inferred from anatomical evidence and from the differences found in neonatal white matter where myelination has not taken place (Table 8). Studies on the composition of the myelin sheath of peripheral nerve confirm this impression (113). While these data are

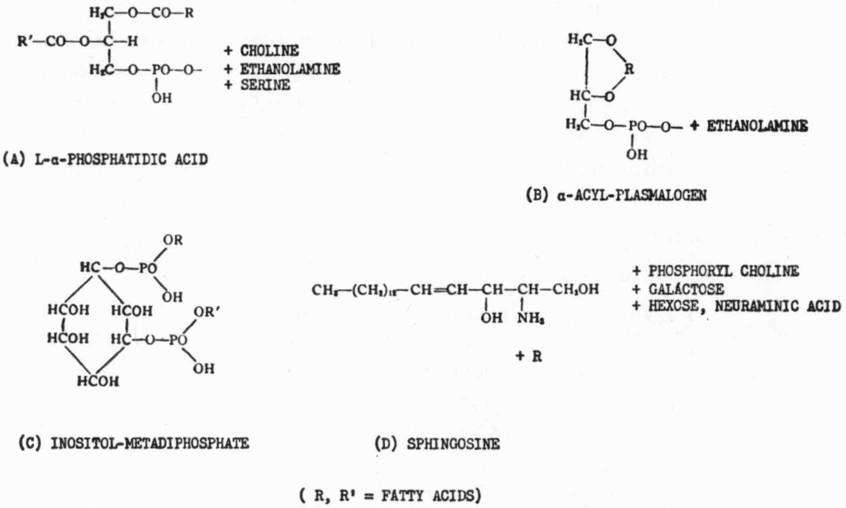

(A) L-α-PHOSPHATIDIC ACID

(B) α-ACYL-PLASMALOGEN

(C) INOSITOL-METADIPHOSPHATE   (D) SPHINGOSINE

(R, R' = FATTY ACIDS)

Fig. 91.—Basic structures of brain lipids. The addition of the side-chain groups listed, to the parent compound, forms phosphatides (A, B), diphosphoimositides (C), and Sphingosides (D).

perhaps incomplete both in terms of compounds as well as concentration and distribution, they provide some idea of the major components present.

Protein.—The manner in which simple lipid units are complexed into

TABLE 8

Concentrations of lipids in human brain (% dry weight)

	Adult*		Infant*	
	Gray	White	Gray	White
Cholesterol (free)	6.3	14.3	5.1	7.0
Phosphatides	21.0	23.8	19.6	22.1
Lecithin	6.3	4.6	7.8	9.1
Cephalins	11.7	12.4	10.5	11.6
Sphingomyelin	3.0	6.8	1.3	1.4
Cerebrosides	5.5	16.3	5.6	6.2

* Water content:	Gray	White
Adult	84%	71%
Infant	90.5%	90.5%

Data from Johnson, McNabb, and Rossiter (60).

such compounds as myelin is still virtually unknown. The majority of cerebral lipids exist as lipoproteins or liponucleoproteins, substances which behave chemically like proteins but contain lipid. In addition, a group of substances which behave as lipids but contain protein, the proteolipids, have recently been reported (37). These latter are particularly prominent in white matter. These data are summarized in Table 9.

TABLE 9

Protein in brain*

    I LIPONUCLEOPROTEINS (75% of brain lipids)
       A. Neurokeratin Fraction (proteolytic resistant)
       B. Albumin—Globulin Fraction
       C. Water-insoluble, proteolytic susceptible Fraction

    II PROTEOLIPIDS (25% of brain lipids: 20% of white, 6–8% gray solids)
       A. Fraction "B" (50% protein—50% lipid)
       B. Fraction "C" (75% protein—25% lipid)

    III NUCLEOPROTEINS

       A. Pentose nucleic acid type (cytoplasm, nucleolus)
       B. Desoxypentose nucleic acid type (nucleus)

* From Folch-Pi and Lees (37), Folch-Pi (38), Rossiter (114), and Hyden (58).

Despite the fact that proteins comprise a substantial portion of central nervous system solids (Fig. 90), little is known of their nature, composition, or distribution beyond that given in Table 9. This is a serious deficiency in knowledge since proteins contribute substantially to the structure of nervous tissue and serve as the basic templates for the activities of the enzyme systems of the central nervous system. In addition it has been suggested (47) that the storage of information by neuronal circuits may involve orientations or adaptations of protein moieties.

Proteins are structurally composed of amino acids linked by peptide bonds to form macromolecules with chain or globular configurations, their properties and specificities being due in part to the accessible side chains or polar groups exhibited at their surfaces. In many instances the active whole unit requires an additional group or groups (such as the porphyrin heme in hemoglobin). One such "complexing" group may be the nucleic acid, either of the pentose or desoxypentose type (the pentose being ribose or desoxyribose in all nucleic acids studied so far), which in association with protein forms the nucleoprotein group. The desoxypentose types occur almost exclusively in the cell nucleus, associated with nuclear chromatin, and their concentration is little affected by cellular metabolism or environmental factors. The relative constancy of desoxy-pentose nucleic acid concentration per species tissue nucleus has been used for an estimate of cell population (49). This type of nucleic acid and its associated protein is generally assumed to be concerned with the chromosomal constitution of the cell nucleus and to participate in cellular divisions. The pentose nucleic acid types occur in the nucleolus of nerve cells and in the cytoplasm, where they are intimately associated with the Nissl substance. This type of nucleic acid may be markedly affected by cellular metabolism and environmental factors. The relationships of nucleic acids to protein synthesis and enzyme production have been suggested but remain to be substantiated and detailed.

Ultrastructure.—Up to now relatively gross units of the central nervous tissue have been considered. Recently, a number of studies at the microscopic and submicroscopic levels have carried neurochemical investigations within the neuron and its component parts. Some of these data are summarized in Table 10, which has been constructed in terms of anatomical subdivisions of the neuron, describing the electron microscope picture (93) and analyses for water, lipid, protein, and nucleic acids (58, 90) for each subdivision. While these data are related mostly to spinal anterior horn motor neurons and are preliminary and incomplete, it is probable that they are fairly representative for mammalian neurons.

Note that the nucleolus has a very high concentration of solids, mostly protein in nature. With the exception of the nucleus, there is a graded increase in water concentration and decrease in nucleic acid concentration as one moves peripherally in the neuron. Lipids are apparently confined largely to nucleus and perikaryal cytoplasm and to the nerve sheath.

There are other types of studies which have been carried out at this level. Ultra-centrifugation of neurons results in four principal fractions, nucleus, mitochondria, microsomes, and the soluble or final supernatant fraction. The microsomal fraction is probably associated with the Nissl substance and contains little oxidative enzyme activity but a major share of the cytoplasmic pentose nucleic acid. The mitochondrial fraction apparently contains the majority of oxidative enzymes concerned with energy metabolism and nutrition of the neuron but only about one-fifth of the cytoplasmic nucleic acid. Relatively the soluble fraction is less important both in terms of enzyme and nucleic acid content. Nuclei have been found to contain appreciable enzyme activity, including cholinesterase (107). Differences in enzyme distribution or activity among neurons in different layers of cerebral cortex and among various parts of the neuron have been reported, using ultramicrochemical techniques on single cells or cell layers (76) or histochemical methods (100). Such studies

TABLE 10

Fine chemical anatomy of neurons*

Subdivision	Ultrastructure†	Solids			
		% H₂O	% Lipid	% Protein	% N.A.‡
1. NUCLEOLUS	Chains or threads of 10–30 mμ diam. granules	25	?	(96)	3.5 (P)
2. NUCLEOLUS ASSOC. CHROMATIN	(a) Nucleolar caps 0.5–2 μ diam., numbering 2–4	:	:	:	... (D)
	(b) Satellite (sex chromatin) 1 μ. diam. in ♀	:	:	:	... (D)
	(c) Chromocenter area—? more prominent in ♂	:	:	:	... (P)
3. NUCLEUS	Possesses double membrane, outer showing cytoplasmic projections and discontinuities up to 30 mμ. wide.	77	25	74	0.5 {P/D 2/1
4. CYTOPLASM (Perikaryon)	(a) *Nissl Bodies:* (1) "Endoplasmic reticulum" of parallel tubules or vesicles 100–200 mμ. in diam. with walls 7–8 mμ. thick in continuous system of lacunae; (2) fine granules 10–30 mμ. in diam. in patterned rows and clusters along tubules (? *Microsomal fraction*—no succinoxidase, 50% of P.N.A.). (b) *Fibrillar Network:* 6–10 mμ. in diam. and 200+ mμ. long, separating Nissl bodies. (c) *Mitochondria:* 80% succinoxidase activity; 20% P.N.A. (d) Lipid droplets and yellow pigment. (e) Cell membrane: single, smooth.	60	25	73	1.5 (P)
5. DENDRITES	Similar in appearance to perikaryon. Synaptic bulbs or end-feet on dendrites resemble simplified version of motor end-plate of Couteaux.	..			...

6. AXON HILLOCK		85	?	±100	0
7. AXON: AXOPLASM	(a) Extension of Nissl "endoplasmic reticulum"; (b) fibrillar network; (c) axoplasmic migration or flow.	90	0(?)	±100	0
SHEATH	Complex of concentric layers of protein interspersed with radially oriented bimolecular layers of lipid, each lamella separated by water spaces (Cf. Fig. 3)	65	55	45	?

* Composite tabulation from data of Nurnberger (90, 91), Hyden (58), Rossiter (114), Palay (93), and Schmitt (118).
† Ultrastructure from electron microscope, X-ray diffusion, ultraviolet spectrometry, and polarized light techniques.
‡ Nucleic acids—P = pentose type; D = desoxypentose type.

are still very preliminary and must await further extension before they can be integrated into data already presented.

Investigations by special physicochemical methods have begun to provide some conception of the molecular arrangement in nervous tissue structures. The myelin sheath has been the only such structure studied in detail. Figure 92, redrawn from Schmitt (118), illustrates the findings.

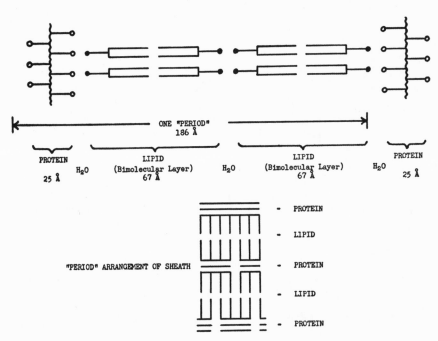

Fig. 92.—Ultrastructure of the myelin sheath (redrawn from Schmitt [118]). The molecular organization of a single protein-lipid "period" and its dimensions are shown at the top. Below is a schematic arrangement of such "periods" in the sheath. (1 Angström = 0.1 millimicron.)

The sheath is apparently composed of biomolecular lipid layers oriented radially between concentrically oriented protein chains probably separated by water channels. These concentric periods or leaflets are wrapped as laminations around the axon in the dimensions indicated. The extension of such studies combined with electron-microscope observations to central nervous system structures should be useful in relating micro-analytical data with macromolecular structure and may in certain pathological conditions reveal structural alterations or differences not visible by ordinary microscopic techniques.

Methods of Study

It must already be apparent that many methods and disciplines are being brought to bear on the problems of chemical constitution of the central nervous system. Still others are being applied to problems of neuronal metabolism. In order to understand and evaluate the data presented, a brief consideration of the general methods available and in use may be appropriate.

In vivo.—Observations carried out on intact, living central nervous tissue *in situ* are clearly the most desirable. So far these have been restricted, to some degree at least, by the anatomical situation and physiological sensitivity of the central nervous system. Two general approaches have been developed.

The one is concerned with overall measurements of cerebral circulation, oxygen consumption, metabolic exchange and the like, utilizing the Schmidt-Kety nitrous oxide technique (67, 68, 117) or modifications thereof. These studies have been of great value in providing an overall picture of the main facets of brain metabolism, such as oxygen consumption and glucose utilization, and how these vary with changes in physiological states, such as anesthesia, sleep, mental activity, anxiety and convulsions (67, 68). A special aspect of this approach has been the use of isotopically-labelled compounds administered systemically with subsequent sampling of cerebral fluids or tissue to determine their fates. The usefulness of compounds which do not freely pass the blood-central nervous system barriers has been restricted in terms of rates of metabolism or turnover within the brain, but information regarding routes of metabolism and relative importances of substrates and alternate metabolic pathways can still be obtained in many instances.

The second approach has been concerned with the study *in situ* of relatively intact, localized brain areas. Local circulation, pH, oxygen tension and the like can be measured in areas of brain either physically isolated or isolated in terms of local circulation (19, 46, 73). In the latter case perfusion of the local area can be carried out to permit assessment of the effects of physiological changes or pharmacological agents upon measurable activities of the area, such as electrical activity, oxygen tension and the like. Such studies have been few, due primarily to the technical difficulties of the method, and they have been largely restricted to accessible and relatively gross surface areas. The development of a procedure for perfusion of the whole isolated brain *in situ* (42) represents a combination of the two general methods which has introduced some new and interesting findings.

Data derived from these in vivo approaches have been of considerable value for correlation with in vitro observations. Yet the in vivo methods are at present limited both in terms of technical difficulties of the experimental set-up and in the problem of studying small or localized areas particularly in less accessible regions of the central nervous system, not just for overall functioning and activity but also for the more detailed aspects of metabolism. One of the greatest challenges in neurochemistry and neurophysiology today is the need to bridge the gap between the extensive and detailed data derived from in vitro studies and the situations encountered in the intact, functioning nervous system. Those working at the latter level are approaching the point in methodology where combined studies can soon be attempted. Until then the extent of the data and the correlations with known biochemical systems will necessarily be restricted to a greater or lesser degree.

In vitro.—Resort to in vitro methods overcomes much of the difficulty inherent in in vivo approaches, but they pose new problems which tend to negate this advantage. Two main elements are lacking in the in vitro preparations—capillary circulation and spontaneous neuronal activity associated with intact neuronal circuits. While these deficiencies can be compensated for to greater or lesser degree, the fact remains that the tissue sample in vitro is no longer in its natural, intact environment and it cannot, therefore, be expected to manifest metabolic behavior identical to that in vivo, if such could be studied. The gap and complementary limitations between in vivo and in vitro studies has made neurochemical investigation of the central nervous system difficult indeed.

Three principal in vitro preparations for studying neuronal metabolism are available, the slice, the homogenate, and the cell-free extract. The tissue slice technique is probably the closest in vitro analogy to the in vivo situation. Here the cell body integrity is maintained, capillary circulation is well compensated for by increased oxygenation, and stimuli (either chemical or physical) can be applied which resemble to some degree neuronal activity. The particular advantage of the slice is that by maintenance of the integrity of the cell body, over-all metabolic reactions are retained. Such system reactions are modified or lost when the cell is fragmented. The slice technique makes it possible to study compounds which depend upon cellular intactness (such as bound acetylcholine) or those which are rapidly metabolized or destroyed upon cell destruction (such as high-energy phosphate compounds). Effects of environmental factors and of drugs or toxins, many of which function either via intact cell membranes or in the presence of intact systems, on metabolic reactions of the neuron are well studied by this technique. In situations of dysfunction the slice preparation may be the only in vitro method to exhibit bio-chemical correlates of such dysfunction since multiple systems may be involved which would lose identity upon cell fragmentation.

However, the slice technique suffers from the disadvantage that it is usually possible to follow only over-all reactions in which the many intermediate steps or alternate pathways cannot be observed or evaluated. Interpretation in terms of mechanisms concerned may be difficult or impossible. When such detailed data are required, fragmentation and fractionation of the cell must be resorted to. Homogenization ruptures cytoplasmic membranes but usually leaves nuclei, mitrochondria, and other major cell units relatively intact. Many enzymatic reactions and the active concentrations of enzymes can be conveniently studied on homog-enates. Further refinements by fractionation or extraction to reduce the number of cellular components and by precipitation or organic extrac-tion procedures to isolate individual enzymes or enzyme systems are in-valuable in providing knowledge about the nature of reactions, kinds of enzymes involved, and factors which affect them.

Such data are relatively far removed from the intact, functioning cell, and they are often misleading or difficult to apply to whole-cell or in vivo systems. These isolated preparations often behave differently alone from the way they behave in series or parallel with other enzymes or systems, the precise constitution of which may not be discernible by the methods employed or available. An example is the phosphatase group of enzymes easily demonstrable in nervous tissue extracts or homogenates, which function there by splitting organic phosphate bonds to give inorganic phosphate. While possible, such a reaction in the intact cell would be most uneconomical since it fails to conserve energy stored in the organic phosphate bond at the cost of a complex series of metabolic reactions. More probable is the view that these phosphatases actually represent frag-ments of phospho-transferase systems in which only the initial removal step remains. This illustrates the caution necessary in interpreting data obtained with such techniques.

In some cases none of the above methods is suitable to solution of the problem. There is a whole body of data derived from the techniques of sampling living brain *in situ*. These are designed primarily to attempt to follow the course of active compounds (such as acetylcholine) in relation to cerebral activity. Simple sampling even in the absence of anesthesia is usually not very fruitful because of the capacity of the neurons to revert to resting or "normal" conditions. Reductions in acetylcholine during con-vulsant activity, for example, would never be detected since resynthesis to inter-ictal levels occurs in seconds or less (63, 106). Thus, rapid immo-

TABLE 11

Micromethods for study of nervous tissue

Method	Procedure	Relative Values
HISTOCHEMISTRY	Staining of microscopic sections by histochemical reactions and microscopic inspection. Radioautography is a special application, using isotopically labelled cpds.	Simple method which gives intracellular localization, but is not quantitative and may give artifacts or false localizations. Not applicable to many important compounds because of lack of suitable methods.
MICROSPECTROGRAPHY	Observation or measurement of absorption spectrum (usually ultraviolet, ? infrared) of compounds, properties in polarized light, or X-ray diffraction, using histological sections.	Complex method but gives excellent intracellular localization and can be quantitated in some cases. Not all substances are suitable for this type of analysis and quantitation may be interfered with by uncontrollable factors.
DIFFERENTIAL CENTRIFUGATION	Fractionation of cell by centrifugation at various speeds to obtain individual cell components.	Good quantitation and localization of a "gross" nature. Retains heterogeneity of tissue sample (glia and neurons) and is not suitable for all enzymes or compounds due to adsorption, diffusion, and inactivation processes.
ULTRAMICROCHEMISTRY	Microdissection of single cells or cell groups and analysis by ultramicrochemical and metabolic reactions.	Good quantitation and specificity but gives little or no intracellular localization and is not adaptable to all types of reactions due to inactivation during preparation.

Summarized from Robins and Smith (110).

bilization, usually by freezing in liquid air or nitrogen, is necessary. This is easily achieved with small animals where the entire animal or head can be dropped in and frozen within a second or two. It is a cumbersome to impossible technique with larger animals or man. Certain data obtained by this general technique have been very useful in demonstrating neurochemical correlates of central nervous system activity. However, there are distinct disadvantages and limitations which restrict its usefulness. Freezing and the thawing necessary before analysis may destroy or modify compounds markedly. More important only a single instantaneous event can be recorded by one specimen. The variations from millisecond to millisecond and from subject to subject limit results to, at best, glimpses of metabolic events which can be fragmentary indeed.

None of these methods permit much localization of cellular reactions or demonstration of differences in types of reactions between cells in such relatively gross tissue samples. Microtechniques have been resorted to for such problems, but no one of these is satisfactory by itself, and combinations are not necessarily complementary. Table 11 summarizes the principal available techniques, derived from a recent review of this subject (110). Such methods and their modifications are only beginning to be applied to study of central nervous system tissues. Much interesting data concerning intracellular and local biochemical organization should be provided, but, in addition to the technical problems inherent in the methods, they suffer from the basic problem of analytical overrefinement. It is possible to obtain and analyze single-cell metabolism but this, as Folch-Pi (39) pointed out, is too great a degree of resolution since it would be necessary to sample myriads of such cells to obtain a valid picture of normal metabolic activity for a given cell type or location. In terms of neuronal dysfunction such a problem would be greatly magnified.

These, then, are the principal tools available to and used by the neurochemist (in addition to recognized classical chemical and physicochemical analytical techniques). They should serve as a background for the analytical and metabolic data presented, emphasizing the technical problems and the limitations which should commend caution to the interpreter of such data in the complex areas of integration into function and behavior.

The Central Nervous System and the Whole Organism

Blood-brain barriers.—In neurological research the central nervous system often comes to be regarded as an almost autonomous unit or the central organ of the body. The mammalian organism is indeed destitute without a functioning central nervous system, but that organ is, in a sense, more dependent upon an intact, well-functioning rest of the body than most of the other organs or tissues. One of the unique safety devices which has evolved to protect the central nervous system from the vicissitudes of daily body life is the blood-brain barrier. The neuron is highly sensitive to changes in its environment so that this mechanism is apparently provided as an homeostatic mechanism to maintain an optimal environment in which the central nervous system can function (143). The anatomical correlate of this mechanism has long been in dispute, but recent studies suggest that the luminal aspect of cerebral capillary endothelium and the ventricular aspect of the choroid plexus epithelium may be the locus of the barrier (111).

Recent studies with isotopically labeled solutes and metabolites (see 56) have clarified the problems of the barrier functions and physiological nature. There is apparently no barrier to water or gas (carbon dioxide, oxygen) exchange between the central nervous system compartment and the general blood circulation. These are freely and rapidly diffusible into and out of the central nervous system. Certain lipid soluble compounds (such as anesthetics) experience little barrier delay, but the majority of substances have their access to the central nervous system delayed, regulated, or even virtually prevented by the barrier mechanism. Electrolytes and solutes, like sodium, potassium, chloride, and glucose meet delays of minutes to hours (characteristic of the substance) before equilibration of plasma and cerebrospinal fluid or tissue concentrations is reached. Other substances such as phosphate or albumen exhibit much longer delays, and penetration of certain compounds is slow indeed. That the barrier is not simply an impedance but a functioning mechanism is illustrated by numerous examples. Glutamic acid, in common with most strong acids, cannot be shown to increase in the central nervous system compartment even after large parenteral doses (119), yet studies of arteriovenous differences clearly indicate that exchange into the central nervous system normally occurs (1). Other factors such as charge, molecular size, and the like, affect the accessibility of substances.

Perhaps the most interesting example of barrier function concerns carbohydrate supply to central nervous tissue. The fact that glucose is essentially the sole source of energy for the brain is well established, yet in vitro brain tissue can utilize numerous other carbohydrates with ease. The explanation of the paradox lies with the blood-brain barrier, which passes glucose much more readily and rapidly than fructose, pyruvate, or other possible substitutes.

These studies exemplify the regulatory nature of the barrier in terms of supply of necessary nutrients and substrates to the central nervous system and the protective function in excluding undersirable or toxic substances. In disease of other organs or particularly of the central nervous system itself, this mechanism can be quite disadvantageous either by its failure, with consequent increased permeability, or by preventing access of essential substrates and therapeutic agents.

The reverse process, disposal of substances liberated from the central nervous system, is not so well studied. Outward transfer or diffusion is apparently rapid for the few substances investigated, but this is not true for all (notably larger molecules). There is a possible discrepancy here since a regulation or inflow without any mechanism to control outflow, at least of essential solutes, does not seem to be an ideal arrangement. Further study is required both on this aspect and on the basic mechanisms whereby the barrier achieves its functional results.

Within the central nervous system compartment there appears to be no subsequent barrier except the cell membrane itself. Cerebrospinal fluid is now considered to be co-extensive with the interstitial fluid of central nervous tissue with rapid and free penetration of solutes from one to the other. The exact limits of the extracellular space in the vicinity of the neuron are not yet clear since space studies with inulin give different dimensions from those with thiocyanate or sucrose, suggesting that certain larger molecules may not have as ready access to the cell (25). For most purposes, however, it does not seem necessary to subdivide the extracellular space.

The site of formation of cerebrospinal fluid was classically assumed to be the choroid plexuses. More recent studies with deuterium and tritium indicate that water may enter the fluid spaces at any point. Isotope studies with solutes on the other hand suggest that the majority enter the cerebral ventricles first, presumably via the choroid plexuses, although smaller fractions evidently enter elsewhere. Similarly, egress from the cerebrospinal fluid spaces, once considered to be limited to the arachnoidal villi, may apparently occur elsewhere. The free and rapid transfers of water permit the maintenance of isotonicity of central nervous system extracellular fluids with other body fluids at all times.

Nutrition.—Central nervous tissue is relatively self-sufficient in its nutritional requirements. The important exceptions are oxygen and glucose. Most of the other substances required for its structure, function, and activity, are apparently synthesized *in situ*, mainly from glucose metabolism. A few components such as vitamins, certain amino acids, and the like are also required from the general circulation, but in relatively small quantities compared with oxygen and glucose. The dependence of central nervous tissue upon these two substances is firmly established. The dysfunctions which attend deprivation of either or both are rapid, dramatic, and often irreversible within very short periods. Skeletal muscle can function under conditions of anoxia for many minutes to hours, and liver can utilize fats in the absence of carbohydrate for days. The brain appears to be devoid of such reserves or alternate pathways, with the sole recourse of consuming its own protein and lipid, which rapidly results in irreversible structural damage.

Integration.—Integration of the central nervous system into the total functioning organism forms an entire subject in itself. Yet it is important to bear in mind significant facets of this aspect since these physiological regulatory mechanisms have in the intact organism fundamental bearings on neuronal function and activity. In addition to the blood-brain barriers, the central nervous system possesses its own mechanism for regulating blood flow, oxygen and carbon dioxide tensions, pH, and the like, which are to a considerable extent independent of general regulatory mechanisms elsewhere in the body. In a reciprocal type of relationship the central nervous system exerts important controls over other organs and body functions, notably respiration, cardiac function, vascular dynamics, hormonal secretions, and renal function. Such important integrative aspects cannot be treated here but must be borne in mind in the subsequent discussions.

CARBOHYDRATE METABOLISM

It is appropriate to begin the consideration of neuronal metabolism with carbohydrate because of the fundamental importance of its metabolism to the central nervous system. Carbohydrate, as glucose, is essentially the sole source of cellular energy for central nervous tissue. It serves as a major source of structural units such as amino and fatty acids. It is the principal source of carbon dioxide for the regulation of pH both extracellularly and intracellularly. Its metabolism, therefore, embraces the basic series of reactions upon which neuronal function and activity depend.

Utilization of Oxygen and Glucose

Oxygen uptake in vivo and in vitro.—By use of the Fick principle in conjunction with the nitrous oxide method for measuring cerebral blood flow, Kety and others have obtained data on cerebral oxygen consumption in vivo for man and various experimental animals (68). In the normal, awake, resting human subject, cerebral oxygen consumption averages 3.3 ml/100 gm/min or a $-Q_{O_2}$ of 9.9.* From studies of physio-

---

* Q values = microliters of gas evolved or taken up (designated by $-Q$), at standard temperature and pressure, per milligram dry weight of tissue per hour. Conversion

logical and pathological factors affecting these values, two groups emerge: (*a*) that in which significant changes in cerebral blood flow occur without much change in oxygen consumption (hyperventilation, inhalation of 10 per cent O_2, cerebral angioma); and (*b*) that in which there are significant changes in $-Q_{O_2}$ without much change in blood flow. The latter are summarized in Table 12. Convulsions are the only case in this

TABLE 12

Cerebral oxygen consumption in vivo

Subject	Mental state	$-Q_{O_2}$	CBF*
MAN	Anxiety (i.v. epinephrine)	15.0	..
	Normal, resting	9.9	54
	Confused	8.1	49
	Anesthesia (thiopental)	6.3	60
	Coma	5.4	64
MONKEY	Convulsing	19.5	
	"Normal"	11.1	
	"Coma" (reversible)	5.6	
	"Coma" (irreversible)	3.5	
CAT	Convulsing	±18	
	"Normal"	±13.5	
	Coma	6.9	

* Cerebral blood flow in ml/100 gm/min. Compiled from Kety (68), Schmidt, Kety, and Pennes (117), and Geiger and Magnes (42).

group where change in cerebral blood flow (increase up to twice "normal") is associated with change in oxygen consumption. In anesthesia the reduction in oxygen uptake may result from decreased neuronal activity rather than from the anesthetic agent.

Only a very few studies of local brain areas in vivo have been reported. With the oxygen electrode, observations of oxygen consumption by the suprasylvian gyrus of cat cerebral cortex have been made (19, 46). These are summarized in Table 13. Data on other areas of cortex and deeper

factors for brain tissue to other common units are the following (23): Q values = ml/gr/hr $\times$ 5; Q values = ml/100 gr/min $\times$ 3; ml/gr/hr = ml/100 gr/min $\times$ 0.6; 1 millimole (mM.) = 22.4 ml.

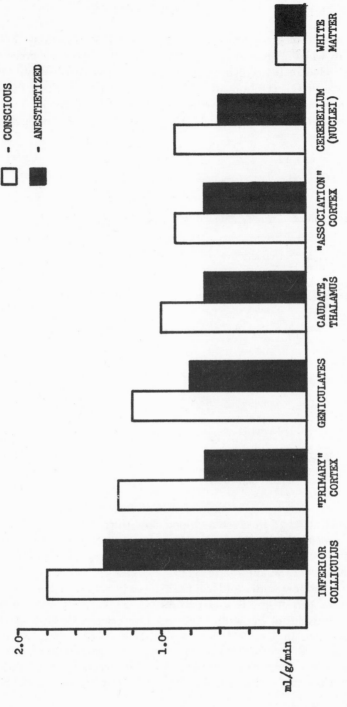

Fig. 93.—Local blood flow in various areas of cat brain. (Modified from data of Landau et al. [73]).

structures would be of interest. Recently Kety and co-workers (73) have been able to estimate local blood flow in various brain areas, using an inert, radioactive gas. Their results are given in Figure 93. Anesthesia apparently reduces blood flow of the more "active" areas to a level relatively uniform with areas of lower blood flow. Such local differences in circulation may reflect local metabolic rates with which oxygen consumption might correlate.

TABLE 13

Local oxygen consumption in vivo (cat cerebral cortex)

Condition	EEG	O_2 Consumption (Change from resting state)
Metrazol convulsions	Paroxysmal bursts	+30%
0.5 mM. Nembutal	Markedly depressed	−25%

From Davies and Remond (19) and Grenell and Davies (46).

There are more extensive data from in vitro studies, but their application to in vivo situations is difficult. Factors which affect in vitro tissue respiration include oxygen tension, substrate type and concentration, pH, electrolytes, drugs, and many others, all of which are closely interwoven with glycolysis (see below). Both in vivo and in vitro respiratory function of brain tissue can be maintained at very low oxygen tensions (4–5 mm. Hg) (26). Unlike brain in vivo, which exhibits normal oxygen consumption without any glucose or substrate (46), slices or suspensions rapidly and irrevocably lose activity in the absence of glucose or related compounds. On the other hand pyruvate, lactate, and glutamic acid will support respiration in vitro but not in vivo (presumably due to their slow penetration of the blood-brain barrier). Stimulation of respiration by increased concentrations of potassium occurs both in vitro and in vivo. There are numerous other observations which cannot be covered here (see 23 for details).

Oxygen uptake in vitro can be correlated with the size of species studied. Respiration per unit weight of brain decreases with increasing size of animal species according to the relationship: $-Q_{O_2} = 18.0 \times W^{-0.1}$ (where W equals average body weight of a given species in grams). (See Figure 96.) The $-Q_{O_2}$ of brain is not high compared with other body tissues. In the rat, retina and kidney cortex respire more actively, and

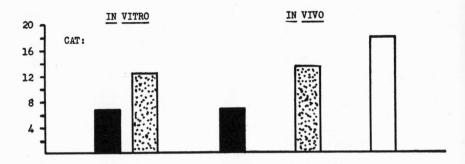

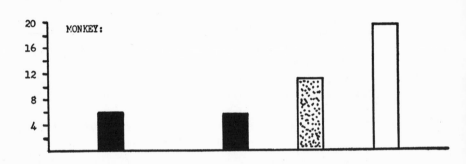

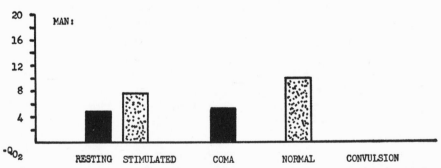

Fig. 94.—Comparison of $-Q_{O_2}$ of whole brain in vitro and in vivo. Values for whole brain in vitro are estimated values (23). The stimulated samples in vitro were obtained by chemical stimulation (cat) or electrical stimulation (man) (71, 77). Data derived from Elliott (23).

many other organs exhibit the same order of activity. A few values for oxygen uptake by various areas of brain are given in Table 14, which may be of interest to compare with Figure 93.

Comparable values for $-Q_{O_2}$ of brain in vivo and in vitro are illustrated in Figure 94. The in vitro figures correspond roughly to those in vivo associated with depressed functional activity. This is not unreasonable since neurons in vitro exhibit no spontaneous activity, and their metabolism cannot be stimulated except by experimental means. If chemical or electrical stimulation is applied, respiration in vitro increases markedly to levels which compare with "normal" or resting rates in vivo.

TABLE 14

$-Q_{O_2}$ of areas of dog brain in vitro

Area	$-Q_{O_2}$
Cerebral cortex	5.8
Cerebellum	7.0
Thalamus and caudate	5.9
Medulla (? gray + white)	3.5
White matter	50% or less rate of gray

From Himwich and Fazekas (54) and Elliott (23).

There is general agreement that respiration both in vivo and in vitro for brain is normally at the expense of glucose. The R.Q. (respiratory quotient)* averages 0.95 in slices, and similar values have been obtained in vivo, i.e., close to 1.0, the theoretical R.Q. for complete combustion of carbohydrate (23). The rate of oxygen usage is probably controlled by the level of high-energy phosphate compounds derived from glucose (see below). In man at any one time the brain will contain about 7 ml. total oxygen, which, at a rate of utilization of some 50 ml/min, would last about 10 sec., with symptoms of anoxia appearing before complete consumption. Survival time of the central nervous system in the face of oxygen deficit is therefore very short, a fact well documented clinically. In contrast, stores of carbohydrate (glucose and glycogen) are such that brain, deprived of its glucose supply, can survive much longer. In deep insulin coma, blood glucose levels are too low to support the observed oxygen consumption, so that brain must be using its own supply. It can be calculated on the basis of its stores (about 2 gm. in man) that, at a rate of oxy-

* R.Q. $= Q_{CO_2}/-Q_{O_2}$.

gen consumption of 1.9 ml/100 gm/min, the supply would last 90 min., which is the approximate limit for insulin coma without irreversible changes (67, 68).

Maintenance of respiration in the absence of glucose suggests that noncarbohydrate substances (glutamic acid, protein, and lipid) are being consumed with consequent damage to neuronal structure and functional capacity. Even at measurable blood levels of glucose, symptoms of hypoglycemia occur, emphasizing the difference between concentrations in blood and at the neuron some distance from the capillary involving the diffusion gradient. Clinical examples of repeated exposures to anoxia or hypoglycemia are consistent with these considerations. To paraphrase Haldane, anoxia or lack of glucose not only stops production but wrecks the machine (68).

$$1 \text{ GLUCOSE} \xrightarrow[\text{Glycolysis}]{\text{No } O_2} 2 \text{ LACTIC ACID} + 54,000 \text{ cals.} \nearrow 2 CO_2 \text{ (Bicarbonate)}$$
$$\downarrow$$
$$2 \sim P$$

$$1 \text{ GLUCOSE} + 6 O_2 \longrightarrow 6 CO_2 + 6 H_2O + 690,000 \text{ cals.}$$
$$\downarrow$$
$$32+ \sim P$$

Fig. 95.—The relative efficiencies of Anaerobic glycosis (top reaction) and complete oxidation (bottom reaction) in production of high-energy phosphate ($\sim P$) from glucose (23).

Glycolysis.—The series of reactions by which glucose is initially broken down in preparation for oxidative metabolism is grouped under the term "glycolysis" (or more specifically, "glucolysis"), which is usually measured as lactic acid production. In brain glycolysis may be either aerobic (oxygen available) or anaerobic (oxygen absent).* Like many other tissues, brain can utilize glucose in the absence of oxygen. In fact, the rate of utilization is several times that under aerobic conditions. Despite this fact the energy yield per glucose molecule is poor by comparison with

* Q values expressed as: Q_A^O (aerobic acid production); Q_A^N (anaeroboic production).

complete oxidation of glucose in the presence of adequate oxygen (Fig. 95).

The average value for glucose consumption of human brain in vivo is 5.4 mg/100 gm/min under normal, resting conditions. The R.Q. and direct measurements indicate that normally all oxygen consumed by the brain is utilized for complete oxidation of glucose, only a small portion (about 15 per cent) going to lactic acid (44, 68). In insulin-induced hypo-glycemia, utilization of glucose from blood is virtually nil, although R.Q. remains unity, indicating metabolism from brain carbohydrate stores to support metabolism at a reduced level. In contrast, supplies of oxygen and glucose to brain are both adequate in diabetic coma or uremia, but there is a similar reduction in oxygen consumption which is apparently correlated with derangement of cellular metabolism in the presence of keto-compounds (68).

Under uniform conditions in vitro glycolytic activity of brain tissue is more variable and more sensitive to accelerating and inhibitory factors than respiration. Thus, comparisons of relative glycolytic rates are less satisfactory. Again, brain does not glycolyze as actively as some other body tissues (notably retina) and is similar in activity to many others (23). Within the brain, cerebral cortex and basal ganglia have the highest rates of anaerobic glycolysis, cerebellum and medulla are intermediate, and white matter quite low (16). Comparisons between species indicate an appreciable increase in anaerobic glycolysis per unit weight of brain tissue with increasing species size (Fig. 96). The concurrent decrease in oxygen consumption, previously noted, accentuates this relationship.

In the presence of oxygen there is suppression of glycolysis (the Pasteur effect), but in certain tissues (cancers, retina, testis, and, to lesser extent, brain) the suppression is less complete and aerobic glycolysis can be detected. In vitro, depleted brain tissue exhibits higher and longer sustained aerobic glycolysis when supplied with glucose than more normally constituted samples (23). Mixed conditions occur if oxygen supply is insufficient to permit adequate diffusion to interior areas.

Of the many factors which affect glycolysis several are important to consider here. Sodium ions are potent depressors of anaerobic glycolysis, at the same time stimulating aerobic glycolysis. Increased concentrations of potassium or ammonium ions or glutamate also stimulate aerobic glycolysis while depressing anaerobic activity, but this effect is limited to brain tissue. It is of interest that addition of adenosine triphosphate (ATP) to slices abolishes the suppression of anaerobic glycolysis by glutamate (128). When potassium concentrations are increased in the incubation medium, the levels of high-energy phosphate compounds decrease

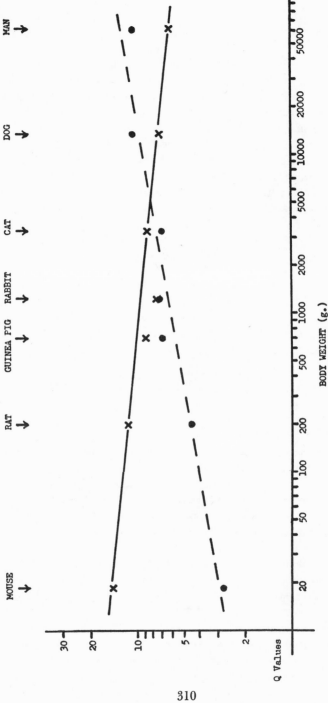

Fig. 96.—Correlation of respiration (**X**) and anaerobic glycolysis (•) of slices of cerebral cortex *in vitro* with average body weight of species (log scales). Units of ordinate in *Q* values. The significance of the correlation of glycolysis has not been established. Data derived from Elliott (23).

significantly in the brain slices (Brodkin and Elliott—unpublished). Electrical stimulation of brain tissue in vitro is associated with both an increase in respiration and in glycolysis (77). In vivo there is normally some lactic acid production by brain and it increases markedly during convulsive activity. Narcotics (anesthesia), which in vivo are associated with decreased oxygen consumption, exhibit a considerable stimulatory effect on aerobic glycolysis in vitro (152). Insulin, which presumably functions at some stage in the glycolytic utilization of glucose in other tissues, apparently does not affect brain tissue metabolism in vitro or directly in vivo (23).

In skeletal muscle and probably also in brain, glycolysis can serve as a rapid but inefficient means of producing energy as high-energy phosphate compounds (cf. Fig. 95), when depletion is exceeding oxygen supply. In the newborn glycolytic activity in brain is relatively higher than respiratory activity and may be adequate for the lower energy demands. These facts may explain the greater resistance of newborn brain to anoxia compared with the adult brain (31, 53). However, the normal occurrence of aerobic glycolysis in vivo suggests another function for glycolysis, that of local or over-all regulation of pH and circulation in brain (23). Increased lactic acid production during hypoxia would liberate more carbon dioxide, which in turn could dilate vessels to assist in increasing circulation and supplies to the area. Changes in intracellular pH by this mechanism could affect the state of functional activity. The effect of narcotics in increasing glycolysis may be related to their actions in depressing neuronal function. The glycolytic mechanism appears to be self-regulating since it slows or ceases as pH drops (23).

Little has been said about the localization of these processes except that they are more active in gray than in white matter. Since gray matter contains not only neurons but glial cells, which account for up to 80 per cent of the total *cells* in cerebral cortex (50), it is important to know the relative capacities of neurons and glia for this type of metabolism. Recently Heller and Elliott (50) have clarified this point in a study of cerebral cortex, cerebellar cortex (containing more neurons per unit weight), and *corpus callosum* (containing as many cells as cerebral cortex but no neurons), as well as glial tumors. Their findings are summarized in Table 15. Per unit weight both cerebral and cerebellar cortex respire more actively than *corpus callosum,* but per cell the rate is highest in cerebral cortex, much lower in *corpus callosum,* and least in cerebellar cortex. Oligodendroglia, which are more numerous in white matter, appear to respire more actively than astrocytes, which predominate in gray matter (see also 146). From these data it can be calculated that at least 70 per cent of cerebral cortex respiration is accounted for by neurons. The difference between cerebral and cerebellar cortex may in part be due to the factor of cell volume, since neurons in the former are generally of much greater volume. Characteristically the tumors show rates of glycolysis relative to respiration higher than in normal white or gray matter, although the absolute rates are much lower. Within the cell itself what data are avail-

TABLE 15

Respiration and glycolysis of various neural elements

Tissue	Cell Type	Cell Density (Nuclei/mm^3 $\times$ 1000)	$-Q_{O_2}$ (tissue)*	O_2 Uptake per 10^6 Nuclei (μl/hr)*	Aerobic Glycolysis (μl/mg/hr)†	Anaerobic Glycolysis (μl/mg/hr)†
CAT						
Cerebral cortex	Mixed	128	12.4	19	0.4	1.35
Corpus callosum	Glial	135	2.5	5.7	0.2	0.4
Cerebellar cortex	Mixed	808	10.6	2.6	...	....
MAN:						
Cerebral cortex	Mixed	131	10.6	14.5	0.6	2.0
Corpus callosum	Glial	.112	....	(4.8)‡	...	0.3
Cortical white	Glial	....	2.7	(6.7)‡	...	....
TUMORS (Human):						
Medulloblastoma		1600	2.2	0.2	0.35	1.25
Astrocytoma*		210	2.7	0.9	0.2	0.3
Oligodendroglioma*		298	....	4.7	0.2	0.6

* Values for phosphate-buffered medium except for two tumors indicated, which were for bicarbonate-buffered medium. Latter values on normal tissues were about 30% lower than in former.

† Fresh weight of tissue.

‡ Assuming *corpus callosum* and white to be similar. Adapted from Heller and Elliott (50).

able suggest that most, if not all, of the respiratory and glycolytic activity is in association with the mitochondrial fraction.

Glucose degradation.—Details of glucose and oxygen ultization to produce cellular energy have been well worked out and have been confirmed in brain (18). The utilization of glucose can be conveniently divided into three stages, glycolysis, oxidation, and production of energy, all of which are intimately related within the functioning cell.

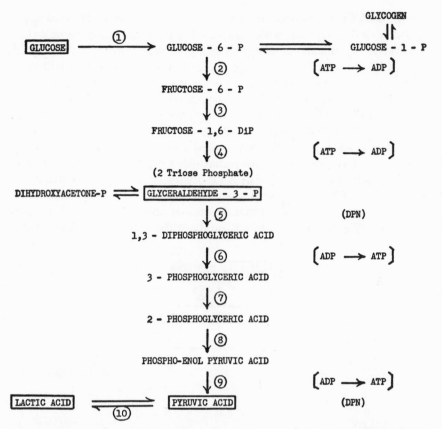

Fig. 97.—The glycolytic reactions. The important compounds are enclosed in boxes. Energy changes are given to the right of the corresponding reaction. Enzymes catalyzing these reactions (circled numbers) are the following: (1) *Hexokinase,* (2) Hexosisomerase, (3) Phosphofructokinase, (4) *Aldolase,* (5) *Triosephosphate dehydrogenase,* (6) Phosphoglyceric phosphokinase, (7) Phosphoglyceric mutase, (8) Enolase, (9) Pyruvic phosphokinase, and (10) *Lactic dehydrogenase* (italicized enzymes are the most important). The abbreviation P = phosphate. Data derived from Coxon (18), Racker (104), and Umbreit (145).

The steps in the glycolytic process are outlined in Figure 97. In this stage glucose is assimilated into the cell, phosphorylated, and either stored as glycogen or split into two 3-carbon compounds which are oxidized to pyruvate (or lactate). These "complex molecular acrobatics" (104) provide relatively little energy but serve to convert the glucose molecule into a form which can be fed into the second stage. Phosphorylation and cleavage to 3-carbon size are essential to this conversion.

Energy as ATP is required at two steps. The common intermediate, gly-ceraldehyde-3-phosphate, which is formed, must be oxidized (using oxygen indirectly) by means of the coenzyme, diphosphopyridine nucleotide (DPN). The subsequent steps regenerate ATP used up and contribute an excess to the energy pool. If lactate is the final step (anaerobic glycolysis), the DPN is reoxidized and no net oxygen consumption need occur.

The activity of the glycolytic stage appears to be regulated by the ratio of ATP to ADP, since 2 ATP are required per molecule of glucose phosphorylated, but 4 ADP are required to accept energy-rich phosphate in succeeding steps (Fig. 97). Meyerhof (85, 86) pointed out that if excessive destruction or utilization of ATP occurs, or if insufficient utilization occurs, the ATP/ADP ratio is upset and glycolysis fails. In the reaction series the rate-limiting step is that dependent upon triose phosphate dehydrogenase (Fig. 97, Step 5), which catalyzes the coupled phosphorylation

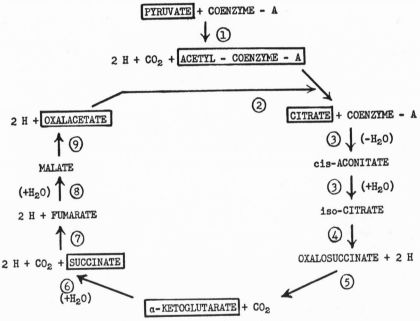

Fig. 98.—Pyruvate metabolism and the Krebs tricarboxylic acid cycle. The important compounds are enclosed in boxes. Enzymes catalyzing these reactions (circled numbers) are the following: (1) *cocarboxylase* (diphosphothiamine), (2) *Condensing enzyme* (Ochoa), (3) *Aconitase,* (4) Isocritric dehydrogenase, (5) Oxalosuccinic decarboxylase, (6) Ketoglutaric dehydrogenase, (7) *Succinic dehydrogenase,* (8) Fumarase, and (9) Malic dehydrogenase (italicized enzymes are the most important). Data derived from Krebs (72).

of glyceraldehyde-3-phosphate to 1,3-diphosphoglyceric acid (104). It is particularly sensitive to various inhibitors and is a key enzyme in the anaerobic production of ATP.

In the presence of oxygen, utilization of glucose does not stop at lactate but continues into the second stage, the familiar Krebs tricarboxylic acid (or citric acid) cycle (Fig. 98). The manner in which pyruvate is fed into the cycle is complex, apparently due in part to the difficulty which the cell has in handling a 2-carbon fragment. Thus, pyruvate undergoes oxidative decarboxylation, catalyzed by diphosphothiamine (cocarboxylase), and the resulting acetyl-fragment combines with coenzyme-A to form acetyl-coenzyme-A. The cell now has a choice of using this complex for acetylation (choline to acetylcholine), for donating acetate to fatty acid synthesis, or for condensation with oxalacetate to form citrate, as the first step in the Krebs cycle.

With the formation of citrate, the cycle proceeds as shown in Figure 98. This series of reactions completes the degradation of the glucose molecule. Its apparent complexity has several important purposes in permitting a number of important functions to be carried out more or less simultaneously. In the cycle six molecules of carbon dioxide are given off for each molecule of glucose utilized, accounting for the six carbons and oxygens in the glucose molecule. The carbon dioxide is important to the cell in the regulation of pH and in regulating cerebral vascular dynamics. In addition hydrogen molecules are given off to complete the disposition of the glucose molecule. These are essential in generating the "energy-rich phosphate" resulting from complete oxidation of glucose (cf. Fig. 95), and are finally converted to cellular water, thus accounting for the remainder of the oxygen consumed in utilization of the glucose molecule. As the cycle is completed oxalacetate is regenerated to start the cycle again.

Krebs (72) has emphasized that the tricarboxylic acid cycle represents the common terminal pathway of oxidation of all foodstuffs. At this point the final stage in utilization of the glucose molecule comes into action to produce cellular energy, a special form of chemical energy stored in the pyrophosphate bonds of ATP, ADP, and phosphocreatine (PC). The utilization of the hydrogen atoms through the series of reactions shown in Figure 99 accomplishes this. The system is designated as an electron transmitter system because most of the steps involve no transfer of hydrogen per se but only a flow of electrons derived from the hydrogen. The reaction in essence is therefore:

$$2\,H \rightarrow (2H^+ + 2e) + \tfrac{1}{2}\,O_2 \rightarrow H_2O + \text{energy}.$$

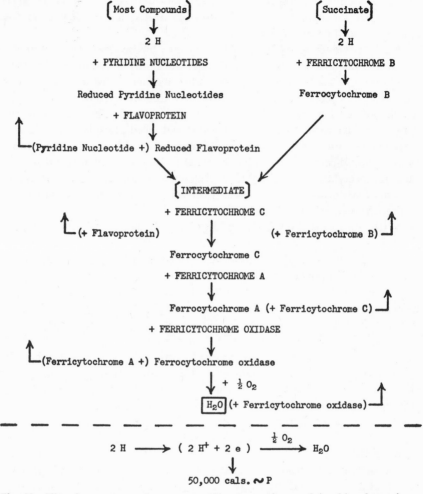

Fig. 99.—The electron transmitter system. The convention used in this scheme is as follows: electron receptor in capital letters, electron donor in small letters, and reconstituted receptor in parentheses. The over-all reacton is shown at the bottom. Data taken from Ball (5).

Again, there are numerous steps involved, probably designed to provide energy from each in small or convenient units (5). The pyridine nucleotides (DPN or TPN) of the first step incorporate nicotinamide in the molecule. There are probably a number of flavoproteins to catalyze the next step, but in all the active group is riboflavine. The final steps are catalyzed by the cytochromes, which are iron-containing ring compounds of the porphyrin type (such as the heme of hemoglobin). The entire system beyond the pyridine nucleotides appears to be a complex found in the mitochondrial fraction of the cell probably as a lipoprotein (5).

Energy derived from the electron transmitter system appears in the form of high-energy phosphate bonds of ATP and PC, which on hydrolysis liberate 12,000 to 14,000 calories of free energy. (Ordinary ester-type bonds release only 2,000 to 4,000 calories on hydrolysis.) Each electron passing through the system can make available some 25,000 calories (5). The mechanism by which energy is transferred is not well understood, but several steps have been worked out. Taking the coupled phosphory-

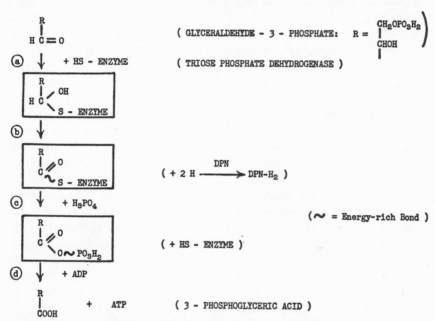

Fig. 100.—Formation of energy-rich phosphate bonds, according to Kreb (72). In step (*a*) substrate and enzyme combine to form an addition compound through the sulfhydryl (HS-) group, in this case of a glutathione moiety. Two hydrogens are then removed in step (*b*) and passed to DPN. The acyl-mercaptan resulting is an anhydride of sulfhydryl and carboxyl groups, which is an energy-rich bond. In step (*c*) phosphorolysis of the acyl-mercaptan occurs, in effect transferring the R-C = O group from thiol to phosphate, resulting in an energy-rich carboxyl-phosphate, also anhydride. (Note the difference between this bond and the low-energy phosphate bond on the R-end of the molecule.) Finally, in step (*d*) in the presence of ADP, the phosphate is transferred from carboxyl to ADP to form ATP with its energy-rich bonds, also anhydride in type. In the example illustrated, glyceraldehyde-3-phosphate is the starting compound, which by means of triose phosphate dehydrogenase is converted successively to 1,3-diphosphoglyceric acid and 3-phosphoglyceric acid (as shown in Figure 97).

lation of glyceralderhyde-3-phosphate as an example, a series of reactions occur which convert an ordinary low-energy bond into an energy-rich bond (Fig. 100). The formation of an anhydride (in this case, acylmercaptan) appears to be the key. Thermodynamically the anhydride structure, which, so to speak, places the molecule under strain, accounts for the appearance, from an ordinary bond of 2,000 to 4,000 calories, of a bond which on hydrolysis releases 12,000 to 14,000 calories of free energy (72). Analogous mechanisms are envisaged for other types of high-energy compounds.

Enzymes and the role of vitamins.—All the foregoing reactions are enzymatic in nature, each involving a specific enzyme system. The enzymes are identified in Figures 97, 98, and 99. They are proteins or lipid-protein complexes, which in most cases also serve as units of cell structure. Enzymes function to facilitate reactions in biological systems which would be slow, difficult, or impossible to carry out by ordinary chemical or physical means. In some cases the enzyme appears to be a single entity which will function well with only the additional presence of a few inorganic ions (notably magnesium) as activators. Cholinesterase is such an enzyme. In most cases the protein portion of the enzyme system is only an apo-enzyme to which must be added a coenzyme to make a functional unit. The apo-enzymes are thus like templates into which specific molecular configurations can be fitted. The coenzyme then accomplishes the actual reaction, often with additional aid of activators. Coenzymes are of particular interest because many of them are vitamins or vitamin derivatives, mostly of the B-vitamin group. Thus, in a number of the steps given in Figures 97, 98, and 99 common B-vitamins are functioning as coenzymes. Nicotinamide appears in the pyridine nucleotides, DPN and TPN. Thiamine with the addition of two phosphate groups becomes co-carboxylase, important in pyruvate decarboxylation. Pantothenic acid is a constituent of coenzyme-A, a somewhat more complex arrangement. Pyridoxine as pyridoxal phosphate is important as the coenzyme catalyzing conversion of α-keto acids of the Krebs cycle to other compounds such as amino acids. Riboflavin is the active component of the flavoproteins which dispose of the hydrogens removed by the pyridine nucleotides. Trace amounts of these and other B-vitamins are thus of importance in facilitating the course of cellular metabolism. The implications of this in deficiency states will be discussed below.

Relationships to Lipid and Protein Metabolism

Important interrelationships between metabolism of glucose and lipid and protein metabolism exist primarily at the Krebs cycle level. The

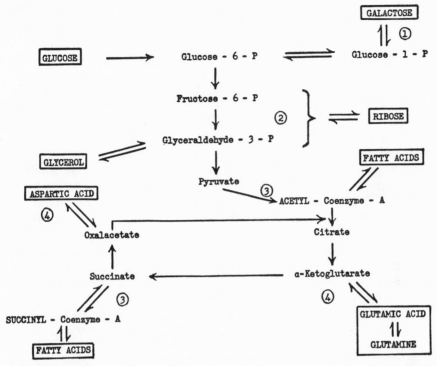

Fig. 101.—Some interrelationships in glucose metabolism. The important points of interchange are indicated by the compounds enclosed in boxes. Enzymes or coenzymes at some of these points (circled numbers) are the following: (1) Galactowaldenase and UDP; (2) Aldolase; (3) Diphosphothiamin; (4) Pyridoxal phosphate. The intervening steps in glycolysis and the Krebs cycle are detailed in Figures 97 and 98.

scheme of reactions has been simplified and modified to show the more important of these in Figure 101.

The sphingolipids of brain contain a hexose unit in the basic molecule which is usually galactose. Since these lipids are probably synthesized *in situ,* the source of the galactose moiety is of interest. Ingested galactose is converted by the liver to glucose. Possibly some reaches the brain and is utilized, but evidence for this is lacking. Recent work on the mechanism of glucose-galactose interconversion (14, 65, 75) suggests the alternative that brain lipid galactose is derived from glucose in brain. The coenzyme for this reaction is a uridine pyrophosphate (UDP or UTP), analogous to ATP but differing in stability and the fact that an actual molecular complex with the hexose, UDPG, is intermediate in the conversion reaction. This complex has been isolated from rat brain as well as other organs, suggesting that it may function *in situ* there (14). These uridine coenzymes may prove to have a much wider field of application than is presently apparent.

Another important constituent of many complex compounds is pentose (usually ribose or desoxyribose), which is the 5-carbon sugar found in the molecules of ATP, DPN, uridine pyrophosphates, and nucleic acids. Ingested pentoses are apparently not utilized to any extent. Recent evidence has accumulated to indicate that ribose, desoxyribose, and related pentoses are derived from hexoses by an alternate pathway of glucose metabolism (see 57 for details). In liver this is a complete system parallel to glycolysis which terminates in ribose. This pathway is absent in skeletal muscle and some other tissues, but no data on brain are in hand. However, as part of this alternate route there is a second entry at the stage in glycolysis of fructose-6-phosphate and the triose phosphates. By a variety of interconversions catalyzed by aldolase and related enzymes, these products from glucose can be converted to ribose or desoxyribose and vice versa. This pathway is active in muscle, and there is some evidence reported for brain. The possiblity that the interconversions suggested in Figure 101 occur in brain is reasonably good.

The fatty acids and glycerol, the linkage unit for phosphatides, have interchange points shown in Figure 101. Acetyl-coenzyme-A is probably the principal channel through which lipid-carbohydrate interconversion occurs (72). In neonatal brain, where active deposition of myelin and other lipids is occurring, anaerobic glycolysis is relatively more active than respiration (reflecting oxidative metabolism of the Krebs cycle). Sperry (125, 126) has suggested that at this time much of the glucose utilization is being channeled via acetyl-coenzyme-A into fatty acid synthesis. Once lipid deposition is accomplished, this pathway need serve only for repair and turnover, so that glucose is channeled into the Krebs cycle, and oxidative metabolism predominates. The alternate route via succinyl-coenzyme-A has been demonstrated but is probably less important.

Finally, there are the highly important interchange points between carbohydrate intermediates, the α-keto acids, and amino acids. Ammonia is basic to these reactions since they all involve transamination or transamidation, i.e., the transfer of ammonia as α-amino or amide group from one compound to another. These types of reactions are distributed widely in tissues and are very active in brain (see 81 for details). The two key reactions for most ammonia transfers are those shown in Figure 101 between α-ketoglutarate and glutamic acid and between oxalacetate and aspartic acid. One or other of these interchanges participates in most transamination reactions. Peptide-bond formation, by which amino acids are linked to form protein, is probably associated with these reactions, especially in terms of rearrangement of amino acids supplies on hand to fit specific structural needs of the cell.

Asparatic and glutamic acids and glutamine are present in large amounts in nervous tissue. Yet the two acids do not readily penetrate the blood-brain barrier. The possibility that they are produced *in situ* from the respective α-keto acids (Fig. 101) gains support from in vitro studies (149). When brain slices are exhausted of glutamic acid stores, they will build back appreciable levels when supplied with only glucose as substrate. Most of these reactions involving amino acids and ammonia transfers require pyridoxal phosphate as coenzyme.

Relationships to Function and Activity

Without the utilization of glucose and oxygen to produce cellular energy as ATP, function and activity of the neuron cease. High-energy phosphate exists primarily in three compounds, ATP, ADP, and PC (phosphocreatine). These are present in measurable concentrations in brain, about 3 uM/gm of adenylpyrophosphate (ATP + ADP) and a like amount of phosphocreatine (130). The level of ATP appears to be maintained at the expense of PC, since the latter is depleted first when energy demands increase. Thus, PC is looked upon as a reserve of high-energy phosphate, storing it from excess ATP or donating it back to ADP as needed (Fig. 102). The use of ADP directly or via the myokinase reaction, as a source of energy, is poor economy, since the resulting monophosphate (AMP) requires still more energy to revert to ATP. Recent studies suggest that the inosine and uridine pyrophosphates may participate in the maintenance and distribution of cell energy (64).

Much of the energy goes into maintenance of the internal environment of the cell, the homeostatic mechanisms. Transport of electrolytes and solutes (potassium, glucose, glutamate) from extracellular fluid across cell membranes requires energy. The maintenance of potassium and glutamic acid within the cell against a concentration gradient (i.e., tendency to diffuse out) requires energy. When it fails, these substances leak out rapidly and completely. Conversely, energy is expended to keep out substances, like sodium, which are inimical to intracellular processes. Energy is also required for synthesis of important and active compounds like acetylcholine and glutamine. Finally the build-up, replacement, and repair of lipid, protein, and enzyme structure depend upon energy.

Excessive activity (convulsions), anoxia, hypoglycemia all rapidly deplete the stores of high-energy phosphate, outstripping the capacity to

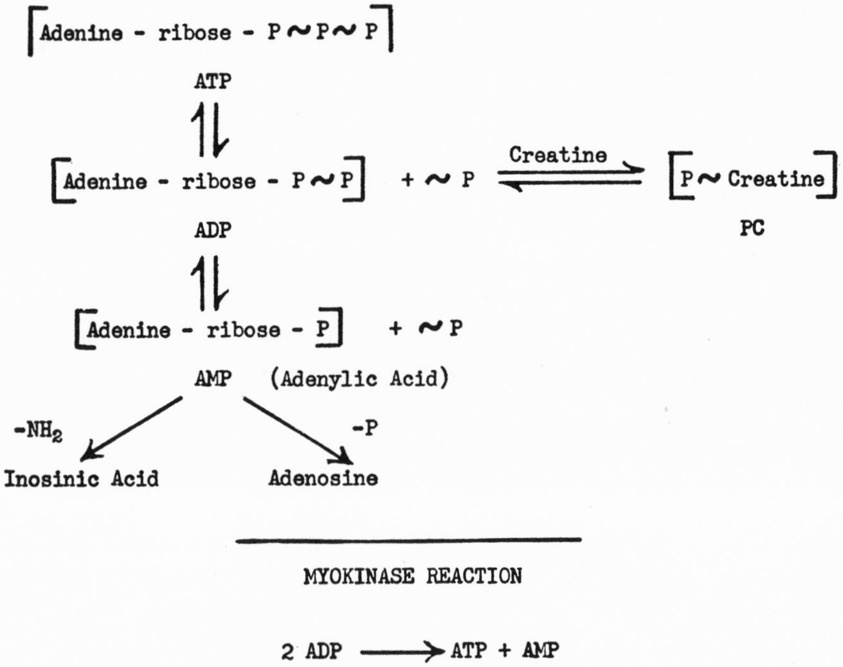

$$\left[\text{Adenine - ribose - P} \sim \text{P} \sim \text{P}\right]$$

ATP

$\uparrow\downarrow$

$$\left[\text{Adenine - ribose - P} \sim \text{P}\right] \ + \sim \text{P} \ \underset{\longleftarrow}{\overset{\text{Creatine}}{\longrightarrow}} \ \left[\text{P} \sim \text{Creatine}\right]$$

ADP   PC

$\uparrow\downarrow$

$$\left[\text{Adenine - ribose - P}\right] \ + \sim \text{P}$$

AMP   (Adenylic Acid)

$-NH_2$ $-P$

Inosinic Acid   Adenosine

MYOKINASE REACTION

$$2 \ \text{ADP} \longrightarrow \text{ATP} + \text{AMP}$$

Fig. 102.—The energy-rich phosphate compounds.

maintain or replenish them. In an effort to maintain some semblance of energy production, the neuron turns upon itself, burning first glutamic and aspartic acids and then its lipid and protein structure. This burning of the furnishings to keep the house warm is the acute, catastrophic picture. More subtle damage occurs when important steps in the energy-producing process cease functioning. From the preceding discussions the reasons for the clinical manifestation of cyanide poisoning (of the electron transmitter system), thiamine deficiency (pyruvate ultization), neurotropic virus action (blocking triose-phosphate dehydrogenase [104]), fluoroacetate poisoning (blocking citrate metabolism), and pyridoxine deficiency (α-keto acid–amino acid interchange) are more apparent. These interferences and destruction of nervous tissue function can be demonstrated in the laboratory in vitro and are evident in the clinic in death, decerebration, beri-beri, encephalitis, and convulsions.

LIPID METABOLISM

In contrast with the wealth of detail on carbohydrate metabolism there is a dearth of information on the metabolism of central nervous system lipids. Their importance in terms of mass, their complexity often peculiar to nervous tissue, and their participation as components of myelin sheaths, cell membranes, and enzyme complexes in association with protein all argue for the need to know more about their metabolism.

Lipid Turnover

Brain lipids used to be thought of as inert insulation material. Perhaps they may function in part as insulation, but recent studies show that they are certainly not inert. The failure to take account of the blood-brain barrier has been responsible for much of the error in interpretation of brain lipid turnover activity. When P^{32} was first used to study phospholipid turnover in brain, so little appeared that it was concluded that turnover at best was minimal. It is now known that P^{32} penetrates the barrier very slowly. The injection of P^{32} into cerebrospinal fluid gives a far different picture since there is a rapid and marked incorporation of P^{32} into brain after such an injection (4).

With the above procedure, rapid incorporation of P^{32} into phospholipid and diphosphoinostide fractions occurs (132), amounting to a turnover in phospholipids of 1.5 per cent in 4 hr. and 11 per cent in 24 hr. and in diphosphoinositide of 10 and 23 per cent, respectively. In another approach, by maintaining constant P^{32} levels in the general circulation, brain phosphatide turnover is calculated to be 11 per cent in 12 hr., 29 per cent in 9 days, and 77 per cent in 50 days with evidence that the cephalins take up more P^{32} than lecithin (51). In neonatal brain P^{32} administered into the general circulation is incorporated much more rapidly, but there is the possibility that this reflects a difference in barrier permeability. In vitro brain slices rapidly incorporate P^{32} into phospholipids in the presence of oxygen and glucose. This incorporation is metabolic since it depends upon an adequately functioning phosphorylating mechanism (114).

Fatty acid turnover in brain has been studied by the use of deuterium. Deuterium-labeled fatty acids given into the general circulation concentrate highly in liver and kidney but fail to appear in brain (124). It is probable that the blood-brain barrier prevents their penetration, since in animals maintained at constant levels of deuterium in body water, significant incorporation into brain fatty acids occurs. The turnover rate is calculated at 20 per cent in a week, compared with 50 per cent in a day for liver (124). Only a trace of deuterium is found in brain cholesterol. In newborn animals maintained on deuterium oxide, the percentage in cholesterol and fatty acid fractions of brain are higher in the first weeks of life than corresponding fractions in liver or carcass. Sperry (124) has come to the conclusion, based on these results, that lipids in the central nervous system are synthesized there and not delivered from other sources. This conclusion is supported by the ability of brain tissue to synthesize phosphatides in vitro (P^{32} studies) and by the unique quantity and in some cases type of lipids in central nervous tissue.

When N^{15}-labeled choline or ethanolamine is fed, there is a small incorporation into brain lipids, but much less than in other organs (129). C^{14}-labeled acetate is not incorporated into brain cholesterol either in vivo or in vitro (114), but in young animals, at least, activity is found in brain sphingosine (156). Labeled glycine also gives activity in the latter (127). Finally C^{14}-labeled glycerol administered to adult animals results in higher activity in brain lipids (unfractionated) than in any other tissue except liver (45). In such whole-animal studies, the compound administered is not necessarily incorporated as such, since metabolism and resyntheses (especially in the liver) can occur prior to its reaching the central nervous system. These few data suggest that the small units such as acetate, glycerol, and glycine may be carried to the brain where, as Sperry suggests, synthesis of lipids occur.

Demyelination

Demyelinating diseases, such as multiple sclerosis, are common, but little is known about initiating factors or mechanisms. Study of this process should reveal much which concerns lipid metabolism in general. Attempts to reproduce demyelinating diseases experimentally have been rather unfruitful. Those lesions produced by experimental allergic meningo-encephalitis do not on close scrutiny mimic the "spontaneous" lesions of man, and the experimental animal exhibits general changes such as lipemia which do not occur in the human group of diseases. Nevertheless these and other studies have provided some insight into the processes of destruction of brain lipids of the myelin type.

Brain slices incubated in vitro under conditions promoting degeneration exhibit changes only in the phospholipid fraction, beginning with the cephalins and followed by sphingomyelin. After 14 days the phospholipid fraction has decreased by about 50 per cent, but no changes in lecithin, cerebrosides, or cholesterol are seen. Peripheral nerve under the same conditions shows similar changes (61).

These findings do not correlate well with observations in vivo on degeneration of myelin sheaths of nerves (Wallerian degeneration) carried out by the same investigators (for details see 113). The process is slower, no change in myelin lipids appearing until the eighth day after section, and the lipids which drop significantly thereafter are primarily cholesterol, cerebrosides, and sphingomyelin. These are, of course, the principal lipid constituents of myelin. The difference between in vitro and in vivo observations may be due to the presence in the latter of macrophages and Schwann cells, which contribute enzymes different from those acting in vitro.

In terms of mechanisms, Sperry and Waelsch (126) have pointed out that there is in normal brain presumably a balance between breakdown and resynthesis of lipids in the course of normal repair and turnover. Demyelination may be looked upon as an imbalance between the two, either from a block of synthesis while breakdown continues or a speed-up of breakdown (and removal) exceeding synthetic capacities. Such a concept seems apt for substances like brain lipids which are apparently synthesized *in situ*.

NITROGEN AND PROTEIN METABOLISM

The importance of proteins in cell structure, as enzymes in association with cerebral lipids, and possibly in integration and recording is unquestioned. But beyond some of the simpler aspects of metabolism, data are nonexistent.

Nitrogen Metabolism

Ammonia is the simplest unit of nitrogen either in synthesis or degradation. It can be derived from amino acids and proteins, from the purine and pyrmidine bases of nucleic acids, and from the lipids containing

TABLE 16

Glutamic acid and glutamine in brain and other organs

Species	Brain		Liver		Kidney	
	GAc	G–NH$_2$	GAc	G–NH$_2$	GAc	G–NH$_2$
Mouse	11.4	4.7	1.3	2.4	5.3	0.7
Rat	10.4	4.0	3.3	3.8	6.5	1.5
Cat	10.0*	5.0*	2.9	3.7	7.1	2.4
Dog	11.0	4.4	...	3.1	...	0.8
Sheep	10.5*	3.8*	5.8	1.7	6.3	1.0
Man	10.0*	5.0*	...	...	...	...

GAc = glutamic acid; G–NH$_2$ = glutamine (both in μM/gm of tissue).

* Values for cerebral cortex; other species values not specified. In sheep white matter: GAc = 6.1; G–NH$_2$ = 3.3.

Modified from Waelsch (151) and Tower (139).

amino alcohol (such as ethanolamine and choline). Only in the case of amino acids are there much data.

In Figure 103 the relative concentrations of nonprotein nitrogen (NPN) constituents are summarized. The α-amino nitrogen fraction (amino acids) accounts for only 0.5 per cent of brain solids, but comprises some 60 per cent of the total NPN. Within this fraction nearly 80 per

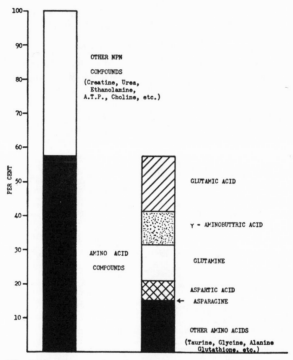

Fig. 103.—Nonprotein nitrogen components of brain tissue (relative concentrations). The figure is based on data from Weil-Malherbe (153) and Tallan *et al.* (135).

cent is contributed by glutamic and aspartic acids and their derivatives (135, 153). The importance of the glutamic-aspartic group is also indicated by the fact that in all species studied their concentration in brain is higher than in any other body organ (Table 16). Per unit weight of brain the concentrations are essentially constant from species to species. During the neonatal period of brain development, their concentration remains constant on a dry weight basis, but since more solids are being deposited and water content drops, there is an incréase in total amount paralleling the increase in protein (151).

The source of glutamic and aspartic acids in brain has been designated as primarily from reductive animation of the appropriate α-keto acid of the Krebs cycle. However, glutamine and asparagine both penetrate the blood-brain barrier well in contrast to the acids (119 and Tower, unpublished), and there are appreciable concentrations of glutamine in serum (0.7 μM/ml) and cerebrospinal fluid (0.5 μM/ml) normally in man (Meister, unpublished). These could be another source of glutamic and aspartic acids in brain. In addition studies of arterio-venous differences in cerebral blood suggest that exchanges of glutamic acid and of glutamine may occur between the blood and central nervous system compartment (1). From various points of view the latter two sources do not seem to be as important as the *in situ* source.

Glutamic acid exemplifies the many reactions in which this group of compounds can participate in brain tissue (Fig. 104). Aspartic acid undergoes identical reactions, with the possible exception of amidation to asparagine. This reaction, demonstrated in liver (81) has not been studied in brain, but there are traces of asparagine present (135). All the reactions given in Figure 104 have been clearly demonstrated in brain (see 151 for review).

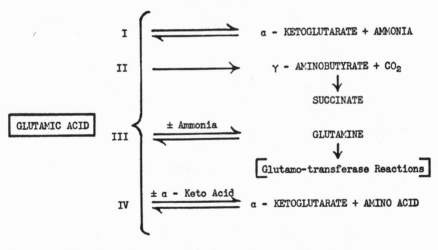

I   Oxidative deamination - Reductive amination

II Decarboxylation

III Amidation - Deamidation

IV Transamination

Fig. 104.—Reactions of glutamic acid (151).

Oxidative deamination to α-ketoglutarate is the means by which brain tissue in vitro can respire with glutamic acid as its sole substrate. This is not an efficient means of "priming" the Krebs cycle, as evidenced by the failure under these conditions of P^{32} incorporation into the slice, of increase in phosphocreatine, and of response to electrical stimulation (114, 151). Human brain is an interesting exception to the last finding. Mc-Ilwain (77) has reported that, in contrast to brain tissue from all other species including the monkey, human brain in vitro can not only maintain respiration with glutamic acid as substrate, but also can respond to electrical stimulation by a marked rise in respiratory rate similar to that seen with glucose as substrate. The reasons for this difference in human brain and its significance are not clear.

Decarboxylation of glutamic acid to γ-aminobutyrate is especially interesting. This reaction is apparently exclusive to central nervous tissue and is more active in gray than white matter (109). The reason for providing such an alternate path of glutamic acid utilization is not clear. The γ-aminobutyrate formed transaminates with α-ketoglutarate to give succinate plus reconstituted glutamic acid. Thus, the only change appears to be production of carbon dioxide. Possibly this added or alternate source is important to the pH regulatory mechanism.

The reactions of amidation, transfer of carbon skeletons (glutamotransferase reaction), and transamination are active in brain. They provide the mechanisms for efficient utilization of ammonia in specific desired channels (see 81, 151 for reviews). It is suggested that the transferase reactions may be important in peptide bond formation by a temporary γ- or β-peptide type bond of the amide group which could rearrange into a new true α-peptide linkage. The amide nitrogen of amide N^{15}-labeled glutamine is handled in the same fashion as α-amino nitrogen of amino acids and not like ammonia. Sixty per cent of the nitrogen, either α-amino or amide, is utilized, mostly in protein synthesis, whereas less than 20 per cent of ammonia nitrogen is so utilized (108).

Changes in Cellular Protein

The data available on protein metabolism itself are derived largely from microspectrographic studies. In other tissues the nucleic acids, associated with much of the cellular protein, have been studied in some detail. Synthesis and degradation of the nucleotide and nucleoside units can be demonstrated in vitro. Such studies have not been done on brain tissue. With P^{32} in vivo and in vitro a rapid turnover of pentose nucleic acids and "phosphoprotein" occurs, but very little takes place for desoxypentose nucleic acids (34, 35, 36, 132). In vitro a dependence of these incorporations of P^{32} on adequate phosphorylating mechanisms (energy) is clear. By microspectrography physiological variations in cytoplasmic nucleoproteins and nucleic acids have been reported, associated with stimulation of neurons (58).

In the development of a neuron from the apolar neuroblast, cytoplasmic substance increases some two thousand times. The ratio of protein to nucleic acids changes from 4:1 to 10:1, indicating a relative increase in protein during differentiation. If the latter is prevented, as in the ganglion cells of a blinded retina, the protein increase does not occur. Hydén (58) points out that large nucleoli and abundant cytoplasmic pentose nucleoproteins, such as are found in neurons, are characteristic of growing cells or cells in which there is intense production of protein. The capacity of the neuron for synthesis is exemplified by the regeneration of a nerve axon after section in which the protein produced may exceed that of the perikaryal cytoplasm by two hundred to one thousand times. When chromatolysis of the neuron occurs, pentose nucleic acids disappear, beginning centrally around the nucleus and progressing until there is little cytoplasmic nucleic acid or protein remaining. During regeneration high concentrations of pentose nucleic acid appear around the nucleus, and there is a large flow of axoplasm peripheralward (58). Weiss (154) has demonstrated that there is a migration of substances from cell body peripheralward in the axon. Migration of ions (28) and of acetylcholine (MacIntosh, unpublished) as well as axoplasmic protein have been demonstrated. Whether these processes of perikaryal cytoplasmic production and axonal flow occur normally or only during regeneration is not established, but there is evidence to suggest that this is a normal process which is intensified during regeneration. While the mechanism of protein production is unknown, Hydén (58) presents evidence that protein is synthesized by the nucleolus, passes to the outer face of the nuclear membrane, and is there converted through the mediation of pentose nucleic acids into cytoplasmic nucleoprotein. An alternate suggestion by Bodian (11) is that these processes occur near the cytoplasmic membrane.

Metabolic Organization

The mechanism by which the differentiation of proteins into specific types or enzymes occurs with characteristic cell and intracellular distribution is most baffling. The brilliant studies of Lowry and co-workers (76, 110) demonstrate how interesting but complex these facets of the problem can be. Their findings for various layers of a special cortical area, Ammon's horn, are summarized in Table 17. In a sense these complement much of the foregoing sections in terms of the organization of structure and function.

Ammon's horn was chosen because of the distinct histological char-

TABLE 17

Characteristics of various layers of cerebral cortex
(Ammon's Horn)

	Units	Layer					
		ALVEUS	ORIENS	PYRAMIDALIS	RADIATA	LACUNOSUM	MOLECULARIS
Thickness	μ.	200	250	50	400	150	200
Histology		Myelinated fibers	Nonmyelinated axons and dendrites	Cell bodies densely packed	Dendrites densely packed	Dendrites + Myelinated fibers	Term. Dendrites + axons + pial vessels
Dry weight	g/L	303	204	170	233	271	206
Lipid	%	58	33	19	31	43	31
Protein	%	31	51	66	54	44	52
Chloride	mM/L*	59	39	40	50	50	40
Acid-sol. org. P	mM/kg protein	142	140	128	127	145	131
Lipid P†		1033	627	297	563	630	515
Sphingomyelin		140	58	29	52	124	80
Cholesterol		841	308	93	272	453	313
Nucleic acid P			23	191	29	27	33

Aldolase	M. Split per kg. of protein per hour	5.3	7.15	5.33	7.86	6.60	4.74
Fumarase		20.6	27.9	38.7	28.0	30.2	40.2
Riboflavin‡		26.8	36.1	35.8	34.9	30.9	49.6
Cholinesterase		2.47	2.98	3.12	2.45	2.60	3.95
ATP-ase		5.53	10.62	7.61	9.56	8.48	

* Assuming 110 mM/L in extracellular fluid and all chloride extracellular, the extracellular spaces would be 35–45% in all layers but alveus (55%).

† Cephalins and lecithin in 1 : 1 ratio, except in alveus (Ceph. 492; Lec. 361).

‡ Expressed as mg/kg of protein.

Table adapted from data of Lowry *et al.* (76).

acter of certain cortical layers, some primarily cell bodies (pyramidalis), some primarily myelinated fibers (alveus), and some primarily dendrites (radiata). The first section of the table illustrates nicely the difference between myelinated fibers and the cell bodies and processes in protein and lipid composition. The association of sphingomyelin and cholesterol with myelinated structures and of nucleic acids with the cell bodies is clear in the next section of the table.

The enzymes chosen for study are representative of important aspects of neuronal metabolism: glycolysis (aldolase), Krebs cycle activity (fumarase), electron transport (riboflavin as an indicator of flavoprotein), cholinergic activity (cholinesterase), and ATP (indicated by the acid-soluble organic phosphate fraction and possibly by ATPase, although its precise function is not clear). Two important points emerge from the data on enzyme activities. First, the dendrite layer (radiata) exhibits high activity. Since dendrites probably compose the bulk of nonmyelinated brain structure, "brain metabolism" is in a sense "dendrite metabolism" (76). Secondly, the activity of the layers containing myelinated fibers is unexpectedly high, suggesting that more of the total metabolic activity derives from these structures than has been supposed. It is from carefully designed studies such as this that much of the data still required will be forthcoming.

FUNCTION AND ACTIVITY METABOLISM

Separation of function and activity metabolism from energy metabolism and structural synthesis is highly artificial, since the two facets of cellular metabolism are tightly interwoven and interrelated. It is only to simplify for purposes of presentation that the distinction is made. The term "activity metabolism" is used here in the context of the special capacity of neurons to receive, conduct, and transmit impulses. Many of the discussions up to this point could be applied with minor modifications to liver, kidney, or other metabolically active cells. Only in the neuron is the property of impulse conduction and transmission so highly developed and specialized. With this distinction go certain features of metabolism which are intimately related to the functioning and maintenance of this activity.

Electrolytes

In peripheral nerve conduction, the central roles of sodium and potassium are well established. The electrical signs of the propagating impulse have their basis in the distribution and movement of these ions across the axonal membrane. Coupled with these phenomena is the expenditure of energy by the nerve to maintain the system in optimal functioning condition (55). How much of the extensive data collected for peripheral nerve is applicable to central nervous system conduction is unknown because available evidence is fragmentary.

The central nervous system exhibits complex and spontaneous electrical activity which must depend both upon energy metabolism and the distribution and movement of ions across membrane. Failure of energy supplies in anoxia is associated with loss of potassium from brain tissue in vitro and in vivo (21, 69). With heightened cerebral activity (induced convulsions) microincineration studies show a change in ion distribution with exit of potassium from, and entry of sodium into, the neuron (17). Increased concentrations of potassium extracellularly not only stimulate respiration in vitro and in vivo, but are associated with heightened electrical activity. The injection of citrate, which immobilizes calcium, into the cerebrospinal fluid is followed by convulsions (24). Magnesium, which is usually considered in its role as activator of enzymes, is an important intracellular ionic constituent of neurons. It is of interest that changes in magnesium concentration also affect cerebral activity. Parenteral administration of magnesium depresses central nervous system activity to the point of anesthesia. Conversely, depletion of magnesium has recently been reported to be associated with delerium and convulsions in man (133). The impression gained from these bits of evidence is that the electrolytes are very important to central nervous system activity and that a close analogy to the peripheral nerve mechanism of conduction is highly probable for the central nervous system.

Bicarbonate is the outstandingly important anion, and it is very intimately concerned with neuronal function and activity. The natural buffering system of the body for pH regulation is a bicarbonate-carbon dioxide system. In the central nervous system the maintenance of extra- and intracellular pH depends upon this system. In addition it has a major role in the regulation of cerebral blood flow. The effects of hyperventilation and of increased carbon dioxide tension in vivo on cerebral activity are familiar examples of the importance of this system.

Neurohumors

Acetylcholine.—The literature on the role of acetylcholine in peripheral and central nervous activity is vast indeed. No attempt will be made to go into details since the subject has been very ably reviewed recently by Burgen and MacIntosh (13). It is now established that the transmission of nerve impulses at the neuromuscular synapse of skeletal muscle and at the preganglionic synapse of autonomic ganglia is effected by acetylcholine. Nachmansohn (89) believes that acetylcholine is essential in nerve conduction as well, but the bulk of evidence does not favor this view. The role of acetylcholine in central nervous activity is still controversial.

There is little doubt that acetylcholine is an important factor in neuronal activity. Its metabolism in nervous tissue has been extensively studied, and the principal features are outlined in Figure 105. The acetyl-

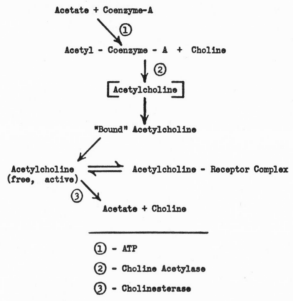

Fig. 105.—Acetylcholine metabolism (89).

choline produced from acetylation of choline by choline acetylase is present in brain almost entirely in a "bound" form. This form is insoluble and biologically inactive by usual test procedures, but the precise nature of the "binding" is not known. Acetylcholine content of brain is essentially content of "bound" acetylcholine, since free, active acetylcholine normally exists in traces, if at all. The "bound" form of acetylcholine may be looked upon as a reserve, which, upon appropriate stimulus, is released as free, soluble, and biologically active acetylcholine. In vitro this release is usually effected by treatment of the tissue by mild acid. In vivo release can be demonstrated on nerve stimulation, by perfusion with potassium and numerous other means. Free acetylcholine is normally very rapidly inactivated by cholinesterase, which hydrolyzes the molecules to acetate and choline. From studies of cholinesterase inhibitors and acetylcholine blocking agents it is apparent that effector activity is mediated by an acetylcholine-receptor complex, distinct from cholinesterase, which functions once the complex is formed to clear the receptor site. Both receptor and cholinesterase exhibit rather rigid requirements for substrate structure, which are optimally met by the acetylcholine molecule.

The system for synthesis, storage, release, and inactivation of acetylcholine is widespread in the nervous system and in nervous tissue of the animal kingdom. Distribution of the principal components in the central nervous system of the dog is summarized in Table 18. Comparisons of choline acetylase activity and acetylcholine content indicate a reasonable degree of correspondence between synthesizing capacity and amount in "storage," suggesting the possibility that these two aspects are usually

TABLE 18

Distribution of the acetylcholine system in dog brain

Area	Choline-acetylase*	Acetylcholine (bound)*	Cholinesterase*†
Cerebral cortex (Av.)	49	43	4
Caudate n.	(100)	(100)	(100)
Thalamus	79	60	12.5
Lentiform n.	56	38.5	66
Superior colliculus	84.5	23.5	24
Hypothalamus	90.5	26.5	8
Corpus callosum	20.5	30	0.4
Cerebellum (cortex)	11.5	2.5	25
Pyramids	10	4.5	2
Dorsal columns: Nuclei	67.5	....	12
Tract	8	5.5	0.95
Spinal cord: Ventral horn	121	36	15.5
Dorsal horn	81	21.5	
Ventral roots	186	214	4
Dorsal roots	....	0.5	0.85
Optic nerve	4.5	4	0.25
Sympathetic ganglia	....	630	....

* All values are relative, referred to Caudate = 100; Actual values for Caudate: ChAc = 410 μg ACh/gm acetone powder/hr; ACh = 7.0 μg/gm fresh wt; ChE = 3936 μl CO_2/gm fresh wt/10 min.

† ChE I ("true" or acetyl-cholinesterase).

Compiled from Feldberg and Vogt (33), MacIntosh (78), and Burgen and Chipman (12).

closely associated. The superior colliculus, hypothalamus, and spinal cord area are exceptions. Reasons for the former are not obvious, but in the case of spinal cord it is possible that the phenomenon of axonal flow may be a factor. Acetylcholine is one of the substances which appears to flow peripheralward in the axon, so that it is not unreasonable to expect some dissociation between synthetic capacity and concentration of stored prod-

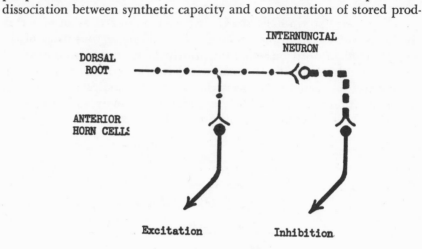

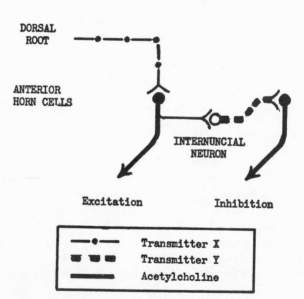

Fig. 106.—Scheme for multiple transmitter mechanisms at central synapses (redrawn from Eccles [22]).

uct in such areas. Comparisons of various areas of the nervous system suggest that production and storage is more active in nuclear areas (i.e., areas of neuron density) than in tracts, nerves, and the like. The cerebellum is an exception to this assumption.

Cholinesterase activity presents a rather different picture both in terms of relation to levels of the other two components and in relation to different areas of the nervous system. In vitro studies suggest that cholinesterase is far in excess of normal requirements by most areas in terms of acetylcholine released for hydrolysis. Although more localized concentrations within the cell might modify this impression somewhat, it is also apparent that diffusion of acetylcholine from the site of action can be an important factor in its inactivation. The concept of cholinesterase excess introduces the requirements of activity into the scheme, since it is presumably easier for the cell to turn out acetylcholine on demand than to synthesize a cholinesterase molecule. Thus, even though under "resting" conditions only a fraction of available cholinesterase need be called upon, sufficient must be on hand to cope with periods of markedly increased activity, i.e., a sort of "safety factor." The compensatory increase in cholinesterase activity seen in epileptogenic foci (101) illustrates this concept. It is of interest that areas of brain with normally intense neuronal activity are rich in cholinesterase.

On the basis of findings such as those in Table 18, it has been proposed that not all central transmission is cholinergic in nature (32). The discrepancy between sensory and motor nerves and tracts, of apparently comparable physiological activity, is great. In addition, a single transmission mechanism is difficult to apply both to excitatory and inhibitory action. The concept of interposed non-cholinergic links has been proposed (32), and support in favor of this has recently been reported for central synapses in spinal cord by Eccles (22). An example of how such a multiple transmitter mechanism might function is shown in Figure 106. A simplified version of this exists in sympathetic ganglia, where acetylcholine effects preganglionic transmission and *nor*-adrenalin is the postganglionic transmitter. In the central nervous system there is little evidence for *nor*-adrenalin as a transmitter with the possible exception of the hypothalamus (147). The nature of other transmitter substances is speculative at present.

Burgen and MacIntosh (13) have summarized the evidence for acetylcholine as a central transmitter as follows:

1. As shown in Table 18, central nervous tissue contains relatively large amounts of acetylcholine and specific enzymes for its synthesis and inactivation.

2. Central neurons are highly sensitive to acetylcholine. Intra-arterial injections of 1 µg. or less produce EEG changes, affect cortical excitability and cord reflex activity, and facilitate mono- and polysynaptic pathways in brain. Local applications of amounts as low as 0.02 µg. stimulate medullary centers.

3. The pronounced central effects of various cholinesterase inhibitors are difficult to explain except by assuming that they result from accumulation of naturally liberated acetylcholine. These agents generally produce excitatory effects which closely resemble analogous experiments with acetylcholine itself.

4. Associated with changes in over-all levels of nervous activity there are transient changes in acetylcholine content. Such findings are shown in Table 19. Acetylcholine appears to be concentrated at synaptic end-

TABLE 19

Changes in acetylcholine content in vivo with changes in levels of brain activity

State of Activity	Acetylcholine Content*
Anesthetized	141
Sleep	115
Normal, awake, "resting"	100
Emotional excitement	70
During convulsions	56

* Values as % of normal = 100. From Richter and Crossland (106).

ings, and the stocks seem to vary, depending upon synaptic activity.

5. Release of acetylcholine in association with neuronal activity occurs. At the cortical surface there is a marked decrease with deep anesthesia. The persistence of acetylcholine in cerebrospinal fluid after seizures is indicative of an increased release at the tissue surface. Recordings of electrocorticogram suggest that output of acetylcholine correlates with high-frequency activity. From the foregoing considerations there seems to be little doubt that acetylcholine is intimately concerned with the activity of a fair portion at least of the central nervous system neurons.

An amplification of the last two points will serve to indicate some of the relationships which may exist between events and metabolism. In Table 20 the effects of narcotics and convulsants on acetylcholine synthesis in vitro are summarized. When these data are set beside those

TABLE 20

Effects of drugs on acetylcholine production in vitro by cerebral cortex

A. *Free* acetylcholine production by slices (rat)

Drug added in vitro*	Free acetylcholine production
Nembutal 0.4 mM/L	50
Control—no drug	100
Metrazol—2.5 mM/L	143†

B. *"Bound"* acetylcholine production by slices (cat)

Drug administered in vivo	"Bound" acetylcholine production
Nembutal—anesthesia 1 hr.	140
Control—no drug	100
Methionine sulfoximine—recurrent seizures	19

All values expressed as % of control = 100

* Drug concentrations correspond roughly to those expected in vivo in extracellular fluid which produce pharmacological effects.

† Similar results obtained with methionine sulfoximine.

Modified from McLennan and Elliott (79) and Tower and Elliott (142).

in Table 19, the parallelism is rather striking. (Direct comparisons are not justified.) The in vitro studies suggest the possibility of cause and effect between drug and acetylcholine which may operate in vivo. It is of interest in this connection that the concentrations employed (Table 20*A*) have minimal or no effects on slice respiration. Effects of high narcotic concentrations in vivo on slice respiration can be reversed by rinsing the slice. When the animal is anesthetized in vivo and the brain subsequently studied for bound acetylcholine production (Table 20*B*), thorough rinsing of the slice does not abolish the enhanced production of bound acetylocholine. Quastel (103) has proposed a mechanism of narcotic action which suggests that the decrease in oxygen consumption associated with anesthesia in vivo is caused by the narcotic, presumably by its interference with phosphorylating mechanisms necessary to produce

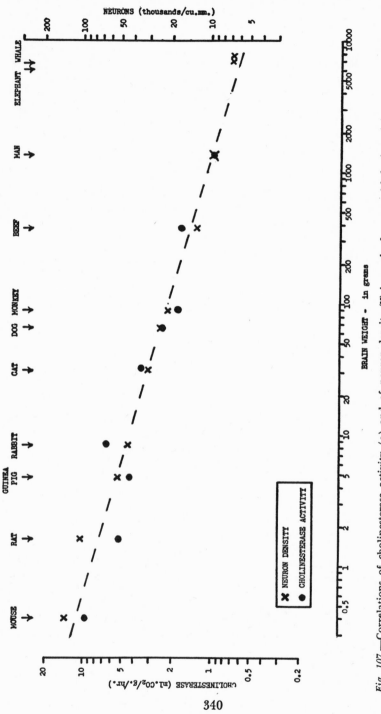

Fig. 107.—Correlations of cholinesterase activity (●) and of neuron density (X) in cerebral cortex with brain weight (log scales). All data taken from Tower and Elliott (141) except for that for elephant and whale, taken from Tower (138). The regression curve is drawn, assuming a regression coefficient of −0.3 (see text). Actual values were −0.27 for cholinesterase (141) and −0.32 for neuron density (138). Brain weights are averages for each species.

340

ATP. The concentrations of narcotics necessary to produce significant inhibition of oxygen uptake in vitro are at least several orders of magnitude greater than pharmacologically effective concentrations in vivo. Before any change in oxygen consumption occurs, ganglionic transmission ceases (74), and changes in levels of acetylcholine and of aerobic glycolysis occur. Quastel (103) suggests that at lower concentrations narcotics may block only an important single step in oxidative metabolism which would have little effect on over-all oxygen uptake. It is alternatively possible that the reduction in neuronal activity associated with narcosis may be the factor in reducing oxygen consumption.

Another type of evidence also indicates a close association with neuronal activity. Of oxygen uptake, glycolysis, tissue potassium concentrations, glutamic acid levels, and acetylcholine metabolism, only the last shows a correlation with brain size and in some way with neuron density from species to species. Oxygen uptake and possibly glycolysis are related to body size of species, and potassium and glutamic acid show essentially the same concentration per unit weight of brain tissue in all species studied. However, for acetylcholine synthesis, content, and esterase activity there is a decrease in cerebral cortex with increasing species brain weight according to the relation $A = K_A W^{-0.3}$ (where A is activity per unit weight; K_A is a constant characteristic of the component measured; and W is average total brain weight for a given species) (141). The neuron density in cerebral cortex also decreases with increasing brain size of species, and the regression coefficient is also -0.3 (120, 138). An example of these findings is given in Figure 107. Since the neuron density from area to area of cortex in a given brain varies significantly but acetylcholine metabolism does not (13, 141), it has been suggested that acetylcholine metabolism is more closely related to some parameter of neuron size (138). Whatever the ultimate interpretation of this relationship is, the foregoing suggests a close association of acetylcholine with the neuron and with neuronal activity.

Other possible neurohumors.—*Nor*-adrenalin is, of course, a recognized neurohumor which mediates postganglionic sympathetic nerve transmission to effector organs (148). There is little evidence for a central role of *nor*-adrenalin with the exception of the hypothalamus, where Vogt (147) has found appreciable concentrations of "sympathin" which may be identical with *nor*-adrenalin. Adrenalin exerts some very striking effects on central nervous activity, but the evidence available indicates that this is mediated via a release of adrenalin from the adrenal medulla into the general circulation and not by release within the central nervous system.

Serotonin or 5-hydroxytryptamine (5-HT) has recently come into prominence as a result of the studies of Brodie and co-workers (99, 121, 144). The serotonin system has many features which make it a likely candidate for transmitter or analogous function in neuronal activity. These are outlined in Figure 108. Serotonin is derived from tryptophan.

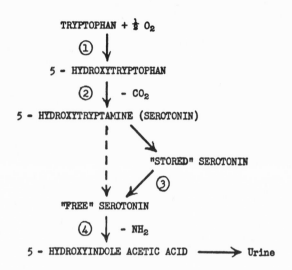

Fig. 108.—Serotonin metabolism and brain content (99, 144). See text for discussion.

Brain Area	Serotonin Concentration (μg./g.)
Cerebral Cortex	0.1
"Midbrain"	0.4
Hypothalamus	1.5

The first step, hydroxylation to 5-hydroxytryptophan, has been difficult to demonstrate in mammalian tissues but has been clearly shown in vivo in the toad and with bacteria. The second step, decarboxylation to serotonin is catalyzed by a decarboxylase which is widely distributed in tissues and various species. It is especially active in liver and brain, where it appears to have a distribution similar to that of serotonin. The enzyme is specific and requires pyridoxal phosphate as coenzyme. The serotonin formed is apparently "bound" in some fashion, but there is a possibility that a small fraction exists free. Little is known about factors affecting its release with the exception of reserpine, which appears to promote a very rapid mobilization. Free serotonin is inactivated rapidly by amine oxidase to 5-hydroxyindole acetic acid, which is excreted in the urine. This enzyme is abundant in brain. In the rabbit the activity is such that 30 μg. of serotonin can be inactivated per milligram per minute. Iproniazide (Marsalid) blocks the action of amine oxidase, permitting accumulation of "free" serotonin under appropriate conditions. Thus, a fairly complete system appears to be present in brain which is closely analogous to the acetylcholine system.

Neuronal activity is markedly affected by agents which appear to act primarily on serotonin metabolism. Serotonin itself, when administered to an animal, exhibits a marked "tranquilizing" effect on behavior. It is now apparent that reserpine (the active principle of the *Rauwolfia* alkaloids), which is a potent "tranquilizing" agent, acts by mobilizing stored serotonin. After large doses of reserpine, brain serotonin is rapidly depleted (up to 75 per cent within 15 min.), and much less rapidly, other stores in the body (gut, platelets) are mobilized with a consequent striking increase in urinary 5-hydroxyindole acetic acid excretion. However, even with therapeutic doses a significant mobilization of brain serotonin occurs (up to 50 per cent by a dose of 0.1 μg/kg body weight) while comparable mobilization from other body stores requires doses about ten times as large. Thus, in the therapeutic range reserpine appears to affect brain serotonin almost exclusively.

Lysergic acid diethylamide (LSD) in microgram doses exerts a marked, disturbing action on central nervous function. Hallucinations, paranoid-type reactions, and many other subjective symptoms result. Evarts and Marshall (29, 30) have found that LSD in the cat exerts a relative block of ganglionic transmission at the lateral geniculate stage in the visual pathway. To inspection such animals appear blind. From this and other observations Evarts (unpublished) has suggested that LSD exhibits the special capacity to block sensory synapses as a sort of curare of the sensory system. The subjective effects of LSD in man are apparently similar to those obtained by Hebb (9, 48) on functional sensory deafferentation by exclusion of all sensory stimuli. It is now apparent from the work of Gaddum (41) and Shore *et al.* (121, 122), that LSD antagonizes the actions of serotonin and of reserpine. Whether this antagonism involves failure to release serotonin or blockage of the site of action of serotonin is not yet clear. It is perhaps not irrelevant that serotonin, reserpine, and LSD are all indole derivatives. It is also of interest that serotonin appears to antagonize the action of acetylcholine in certain preparations (155). The further elucidation of these data will be most important to the subject of neuronal function and activity.*

THE CONCEPT OF A BIOCHEMICAL LESION

The concept of biochemical lesions, although well established, is still unfamiliar to many. In the central nervous system the histopathological bases for important diseases are often obscure or even absent. There is a growing list of clinical entities which result from lesions at the level of cellular metabolism.

Thiamin deficiency is a classical example of this concept. In its co-

TABLE 21

Thiamin deficiency and pyruvate metabolism in pigeon brain

A. Thiamin Content

Status of Animal	Thiamin Content of Brain (μg/g)
Normal	3.0
Deficient diet, no symptoms	1.2
Acute "beri-beri"	0.4

B. Oxidative Metabolism

Time in min.	Rate of Oxygen Uptake by Thiamin-deficient Brain (ml/hr over control)	
	+10 μg Thiamin	+0.05 μg. Diphosphothiamin*
0–10	60	190
10–20	186	130
20–30	100	114

* Brain was able to synthesize 0.05 μg. of diphosphothiamin from 10 μg. Thiamin in 40 min.

Data from Ochoa (92).

* The author is indebted to Drs. Bernard B. Brodie and Sidney Udenfriend of the National Heart Institute and Dr. Edward V. Evarts of the National Institute of Mental Health for making this material available while the respective manuscripts were in press.

enzyme form thiamin catalyzes the oxidative decarboxylation of pyruvate which, as an acetyl radical, combines with coenzyme-A and starts into the Krebs cycle. Some 20 years ago Peters and co-workers (95) observed that brain from thiamin-deficient pigeons is unable to oxidize pyruvate, but this capacity is restored upon addition of thiamin in its coenzyme form (diphosphothiamin). Thiamin itself will also restore pyruvate oxidation, but is slower to act because it must˙ be phosphorylated before becoming effective. These points are illustrated in Table 21. In such thiamin-deficient pigeons marked accumulation of pyruvate can be demonstrated in vivo as evidence of the blocked metabolism. The pigeons become ataxic and unable to fly and in the full-blown deficiency exhibit extreme opisthotonus and disturbance of equilibrium. Within an hour or two after the injection of microgram quantities of thiamin, all symptoms disappear. These stages are illustrated in Plate 27. This simple and dramatic example not only illustrates the concept of a biochemical lesion, but emphasizes the dependence of normal nervous system function upon the intactness of critical steps in its metabolic assembly.

TABLE 22

Classification of lipodystrophies

Disease	Type of Lipid	Organs Involved	Remarks
I LIPID GRANULOMA (Schueller-Christian)	Cholesterol	All, but brain rarely	
II GAUCHER'S DISEASE A. Adult form	Cerebroside	Lymphoid organs rarely brain	Cerebroside contains hexose other than normal galactose.
B. Infantile form	Cerebroside	Brain	Rare, fatal. Cerebroside concentration in brain normal but composition abnormal as in adult.
III NIEMANN-PICK'S DISEASE	Sphingomyelin	Visceral organs	
	Ganglioside	Brain	Brain sphingomyelin normal.
IV TAY-SACHS DISEASE (Familial amaurotic idiocy)	Ganglioside	Brain	No visceral involvement, brain sphingomyelin normal. Fatal.

Compiled from Thannhäuser (136).

*Representative Biochemical Lesions of Central
Nervous System*

Lipodystrophies.—Defects in lipid metabolism of the brain produce
some of the gravest clinical consequences in neurology. The lipodystrophies are a group of rare diseases, some familial in nature, in which lipid
accumulates within cells. If the central nervous system is involved, progressive deterioration and death are the rule. The classification of these
entities, taken from Thannhäuser (136), is given in Table 22. Each involves a different lipid component, and, with one exception, each involves other organs of the body often more commonly than brain. When
the brain is involved, the process appears to be different metabolically
from that in other organs. What the initiating factors and mechanisms
are is unknown.

Fluoroacetate Poisoning.—Fluoroacetic acid ($F\text{-}CH_2\text{-}COOH$) in doses
of a few milligrams (per kilogram body weight) produces in most mam-

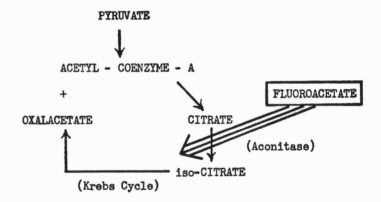

Dose Fluoroacetate	Rat Brain Citric Acid 60 min. after dose ($\mu g./g.$)		
0	21		
5 mg./kg.	166	Cerebrum	123
		Cerebellum	39
		Other areas	89

Fig. 109.—Fluoroacetate poisoning. The fluoroacetate is synthesized into fluorocitrate
which jams the Krebs cycle because of the inability of aconitase to metabolize it further. Brain citrate levels rise as shown in the table (97, 98).

malian species convulsions and death. It is the active principle of a poisonous South African plant and in pure form is widely used as a rodenticide (Compound 1080). As a result of the studies by Peters and co-workers (96, 97), the mechanism of action of fluoroacetate is now apparent. Chemically and biochemically the fluorine-carbon (F-C) bond is extremely stable, and it is this fact which underlies the toxic action of fluoroacetate. Shortly after administration of fluoroacetate to animals, accumulation of excess citrate in brain and other tissues can be demonstrated (Fig. 109). In vitro the fluoroacetyl fragment has been found to be assimilated by synthesis into fluorocitric acid, which blocks the further metabolism of citrate by the Krebs cycle. Flourocitrate itself is highly toxic in vitro and in vivo even under circumstances where fluoroacetate is inactive (presumably due to conditions unfavorable for its assimilation into the cycle). The effect of fluorocitrate is to block competitively the enzyme aconitase, which catalyzes the metabolism of citrate through *cis*-aconitate to *iso*-citrate (Fig. 109). Thus, fluoroacetate, by what Peters (96) calls "lethal synthesis," joins the Krebs cycle to prevent the oxidative stages of glucose metabolism from proceeding. Oxygen consumption consequently is lower, and the production of energy as ATP is seriously curtailed. In the brain it is not surprising that this chain of events is reflected in dire clinical consequences. Since citrate accumulation itself does not appear to be the primary cause of symptoms, it is likely that factors related to defective operation of the Krebs cycle are responsible (6, 66).

Methionine-sulfoximine.—The "improvement" of wheat flour during bleaching by treatment with nitrogen trichloride (Agene) has been found

TABLE 23

Methionine sulfoximine toxicity to mice in vivo: effects of treatment with glutamine

Group*	% Dead†	% Surviving† Seizure-free
Control—injected with saline intraperitoneally	100	0
Injected with saline containing *L*-Glutamine in dose of 10 mM/kg intraperitoneally.	0	100

* All mice averaged 15 seizures/hr at time of random sampling for test, 8 hr. after 150 mg/kg methionine sulfoximine i.p.

† Death in *status epilepticus*. In the group receiving glutamine, % survival calculated from 30 min. after injection to allow time for absorption.

Data from Tower (unpublished).

to alter the methionine in flour to a toxic derivative, methionine sulfoximine (7, 88). Dogs fed diets high in "agenized" flour develop ataxia, running fits, and generalized seizures usually with fatal consequences (82, 83). Methionine sulfoximine itself produces seizures in all mammalian species from mouse to monkey, inclusive (43, 105). Although the complete mechanism of action is not known, it is apparent that the toxic agent interferes with methionine metabolism in some fashion, since animals can be protected or cured by large doses of methionine (105). From enzymatic studies in vitro there is evidence that methionine sulfoximine also inhibits synthesis of glutamine from glutamic acid (123). The connection between these two findings is not obvious, but the latter is not incidental, since the toxicity can be abolished in vivo by administration of glutamine, as shown in Table 23 (Tower, unpublished). Defective glutamine metabolism of slices of cerebral cortex from methionine sulfoximine-intoxicated animals has also been found (139). It is of interest that such slices in addi-

TABLE 24

Effect of methionine sulfoximine in vivo on acetylcholine metabolism

A. In vitro production of "bound" acetylcholine by slices of cerebral cortex from cats with seizures induced by 10 mg/kg i.p. methionine sulfoximine prior to sampling of brain:*

Sample	Increase in "Bound" Acetylcholine (μg/gm tissue/hr)	Same + 10 mM. L-Glutamine in vitro
Normal—control	2.55	2.5
Methionine sulfoximine in vivo	0.05	2.3

B. In vivo levels of acetylcholine in cerebrospinal fluid of dogs with seizures induced by agenized-flour diet:†

Sample	Acetylcholine (μg/100 ml)
Controls—both dogs	0
Dog #1—Diet 6 days, seizures 2 days.	0.3
Dog #2—Diet 12 days, seizures 9 days.	2.0

* From Tower and Elliott (142).
† From Tower (unpublished).

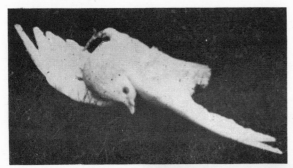

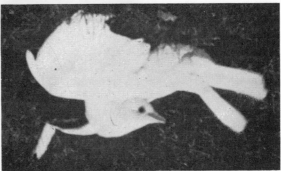

Plate 27.—Effects of Thiamin Deficiency in the Pigeon: *A*, top) After 10 to 12 days on deficient diet: muscular weakness, ataxia, inability to fly; *B*, middle) After 14 days on diet: extreme opisthotonus and disturbance of equilibrium; *C*, bottom) Same pigeon as in *B* 1½ hr. after intravenous injection of 25 μg. thiamin hydrochloride. Deficiencies produced by tube-feeding diet of Swank and Bessey (134). Blood sample at stage *C* showed pyruvate "excess" (131) of 3.7 to 5 mg/100 ml, compared with controls of 0.3 or less. Photographs reproduced from 16 mm. movie film of pigeon's activity (Tower, unpublished).

tion exhibit defective acetylcholine metabolism, characterized by inability to produce "bound" acetylcholine. This defect can be reversed by addition of glutamine to the incubation medium (142). Data in Table 24 illustrate these findings. Complementary studies in vivo on dogs fed a diet high in "agenized" flour (containing the toxic principle) demonstrate that acetylcholine appears in the cerebrospinal fluid after the onset of seizures and epileptiform activity is present in the EEG (Tower, unpub-

EXPERIMENTAL CANINE EPILEPSY
(DUE TO AGENIZED WHEAT FLOUR)

DOG: "PETE" (P8-57)

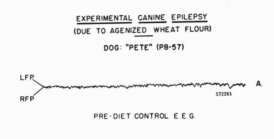

PRE-DIET CONTROL E.E.G.

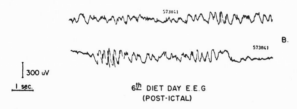

6ᵗʰ DIET DAY E.E.G
(POST-ICTAL)

Fig. 110.—Effect of methionine sulfoximine toxicity on the EEG of the dog. Record *A* was taken with implanted dural electrodes in the waking state prior to institution of diet high in "agenized" flour (see text). Record *B* taken under the same conditions six days after start of diet. At the time of recording the dog exhibited severe ataxia. Running fits has been observed during the previous 12 hrs., and a generalized seizure preceded the recording. Similar records were obtained inter-ictally (Tower, unpublished). (Calibrations for both records at lower left. Recordings taken from right and left frontoparietal leads.)

lished). Representative findings are illustrated in Table 24 and Figure 110. Thus, relatively small changes in methionine structure in nervous tissue result in a variety of metabolic abnormalities which are associated with clinical cerebral dysfunction. Both the in vitro defects and clinical changes can apparently be completely corrected by glutamine or methionine.

Di-isopropylfluorophosphate (DFP) and other cholinesterase inhibitors.—Of the known neurotoxic agents, a great majority act by disturbance of acetylcholine metabolism. Many of these agents (insecticides, industrial chemicals, and the "nerve gases") are potent inhibitors of cholinesterase activity. There are sufficient clinical examples of poisoning and death on record to make these agents of practical as well as theoretical importance. Burgen and MacIntosh (13) have summarized the evidence that these agents exert their effects in vivo through the accumulation of free acetylcholine consequent to cholinesterase inhibition. They parallel the effects of acetylcholine itself under comparable conditions so that there seems little doubt of the correctness of this explanation. Both peripheral and central nervous tissue are affected, so that clinical symptoms

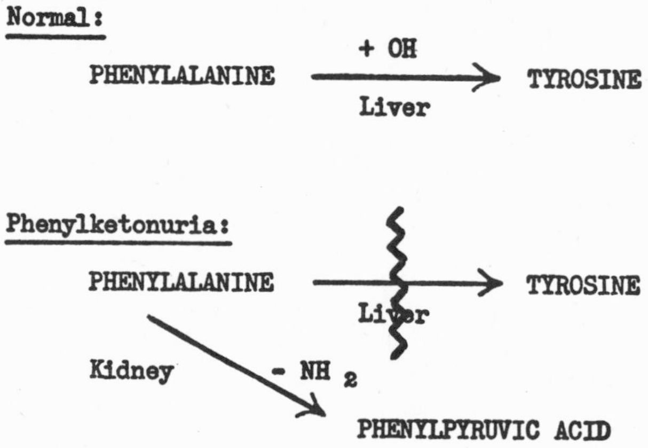

Normal:

$$\text{PHENYLALANINE} \xrightarrow[\text{Liver}]{+ \text{ OH}} \text{TYROSINE}$$

Phenylketonuria:

PHENYLALANINE ⟶ TYROSINE (Liver)

Kidney ⟶ - NH$_2$ PHENYLPYRUVIC ACID

	Serum (mg. %)		CSF (mg. %)		Urine (mg./day)
	PhA	PhP	PhA	PhP	PhP
NORMAL	1.0	None	Trace	0	None
PHENYLKETONURIA	30.0	0 - 3	7.0	±	1000
" + Diet	1.0	None	-	-	None

PhA = Phenylalanine
PhP = Phenylpyruvic Acid

Fig. 111.—Phenylalanine metabolism in the normal subject and in phenylketonuria (150).

are composed of cholinergic hyperactivity from both sources. Irritability, restlessness, anxiety, and seizures are the common central nervous manifestations of such toxicity. Atropine, which is effective treatment early in the development of toxicity, acts by blocking peripheral and to some extent central action of acetylcholine on effector sites. If the accumulation of acetylcholine continues, depression of brain function, coma, and death ensue. These phenomena parallel those of large doses of acetylcholine experimentally. The cholinesterase inhibitors can be subdivided into those which are reversible, such as eserine, and those which are essentially irreversible, such as alkyl phosphates exemplified by DFP. The latter combine in a complex with cholinesterase, which can apparently only be handled in the body by degradation and the synthesis of new cholinesterase as replacement. This situation explains the profound and persistent effects of this type of cholinesterase inhibitor.

Phenylketonuria.—Phenylketonuria (phenylpyruvic oligophrenia) is a rare, hereditary disease characterized by severe mental retardation, dermatitis, and often seizures and spasticity. These clinical manifestations are associated with a defect in the metabolism of the amino acid, phenylalanine, characterized by failure of its normal conversion to tyrosine (Figure 111). Phenylalanine content of most dietary proteins is similar. As a result phenylalanine from the diet accumulates in body fluids and is excreted by the kidney as phenylpyruvic acid in large quantities (up to 1 gm. daily). Normally only traces of phenylalanine are found in body fluids, and no phenylpyruvic acid is detectable in the urine. Typical analyses in the disease are shown in Figure 111. It is generally recognized that the metabolic abnormality is due to a single defective gene, and its site of occurrence is in the liver. Thus, the cerebral counterparts are consequences of the hepatic biochemical lesion. Temporary reduction in phenylpyruvate excretion has been reported after instituting protein-free diets (94), but the mobilization of endogenous protein soon terminated this improvement.

Recently, impressive long-term results have been obtained using a special phenylalanine-free or deficient diet (3). On such a diet all biochemical abnormalities are reversed (Fig. 111), and the dermatitis, due to excess phenylalanine in sweat, rapidly clears. In addition, the seizures cease spontaneously, and EEG abnormalities improve or disappear. Changes in mental and motor function are slower and less dramatic but in all cases have been in the direction of improvement. Better results seem to be obtained in younger patients with shorter duration of disease. Reinstitution of regular diet induces prompt biochemical relapse and slower regression of cerebral symptoms. When given acutely in large amounts, phenylpyruvic acid has been found to be toxic to the central nervous system. Thus, a toxic effect of phenylalanine, of its abnormal metabolites, or of biochemical abnormalities induced by them, appears to be responsible for the central nervous system effects.

Hepatic coma.—That normal hepatic function is essential to the wellbeing of the central nervous system is further illustrated by the condition of hepatic coma. This is characterized clinically by a usually fatal depression of cerebral function associated with severe liver disease (usually cirrhosis). In liver disease, or after experimental hepatectomy, there is an increase in urinary amino acid excretion and a rise in circulating amino acid concentrations. In addition, significantly elevated levels of free ammonia in blood occur regularly (Table 25). These disturbances are ex-

TABLE 25

Blood ammonia and hepatic coma

Clinical Status	Arterial NH$_3$	Cerebral A-V Difference
Normal (mean)	0.76	−0.02
Hepatic Disease (mean)	3.43	+0.52
Alert (av.)	1.73	+0.12
Confused (av.)	2.64	+0.43
Comatose (av.)	4.26	+0.74

All values in μg/ml of ammonia N.

A-V Differences: + indicates uptake; − liberation by brain.

Modified from Bessman and Bessman (8).

plicable in terms of defective liver function, since liver normally accounts for much of the amino acid metabolism and transamination and ammonia disposal reactions in the body. Neither urea synthesis nor amidation is defective so that the source of elevated blood ammonia is not yet clear. Several investigators have demonstrated that the administration of ammonia to a non-comatose patient with liver disease may result in coma (8).

Recent studies of Bessman and Bessman (8) suggest a possible mechanism for this observation. Measurements of arterio-venous differences of ammonia in the cerebral circulation (Table 25) demonstrate that normally there is no significant A-V difference, indicating equilibrium between plasma and brain fluids exists, but in hepatic disease a significant uptake of ammonia by brain occurs. There appears to be a close correlation between the *arterial* ammonia level and both the A-V difference (brain uptake) and the mental state of the patient. The ammonia uptake by brain might be accounted for by glutamine synthesis, which requires ATP. Resultant exhaustion of energy stores could result in coma. This possibility does not appear to be tenable since the uptake of some 4 micromoles of ammonia/100 g of brain/min at the usual rate of cerebral blood flow would soon exhaust available supplies of glutamic acid necessary for such synthesis. Bessman and Bessman (8) suggest that α-ketoglutarate of the Krebs cycle is being reductively aminated to glutamic acid (which may also be further amidated to glutamine). This siphoning-off of α-ketoglutarate would in effect by-pass half of the Krebs cycle (Fig. 98), thus reducing oxygen requirements for the inactivated oxidative metabolism and interfering with the build-up of energy stores. Failure of ATP supplies within the neuron would certainly result in depression of function and its clinical manifestation, coma. It should be pointed out that the uptake of ammonia by brain in hepatic disease does not seem to be peculiar to that condition except insofar as the liver is unable to assimilate the excess blood ammonia to protect the brain from exposure. If the correlation data are correct, increasing ammonia in the cerebral arterial blood of normal brain should give the same result. Experimental confirmation is lacking at present.

Treatment of hepatic coma with glutamic acid would, thus, have a rational basis. In some cases such treatment has been quite dramatic, but results are far from uniform. This is not surprising in view of the difficulty of getting glutamic acid into the central nervous system and also because this is not likely to affect the basic problem of a damaged liver.

Hepato-lenticular degeneration (Wilson's Disease).—Wilson's disease is a familial disease which is characterized by cirrhosis of the liver and gliosis and occasionally cavitation of the nervous system, particularly in the lenticular nucleus. The latter lesions are associated with involuntary movements of a tremorous or athetoid type, rigidity, and other signs typical of an extra-pyramidal disease. As might be anticipated, there is an increased excretion of amino acids in the urine, a finding which appears to be general in hepatic disease. Of more interest is the finding of an increased excretion of copper in the urine and deposition of abnormal amounts of copper in liver and brain (20). This is not an incidental finding, since the treatment of such patients with BAL or versene, which are metal chelating (complexing) agents, has alleviated symptoms in association with mobilization of copper from tissue stores. Denny-Brown (20) has suggested that the results of treatment indicate an association of symptoms with the accumulation of copper in central nervous tissue. The explanation for the tissue accumulation is now fairly apparent. There is normally in plasma a copper-protein complex, ceruloplasmin, to which 90 per cent of the circulating copper is bound (115). In Wilson's disease this plasma protein is markedly deficient, probably due to a decreased rate of synthesis (? in liver) (116). As a result, circulating diffusible copper is higher, even though total plasma copper is decreased. Studies with isotopic copper, Cu^{64}, suggests that in Wilson's disease there is also a greater retention of ingested copper than normal and that whereas normally most of the plasma activity of administered Cu^{64} appears after some delay in the ceruloplasmin fraction, none appears in this fraction in Wilson's disease, and the total plasma activity in such patients is much lower (15). Copper in brain tissue in this disease appears to be associated with tissue as a protein complex (102). Examples of other metals, particularly polyvalent ions (such as lead), are familiar in brain toxicology. Their precise mechanism of action is unknown, but it is suggested that they may act by chelation with functional enzyme groups or by displacement of the ions normally present as enzyme activators (2).

Summary.—The foregoing metabolic abnormalities have been presented to illustrate the importance of the concept of a biochemical lesion in the consideration of central nervous system dysfunction. The examples have been intentionally chosen, without regard to relative clinical importance, to focus attention on the important areas of central nervous system metabolism which are basic to normal neuronal function and activity: glucose and oxygen utilization, amino acids (particularly glutamic acid), nitrogen metabolism, acetylcholine, inorganic ions (electrolytes), and cerebral lipids. Some of the examples involve simple interference at a single vital step, others exhibit a variety of disturbances, but all, provided structural damage has not taken place or is not too extensive, are reversible to some degree (with the exception of the lipodystrophies at present). Many other similar lesions can be cited. Human focal epilepsy has on study yielded several important biochemical defects (acetylcholine, glutamic acid, and potassium) which are reversible in vitro by glutamine or asparagine. Trials of these amides clinically is meeting with rather significant control of seizures (139, 140). The problem of congenital anomalies of the central nervous system is beginning to assume a semblance of order and clarification (52, 59). Some of the factors which contribute cases to that mixture of conditions, cerebral palsy, must be apparent from these studies and examples. And even disturbances in the mental sphere of cerebral activity are taking on new meaning as a result of recent findings. It is foolish to suppose that any one approach can solve the many problems to which an organ of the complexity of the brain is subject, but the biochemical approach, so relatively recent in application, is certain to assist materially in final understanding and correction.*

INTEGRATION AND BEHAVIORAL PHENOMENA

The neurochemical substrates of cerebral function and activity must be integrated into the neurophysiological and behavioral structure of the central nervous system. Where such a synthesis is defective at the neurochemical level, function and behavior alter. To the neurochemist, the neurophysiologist, and the neuropharmacologist, behavior often has a different connotation from that of the psychologist and clinician. Enzyme systems behave, neuronal circuits behave, and animals with drugs behave. These are not things apart from the behavior about which the psychologist speculates. They are units in the total pattern which is physical, mental, and social behavior. Ethyl alcohol is perhaps the commonest mediator of behavioral changes at the mental and social level. The complete dossier on ethyl alcohol has not been written, but a great deal is known at the biochemical, physiological, pharmacological, and pathological levels about its mode of action and its effects. It alters behavior all along the line. With so much background from such examples, the disturbances of behavior which originate apparently spontaneously, the psychoneuroses and psychoses, should not be set apart. Already links between psychical and neurochemical mechanisms are being forged, and others at all levels of integration are following suit. Lysergic acid diethylamide is not the cause of, nor does it produce, schizophrenia, but its mechanisms of action and the systems upon which it acts may be concerned.

There is then the need for integration of scientific assault upon the behavioral mechanisms complex, a need which has stimulated the hold-

---

* The preceding material on brain chemistry and metabolism has not been an exhaustive review. Much has been omitted in favor of emphasis on aspects germane to this symposium. Where feasible, references to review articles rather than specific papers have been preferred. For greater details on these and other aspects of neurochemistry, three recent volumes on this subject will be found useful (27, 84, 87). Since the presentation of this paper in September, 1955, numerous advances have clarified and added to the foregoing data, but subsequent reports have not necessitated revision or deletion of any material originally presented. More recent data on synthesis and turnover of cerebral lipids and proteins, on the oxidative shunt pathway for glucose metabolism, on the roles of γ-aminobutyric acid and serotonin, on the reversal of DFP poisoning, and on phenylketonuria, hepatic coma, and galactosemia may be found in monographs and journal papers published since 1955. The interested reader is referred particularly to papers in the *Journal of Neurochemistry,* to the neurochemistry supplement of volume 8 of *Neurology,* and to published proceedings of the Korey-Nurnberger Progress in Neurobiology symposia and the papers published from the International Neurochemical Symposia of 1954, 1956, and 1958.

ing of this Symposium. In the succeeding paper (112) an ambitious attempt to correlate behavior with neurochemical substrates is presented. Regardless of its ultimate evaluation, it is a signal event because it is one of the first forays into this aspect of behavioral integration. As such, it is not surprising that serious problems in bridging the gap between neurochemical substrates of the acetylcholine system and the integrated function of maze behavior have been encountered. The nature of the neurochemical problems may illustrate to the psychologist a portion of the interdisciplinary problem. For the neurochemist's benefit the psychologist must do likewise.

To suggest an association between acetylcholine metabolism and the maze behavior of rats is appealing to the neurochemist, who is impressed with the many apparently important functions of acetylcholine in cerebral activity. However, such a reaction is immediately tempered by neurochemical facts. The role of acetylcholine in the central nervous system is controversial. It has not been demonstrated to be a central transmitter, although the evidence is strong in favor of such a function. It clearly seems to be of less or no importance to certain major systems, including much of the sensory apparatus upon which maze behavior is dependent. The use of cholinesterase activity as a criterion of acetylcholine metabolism or function is questionable. The method of measurement does not apparently take account of the type of cholinesterase, whether type I ("true" or acetylcholinesterase) or type II ("pseudo" or serum cholinesterase), since both occur in brain, but only type I participates in acetylcholine hydrolysis. In addition, the fact that cholinesterase in brain is apparently far in excess of requirements makes any correlation with function or activity difficult.* Finally, there is the fact that activity of the acetylcholine system is correlated with species brain size and probably with neuron density and/or size. When differences in maze behavior of two distinct strains, so-called, bright and dull, appear to relate to differences in cholinesterase activity in respective brains, might this not represent differences in cell densities or sizes which, so-to-speak help make such animals bright or dull?

This critique is not intended to detract from the idea or the results of such a study. It is stated merely as an example of the problems in bridg-

* A preliminary report by Jones *et al.* (62) on chick embryo nervous tissue in vitro indicates that exposure of the tissue to acetylcholine induces production of additional cholinesterase (type I) up to 100 per cent of controls without change in total protein. Analogous changes in cholinesterase activity possibly due to excess acetylcholine are found in epileptogenic cortical foci of adult brain (101, 140). These changes are gross by comparison with the changes reported by Rosenzweig *et al.* (112), which are close to, or within the probable limits of, error of sampling and analysis.

ing the gap between the integrated structure of behavior and the basic units of the structure. The interpretation in this case appears oversimplified in ignoring the many other units and systems of the structure which must and do function in behavioral mechanisms. Yet the start in bridging the gap must be made somewhere and in terms which do not exceed the experimental limitations. It is with the latter that this Symposium has most to offer the investigator at whatever level of integration he is working. This discussion of the chemistry of the brain has been designed to illustrate the type of information available to other fields and the limitations inherent in its application to them.

In conclusion it is appropriate to quote a portion of Professor G. H. Bishop's thinking on this subject:

> Every chemical process in a nerve cell is presumably represented by an electrical change, and every electrical phenomenon presumably correlates with mental function. However precisely measured, at present these potentials are in a sense nonspecific; an electrical change does not tell what chemical change produced it nor what mental phenomenon results from it . . . we must have the chemical information in terms of observable neural functions. It is not enough to know, for instance, that certain enzymes accomplish substrate oxidation in nerve; we must know how these chemical reactions result in electrochemical excitability and response. On the other hand we should have mental behavior broken down into components capable of corresponding to practicably recordable patterns of neural behavior. That such a breakdown should be possible follows from the premise that mental behavior is a function of nervous tissue. It is difficult to conceive of a neural pattern corresponding to anxiety, or to a dissociation from reality; if there is one, it must be too hopelessly complex to be recorded by any current apparatus. There must be simpler mental components conceivable, as there will certainly be more complex electrical recordings possible, in terms of which the neurophysiologist and the psychologist can find a common ground; but this common ground must be approached from both directions (10, pp. 160–61).

REFERENCES

1 Adams, J. E., H. A. Harper, G. S. Gordan, M. Hutchin, and R. C. Bentinck. Cerebral metabolism of glutamic acid in multiple sclerosis. *Neurology*, 1955, 5: 100–107.

2 Aring, C. D., and S. A. Trufant. Effects of heavy metals on the central nervous system. *Res. Publ. Ass. nerv. ment. Dis.*, 1953, 32: 463–74.

3 Armstrong, M. D., and F. H. Tyler. Studies on phenylketonuria. I. Restricted phenylalanine intake in phenylketonuria. *J. clin. Invest.*, 1955, 34: 565–80.

4 Bakay, L., and O. Lindberg. Studies on the rôle of the cerebrospinal fluid

in brain metabolism as measured with radioactive phosphate. *Acta physiol. scand.,* 1949, *17:* 179–90.

5 Ball, E. G. Oxidation and reduction in brain tissue. In *The biology of mental health and disease.* New York: Hoeber, 1952, pp. 74–82.

6 Benitez, D., G. R. Pscheidt, and W. E. Stone, Formation of ammonium ion in the cerebrum in fluoroacetate poisoning. *Amer. J. Physiol.,* 1954, *176:* 488–92.

7 Bentley, H. R., E. E. McDermott, and J. K. Whitehead. Action of nitrogen trichloride on proteins: A synthesis of the toxic factor from methionine. *Nature,* 1950, *165:* 735.

8 Bessman, S. P., and A. N. Bessman. Cerebral and peripheral uptake of ammonia in liver disease with an hypothesis for the mechanism of hepatic coma. *J. clin. Invest.,* 1955, *34:* 622–28.

9 Bexton, W. H., W. Heron, and T. H. Scott. Effects of decreased variation in the sensory environment. *Canad. J. Psychol.,* 1954, *8:* 70–76.

10 Bishop, G. H. Neurophysiology and behavior. Electrical manifestations of action in neurons. Discussion. In *The biology of mental health and disease.* New York: Hoeber, 1952, pp. 159–61.

11 Bodian, D. Nucleic acid in nerve-cell regeneration. *Symp. Soc. exp. Biol.,* 1947, *1:* 163–78.

12 Burgen, A. S. V., and L. M. Chipman. Cholinesterase and succinic dehydrogenase in the central nervous system of the dog. *J. Physiol.,* 1951, *114:* 296–305.

13 Burgen, A. S. V., and F. C. MacIntosh. The physiological significance of acetylcholine. In K. A. C. Elliott, I. H. Page, and J. H. Quastel (Eds.), *Neurochemistry: The chemical dynamics of brain and nerve.* Springfield, Ill.: Charles C Thomas, 1955, pp. 311–89.

14 Caputto, R., L. F. Leloir, C. E. Cardini, and A. C. Paladini. Isolation of the coenzyme of the galactose phosphate—glucose phosphate transformation. *J. biol. Chem.,* 1950, *184:* 333–50.

15 Cartwright, G. E., J. A. Bush, H. Markowitz, J. P. Mahoney, and C. J. Gubler. Further studies on the abnomalities in the metabolism of copper in Wilson's disease. *J. clin. Invest.,* 1955, *34:* 925 (Abstract).

16 Chesler, A., and H. E. Himwich. Glycolysis in the parts of the central nervous system of cats and dogs during growth. *Amer. J. Physiol.,* 1944, *142:* 544–49.

17 Colfer, H. F., and H. E. Essex. The distribution of total electrolyte, potassium and sodium in the cerebral cortex in relation to experimental convulsions. *Amer. J. Physiol.,* 1947, *150:* 27–36.

18 Coxon, R. V. Carbohydrate metabolism in nervous tissue. In R. T. Williams (Ed.), *Metabolism and function in nervous tissue (Biochemical Society Symposia No. 8).* Cambridge: The Univer. Press, 1952, pp. 3–15.

19 Davies, P. W., and A. Rémond. Oxygen consumption of the cerebral cortex of the cat during Metrazol convulsions. *Res. Publ. Ass. nerv. ment. Dis.,* 1947, *26:* 205–17.

20 Denny-Brown, D. Abnormal copper metabolism in hepatolenticular degeneration. *Res. Publ. Ass. nerv. ment. Dis.*, 1953, *32:* 190–97.

21 Dixon, K. C. Anaerobic leakage of potassium from brain. *Biochem. J.*, 1949, *44:* 187–90.

22 Eccles, J. C. *The neurophysiological basis of mind: The principles of neurophysiology.* Oxford: The Clarendon Press, 1953.

23 Elliott, K. A. C. Brain tissue respiration and glycolysis. In K. A. C. Elliott, I. H. Page, and J. H. Quastel (Eds.), *Neurochemistry: The chemical dynamics of brain and nerve.* Springfield, Ill.: Charles C Thomas, 1955, pp. 53–93.

24 ———. Chemical studies in relation to convulsive conditions. In K. A. C. Elliott, I. H. Page, and J. H. Quastel (Eds.), *Neurochemistry: The chemical dynamics of brain and nerve.* Springfield, Ill.: Charles C Thomas, 1955, pp. 677–95.

25 ———. The relation of ions to metabolism in brain. *Canad. J. Biochem. Physiol.*, 1955, *33:* 466–77.

26 Elliott, K. A. C., and M. Henry. Studies on metabolism of brain suspensions. III. Respiration at low oxygen tension. *J. biol. Chem.*, 1946, *163:* 351–59.

27 Elliott, K. A. C., I. H. Page, and J. H. Quastel. *Neurochemistry: The chemical dynamics of brain and nerve.* Springfield, Ill.: Charles C Thomas, 1955.

28 Engström, A., and H. Lüthy. The distribution of mass and lipids in the single nerve fiber. *Exp. Cell. Res.*, 1950, *1:* 81–91.

29 Evarts, E. V., W. M. Landau, W. H. Freygang, Jr., and W. H. Marshall. Some effects of lysergic acid diethylamide and bufotenine on electrical activity in the cat's visual system. *Amer. J. Physiol.*, 1955, *182:* 594–98.

30 Evarts, E. V., and W. H. Marshall. The effects of lysergic acid diethylamide on the excitability cycle of the lateral geniculate. *Trans. Amer. neurol. Ass.*, 1955, *80:* 58–60.

31 Fazekas, J. F., F. A. D. Alexander, and H. E. Himwich. Tolerance of the newborn to anoxia. *Amer. J. Physiol.*, 1941, *134:* 281–87.

32 Feldberg, W. The role of acetylcholine in the central nervous system. *Brit. med. Bull.*, 1950, *6:* 312–21.

33 Feldberg, W., and M. Vogt. Acetylcholine synthesis in different regions of the central nervous system. *J. Physiol.*, 1948, *107:* 372–81.

34 Findlay, M., R. J. Rossiter, and K. P. Strickland. Factors affecting the incorporation of radioactive phosphate into the pentose nucleic acids of brain slices. *Biochem. J.*, 1953, *55:* 200–204.

35 Findlay M., W. L. Magee, and R. J. Rossiter. Incorporation of radioactive phosphate into lipids and pentosenucleic acid of cat brain slices. The effect of inorganic ions. *Biochem. J.*, 1954, *58:* 236–43.

36 Findlay, M., K. P. Strickland, and R. J. Rossiter. Incorporation of radioactive phosphate into non-nucleotide protein-bound phosphorus fractions of respiring brain slices. *Canad. J. Biochem. Physiol.*, 1954, *32:* 504–14.

37 Folch-Pi, J., and M. Lees. Proteolipids, a new type of tissue lipoproteins. *J. Biol. Chem.,* 1951, *191:* 807–17.

38 Folch-Pi, J. Chemical constituents of brain during development and in maturity. In *The biology of mental health and disease.* New York: Hoeber, 1952, pp. 11–16.

39 ――――. A quantitative histochemical study of eight enzymes of the cerebellar cortex and subjacent white matter in the monkey. Discussion. *Res. Publ. Ass. nerv. ment. Dis.,* 1953, *32:* 322–23.

40 Folch-Pi, J., and W. M. Sperry. Chemistry of the lipids. *Annu. Rev. Biochem.,* 1948, *17:* 147–68.

41 Gaddum, J. H. Antagonism between lysergic acid diethylamide and 5-hydroxy-tryptamine. *J. Physiol.,* 1953, *121:* 15P (Abstract).

42 Geiger, A., and J. Magnes. The isolation of the cerebral circulation and the perfusion of the brain in the living cat. *Amer. J. Physiol.,* 1947, *149:* 517–37.

43 Gershoff, S. N., and C. A. Elvehjem. The effect of methionine sulfoximine on different species of animals. *Fed. Proc.,* 1951, *10:* 188 (Abstract).

44 Gibbs, E. L., W. G. Lennox, L. F. Nims, and F. A. Gibbs. Arterial and cerebral venous blood: Arterial-venous differences in man. *J. biol. Chem.,* 1942, *144:* 325–32.

45 Gidez, L. I., and M. L. Karnovsky. The metabolism of C^{14}-glycerol in the intact rat. *J. biol. Chem.,* 1954, *206:* 229–42.

46 Grenell, R. G., and P. W. Davies. Respiration of cerebral cortex in vivo, in the absence of glucose. *Fed. Proc.,* 1950, *9:* 52 (Abstract).

47 Halstead, W. C. Brain and intelligence. In L. A. Jeffress (Ed.), *Cerebral mechanisms in behavior.* New York: Wiley, 1951, pp. 244–88.

48 Hebb, D. O. Drives and the C.N.S. (Conceptual nervous system). *Psychol. Rev.,* 1955, *62:* 243–54.

49 Heller, I. H., and K. A. C. Elliott. Desoxyribonucleic acid content and cell density in brain and human brain tumors. *Canad. J. Biochem. Physiol.,* 1954, *32:* 584–92.

50 Heller, I. H., and K. A. C. Elliott. The metabolism of normal brain and human gliomas in relation to cell type and density. *Canad. J. Biochem. Physiol.,* 1955, *33:* 395–403.

51 Hevesy, G. Some applications of radioactive indicators in turnover studies. *Advanc. Enzymol.,* 1947, *7:* 111–214.

52 Hicks, S. P. Effects of ionizing radiations on the adult and embryonic nervous system. *Res. Publ. Ass. nerv. ment. Dis.,* 1953, *32:* 439–62.

53 Himwich, H. E., O. A. Bernstein, H. Herrlich, A. Chesler, and J. F. Fazekas. Mechanisms for the maintenance of life in the newborn during anoxia. *Amer. J. Physiol.,* 1942, *135:* 387–91.

54 Himwich, H. E., and J. F. Fazekas. Comparative studies of the metabolism of the brain of infant and adult dogs. *Amer. J. Physiol.,* 1941, *132:* 454–59.

55 Hodgkin, A. L., and R. D. Keynes. Active transport of cations in giant axons from Sepia and Loligo. *J. Physiol.,* 1955, *128:* 28–60.

56 Holmes, J. H., and D. B. Tower. Intracranial fluids. In K. A. C. Elliott, J. H. Page, and J. H. Quastel (Eds.), *Neurochemistry: The chemical dynamics of brain and nerve.* Springfield, Ill.: Charles C Thomas, 1955, pp. 262–93.

57 Horecker, B. L., and A. H. Mehler. Carbohydrate metabolism. *Annu. Rev. Biochem.,* 1955, *24:* 207–74.

58 Hydén, H. Nucleic acids and proteins. In K. A. C. Elliott, I. H. Page, and J. H. Quastel (Eds.), *Neurochemistry: The chemical dynamics of brain and nerve.* Springfield, Ill.: Charles C Thomas, 1955, pp. 204–33.

59 Ingalls, T. H. Biologic implications of mongolism. In *The biology of mental health and disease.* New York: Hoeber, 1952, pp. 389–401.

60 Johnson, A. C., A. R. McNabb, and R. J. Rossiter. Concentration of lipids in the brain of infants and adults. *Biochem. J.,* 1949, *44:* 494–98.

61 ———. Lipids of the nervous system during *in vitro* degeneration. *Canad. J. Res., Sect. E,* 1949, *27:* 63–71.

62 Jones, M., R. M. Featherstone, and S. L. Bonting. Acetylcholine-induced enzyme formation in vertebrate cells cultivated *in vitro. Anat. Rec.,* 1955, *121:* 472 (Abstract).

63 Kahlson, G., and F. C. MacIntosh. Acetylcholine synthesis in a sympathetic ganglion. *J. Physiol.,* 1939, *96:* 277–92.

64 Kalckar, H. M. The enzymes of uridine polyphosphates. *Science,* 1954, *119:* 479–80.

65 Kalckar, H. M., B. Braganca, and A. Munch-Petersen. Uridyl transferases and the formation of uridine diphosphogalactose. *Nature,* 1953, *172:* 1038.

66 Kandel, A., and M. B. Chenoweth. Metabolic disturbances produced by some fluoro-fatty acids: Relation to pharmacologic activity of these compounds. *J. Pharmacol.,* 1952, *104:* 234–47.

67 Kety, S. S. Cerebral circulation and metabolism. In *The biology of mental health and disease.* New York: Hoeber, 1952, pp. 20–31.

68 ———. Blood flow and metabolism of the human brain in health and disease. In K. A. C. Elliott, I. H. Page, and J. H. Quastel (Eds.), *Neurochemistry: The chemical dynamics of brain and nerve.* Springfield, Ill.: Charles C Thomas, 1955, pp. 294–310.

69 Keynes, R. D., and P. R. Lewis. Electrolytes and nerve function. In K. A. C. Elliott, I. H. Page, and J. H. Quastel (Eds.), *Neurochemistry: The chemical dynamics of brain and nerve.* Springfield, Ill.: Charles C Thomas, 1955, pp. 440–57.

70 Klein, J. R., and N. S. Olsen. Effect of convulsive activity upon concentration of brain glucose, glycogen, lactate, and phosphates. *J. biol. Chem.,* 1947, *167:* 747–56.

71 Krebs, H. A. Body size and tissue respiration. *Biochem. biophys. Acta,* 1950, *4:* 249–69.

72 ———. Some aspects of the energy transformation in living matter. *Brit. med. Bull.,* 1953, *9:* 97–104.

73 Landau, W. M., W. H. Freygang, L. P. Roland, L. Sokoloff, and S. S. Kety.

The local circulation of the living brain: Values in the unanesthetized and anesthetized cat. *Trans. Amer. neurol. Ass.*, 1955, *80:* 125–29.

74 Larrabee, M. Effects of anesthetics on oxygen consumption and synaptic transmission in sympathetic ganglia. In *The biology of mental health and disease.* New York: Hoeber, 1952, pp. 384–88.

75 Lipton, S. H., S. A. Morell, A. Frieden, and R. M. Bock. Uridine-5'-triphosphate. *J. Amer. chem. Soc.*, 1953, *75:* 5449–50.

76 Lowry, O. H., N. R. Roberts, K. Y. Leiner, M. L. Wu, A. L. Farr, and R. W. Albers. The quantitative histochemistry of brain. III. Ammon's horn. *J. biol. Chem.*, 1954, *207:* 39–49.

77 McIlwain, H. Substances which support respiration and metabolic response to electrical impulses in human cerebral tissues. *J. Neurol. Psychiat.*, 1953, *16:* 257–66.

78 MacIntosh, F. C. Distribution of acetylcholine in peripheral and central nervous system. *J. Physiol.*, 1941, *99:* 436–42.

79 McLennan, H., and K. A. C. Elliott. Effects of convulsant and narcotic drugs on acetylcholine synthesis. *J. Pharmacol.*, 1951, *103:* 35–43.

80 Manery, J. F. Inorganic metabolism of the brain. In *The biology of mental health and disease.* New York: Hoeber, 1952, pp. 124–32.

81 Meister, A. Enzymatic transfer of alpha-amino groups. *Science*, 1954, *120:* 43–50.

82 Mellanby, E. Diet and canine hysteria: Experimental production by treated flour. *Brit. med. J.*, 1946, *2:* 885–87.

83 ———. Further observations on production of canine hysteria by flour treated with nitrogen trichloride (Agene process). *Brit. med. J.*, 1947, *2:* 288–89.

84 Merritt, H. H., and C. C. Hare (Eds.). *Metabolic and toxic diseases of the nervous system (Res. Publ. Ass. nerv. ment. Dis.,* v. 32). Baltimore: Williams and Wilkins, 1953.

85 Meyerhof, O. The origin of the reaction of Harden and Young in cell-free alcoholic fermentation. *J. biol. Chem.*, 1945, *157:* 105–119.

86 Meyerhof, O., and J. R. Wilson. Comparative study of the glycolysis and ATP-ase activity in tissue homogenates. *Arch. Biochem.*, 1949, *23:* 246–55.

87 Milbank Memorial Fund (27th Annual Conference). *The biology of mental health and disease.* New York: Hoeber, 1952.

88 Misani, F., and Reiner, L. Studies on nitrogen trichloride-treated prolamines. VIII. Synthesis of the toxic factor. *Arch. Biochem.*, 1950, *27:* 234–35.

89 Nachmansohn, D. Metabolism and function of the nerve cell. In K. A. C. Elliott, I. H. Page, and J. H. Quastel (Eds.), *Neurochemistry: The chemical dynamics of brain and nerve.* Springfield, Ill.: Charles C Thomas, 1955, pp. 390–425.

90 Nurnberger, J. I. Combined use of soft X-rays and monochromatic ultraviolet light for microabsorption measurements of nerve cell components. Histopathology of schizophrenia and other psychoses of unknown origin—

discussion. In *The biology of mental health and disease*. New York: Hoeber, 1952, pp. 491–95.

91 ———. Clinical and metabolic effects of exposure to low environmental temperatures on the central nervous system and related visceral structures. *Res. Publ. Ass. nerv. ment. Dis.*, 1953, *32*, 132–173.

92 Ochoa, S. Pyruvate oxidation in brain. Carbohydrate metabolism in brain tissue. Discussion. In *The biology of mental health and disease*. New York: Hoeber, 1952, pp. 97–104.

93 Palay, S. L. Structure and function in the neuron. In S. R. Korey, and J. I. Nurnberger (Eds.), *Progress in neurobiology*. Vol. 1. *Neurochemistry*. New York: Hoeber, 1956, pp. 64–82.

94 Penrose, L., and J. H. Quastel. Metabolic studies in phenylketonuria. *Biochem. J.*, 1937, *31*: 266–74.

95 Peters, R. A. The biochemical lesion in vitamin B_1 deficiency: Application of modern biochemical analysis to its diagnosis. *Lancet*, 1936, *230*: 1161–64.

96 ———. Croonian lecture: Lethal synthesis. *Proc. roy. Soc., Ser. B.*, 1952, *139*: 143–70.

97 ———. Significance of biochemical lesions in the pyruvate oxidase system. *Brit. med. Bull.*, 1953, *9*: 116–22.

98 ———. Pyruvate metabolism in the central nervous system. In K. A. C. Elliott, I. H. Page, and J. H. Quastel (Eds.), *Neurochemistry: The chemical dynamics of brain and nerve*. Springfield, Ill.: Charles C Thomas, 1955, pp. 111–33.

99 Pletscher, A., P. A. Shore, and B. B. Brodie. Serotonin as a mediator of reserpine action in brain. *J. Pharmacol.* 1956, *116*: 84–89.

100 Pope, A. Quantitative distribution of dipeptidase and acetylcholine esterase in architectonic layers of rat cerebral cortex. *J. Neurophysiol.*, 1952, *15*: 115–30.

101 Pope, A., A. A. Morris, H. Jasper, K. A. C. Elliott, and W. Penfield. Histochemical and action potential studies in epileptogenic areas of cerebral cortex in man and the monkey. *Res. Publ. Ass. nerv. ment. Dis.*, 1947, *26*: 218–33.

102 Porter, H., and Folch-Pi, J. Fractionation of brain copper proteins. In S. R. Korey, and J. I. Nurnberger (Eds.), *Progress in neurobiology*. Vol. 1. *Neurochemistry*. New York: Hoeber, 1956, pp. 40–51.

103 Quastel, J. H. Biochemical aspects of narcosis. In K. A. C. Elliott, I. H. Page, and J. H. Quastel (Eds.), *Neurochemistry: The chemical dynamics of brain and nerve*. Springfield, Ill.: Charles C Thomas, 1955, pp. 648–76.

104 Racker, E. The mechanisms of glycolysis. In K. A. C. Elliott, I. H. Page, and J. H. Quastel (Eds.), *Neurochemistry: The chemical dynamics of brain and nerve*. Springfield, Ill.: Charles C Thomas, 1955, pp. 134–52.

105 Reiner, L., F. Misani, and P. Weiss. Studies on nitrogen trichloride-treated prolamines. VI. Suppression of development of convulsions with methionine. *Arch. Biochem.*, 1950, *25*: 447–49.

106   Richter, D., and J. Crossland. Variation in acetylcholine content of brain with physiological state. *Amer. J. Physiol.*, 1949, *159:* 247–55.

107   Richter, D., and R. P. Hullen. Isolated nuclei from cells of the cerebral cortex: Preparation and enzyme content. *Biochem. J.*, 1951, *48:* 406–10.

108   Rittenberg, D. Nitrogen metabolism in the brain. Discussion. In *The biology of mental health and disease.* New York: Paul B. Hoeber, 1952, pp. 112–14.

109   Roberts, E. Formation and utilization of γ-aminobutyric acid in brain. In S. R. Korey, and J. I. Nurnberger (Eds.), *Progress in neurobiology.* Vol. 1. *Neurochemistry.* New York: Hoeber, 1956, pp. 11–25.

110   Robins, E., and D. E. Smith. A quantitative histochemical study of eight enzymes of cerebellar cortex and subjacent white matter in the monkey. *Res. Publ. Ass. nerv. ment. Dis.*, 1953, *32:* 305–27.

111   Rodriguez, L. A. Experiments on the histologic locus of the hemato-encephalic barrier. *J. comp. Neurol.*, 1955, *102:* 27–45.

112   Rosenzweig, M. R., D. Krech, and E. L. Bennett. Brain chemistry and adaptive behavior. Pp. 367 in this volume.

113   Rossiter, R. J. The biochemistry of demyelination. In K. A. C. Elliott, I. H. Page, and J. H. Quastel (Eds.), *Neurochemistry: The chemical dynamics of brain and nerve.* Springfield, Ill.: Charles C Thomas, 1955, pp. 696–714.

114   Rossiter, R. J. Chemical constituents of brain and nerve. In K. A. C. Elliott, I. H. Page, and J. H. Quastel (Eds.), *Neurochemistry: The chemical dynamics of brain and nerve.* Springfield, Ill.: Charles C Thomas, 1955, pp. 11–52.

115   Scheinberg, I. H., Relation of ceruloplasmin and plasma copper to hepatolenticular degeneration (Wilson's disease). In S. R. Korey, and J. I. Nurnberger (Eds.), *Progress in neurobiology.* Vol. 1. *Neurochemistry.* New York: Hoeber, 1956, pp. 52–63.

116   Scheinberg, I. H., D. T. Dubin, and R. S. Harris. The survival of normal ceruloplasmin in patients with hepatolenticular degeneration (Wilson's disease). *J. clin. Invest.*, 1955, *34:* 961 (Abstract).

117   Schmidt, C. F., S. S. Kety, and H. H. Pennes. The gaseous metabolism of the brain of the monkey. *Amer. J. Physiol.*, 1945, *143:* 33–52.

118   Schmitt, F. O. The ultrastructure of the nerve myelin sheath. *Res. Publ. Ass. nerv. ment. Dis.*, 1950, *28:* 247–54.

119   Schwerin, P., S. P. Bessman, and H. Waelsch. The uptake of glutamic acid and glutamine by brain and other tissues of the rat and mouse. *J. biol. Chem.*, 1950, *184:* 37–44.

120   Shariff, G. A. Cell counts in the primate cerebral cortex. *J. comp. Neurol.*, 1953, *98:* 381–400.

121   Shore, P. A., S. L. Silver, and B. B. Brodie. Interaction of reserpine, serotonin, and lysergic acid diethylamide in brain. *Science,* 1955, *122:* 284–85.

122   ———. Interaction of serotonin and lysergic acid diethylamide (LSD) in the central nervous system. *Experientia,* 1955, *11:* 272–73.

123 Speck, J. F. The enzymatic synthesis of glutamine, a reaction utilizing adenosine triphosphate. *J. biol. Chem.*, 1949, *179:* 1405–26.

124 Sperry, W. M. Lipid metabolism of the brain. In *The biology of mental health and disease.* New York: Hoeber, 1952, pp. 116–23.

125 ———. The biochemistry of the brain during early development. In K. A. C. Elliott, I. H. Page, and J. H. Quastel (Eds.), *Neurochemistry: The chemical dynamics of brain and nerve.* Springfield, Ill.: Charles C Thomas, 1955, pp. 234–61.

126 Sperry, W. M., and H. Waelsch. The chemistry of myelination and demyelination. *Res. Publ. Ass. nerv. ment. Dis.,* 1950, *28:* 255–67.

127 Sprinson, D. B., and A. Coulon. The precursors of sphingosine in brain tissue. *J. biol. Chem.,* 1954, *207:* 585–92.

128 Stern, J. R., L. V. Eggleston, R. Hems, and H. A. Krebs. Accumulation of glutamic acid in isolated brain tissue. *Biochem. J.,* 1949, *44:* 410–18.

129 Stetten, DeW., Jr. Biological relationships of choline, ethanolamine, and related compounds. *J. biol. Chem.,* 1941, *140:* 143–152.

130 Stone, W. E., J. E. Webster, and E. S. Gurdjian. Chemical changes in the cerebral cortex associated with convulsive activity. *J. Neurophysiol.,* 1945, *8:* 233–40.

131 Stotz, E., and O. A. Bessey. The blood lactate-pyruvate relation and its use in experimental thiamine deficiency in pigeons. *J. biol. Chem.,* 1942, *143:* 625–31.

132 Strickland, K. P. Nucleic acids and other protein-bound phosphorus compounds of cat brain: Incorporation of P^{32} after intracisternal injection. *Canad. J. med. Sci.,* 1952, *30:* 484–93.

133 Suter, C., and W. O. Klingman. Neurologic manifestations of magnesium depletion states. *Neurology,* 1955, *5:* 691–99.

134 Swank, R. L., and O. A. Bessey. III. Avian thiamine deficiency: Characteristic symptoms and their pathogenesis. *J. Nutr.,* 1941, *22:* 77–89.

135 Tallan, H. H., S. Moore, and W. H. Stein. Studies on the free amino acids and related compounds in the tissues of the cat. *J. biol. Chem.,* 1954, *211:* 927–39.

136 Thannhäuser, S. J. Diseases of the nervous system associated with disturbances of lipide metabolism. *Res. Publ. Ass. nerv. ment. Dis.,* 1953, *32:* 238–68.

137 Thudichum, J. L. W. *A treatise on the chemical constitution of the brain.* London: Baillière, Tindall and Cox, 1884.

138 Tower, D. B. Structural and functional organization of mammalian cerebral cortex: the correlation of neurone density with brain size. Cortical neurone density in the fin whale (Balaenoptera physalus L.) with a note on cortical neurone density in the Indian elephant. *J. comp. Neurol.,* 1954, *101:* 19–52.

139 ———. Nature and extent of the biochemical lesion in human epileptogenic cerebral cortex: An approach to its control in vitro and in vivo. *Neurology,* 1955, *5:* 113–30.

140 ——. The neurochemistry of seizures. In S. R. Korey and J. I. Nurnberger (Eds.), *Progress in neurobiology*. Vol. 1. *Neurochemistry*. New York: Hoeber, 1956, pp. 169–97.

141 Tower, D. B., and K. A. C. Elliott. Activity of acetylcholine system in cerebral cortex of various unanesthetized mammals. *Amer. J. Physiol.*, 1952, *168:* 747–59.

142 ——. Experimental production and control of an abnormality in acetylcholine metabolism present in epileptogenic cortex. *J. appl. Physiol.*, 1953, *5:* 375–91.

143 Tschirgi, R. D. Blood-brain barrier. In *The biology of mental health and disease*. New York: Hoeber, 1952, pp. 34–46.

144 Udenfriend, S., and E. Titus. The 5-hydroxyindole pathway of tryptophan metabolism. In W. D. McElroy, and H. B. Glass (Eds.), *Amino acid metabolism*. Baltimore: Johns Hopkins Press, 1955, pp. 945–49.

145 Umbreit, W. W. *Metabolic maps*. Minneapolis: Burgess, 1952.

146 Victor, J. V., and A. Wolf. Metabolism of brain tumors. *Res. Publ. Ass. nerv. ment. Dis.*, 1937, *16:* 44–58.

147 Vogt, M. The concentration of sympathin in different parts of the central nervous system under normal conditions and after the administration of drugs. *J. Physiol.*, 1954, *123:* 451–81.

148 Von Euler, U. S. Noradrenaline in adrenergic nerves. In K. A. C. Elliott, I. H. Page, and J. H. Quastel (Eds.), *Neurochemistry: The chemical dynamics of brain and nerve*. Springfield, Ill.: Charles C Thomas, 1955, pp. 426–39.

149 Waelsch, H. The metabolism of glutamic acid. *Lancet*, 1949, *257:* 1–4.

150 ——. Quantitative aspects of the metabolic error in oligophrenia phenylpyruvica. Mental deficiency and abberrant metabolism. Discussion. In *The biology of mental health and disease*. New York: Hoeber, 1952, pp. 430–33.

151 ——. Metabolism of glutamic acid and glutamine. In K. A. C. Elliott, I. H. Page, and J. H. Quastel (Eds.), *Neurochemistry: The chemical dynamics of brain and nerve*. Springfield, Ill.: Charles C Thomas, 1955, pp. 173–203.

152 Webb, J. L., and K. A. C. Elliott. Effects of narcotics and convulsants on tissue glycolysis and respiration. *J. Pharmacol.*, 1951, *103:* 24–34.

153 Weil-Malherbe, H. Glutamic acid and its relation to the nervous system. In R. T. Williams (Ed.), *Metabolism and function in nervous tissue (Biochemical Society Symposia No. 8)*. Cambridge: The Univer. Press, 1952, pp. 16–26.

154 Weiss, P., and H. B. Hiscoe. Experiments on the mechanism of nerve growth. *J. exp. Zool.*, 1948, *107:* 315–95.

155 Welsh, J. H. Excitation of the Heart of Venus mercenaria. *Arch. exp. Path. Pharmak.*, 1953, *219:* 23–29.

156 Zabin, I., and J. F. Mead. The biosynthesis of sphingosine. I. The utilization of carboxyl-labeled acetate. *J. biol. Chem.*, 1953, *205:* 271–77.

Mark R. Rosenzweig, David Krech, Edward L. Bennett

Brain Chemistry and Adaptive Behavior

This research program was made possible by a grant from the National Science Foundation and is also supported, in part, by the U.S. Atomic Energy Commission. We wish to acknowledge the aid of the following graduate students in the conduct of the experimental work: Walter Coppock, Alvin Halevy, Barbara Krueckel, James McGaugh, Trevor Peirce, and Thomas Roderick.

Many of the papers in this Symposium reflect a fruitful collaboration of long standing between behavioral and neurological sciences. In comparison, relatively few examples of research can be found involving collaboration between behavioral and biochemical sciences. The field of hormones and behavior, as exemplified by the work of Frank Beach, is one notable exception.

It seems to us that the time is now favorable for extended interdisciplinary research between the behavioral and biochemical sciences. We would argue that such collaboration is well suited to develop many of the valuable leads already available from research in psychology, neurophysiology, and neuroanatomy. A brief review of some problems that seem to call for a joint attack by behavioral and biochemical methods may suggest our reasons for stressing the importance of such collaboration.

The study of changing dynamic properties of the nervous system in its control of behavior seems to be an area peculiarly fitted for such an approach. Under this heading we might list problems such as these:

1. What changes in the nervous system accompany learning? Though learning is generally considered to involve structural changes, and though the search for such changes has been the preoccupation of many experimenters and theorists, the complexities of the anatomy of the nervous system seem so far to have prevented the detection of such changes. A biochemical analysis which could integrate changes over thousands of neural units might provide an entering wedge to the solution of this problem. Further analysis might then focus more narrowly on the exact sites of change. Behavioral techniques would, of course, be equally necessary in such research where one of the variables is "learning."

2. How is the development of behavior during maturation related to the development of neural metabolism? There is available a large body of knowledge about the sequence of behavioral and neurological

development. Knowledge about biochemical changes in maturation is also being gathered. It is already possible, using separate sources of data for each variable, to find certain relationships among the behavioral, anatomical, and biochemical sequences of development. Interdisciplinary research could aid progress here by capitalizing upon individual differences. If each experimental subject is tested both behaviorally and biochemically, then the precision of the research can be greatly enhanced. Powerful statistical tools become available which cannot be used when related data are drawn from different test samples.

3. What are the possibilities for chemotherapy in behavioral disorders? Much current research is being done with the effects of various drugs upon behavior disorders. While the first results seem most promising, it is probably fair to say that most of this work can be characterized as purely empirical, trial-and-error scouting expeditions. It would seem obvious that a better understanding of the role of neural-biochemical events in the integration of behavior would provide direction to such research and might increase its effectiveness.

Perhaps the major obstacle in the way of such joint research derives from the lack of familiarity by members of each discipline with the methods, states of knowledge, and possible contributions of the other discipline. The biochemical sciences have a number of promising hypotheses concerning metabolic processes that underlie neural functioning, and they have reliable and sensitive measures of such processes. The behavioral scientist might do well to give these biochemical hypotheses more serious consideration and to seek to exploit them in his quest for the physiological foundations of behavior.

For the biochemical scientists we would like to make the point that the precise measurement and experimental control of behavior are neither easy nor, on the other hand, impossible. Most biochemists who are interested in the nervous system tend to ignore the problems of the observation and the experimental manipulation of behavior. Thus, for example, a series of conferences that were initially conceived under the heading of "chemopsychology" have appeared under the title of "neuropharmacology" (1), and the index of the first conference report makes no mention of either "behavior" or "psychology." Similarly, the editors of an impressive new volume on neurochemistry have written, "The ultimate objective of Neurochemistry, in partnership with Neurophysiology and Neuropathology, is the understanding of the phenomena underlying the behavior of nerve, brain and mind, and the maladies to which they are subject" (9). Not only are the behavioral sciences ignored in the enterprise of understanding the behavior of nerve, brain, and mind, but also the topic of behavior is mentioned only once in the index and, then, in regard to behavior disorders! When behavioral categories *are* used in these studies, they tend to be gross ones such as "sleep," "wakefulness," "coma," and the categories of pathological behavior. While it would be of value to discover biochemical correlates of these broad categories, such categories do not begin to classify the kinds of behavior that are important in the normal adjustments of the organism. More discriminating and objective classifications must be employed to match the precision available in biochemical techniques. Interdisciplinary research has many implications, but among these, we would suggest, is the implication that at least two sets of *disciplined* workers are coöperating.

Enzymes and Brain Metabolism

Before turning to our own work we wish to review briefly the general role of enzymes in brain metabolism and then to discuss some behavioral studies implicating brain enzymes.

To maintain its structure and to accomplish its functions, the nervous system requires a host of different enzymes. Energy is necessary to synthesize complex biological compounds in the neuron and to transmit neural impulses. The energy is obtained in the nervous system by oxidizing glucose to the end products of carbon dioxide and water. But special conditions are imposed upon this oxidation. It must occur at the moderate temperature and at the moderate pH of the neuron. And the energy released must not escape as heat but must be stored in a way that will allow ready utilization. The complete oxidation of glucose in the cell requires about two dozen steps, almost each of which is catalyzed by an enzyme that is specific to that step. In this process about 70 per cent of the total free energy is transferred, through the action of an electron transport system, to the energy-rich phosphate bonds of adenosine triphosphate (ATP).

One substance synthesized at the expense of energy-rich phosphate bonds is the neurohumor acetylcholine (ACh). Acetylation of choline also requires the aid of both the enzyme choline acetylase (ChA) and coenzyme A. Acetylcholine and its enzyme system will be of special interest to us in behavioral studies that will be described later, so it is appropriate to consider its functions briefly here. The physiological significance of ACh has been treated in several recent reviews (3, 6, 10, 20). There is fairly general agreement in these reviews that ACh is essential in neuromuscular transmission. ACh is released at the neuromuscular junction during activity, and perfusion of this region with minute amounts of ACh evokes a muscle-twitch. While ACh stimulates in small amounts, accumulation of ACh beyond a certain concentration will paralyze transmission. This observation led to the search for a substance that would inactivate ACh rapidly after its release. It was soon found that an enzyme, cholinesterase (ChE), exists at the necessary sites and in amounts sufficient to hydrolyze ACh almost instantaneously. Within the central nervous system it is not clear that ACh is essential for synaptic transmission, although there is strong evidence in favor of this hypothesis. Among such evidence Burgen and MacIntosh (6) stress the following points: (1) The presence of relatively large amounts of ACh, ChA, and ChE in the central nervous system; (2) the high sensitivity of some central neurons to ACh; (3) the striking effects of anti-ChE drugs, which can best be explained by assuming that they allow accumulation of ACh; (4) changes in the general level of neural activity are accompanied by transient changes in ACh content of the brain; (5) ACh is released at the cerebral cortex during physiological activity. Finally, there is some evidence (not without its counterevidence, however) that ACh is necessary for conduction of the impulses along the neuron as well as for interneuron transmission.

Provisionally we can conclude that ACh metabolism is important in some if not all synaptic transmission and that it may also be important in neural conduction. Many workers are currently contributing to this problem and new evidence is accumulating rapidly.

Previous Behavioral Studies Implicating Brain Enzymes

In spite of the vital role of enzymes in brain function, relatively few studies have attempted to relate enzyme activity to adaptive behavior, and even these few studies (with one exception) have concerned themselves with the problem only indirectly.*

In a few experiments, anti-ChE agents have been employed. Platt and Wickens (28) trained rats on a T-maze, and after criterion was reached, the experimental animals were injected with di-isopropylfluorophosphate (DFP), a powerful anti-ChE agent. Ten weeks later the rats were retrained to the same criterion. No effects of the DFP upon retention were found. Russell (30) has reported that inhibiting ChE with an organic phosphorous poison does have effects on a variety of learning and discrimination performances in the rat. While he apparently did measure the level of ChE after experimental treatment by the poison, his report, unfortunately, is in the form of a very brief abstract, and a detailed analysis or discussion of his findings cannot now be made.

In an early study Lashley (19) showed that moderate doses of strych-

* We wish to thank James McGaugh and Lewis Petrinovich of our laboratory for bibliographic aid here. In a forthcoming publication they will present a detailed and critical review of this topic.

nine *enhanced* the learning of rats in a circular maze. Enhancement as great as 40 per cent was found with some groups. As far as we can determine, no investigator has attempted to repeat this striking observation. In the present connection, the interest of this study derives from the fact that strychnine has been shown to inhibit ChE in vitro (25).

The effects of various narcotic agents upon behavior should also be considered here since there is evidence that narcotics may inhibit enzyme-catalyzed processes such as the synthesis of ATP and ACh in the cerebral cortex (29), and anesthesia has been found to lead to a decrease in the utilization of ACh in vivo (6). Several studies indicate that prolonged administration of barbiturates to fetal or young rats results in deleterious effects upon later learning (reviewed in Munn [24]). It would appear that in part these effects may be due to impaired development of the nervous system. In part they may also be due to the reduction of exploratory behavior and other experience in animals that were drugged daily for long periods. Such experiments do not seem to be well designed to provide information about the effects of drugs on neural functioning.

Conditioning of cats under acute sodium epival anesthesia was reported by Sterling and Miller (32). Some of the experimental animals gave conditioned responses upon recovering from anesthesia, although they had shown no conditioned responses during training. Most animals, however, showed no signs of conditioning upon recovery from the anesthetic, although they had been given many more training trials than had been found necessary for unanesthetized animals.

Dews (7) has reported that pigeons in the Skinner box perform less well in a conditional situation when either pentobarbital or methamphetamine is administered. Scopalamine did not interfere with the appropriateness of the response. In another study (8), Skinner box performance with various reward schedules was differentially affected by different dosages of pentobarbital.

Finally we should note an interesting series of studies by Kennard and her associates on recovery of function after removal of the motor cortex in monkeys. Drugs which have a stimulating, "cholinergic" effect on neural functioning—strychnine, thiamin, and doryl—were found to speed recovery of function (36). On the other hand, anticonvulsant drugs—phenobarbital and dilantin—were found to slow the recovery of function (37). This was true even when the dose of phenobarbital was so small that it had no obvious observable effect on the general cage behavior of the monkey.

While many of these studies are significant in suggesting relationships between brain enzyme activity and behavior, it is clear that the data remain no more than suggestive. In only one case cited above (nor have we discovered any other in the literature) has the activity of any brain enzyme been measured directly and its relation to adaptive behavior determined.

OUTLINE OF OUR EXPERIMENTS

In 1953 the two psychologists of our team began to plan an experimental investigation of the relationships between brain chemistry and behavior. Recognition that such an experiment necessitated an interdisciplinary team led to discussion with Professor Melvin Calvin, whose interest in interdisciplinary research is well known. It was through his offices that Dr. Bennett became interested in the problem and joined the investigation. Thus we had an experimental psychologist, a physiological psychologist, and a biochemist to plan and execute the investigation. As previously noted, such a study demands careful selection and reliable measurement of variables in the two quite different disciplines. The final criteria adopted to guide us in the behavioral and chemical experimentation were these:

On the behavioral side we wanted a measure (1) on which animals would show large and reliable individual differences; (2) which would reflect stable characteristics of the individual rather than ephemeral situational influences; (3) which would have adaptive significance in the *normal* repertoire of the animal, rather than behavior determined by pathological conditions; and, finally, (4) we wanted behavior whose neurological basis was already understood, to some extent at least.

For our chemical variable we had similar desiderata: We wanted to measure a substance that would (1) discriminate reliably among different individuals, (2) reflect stable characteristics of the individual, (3) be significant in normal neural functioning, and (4) be a substance that, on the basis of already existing knowledge or theory, plays a role in interneural functioning.

For our behavioral variable we chose "hypothesis" behavior and the Krech unsolvable maze as its measuring instrument. This choice met, we felt, the criteria listed above. (1) Previous work by Krech (14, 15, 16) had amply demonstrated individual differences in hypothesis behavior in the laboratory rat. (2) These individual differences had been shown to be stable characteristics of the organism: Hypothesis behavior remains stable over at least a four-week period as measured by a test-retest study (18), and it differs for different strains of rats (17), thus implicating genetic factors. (3) Hypothesis behavior is significant in the animal's normal adaptive functioning in that it reflects perceptual selectivity—and such perceptual selectivity must occur if the animal is to organize the welter of stimuli which impinge upon it in its normal environment. (4) Finally, this behavior can be altered predictably by ablations in the visual and somesthetic areas of the cerebral cortex (18). This not only tied the behavior down to already determined functional areas in the cortex, but it also suggested profitable loci for chemical analysis.

For our chemical substance we chose the enzyme cholinesterase. (1) As has already been indicated, there is strong evidence that the system including choline acetylase, acetylcholine, and cholinesterase is involved in transmission at central synapses. Of this ChA-ACh-ChE system we chose ChE because it is a relatively stable and easily measured substance, because there is general agreement and some evidence that ChE can be used as an index for the other members of the system (5), and, finally, because cholinesterase has a well-defined pattern of distribution in the nervous system as opposed to those enzymes that seem to be rather uniformly distributed. On this last point we followed Ashby's suggestion that "It is the enzymes with a well-defined pattern of quantitative distribution which are probable factors in determining functional integration . . ." (2, p. 468). (2) The choice of ChE also permitted us to meet our measurement criteria. An automatic titrator, developed at the biochemistry laboratories of the University of California (27), made possible the reliable and objective determination of ChE activity with fairly small samples. (3) Concerning individual differences in ChE activity we could not be certain. Data in the literature indicated variability, but some authors (5) tended to attribute this to experimental error. Our results, however, have since shown individual differences which appear to exceed the error of measurement.

In the next section we present a detailed account of the measurement techniques used for both the behavioral and chemical variables investigated. Our findings and conclusions will be given in three sections. In the first of these we will present evidence that different functional areas of the cortex differ significantly in ChE activity, that these differences among functional areas are positively correlated within the individual animal, and that ChE activity shows a progressive decline with age. In the second section we will present the data which indicate that individual differences in hypothesis behavior are related in a systematic fashion to individual differences in ChE activity of normal animals. In the final section of our results and conclusions we will show that experimental modification of brain chemistry, by the use of a drug, leads to predictable modification of hypothesis behavior.

METHODS

Behavioral Methods

The floor plan of the apparatus used for our behavioral tests is shown in Figure 112. At each of the four choice-points the rat finds one alley lighted and the other dark. One alley is open at its far end and allows the rat to progress toward the goal-box; the other alley is blocked at its far end by a door. Curtains prevent the rat from seeing whether the alley is blocked or open.

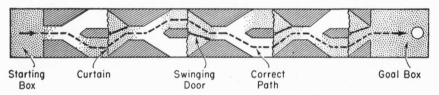

| Starting | Curtain | Swinging | Correct | Goal Box |
| Box | | Door | Path | |

Fig. 112.—Floor plan of apparatus used in behavior tests. (Adapted from Krech [16].)

The rat cannot learn to avoid the blocked alleys since, for each trial, the experimenter changes the pattern of lights and of open doors according to a prearranged sequence. Each trial includes four choices, and 12 trials are given per day. The sequence is balanced so that, in the 12 trials, any one cue (lighted alley, dark alley, right alley, left alley, etc.) is associated with the open alley only half the time. Thus a consistent approach to any one cue will bring only chance "success." This balanced pattern is repeated each day.

Before the rat is tested, it is pretrained in a special runway for 10 days. For almost all rats in the present study, pretraining began when the animal was about 75 days old and testing began about the 85th day. In this rather long pretraining period the rat is accustomed to the 24-hr. deprivation schedule, and it learns to leave a starting box, to push through curtains on the way to the goal-box, to eat in the goal-box, and, in general, becomes "maze-adjusted."

After completion of the pretraining period the animal is tested in the apparatus in a darkened and quiet room where the only effective lights, as far as the rat is concerned, come from the 15-watt bulbs over the lighted alleys and an extremely weak light over the food-dish in the goal-box which permits observation of the animal's entry into the goal-box. Throughout the running of a trial, the experimenter remains behind the starting box and observes the animal through mirrors, thus avoiding, we hope, influencing the animal by involuntary cues. On test days 1 and 2 the rat is run only 6 trials per day. These 12 trials are considered to be one "running day" in analysis of data. On days 3 and 4 the animal is given its full complement of 12 trials. Thus, a total of 144 choices is made by the animal in this period (4 choices per trial, 12 trials per day, 3 "running days"). The only food the animal obtains during this testing period is in the goal-box of the apparatus. There it may eat for 30 sec. after each trial, except after the last trial of the day, when it remains in the goal-box 60 sec.

Although the rat cannot "solve" the maze, it does not behave randomly, but typically displays systematic patterns of choices which we call "hypotheses." Its behavior is analyzed for eight different hypotheses divided into two major groups: visual and spatial.

Among the visual hypotheses, an animal may systematically choose the lighted alleys (a "Light Hypotheses") or the dark alleys (a "Dark Hypothesis"). Sometimes an animal tends to choose an alley in terms of the similarity of its visual characteristics to the immediately preceding "correct" alley (e.g., choosing a lighted alley if the previous lighted alley had proved to be correct, etc.). This behavior is termed a "Perseverative Visual Hypothesis." Conversely, the rat may show an "Alternating Visual Hypothesis" (e.g., choose a dark alley if the immediately preceding lighted alley had been correct, etc.).

The other general category of hypotheses—spatial—also has four possibilities. The rat may systematically choose the alley on the right side (irrespective of its visual characteristics), or the alley on the left, or choose the side that had been correct at the previous choice point, or the side opposite to the previous correct one. In other words, there are "Right," "Left," "Perseverative Spatial," and "Alternating Spatial" hypotheses.

An animal is credited with displaying a "hypothesis" only when its choices during a day deviate from 50 per cent, for any cue, by at least 2.5 standard deviations.

On each test day the animal's choices are used to calculate a Spatial-Visual Preference Score in the following manner: The less random the animal's behavior, the more its score differs from 50 per cent for some one hypothesis. We first determine for each animal the percentage deviation (from 50 per cent) for every hypothesis. We next sum all the percentage deviations for the four visual hypotheses, and then the deviations for the spatial hypotheses. The difference between these sums is a measure of the extent to which the animal prefers visual or spatial responses. These daily Preference Scores are then summed to give a three-day total Preference Score.

The Preference Score is assumed to measure perceptual selectivity because of the following considerations: The animal is presented with a situation in which there are various stimuli confronting it and various choices possible. In such a situation, a paradigm of any animal's "normal" environment, the animal must first select the stimuli it will "attend to." Here it is given "free choice" in the sense that choosing *either* the visual or spatial characteristics of the box will not be *differentially* rewarded or punished. The Preference Score gives us a quantitative measure of the animal's perceptual selectivity.

In order to measure the reliability of our instrument and our scoring procedure, a point stressed by Harlow in his paper, we computed two sets of reliability indices. The first set is intended to measure the reliability of our basic observations. As the animal proceeds through the maze, the experimenter records whether the animal chooses a light or dark alley at each choice point. (It is from these observations that scores on each of the eight hypotheses are determined.) To ascertain whether these basic measures are reliable, we have used the split-half reliability index. For 55 randomly selected animals separate light-dark scores were computed for the even- and odd-numbered trials for each day. The product-moment correlation coefficients for these two sets of subscores were computed and corrected by the Spearman-Brown formula. These are presented in Table 26. It will be seen that these correlations are all .80 or above, including the very first day.

TABLE 26

Reliability of behavioral measurements—odd even correlations (corrected by Spearman-Brown Formula)

Light scores			Preference score
Day 1	Day 2	Day 3	Sum for days 1–3
.82	.80	.85	.74

There remains, however, another question. Although the measuring technique seems satisfactorily reliable, we must know the reliability of our Preference Scores, for it is these derived Preference Scores which we use in our analysis. Here the question is, essentially, How consistent is the animal's preference? We again used the split-half method. We computed daily Preference Scores for the even and for the odd trials for each animal separately and then summed the even scores and the odd scores for the three days. The product-moment correlation between these two Preference Scores with the Spearman-Brown correction is .74 (Table 26).

On the basis of these correlations we can conclude that the reliability of our behavior-measurement technique is acceptable and that our scoring method measures behavior which is rather consistent for the individual animal.

Chemical Methods

In choosing the cortical areas for analysis, we were guided by Krech's earlier finding that ablation of cortex in one region ("spatial") caused rats to perform visually in the maze while destruction in another region ("visual") caused rats to perform spatially (18). These regions are shown in Figure 113*A*. We decided to sample in the motor cortex as well. More

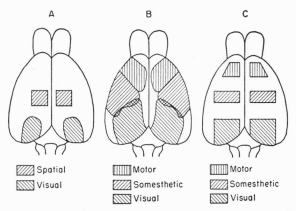

A   B   C

Spatial
Visual

Motor
Somesthetic
Visual

Motor
Somesthetic
Visual

Fig. 113.—Diagrammatic representation of brain areas of the rat. (Drawn approximately to same scale.)

recently the rat's cortex has been mapped by electrophysiological techniques; the results of Woolsey and LeMessurier are shown in Figure 113*B*, which is adapted from Zubek (38). We took samples of cortex from the visual, somesthetic, and motor areas of both hemispheres, as shown in Figure 113*C*. (Hereafter we will refer to these areas as V, S, and M, respectively.) The animals were delivered for chemical analysis under code designations which gave no information about their performance in the behavioral test. Thus, the behavioral and chemical analyses were completely independent. To obtain the samples, we decapitated the animals and removed the sample rapidly by gross dissection. Since the rat's cortex provides no external landmarks, the areas to be removed were determined with the aid of a special plastic guide appropriately calibrated. Each sample of V contained 20–25 mg. of tissue, and each sample of S and M contained 12–18 mg.* We attempted to avoid subcortical white matter in the

* The order of removal, weighing, and homogenization of the sections was left hemisphere, somesthetic area (LS), right hemisphere, somesthetic area (RS), LM, RM, LV, and RV. The order of enzymatic assay was LV, LS, LM, RM, RS, RV, RV, and LV. The time required for the assay was approximately 3½ hr., but no significant difference was found between the first and last LV sample assayed.

samples, since it has been shown to be very low in ChE activity (5). The brains were preserved for more exact determination of the sites of the ablations.

The samples of tissue were weighed rapidly on a projection analytical balance. The removal and weighing of the samples required approximately 10 min. after the cortex had been exposed. The samples were then homogenized in a Potter-type homogenizer (Teflon pestle) (4) in 5 ml. of cold 0.9 per cent NaCl and diluted to 10 ml.

The enzymatic activity was determined under standardized conditions by the rate of hydrolysis of acetylcholine perchlorate (ACh) (26). We used a pH meter equipped to maintain constant pH and record the volume of reagent added from a syringe buret as a function of time on a Brown recorder (27). The determination was made at 37° and pH 7.95. The capped titration cell was continuously swept with a stream of nitrogen to maintain anaerobic conditions and to keep out carbon dioxide. For each determination, an aliquot portion containing 8–12 mg. of tissue was

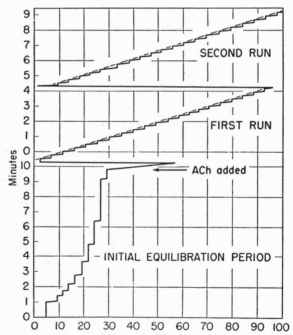

Fig. 114.—Typical record of ChE determination obtained with Neilands and Cannon automatic titrator. Tissue sample: 11.0 mg. taken from somesthetic area, right hemisphere.

pipetted into the thermostated cell assembly, and sufficient saline was added to bring the volume to 12 ml.

An example of a typical ChE determination record is shown in Figure 114. During an initial equilibration period of approximately 10 min., 0.005 M NaOH was added at a decreasing rate to maintain the pH constant. When the rate of addition of NaOH became less than 5 per cent of the expected rate after the addition of ACh, 1 ml. of 0.01 M ACh was added and its rate of hydrolysis was determined over a 10- to 12-min. period from the rate of addition of 0.005 M NaOH. The sensitivity of the Brown recorder was so adjusted that full scale was equivalent to 0.08 ml. of 0.005 NaOH. About 4 to 6 min. was required for the addition of this amount of NaOH. The hydrolysis rate was nearly linear over a 15-min. period.

The "blank" hydrolysis rate of ACh was determined under similar conditions, and corrections were made for this hydrolysis, which was approximately 8 per cent of the uncorrected rate.* After subtraction of the blank, the results were calculated on the basis of moles of ACh hydrolyzed per milligram of the tissue used for each analysis.

The net slope of the curve divided by the weight of the sample gives a measure of the ChE activity of the tissue sample. This will be expressed as moles ACh $\times$ 10^{10} hydrolyzed per minute, per milligram of tissue.

Usually two determinations were made for each V sample. As a test of the reliability of the chemical anlysis, the two values obtained for LV were correlated for a random sample of 30 experimental animals. The correlation, corrected by the Spearman-Brown formula, was .91, indicating that the analysis is highly reliable.

RESULTS AND DISCUSSION

Differences Among Cortical Areas in Cholinesterase Activity

Localization of function within the cerebral cortex has been demonstrated by a number of techniques—surgical, electrophysiological, and histological. It is to be expected that biochemical differences will be found to be correlated with functional differences among areas of the cortex. Previous research in this area has not, however, given decisive results, possibly because of the failure of investigators to seek biochemical differences among cortical areas already delimited by functional and histological criteria. Thus, as McIlwain has pointed out, "A major limitation in present

---

* It was found that the "blank" hydrolysis gradually increased over a period of days when numerous analyses were made because of adsorption or precipitation of the enzyme upon the titration cell wall. This was overcome by leaving 0.1 M HCl in the cell assembly overnight and by rinsing frequently with acetone.

knowledge of metabolic events in the brain is that the majority of bio-chemical investigations have been carried out with the organ as a whole or with preparations from relatively large portions of it" (21, p. 1529).

In the case of cholinesterase, activity has been shown to vary widely from one *level* of the nervous system to another, but there has been little evidence that it varies significantly from area to area within the cerebral cortex. Thus, Tower and Elliott (34) conclude from their work on eight species among which was the rat, "No obvious differences between different cortical areas in the same mammalian species was observed" (p. 758). Burgen and Chipman (5) state that while the visual cortex has the lowest values and the uncinate cortex the highest values in the dog, "Otherwise there is no obvious segregation of cortical areas into groups and it is especially noteworthy that there is no important difference between the motor and sensory areas" (p. 299). The failure of both these sets of investigators to report significant differences stands in contradiction to the findings we wish to present in this paper. In our own work we have measured ChE activity in 129 rats of seven strains, both sexes, and several ages. For every group tested, our data show consistent and significant differences between the ChE activity of the motor, somesthetic, and visual areas of the cortex. We will reserve a discussion of the apparent contradiction between our results and those of previous investigators until after we have presented our data.

Results.—The values of ChE activity for the two hemispheres of an

TABLE 27

Cholinesterase activity in three cortical areas for animals of five strains and both sexes

Strain	Sex	Mean age	No.	Means, ChE activity		
				V	S	M
S_1	M	104	18	58.94	69.28	74.94
S_{13}	M	109	12	53.92	67.00	68.92
S_3	M	113	12	54.67	65.25	72.83
GI	M	154	6	54.67	58.50	66.50
GB	M	118	5	59.20	67.20	78.00
All males*			53	56.38	66.43	72.43
S_1	F	132	13	58.38	66.92	72.00
S_{13}	F	146	5	60.40	74.60	75.80
All Females*			18	58.94	69.06	73.06

* Total and Averages

animal usually agreed closely. For 95 male rats, the mean ChE activity
was 53.94 in the visual area of the left hemisphere and 54.77 in the visual
area of the right hemisphere; 64.05 in the left somesthetic area and 64.59
in the right somesthetic area; 68.63 in the left motor area and 69.50 in
the right motor area. For the female rats the interhemisphere agreement
was equally good. None of these small interhemispheric differences approached statistical significance. Because of this, it was decided to combine the readings of both hemispheres for any one area and for any one
animal. In the rest of this paper, the values reported for each cortical
area will be the mean of the values obtained at the two hemispheres.

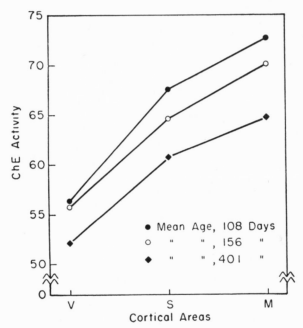

Fig. 115.—ChE activity in areas V, S, and M. Age is the
parameter.

Table 27 presents the ChE values thus obtained for each of the three
cortical areas investigated.* Separate values are given for male rats of five
strains and for female rats of two strains (each subgroup being homogeneous in age). In each of these seven subgroups the very same pattern
of ChE activity was found, i.e., ChE activity level increased from the visual

* We wish to thank Professor Leo J. Postman for invaluable advice in the statistical
analyses.

area (V) to the somesthetic area (S) to the motor area (M). For all male animals combined, ChE is 18 per cent greater in S than in V, 29 per cent greater in M than in V, and 9 per cent greater in M than in S. For the female animals, the corresponding percentages are 17, 24, and 6.

Not only does ChE activity differ among these area, but as the age of the animal increases, the values of ChE activity decrease. The top curve in Figure 115 shows the ChE values for male animals of the S_1, S_{13}, and S_3 strains with a mean of 108 days. The next curve, for a group of male animals whose mean age was 156 days, shows somewhat lower ChE values. The bottom curve is for a third group whose mean age was considerably greater—401 days; in this curve the ChE values are again lower. All three curves are generally similar in shape, but they are closer together for V than for M.

Since ChE activity varies as a function of both age and cortical area, an analysis of variance was computed for the three groups of animals represented in Figure 115 in order to test the significance of these factors. Though the n's at each age are different, the numbers of cases in the subclasses are strictly proportional, and so a standard analysis of variance

TABLE 28

Analysis of variance for cholinesterase activity as a function of age and cortical area

Source	Sum of squares	df	Mean square	Error term	F
a. Ages	2,466.48	2	1,233.24	d	16.91*
b. V-S-M	10,441.99	2	5,221.00	c	22.68†
c. V-S-M Ages	920.75	4	230.19	e	19.59*
d. Subjects	6,708.98	92	72.92	e	6.20*
e. Residual	2,162.59	184	11.75		

* Ratio significant at the .001 level of confidence.
† Ratio significant at the .01 level of confidence.

could be performed (31, pp. 281–284). The results of the analysis are presented in Table 28.*

The F ratios show that every source of variance tested is highly significant, none of the p's being as great as .01. This means that (1) ChE activity differs significantly from area to area over the cortex, (2) the drop

---

* Our S_1 strain is Tryon's (35) maze-bright animals; the S_3 strain is Tryon's maze-dull animals. The S_{13} strain is a cross between the S_1 and S_3 strains. The GI and GB strains are two highly inbred strains obtained from the University of California Genetics Laboratory.

of ChE activity with age is significant, (3) there is a significant interaction between the effects of age and cortical area, the decrease of ChE activity with age being less in V than in S or M, (4) individual animals differ significantly from each other in mean ChE activity. Since the effect of cortical areas is significant, we computed t tests for the animals included in Table 27 and found that the differences between pairs of areas are highly significant (see Table 29).

TABLE 29

Significance of differences in cholinesterase activity among cortical areas for all male and female animals of Table 27

	Cortical areas compared		
	S-V	M-V	M-S
53 Male Animals:			
Mean Diff.	10.06	16.04	6.00
t	15.24	23.25	8.45
p	.001	.001	.001
18 Female Animals:			
Mean Diff.	10.12	14.12	4.00
t	7.72	14.70	2.86
p	.001	.001	.01

Another way to test the generality of this patterning was to tabulate the number of *individual* rats (of all strains and ages and of both sexes) that showed the progressive increase from V to S to M. Of the 129 animals, 104 fitted this order exactly, and 122 animals showed greater ChE activity in S than in V.

Since for each cortical area animals show individual differences in ChE activity, we sought to determine whether the ChE values of the different areas vary together. Table 30 presents product- moment correlation coefficients between the cortical areas for three age ranges. The top row is based on 42 male rats of the S_1, S_{13}, and S_3 strains, with a mean age of 108 days. These intercorrelations are all above .60 and are significantly greater than zero at better than the .001 level of confidence. The next age group consisted of only 13 male animals, and the first two of the resulting correlations are not significantly different from zero, probably owing to the small number of cases involved. The last group included

TABLE 30

Intercorrelations among cortical areas in cholinesterase activity for male animals of three different age ranges

Age range (days)	N	Product-moment correlation coefficients		
		r_{VS}	r_{VM}	r_{SM}
80–125	42	.68	.69	.65
126–175	13	−.25	.05	.65
176–605	40	.45	.59	.76

male animals of a wide range of ages. In order to avoid inflating the correlations by combining groups whose values differed widely, we subdivided this range into subgroups. Standard scores were computed for each subgroup, and these standard scores were used in computing the correlations. The resulting correlation coefficients (bottom row) are significantly greater than zero at a high level of confidence and range from .45 to .76. These positive correlations carry the additional implication that the absolute level of ChE activity is a fairly *general* characteristic of the individual.

Discussion.—Since the differences in ChE activity among three different cortical areas are consistent in all groups of animals and are all statistically significant, it becomes necessary to account for the discrepancy between our findings and conclusions and those of the previous investigators already cited, Tower and Elliott (34) and Burgen and Chipman (5).

In the case of Tower and Elliott there are two considerations which seem relevant. In the first place, it should be clear that only very obvious differences could have been found with the statistical techniques used in their paper. These investigators made no more than seven determinations for any one species. In the light of the ubiquitous individual differences found in dealing with biological material, an *n* of 7 would seem inadequate to demonstrate either the existence of a difference or a lack of it without careful statistical analysis. Where Tower and Elliott do report differences, no appropriate measures of variability are given which would permit a test of significance. Lacking such a test, we must conclude that their data are indeterminate on this question. In the second place, Tower and Elliott did not use cortical areas that were defined functionally or cytoarchitectonically. Their different cortical areas were defined merely as "dorsal anterior," "dorsal posterior," etc. Because they did not use functional areas and we did, the two studies are not strictly comparable.

Burgen and Chipman did find relatively large differences between well-defined areas of the cortex of the dog though they tested not more than six animals for any area and used dogs of different breeds and ages. Fortunately they provide the necessary data from which some tests of significance can be computed. Using their data, we have computed t tests and find that their results for area 6a (motor) show a higher ChE activity than area 3 (primary sensory) at the .01 level of confidence; their values for area 6a show higher ChE activity than area 17 (visual) at better than the .01 level of confidence; and their values for area 3 are higher than for area 17, though this difference does not reach the .05 level of confidence. It must also be noted that the cortical pattern of ChE activity in the dog is similar to our typical pattern for the rat, i.e., motor higher than the primary sensory, and primary sensory higher than visual. It would appear, then, that a comparison between Burgen and Chipman's study and our study (in so far as these studies are at all comparable) shows more similarities than differences in data. The differences seem to be in conclusions reached.

We have found very few previous studies that we can use to check upon our results correlating age with changes in ChE activity. Changes in ChE activity with age have mainly been studied with fetal or immature animals. Some data for older rats are reported by Metzler and Humm (23). Using the whole brain, they have reported a drop in ChE activity between 75 and 120 days and no decline thereafter—or even a slight rise—in adult rats. For ages 75 days, 120 days, and "adult" they apparently made a total of only eight determinations. It will be remembered that our data showed a consistent drop in ChE activity after the age of 120 days. The difference between our results and those of Metzler and Humm may result from the fact that our determinations were made on cortical tissue and theirs were made on the whole brain. More likely, the difference relates to the unreliability of their data. For the "adult" age, they had only two cases.

Thus, we have not found any conclusive studies in the literature that contradict our basic findings that ChE activity in the rat differs significantly among cortical areas and that it drops significantly with age from the one-hundredth to the four-hundredth day.

Relationship between Individual Differences in Hypothesis Behavior and in Cortical Cholinesterase Activity

Our main objective in all these studies is to relate biochemical activities in the cortex to adaptive behavior-patterns, and we now turn to an analysis of the relationship between hypothesis behavior and ChE activity which is based on the records of 95 male rats of five different age groups.

Results.—The basic question we wish to examine is the possible relationship between hypothesis preference (spatial or visual) and ChE activity level. However, since age has a significant effect on ChE activity level, and since our animals were assayed for the ChE activity at various ages, it becomes necessary to keep age constant in making comparisons between the spatial and visual animals. Figure 116 presents the summary data for the present section of our report. The curves represent the change with age in ChE activity* for the spatial rats and visual rats separately. This permits us not only to compare the spatial and visual rats at various age levels, but also to note some very interesting differences in the shapes of the curves.

Regarding first the shapes of the curves, we see that in the *spatial* animals ChE activity declines slowly and almost linearly with age. Over a span of 450 days, there is a drop of only 5.25 units. The *visual* animals show a very different pattern; ChE activity declines very rapidly between 110 and 230 days and thereafter levels off.† It appears as if the spatial

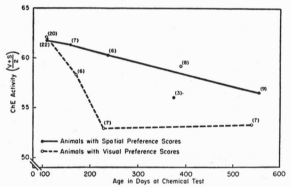

Fig. 116.—Comparison between spatial and visual animals for ChE activity at various ages. The number of animals tested at each age is given in parentheses.

* Throughout this section we will use, for our index of ChE activity level, the average of the ChE activities in the two sensory areas, V and S, i.e., V+S/2. This is the same index that we used in our preliminary report (13).

† In drawing the curves, we have not connected the points for the 3 spatial animals and the 8 visual animals of the 390-day-old group. Their data were aberrent in several respects. In this sense the curves are "smoothed" curves. However, in testing for statistical significance, the data of these 11 animals *are included*. In other words, we preferred to have these curves represent our best estimate of the general trends of the data, but in the *quantitative* analysis, we have included all the data.

animals had not yet reached their "floor" at age 550 days, whereas the visual animals had reached their "minimum" as early as age 230 days. The second generalization which these curves seem to support is that after age 100 days, the spatial animals have higher ChE activity levels than do their visual age-mates.

In order to test the statistical significance of the differences suggested by these two curves, we performed an analysis of variance for our total of 95 animals, correcting for unequal n's in the groups according to the technique detailed by Snedecor (31, pp. 289–293). From the results given in Table 31 it will be seen that all the differences tested prove to be sig-

TABLE 31

Analysis of variance for the effects of hypothesis preference and age on cholinesterase activity (all age groups)

Source	Sum of squares	df	Mean square	Error term	F
a. S-V Preference	72.50	1	72.50	d	4.09*
b. Ages	708.36	4	177.09	d	9.99†
c. Interaction	222.20	4	55.55	d	3.13*
d. Residual	1,506.49	85	17.72		

* *F* ratio significant at the .05 level of confidence.
† *F* ratio significant at the .001 level of confidence.

nificant. Thus, differences in age produce highly significant variations in ChE activity, the confidence level being better than .001. The difference between spatial and visual animals in ChE activity is significant at the .05 level of confidence. Finally, there is a significant interaction between age and spatial-visual behavior, the confidence level of this interaction effect being between .05 and .01. It would appear that the differences suggested by our "smoothed" curves stand up to statistical anlysis: The spatial animals show higher cortical ChE activity and exhibit a slower and more regular decline of ChE with age than do the visual animals.

We have already noted that the chemical differentiation between the spatial and visual animals appears only after age 110 days. At that age, and probably prior to that age, there is no detectable difference between the two groups of rats. We will reserve for a latter discussion some possible reasons for the failure of these young animals to show differences in ChE activity, but this empirical finding (whatever its causes) suggests that the most favorable test for a chemical difference between the spatial and visual rats should be made with animals older than 125 days. We have therefore made a separate analysis of variance on all rats sacrificed at ages greater than 125 days. Despite the fact that we thereby reduce our n, and despite the fact that our 11 "aberrant" cases now have a greater weight in the over-all results, this new analysis of variance yields highly significant F ratios (Table 32). We now find that the effect of age upon ChE activity, the differences between spatial and visual animals in ChE activity, and the interaction between age and behavior upon ChE activity are *all* significant at, or better than, the .01 level.

TABLE 32

Analysis of variance for the effects of hypothesis preference and age on cholinesterase activity (four age groups)

Source	Sum of squares	df	Mean square	Error term	F
a. S-V Preference	82.88	1	82.88	d	7.96*
b. Ages	181.48	3	60.49	d	5.81*
c. Interaction	150.47	3	50.16	d	4.82*
d. Residual	568.33	45	10.41		

* F ratio significant at the .01 level of confidence.

Finally, in order to get some indication of the *degree* of relationship between ChE activity level and behavior, we computed the product-moment correlation coefficient for all rats over 125 days of age between individual ChE scores and individual Preference Scores (treating preference now as a continuous variable rather than a dichotomous one). The resulting correlation is .28, which is significantly greater than zero at the .05 level of confidence.

The following general conclusion seems warranted: Individual differences in hypothesis behavior are correlated in a systematic fashion with the level of cortical ChE activity and with progressive change in such levels as a function of age.

Discussion.—Our findings of a significant relationship between the behavior measured by our test and brain chemistry lead us to speculate about the mechanism involved. This necessitates interpretations of the functional significance of both variables, ChE activity and hypothesis behavior.

We have already noted evidence that ACh metabolism is importantly involved in transmission in the central nervous system. We would now suggest that animals with higher rates of ACh metabolism also show readier transmission of nerve impulses. No causal relationship is specified here—we are merely positing a correlation between the two. We would next accept the common assumption that an animal whose nervous system is capable of relatively efficient transmission would tend to manage new problem situations more effectively than an animal whose transmission of nerve impulses is less efficient. Such an assumption would also involve, of course, limiting factors. It is conceivable, for example, that too ready transmission of nerve impulses may interfere with effective behavioral adjustment, and we intend soon to put this to experimental test. In any event, the reasoning indicated here would assume that animals with higher rates of ACh metabolism (within limits) would tend to show more effective behavioral adjustment than animals with lower ACh metabolism.

On the behavioral side, we believe that animals that show a spatial Preference Score are more adaptive than animals that show a visual Preference Score. We make this interpretation for the following reasons: (1) As we have already pointed out, our test is designed to measure the animal's perceptual selectivity. (2) We next assume that adaptive behavior is correlated with the ability of an animal to "pay attention to" various stimulus aspects of its environment when confronted with a problem. Thus, for example, Tolman (33) stresses the importance of determining the ". . . conditions which favor relatively rapid shifts in the dimension of discrimination of a sign or of a significate . . ." in understanding differential effectiveness of performance. (3) In our maze, under the conditions of training that we have used, almost all animals show a light-going preference on their first few trials. (Data which demonstrate this will be presented in the next section of this paper.) Achieving a spatial Preference Score therefore requires that an animal ignore the dominant illumination cue and pay attention to the less obvious cue of location in space. In other words, an animal that develops a spatial preference shows readier "shifts in the dimension of discrimination" than an animal whose behavior remains controlled by the visual cues. This interpretation is discussed further in the next section, where it will also receive support from another experiment.

These proposed interpretations of the functional significance of ACh metabolism and hypothesis behavior suggest, in most general terms, a rationale for the observed correlation between ChE activity and hypothesis behavior. Cortical ChE activity level provides a measure of the readiness of nerve impulse transmission in the central nervous system; the relative ease of nerve impulse transmission is correlated with capacity for more adaptive behavior; a spatial Preference Score in our maze is indicative of a more adaptive animal; therefore, one might expect a positive correlation between level of ChE activity and a spatial Preference Score.

We realize of course that the differences in ChE may be related to cytoarchitectonic variations. It is also probable that other biochemical measures may be found to differentiate among our subjects that behave differently. Several questions concerning our interpretation can be raised:

The size of the over-all difference in ChE activity between spatial and visual animals is about 5 per cent. We have been asked whether such a "small" difference could have behavioral consequences in view of the fact that much larger changes are required to block peripheral conduction. Any answer to this question must take into account the following considerations: (1) In our test no pathological alterations have been induced in the nervous system or in metabolism, and we do not observe pathological behavior. It is probable that normal behavioral variations may be correlated with relatively small variations in metabolism within the normal range, whereas pathology may require much more extensive changes in the nervous system. Our maze may be a rather sensitive indicator of cerebral functioning. In this connection our general observation may merit repeating: Too frequently have investigators been content with rather gross, unreliable, and qualitative "measures" of behavior while demanding precise and careful measures of biochemical changes. The validity of a correlation depends upon the reliability and validity of the *two* variables being correlated. (2) The over-all difference in ChE activity that we have noted may not reflect accurately the extent of differences at specific sites in the cortex. Clear differences between cortical layers have been shown for a number of substances. It is possible that an over-all difference of 5 per cent may represent a very much larger difference at certain cortical layers or in certain types of cells, for example, and these relatively large differences at such specific sites may well be the important determinants of adaptive behavior.

In the light of these and other considerations we cannot admit as definitive the objection that our observed differences in ChE activity levels are too small to make our hypothesis tenable.

There is an additional difficulty with our hypothesis which we wish to discuss. It will be recalled that when animals were sacrificed before 126 days of age, spatial and visual animals showed no difference in ChE activity. The finding of significant differences in older animals, then, is paradoxical, since *all* animals had their *behavioral* tests at about the same age—85 days. We would suggest three possible explanations, all of which are now being tested in our laboratory.

1. ChE may not be an adequate index of ACh metabolism until about 150 days of age. Before this time, ChE may be present in "functional excess." It is, of course, a common finding that there is a large "safety

factor" in the supply of many biological substances in the organism. This excess may be enough to obliterate any differences between animals. After the age of 150 days, the production of ChE may be regulated to conform more closely with the functional ACh metabolism.

2. The ChE we are measuring may be a composite of both specific ("true") ChE and nonspecific ChE. It may be that nonspecific ChE is more abundant in the younger animals, and, therefore, our measures of the younger animals may give uniformly high and false estimates of specific ChE.

3. Finally, and this is perhaps the most interesting alternative, the behavioral testing itself may affect ChE activity. Before the test begins, animals that will show themselves to be spatial may have a higher ChE level than those that will be visual. But the problem-solving behavior in the test situation may raise ChE to a ceiling in all animals, thus making differentiation impossible when assayed chemically immediately after behavioral testing. After behavioral testing, ChE activity may subside to a resting level, and chemical analysis at this stage will result in differential readings. We have a combined genetic, behavioral, and chemical study planned to examine this possibility.

Effects of Pentobarbital Sodium on Adaptive Behavior-Patterns

The experimental hypothesis.—Having observed the behavioral effects of naturally occurring differences in ACh metabolism, we next attempted to vary the metabolism experimentally and to predict the behavioral effect. We based our prediction, for this experiment, upon the following assumptions and considerations, some of which we have already discussed:

1. Illumination is evidently the initially dominant cue in our apparatus. This assumption was made on two grounds. In the first place, the animal was tested in a darkened room where the only source of light came from 15-watt lamps in the lighted alleys. Thus, the difference in illumination between the lighted and darkened alley was quite large. The difference between the right and left alley, in terms of spatial separation, was only 60 degrees. Because of these stimulus differences we assume that the *perceptual* difference between the two alleys was greater in visual than in spatial characteristics. In the second place, and more compellingly, almost all animals show a light-going preference on their first few trials. In other words, we had behavioral data suggesting the initial dominance and saliency of the light cue over the spatial cue.

2. We assume, for the reasons given previously, that an animal that develops a spatial preference is more flexible than an animal whose behavior remains controlled by the visual cues.

3. As we have seen in the previous section, animals with lower ChE

activity tend to display visual preferences, while animals with higher ChE activity tend to abandon this preference and to develop a spatial preference.

4. ChE activity is assumed to be an index to the rate of ACh metabolism, for the reasons previously discussed.

5. Finally, pentobarbital sodium is one of the agents that have been shown to reduce the rate of synthesis of ACh in the cortex (22).

These five points can be rephrased in the following experimental hy-

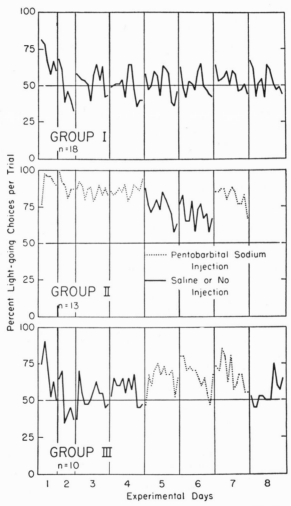

Fig. 117.—Percentage of light-going choices per trial, for pentobarbital and control animals.

pothesis: A low rate of cortical ACh metabolism makes for animals that are stimulus-bound and relatively incapable of ignoring the dominant visual cue in our apparatus. Therefore, pentobarbital, by depressing the synthesis of ACh, should increase this tendency, and animals treated with pentobarbital should show an increased light-going behavior in our apparatus.

Results.—All animals in this experiment were male rats of our S_{13} strain. Our experimental group, Group II, consisted of 13 animals run under pentobarbital on days 1 through 4. Ten mg/kilo body-weight was injected intraperitoneally about 15 min. prior to testing. In all other respects these animals were run according to the standard procedure. The performance of these experimental animals was then compared with control groups. The pentobarbital dosage did not reduce eating in the maze, and no adverse effects upon motivation as compared with the control animals were observed. Although most of the experimental animals showed some motor incoördination, running time in the apparatus was not increased. The dosage was tested on the animals during pretraining. In a few instances it was necessary to reduce the dosage to avoid causing too much incoördination.

Figure 117 shows the percentage of light-going choices per trial for three groups of animals. The primary control group, Group I, shows the typical initial light-going tendency. These light-going choices, however, soon fall to the chance level of 50 per cent and fluctuate rather closely around that level thereafter. The hypotheses of Group I during days 1–4 are distributed fairly evenly among Light, Dark, Left, and Right (Table 33). Too few perseverative hypotheses occurred to warrant tabulating here.

The experimental animals (Group II) start with about the same percentage of light-going choices as the control animals. But almost imme-

TABLE 33

Frequency of various hypotheses per rat per day in the pentobarbital experiment

Group	Days 1–4 Hypotheses					Days 5–6 Hypotheses				
	Light	Dark	Left	Right	Total	Light	Dark	Left	Right	Total
I	.19	.11	.19	.15	.64	.20	.06	.30	.08	.64
II	.90	.00	.00	.05	.95	.58	.00	.04	.04	.64
III	.30	.10	.07	.10	.57	.40	.10	.05	.10	.65

diately the light-going behavior of the experimental animals rises sharply and remains high as long as the barbiturate is administered. On days 5 and 6, when pentobarbital was not administered, the light-going choices fall off. Administering the drug again on day 7 raises the frequency of light-going choices once more. The *t* test (Table 34) shows that the dif-

TABLE 34

t tests of differences between groups in the pentobarbital experiment (light-going scores)

Groups compared	Experimental days					
	1–2	3	4	5	6	7
I and II	7.62*	5.81*	6.15*	3.88*	3.07†	4.08*
II and III	7.61*	4.14*	3.35†	1.06	0.32	1.65
I and III	0.08	0.14	1.10	1.88	2.37§	1.86

* *t* significant at .001 level of confidence.
† *t* significant at .01 level of confidence.
§ *t* significant at .05 level of confidence.

ferences are highly significant, Group II showing more light-going behavior even on days 5 and 6 when it no longer received the drug.

The frequencies of hypotheses of Group II also differ from those of Group I (Table 33), most experimental animals displaying a Light Hypothesis on every pentobarbital day. When the drug was not administered (days 5 and 6), the Light Hypotheses and total hypotheses fell off.

The drugged animals showed several pecularities of behavior. In spite of some motor incoördination, most experimental animals reached the goal-box more quickly than did the control animals. In part the faster time of the drugged animals can be attributed to a more rapid gait. In part it can be attributed to the fact that, in contrast to the control animals, the experimental animals spent very little time in exploratory or "vicarious trial-and-error" behavior. A further peculiarity was the exaggerated tendency of the experimental animals, on the first day or two, to re-enter some of the alleys repeatedly before trying the other alley. In general, the behavior of the drugged animals was rapid and machine-like. The whole picture was one of extreme stereotypy of behavior.

The striking effects observed with pentobarbital raised the question whether the drug might have induced a simple phototropism in the animal and made it unresponsive to the "correctness" of its choice (i.e.,

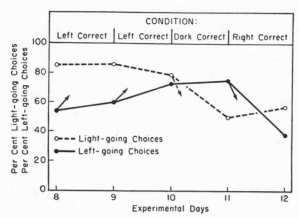

Fig. 118.—Changes in response with changes in stimulus conditions for pentobarbital animals.

a "blind phototropism"!). As one test, ten animals of Group II were later trained—again under pentobarbital—with the maze made *solvable*. The animals had not been run for a week or more, so they first were run for one more day with the maze unsolvable (Fig. 118, day 8). Figure 118 gives percentages for the last six trials of each day. On days 9 and 10 all the *left* alleys were made correct; on day 11, all the *dark* alleys were made correct; and, on the final day, the *right* alleys were made correct. The arrows in Figure 118 indicate the demanded changes in behavior. Though learning was rather slow (and though a few animals remained light-going throughout), the test indicated that animals under pentobarbital can ignore the lighted alleys and tend to adopt the consistently rewarded cue.

As a further test, Group III was run under normal conditions for four days and then under the barbiturate. For days 1–4, their behavior was similar to that of Group I (see Fig. 117 and Table 33, row 3). When pentobarbital was administered on days 5–7, the percentage of light-going choices rose moderately, but only on day 6 did it differ significantly from that of Group I. When Group III received the drug and Group II did not (days 5 and 6), there was no significant difference between their light-going percentages, and Group III actually displayed fewer light-going hypotheses than did Group II. Clearly, pentobarbital does not induce a simple, overriding phototropism. There is an interaction between the biochemical and experiential variables, since the drug has its chief effect in our test when it is administered while the situation is novel. When an animal has already tested out the dominant stimulus and has begun to discard it, the administration of the drug does not cause any marked reversion. The animal continues to show the same behavior after drug administration which it showed before. The animal, even under the drug, is "trying to solve" the problem—within the limits of its "attention" capacity.

Discussion.—Both the results of this pentobarbital experiment and those of the previous section seem to be consistent with the general hypothesis that differences in adaptive behavior-patterns are related to the rate of cortical ACh metabolism. However, our last results together with some recent findings reported by Hernández-Peón and Scherrer (12) suggest a complementary and more specific interpretation.

According to the Hernández-Peón and Scherrer report, afferent channels show habituation to repeated stimuli. These authors conceive of habituation as ". . . simple learning not to respond to stimuli which tend to be insignificant for the organism" (p. 71). Such habituation has been demonstrated to be due to inhibitory impulses from the brain-stem reticular formation and, further, anesthesia with pentobarbital or lesions of the midbrain tegmentum have been found to prevent the occurrence of habituation. Since inhibition of afferent impulses (habituation) has also been produced by electrical stimulation of motor and sensory areas of the cortex (as well as by stimulation of the brain-stem reticular formation), presumably the higher centers exert their inhibitory effect through their connections with the reticular formation (11). Indeed, stimulation in one sensory modality may lead to inhibition of afferent transmission in another modality. In one demonstration, impulses were recorded at the cochlear nucleus of an awake cat. Showing the cat two mice caused the auditory impulses to be blocked. Hernández-Peón and Scherrer suggest ". . . that this selective inhibitory mechanism plays an important role during 'focussing of attention' for sensory perception" (p. 71).

It will be seen that the above observations and conclusions may be relevant to our own data. We wish to suggest that the central initiation of afferent habituation may require a given rate of cortical ACh metabolism. The rats that are normally visual in our maze are those that do not "habituate" to the illumination cue—a cue that does not help them solve the problem—and therefore these visual rats are animals which do *not* learn "not to respond to stimuli which tend to be insignificant for the organism." Such rats, we have seen, are the animals that tend to show a relatively low level of ChE activity. These are the animals whose perceptual selectivity is limited to the dominant stimulus.

On the other hand, if a rat does "habituate" to the dominant stimulus, it can then "attend to" the spatial cues and can go on to test a spatial hypothesis. Such animals are not "stimulus-bound" and have a more effective perceptual selectivity. Again, it will be remembered, these are the rats which have a relatively higher level of ChE activity. Thus, our correlation between spatial-visual *preferences* and ChE activity may be but another way of expressing a correlation between individual differences in rate of *habituation* and cortical ACh metabolism.

Barbiturate anesthesia has been shown to eliminate habituation, presumably because the reticular formation is particularly sensitive to anesthetics. In our experiment with pentobarbital, the relatively light dosage may have had its primary effect upon the reticular formation, or upon the cortical activity which channels into the reticular formation, or finally, effects may have occurred at both levels. These possibilities are yet to be tested. We are hypothesizing, of course, that cortical ACh metabolism is involved in habituation. In making this hypothesis we are proposing a biochemical determinant of perceptual selectivity to complement the valuable suggestions which have already been made for neurological mechanisms.

CURRENT AND PROJECTED RESEARCH

Our research on brain chemistry and adaptive behavior is only begun. We are in the process of replicating and extending some of our present observations, and we are beginning certain further experiments. The main observations that we are attempting to replicate concern the differences in ChE activity between spatial and visual animals as a function of the age at which the chemical analysis is performed (Fig. 116). We are especially interested in adding to the number of older animals tested.

Several rather direct extensions of present observations have been undertaken in our laboratories. A more detailed mapping of ChE activity in the cortex is being done by Trevor Peirce and Alvin Halevy. Mr. Halevy is also attempting to determine how much of the ACh is hydrolyzed by specific ChE and how much by nonspecific ChE in each sex. Following up the observations on the effects of pentobarbital sodium on hypothesis behavior, other drugs are being tested. James McGaugh and Lewis Petrinovich are attempting to repeat the effects of strychnine on learning that Lashley reported.

We have also begun to test in other behavioral situations the hypothesized relationship between ACh metabolism and adaptive behavior. For the present, the other behavioral tests are being run in the same apparatus, but with the maze solvable or partly so. Later, after we have explored these related tests, we plan to use completely different test situations.

To aid the interpretation of our results, we wish to test the use of ChE as an index of ACh metabolism, since this is not founded upon direct observations. In discussing the interaction of age and ChE activity, we hypothesized, in fact, that ChE activity might be a better index of ACh metabolism at older ages than at younger ages. For this reason, we are preparing to measure both ChA and ChE in animals of different ages. It is difficult to measure ACh directly by chemical means. ChA, being necessary for the synthesis of ACh, will afford a more direct estimate of ACh metabolism than does ChE. An analysis for both ChA and ChE will be made from the same samples of tissue, and this will permit us to compare and correlate the concentrations of the two enzymes.

Among the new directions of research now underway in our laboratories is a genetic study of the determinants of ChE activity in the brain, an attempt to automatize the measurements of perceptual selectivity, and a study of the effects of cortical injury upon ChE activity. A selective breeding program in rats has been undertaken by Thomas Roderick. High and low ChE activity will be selected for in two separate, highly heterogeneous foundation stocks. This program, under the guidance of Professor E. R. Dempster of the Genetics Division, is now in its first generation. Determining whether there exists a correlated response in behavior preference between the lines selected for high and low ChE activity will constitute the major point of study. Separated strains would also be valuable for investigating other possible anatomical and biochemical correlates of behavior. James McGaugh has designed an apparatus to measure hypothesis behavior automatically. And finally, Trevor Peirce is investigating the effects of localized cortical ablation on ChE activity in the remaining cortex, studying both the effects on adjacent areas and on areas in the contralateral hemisphere.

The program, stated generally, involves extension in five main directions: (1) the attempt to correlate other chemical substances with adaptive behavior, (2) the use of other behavioral situations to test the generality of the relationships between chemistry and adaptive behavior, (3) the measurement with reliable behavioral tests of the effects of drugs with known phamacological properties, (4) the use of genetic techniques to test the relationship between brain chemistry and behavior, and (5) the effect of cortical injury and other pathology on brain chemistry.

We can take up only a few of the many leads that seem promising. We have been encouraged by the interest shown in our efforts by workers in many allied fields—chemistry, medicine, pharmacology, physiology, and zoology—and by the fact that there are already plans to repeat part of our work in other laboratories. It is our hope that still other interdisciplinary teams will join in attacking the problems of brain chemistry and adaptive behavior.

REFERENCES

1. Abramson, H. A. (Ed.) *Neuropharmacology. Transactions of the first conference.* New York: Josiah Macy, Jr. Foundation, 1955.

2. Ashby, W. M. Discussion. In *The biology of mental health and disease.* New York: Hoeber, 1952, pp. 467–68.

3. Augustinsson, K. -B. Cholinesterases: A study in comparative enzymology. *Acta physiol. scand.,* 1948, *15:* Suppl. 52.

4. Brendler, H. A simple, inexpensive microhomogenizer. *Science,* 1951, *114:* 61–62.

5. Burgen, A. S. V., and L. M. Chipman. Cholinesterase and succinic dehydrogenase in the central nervous system of the dog. *J. Physiol.,* 1951, *114:* 296–305.

6. Burgen, A. S. V., and F. C. MacIntosh. The physiological significance of acetylcholine. In K. A. C. Elliott, I. H. Page, and J. H. Quastel (Eds.), *Neurochemistry: The chemical dynamics of brain and nerve.* Springfield, Ill.: Charles C Thomas, 1955, pp. 311–89.

7. Dews, P. B. Operant behavior. *Fed. Proc.,* 1955, *14:* 333 (Abstract).

8. ———. Studies on behavior. I. Differential sensitivity to pentobarbital of pecking performance in pigeons depending on the schedule of reward. *J. Pharmacol.,* 1955, *113:* 393–401.

9. Elliott, K. A. C., I. H. Page, and J. H. Quastel. (Eds.) *Neurochemistry: The chemcial dynamics of brain and nerve.* Springfield, Ill.: Charles C Thomas, 1955.

10. Gerard, R. W. The acetylcholine system in neural function. *Recent Progr. Hormone Res.,* 1950, *5:* 37–61.

11. Hagbarth, K. -E., and D. I. B. Kerr. Central influences on spinal afferent conduction. *J. Neurophysiol.,* 1954, *17:* 295–307.

12. Hernández-Peón, R., and H. Scherrer. "Habituation" to acoustic stimuli in cochlear nucleus. *Fed. Proc.,* 1955, *14:* 71 (Abstract).

13. Krech, D., M. R. Rosenzweig, E. L. Bennett, and B. Krueckel. Enzyme concentrations in the brain and adjustive behavior-patterns. *Science,* 1954, *120:* 994–96.

14. Krechevsky, I. "Hypotheses" in rats. *Psychol. Rev.,* 1932, *39:* 516–32.

15. ———. "Hypotheses" versus "chance" in the pre-solution period in sensory discrimination-learning. *Univ. Calif. Publ. Psychol.,* 1932, *6:* 27–44.

16. ———. The genesis of "hypotheses" in rats. *Univ. Calif. Publ. Psychol.,* 1932, *6:* 45–64.

17. ———. Hereditary nature of "hypotheses." *J. comp. Psychol.,* 1933, *16:* 99–116.

18. ———. Brain mechanisms and "hypotheses." *J. comp. Psychol.,* 1935, *19:* 425–48.

19. Lashley, K. S. The effects of strychnine and caffeine upon the rate of learning. *Psychobiology,* 1917, *1:* 141–70.

20. Lilienthal, J. L., Jr. Role of quaternary compounds in neural activity. In

The biology of mental health and disease. New York: Hoeber, 1952, pp. 162–77.

21 McIlwain, H. Brain metabolism and activity. *Brit. med. Bull.*, 1950, *6:* 301–3.

22 McLennan, H., and K. A. C. Elliott. Effects of convulsant and narcotic drugs on acetylcholine synthesis. *J. Pharmacol.*, 1951, *103:* 35–53.

23 Metzler, C. J., and D. G. Humm. The determination of cholinesterase activity in whole brains of developing rats. *Science*, 1951, *113:* 382–83.

24 Munn, N. L. *Handbook of psychological research on the rat.* Boston: Houghton Mifflin, 1950.

25 Nachmansohn, D. Sur l'action de la strychnine. *C. R. Soc. Biol.*, Paris, 1938, *129:* 941–43.

26 Nachmansohn, D., and I. B. Wilson. Acetylcholinesterase. In S. P. Colowick and N. O. Kaplan (Eds), *Methods in enzymology.* Vol. 1. New York: Academic Press, 1955, pp. 642–51.

27 Neilands, J. B., and M. D. Cannon. Automatic recording pH instrumentation. *Analyt. Chem.*, 1955, *27:* 29–33.

28 Platt, C. E., and D. D. Wickens. The effects of anticholinesterase agents upon animal behavior: The effects of subcutaneous injection of di-isopropyl fluorophosphate on the retention of a maze habit by the albino rat. *Amer. Psychologist*, 1950, *5:* 254 (Abstract).

29 Quastel, J. H. Biochemical aspects of narcosis. In K. A. C. Elliott, I. H. Page, and J. H. Quastel (Eds.), *Neurochemistry: The chemical dynamics of brain and nerve.* Springfield, Ill.: Charles C Thomas, 1955, pp. 648–76.

30 Russell, R. W. Effects of reduced brain cholinesterase on behavior. *Bull. Brit. psychol. Soc.*, 1954, *23:* (Inset), 6 (Abstract).

31 Snedecor, G. W. *Statistical methods.* (4th Ed.) Ames, Ia.: Iowa State College Press, 1946.

32 Sterling, K., and J. G. Miller. Conditioning under anesthesia. *Amer. J. Psychol.*, 1941, *54:* 92–101.

33 Tolman, E. C. Performance vectors and the unconscious. *Proc. Fourteenth int. Congr. Psychol.*, 1954, 31–40.

34 Tower, D. B. and K. A. C. Elliott. Activity of acetylcholine system in cerebral cortex of various unanesthetized mammals. *Amer. J. Physiol.*, 1952, *168:* 747–59.

35 Tryon, R. C. The genetics of learning ability in rats: Preliminary report. *Univ. Calif. Publ. Psychol.*, 1929, *4:* 71–89.

36 Ward, A. A., Jr., and M. A. Kennard. Effect of cholinergic drugs on recovery of function following lesions of the central nervous system in monkeys. *Yale J. Biol. Med.*, 1942, *15:* 189–228.

37 Watson, C. W. and M. A. Kennard. The effect of anticonvulsant drugs on recovery of function following cerebral cortical lesions. *J. Neurophysiol.*, 1945, *8:* 221–31.

38 Zubek, J. P. Studies in somesthesis. I. Role of the somesthetic cortex in roughness discrimination in the rat. *J. comp. physiol. Psychol.*, 1951, *44:* 339–53.

Physiological Plasticity and
Brain Circuit Theory

The standard Sherringtonian picture of central nervous integration has not received universal acceptance. Students of behavior, in particular, have on numerous occasions expressed dissatisfaction with the conventional fiber circuit concepts. They argue that the central switchboard analogies and reflex circuit diagrams of classical neurology may be all right for the anesthetized and spinal preparations, but that they are hardly adequate to account for the tremendous plasticity and the amazing purposive adaptibility of the normal intact animal. Other objections to conventional circuit theory with direct experimental foundation attained substantial proportions during the twenties and thirties. Outstanding were those that stemmed from brain lesion studies demonstrating the ability of the brain to approximate normal function in the face of extensive cerebral damage. Cortical lesions produced initially in the expectation that whole blocks of memory and categories of experience and behavior would be wiped out proved in many cases to have so slight an effect on functional organization and memory as to tax the ingenuity of the investigator to detect any behavioral deficits. The question of the locus and nature of the memory trace or engram became recognized, through the work of Lashley (13), in particular, as one of the most baffling of all neurological problems. Almost any engram scheme that might be expressed within the framework of the traditional approach to cerebral integration, i.e., in terms of specific fiber connections, seemed to be ruled out.

The case against the conventional connectivist approach was supported further by numerous clinical and experimental observations on nerve crossing and muscle transplantation which seemed to indicate a complete functional interchangeability of neuronal connections, undermining thereby the basic thesis that functional specificity depends on differential fiber connections. Additional objections arose out of the widespread demonstrations of Gestalt principles in perception, principles that emphasized the importance of the whole pattern in brain excitation and at the same time ruled out functional specificity among the neuronal elements. Concomitantly, a series of studies on the puzzling phenomenon of homologous response (50) and its various ramifications seemed also

401

to rule out differential connectivity as a basis of integration, pointing to some kind of resonance principle as an alternative.

Bolstered by the foregoing and other lines of evidence, the anti-connectivity movement had become strong and was gaining rapidly by the late thirties. On the other hand, such constructive suggestions for brain theory as had emerged from the separate lines of evidence remained diverse and inconsistent. In each case the new hypotheses accounted satisfactorily for one or for a few of the plasticity phenomena on which they were directly based, but they remained inadequate with respect to others. In the following I shall attempt to consider, one at a time, some of the more substantial and impressive lines of evidence and related arguments that have been advanced against orthodox reflexology, i.e., the evidence and arguments that have seemed to be the most convincing and demanding of some answer or explanation.

RE-EDUCATION AFTER NERVE CROSSING AND MUSCLE TRANSPOSITION

Many kinds of nerve cross-union and muscle transplantation have been described in the early literature (2, 3, 7) with statements that they lead to complete functional readaptation. Readjustments in the hind limbs were reported to survive spinal transection, implying a type of spinal learning and a basic plasticity in some of the most primitive and supposedly most fixed pathways of the neuraxis. Many investigators emphasized that these readjustments occur immediately and spontaneously with no necessity for any relearning. From these latter, especially, the conclusion was drawn that central coördination mechanisms are independent of any exact morphology in neuronal connections, and that we must therefore seek some entirely new principles of integration, quite different from those envisaged by Sherrington and his followers.

Some fifteen years ago it seemed that a good approach to problems concerning the brain engram and functional plasticity in general might be made through an analysis of the neural changes underlying readjustments of this type. The central nervous changes involved promised to be relatively simple, direct, and circumscribed compared with those for the maze, problem box, and perceptual discrimination habits previously studied. By combining cord and brain transections at various levels with cortical lesions and electric stimulation and recording, it looked as though one ought to be able to pin point the location, and perhaps determine something about the nature, of the underlying neural changes.

When we embarked on this project, our efforts were thwarted from the start by the repeated inability of our animals to effect any significant

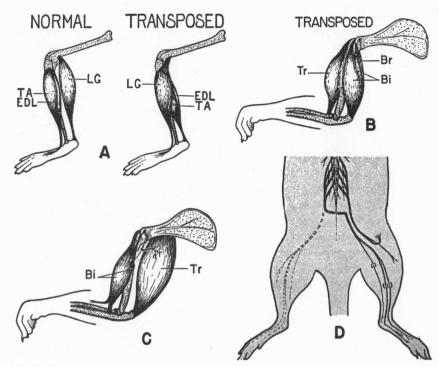

Fig. 119.—Some nerve-end organ disarrangements which have produced in rats corresponding sensory and motor dysfunction that remained uncorrected by re-education. *A.* Transposition of opposing flexor and extensor muscles of hind limb (25, 26). *B.* Same in forelimb (27). *C.* Reinnervation of triceps extensor muscle by antagonist nerve from biceps flexor muscle (27). *D.* Contralateral crossed innervation of right foot by nerves from left foot (28).

central reorganization in response to the surgical alterations produced in the periphery. The rearrangement of nerve-end organ connections resulted repeatedly in corresponding functional disorder that tended to persist indefinitely with little or no correction by re-education. For example, rats with flexor and extensor nerves of the leg interchanged, or with the corresponding muscles transposed as early as the third week after birth (Fig. 119), would go through the remainder of their lives making all movements of the affected foot in reverse (26). Monkeys with the nerve supply of the brachial biceps and triceps muscles interchanged learned quickly to inhibit the resultant reversal of elbow movement, but failed in a period of three years to effect any generalized positive correction of the reversed muscle action (35). After sensory nerves had been crossed in rats from the left to the right leg, the development of painful trophic sores on the sole of the reinnervated right foot in some of the animals caused them to hop about on three legs, bearing extra weight on the inflamed right foot in order to hold up protectively the uninjured left leg. This maladaptive behavior continued uncorrected throughout the waking day for six to nine weeks until the aggravated ulcers eventually healed. In one case the reflex rigidity was fatal (28). Frogs, newts, and fishes with their eyes surgically rotated 180 degrees responded thereafter as if the visual field had the illusory appearance of being upside down (29, 31, 37). Application of conditioning techniques and other special training measures failed to bring about readaption of these and similar types of functional disorder.

A critical revaluation of the older studies undertaken in the light of these contradictory results disclosed that in nearly all cases the earlier optimistic interpretations were suspect (32). In many instances, it is quite obvious that other factors such as vicarious muscle function, anomalous innervation, two-joint tendon action and the like, were mistaken for reorganization in the central circuits of the nerves involved. Although the evidence indicates that some reorganization is possible, particularly with respect to muscle transposition in man, it is definitely restricted and appears not to exceed that achieved in other types of sensory and motor learning.

In brief, the earlier counterindications for traditional connectivity theory are now superseded by data leading to a much more conservative estimate of central nervous plasticity. Instead of demanding new mechanisms of integration as seemed originally to be the case, the nerve cross and muscle transplantation data have now backfired and offer instead strong support for the old idea that specificity of function is closely associated with specificity in the morphology of nerve fiber connections.

MYOTYPIC (HOMOLOGOUS) RESPONSE AND RESONANCE

One exception among the foregoing remained unaccounted for. This was the observation that disarrangement of nerve-muscle connections in the limbs of larval amphibians fails to produce any corresponding functional disorder. In a series of investigations beginning in 1922 Weiss (49, 50) had shown that muscle coördination undergoes an orderly recovery following various kinds of surgical alterations in the normal innervation pattern. More recent experiments, published in part, have revealed the same type of motor recovery in adult *Triturus,* the water newt, and in the fin and trigeminal musculature of the adults of several species of fishes (38, 45). Adult toads and frogs, on the other hand, are incapable of the same kind of recovery (50), and it has been found to fail also in the oculomotor system of amphibians, and certain fishes (33, 45).

The studies by Weiss had demonstrated that this "myotypic" form of motor recovery can be obtained under conditions that clearly eliminate any kind of relearning process or reflex form of readjustment. The results seemed entirely incompatible with the idea that spinal reflex integration is based on specific fiber connections. As an alternative it was proposed that each muscle acts like a resonator responding selectively to a particular frequency of discharge, and that all frequencies are emitted over all the muscle nerves. On this basis it would make no difference to which nerve a given muscle is connected.

This form of the hypothesis was disproved in 1931 by Wiersma (52) with electric recording methods. Wiersma then modified the original interpretation with the suggestion that the muscles impose their specific resonance properties on the motoneurons such that the entire motor unit, rather than just a muscle, acts as the resonator. This modification of the resonance theory has survived to the present. The change in the motoneuron induced by a foreign muscle is called "modulation." Meanwhile the idea that frequency of discharge is the basis for the selective central activation has given way to the notion of qualitatively distinct modes of central excitation, a specific mode for each muscle of the limb (50, 51).

When we tried to reconcile this interpretation with the conflicting results in mammals mentioned above, it became apparent that most aspects of the myotypic response phenomena could be accounted for if one assumed that alteration of the peripheral connections of a motoneuron somehow leads to a compensatory switch in its synaptic relations within the centers (26). The influence of the muscle on its motoneuron as conceived by Wiersma and Weiss could be interpreted as having its direct effect, not on selective receptivity to specific modes or frequencies of central excitation, but on selective tolerance for specific types of synaptic end-feet. Specific chemical affinites between the motoneurons and the different classes of central fibers, might then account for the selective synaptic contacts. Regeneration of a motor axon into a new muscle could be conceived to cause some kind of trophic breakdown in the synaptic end-feet on that motoneuron to be followed by the formation of new end-feet from other fibers having the proper chemical affinity. Such an hypothesis would explain the recovery of normal motor coördination with abnormal nerve-muscle connections. The lack of similar recovery in the rat and other mammals could be ascribed to an early loss in mammals of the embryonic plasticity required for such tissue breakdown and respecification.

Such an explanation had the advantage of not requiring any drastic revision of established neurophysiological principles. Furthermore, it seemed likely that the same factors would be operating under the conditions of normal development to insure the initial establishment of proper reflex relations. If so, one would have here the basis for a general theory of the developmental patterning of synaptic end-feet, a theory to replace older explanations that were based on neurobiotaxis (12) and had leaned heavily on function and experience to account for the developmental organization of the nerve centers.

Such a reinterpretation was in conflict at first with the prevailing view of the thirties that the regeneration and termination of nerve fibers is nonselective and that the central nervous system is incapable of functional regeneration on the scale required. Subsequent investigation has since shown that the central nervous system of amphibians and fishes has extensive regenerative capacity even in the adult. Full functional recovery has been observed after regeneration of the transected midbrain, spinal cord, optic nerve, and vestibular, trigeminal, and dorsal spinal nerve roots. The recovery, furthermore, is always of an orderly type, suggesting a strictly selective re-establishment of synaptic terminals (23, 39, 40). There has not as yet been any direct morphological demonstration of the inferred selective synapsis, however, and the issue remains unresolved to the present. The connectivity interpretation is favored by the broad background of neurological data that has led to the general discard of specific nerve energy and resonance concepts in favor of selective synaptic relations as a basis for central integration.

CHEMOAFFINITY IN THE PATTERNING OF NEURONAL CONNECTIONS

The general picture of the developmental patterning of neural circuits in terms of selective chemoaffinities becomes increasingly credible. Supporting evidence has been extended to include synaptic patterning in the visual, vestibular, and cutaneous pathways, and in the central tectobulbar, tectospinal, and associated mesencephalic and spinal fiber tracts (see Fig. 120). The consistent results suggest general application to the entire nervous system. Since the general scheme and supporting evidence have recently been presented in some detail elsewhere (39, 40, 43), only the broad outlines are mentioned below.

Essentially the hypothesis supposes that the neuron population undergoes an extremely refined embryonic differentiation somewhat as follows: After the embryonic cells for the nervous system have been separated from those for muscle, bone, cartilage, etc., the neuroblasts continue to differentiate among themselves. At first the differentiations are broad: into motor and sensory systems, cephalic and spinal, brachial and thoracic. Later within these groups subgroups are formed, and differentiation continues, producing greater and greater refinement and complexity. Even-

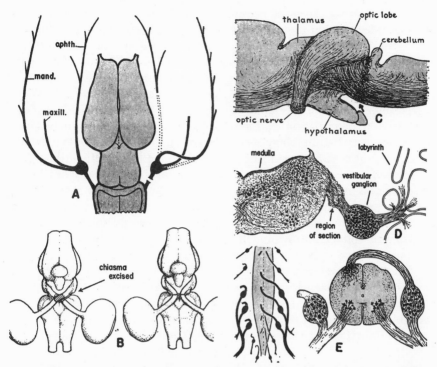

Fig. 120.—Regeneration of central synaptic connections in the following and similar situations is found to effect an orderly re-establishment of reflex functions: *A*. Regeneration of divided trigeminal nerve root, with peripheral cross-union of ophthalmic and mandibular nerves (39). *B*. Regeneration of divided optic nerves into wrong side of brain (39). *C*. Regeneration of sectioned mesencephalic fiber tracts with eyes rotated 180 degrees (36). *D*. Regeneration of divided vestibular nerve root with optic nerve resected (39). *E*. Regeneration of crossed sensory roots of hind limb (40).

tually the primary motor neurons become stamped with additional specificity by the muscles they innervate. Similarly, the primary sensory neurons, after being divided into different classes for the different modalities of sensibility, are further specified within each sense modality to mediate various local sign properties as in the retina, cochlea, skin, tendons, joints, etc. An equally refined and even more complicated differentiation must take place concurrently and in the later stages among the association neurons in the centers. The final specificity of the neuron is determined in many cases by inductive effects transmitted through terminal contacts from other neurons and end organs.

Once the qualitative individuation of the nerve cell population is achieved, it becomes possible for selective interconnections to be made between different classes of neurons on the basis of specific chemical affinities. The fact that the particular patterns of chemoaffinity produced in ontogeny happen to result in circuit connections that are functionally adaptive may be ascribed to evolutionary selection. The developmental mechanisms directly responsible in ontogeny remain largely obscure although some of the broader principles of the developmental process are becoming clear. Organizer and inductor effects, embryonic fields, self-differentiation, potentiation, and most of the other basic concepts developed in experimental embryology seem to have application in the patterning of the neural circuits. According to this view, the final prefunctional patterning of precise synaptic relations merely involves a refinement of developmental and cytologic mechanisms long recognized in grosser form in other phases of ontogeny. From the embryological standpoint, the chemoaffinity concept of the developmental patterning and maintenance of synaptic connections brings the ontogeny of inherited behavior mechanisms into line with the development of other organ systems.

Like most developmental processes, the specification of nerve cells exhibits adaptive plasticity and reversibility in early stages. Only in later stages of development does the specificity tend to become fixed and irreversible. If surgical alterations are performed during the early plastic period, embryonic adjustments leading to functional readaptation ensue. In the fishes and amphibians neuronal specificity remains plastic for long periods, even into adult stages. This is paralleled by other evidences of tissue plasticity in these forms such as the ability to regenerate limbs, fins, and tails, the lens of the eye, the retina and optic nerve, and central nervous fiber tracts. Most of the phenomena of neural readaptation following surgical alterations in the lower vertebrates are to be understood in these terms. The plasticity is one of embryonic development rather than of neural function.

The selectivity of staining reactions in different parts of the nervous system and the selectivity of drug action, of toxicity effects, of bacterial and viral invasion, of the incidence of degeneration, and the like are all indicative of chemical differentiation generally at a much more crude level than that involved in the patterning of synaptic relations. With regard to future possibilities for specific chemotherapy in nervous and mental disease the above picture of refined chemical differentiation among the neural centers is an encouraging one. That the elaborate qualitative specificity within the neuron population has utility, beyond the establishment and maintenance of synaptic relations, is suggested in the direct response of certain nuclei to different blood constituents. What further direct role it may play in integration remains to be determined.

In summary, it is possible in these terms to account for myotypic response and related phenomena without departing from orthodox connectivity principles. The data have extended further the evidence for the existence of a high degree of qualitative, presumably chemical, specificity among nerve cells correlated closely with the inherent functional differentiation. The results further emphasize that in lower vertebrates, at least, the basic features of space perception, including retinal, vestibular, and cutaneous local sign, and position sense as well as the basic elements of motor coördination and of other functions at reflex and higher levels, are built into the nerve centers under genetic control and are not subject to major reorganization through experience and training. Finally, the findings support a plausible working picture, outlined elsewhere (40, 43), of the way in which these inherited features of neural organization can be organized prefunctionally in the growth process itself.

ELECTRIC FIELD THEORY

The electric field hypothesis of cerebral integration proposes a revision in neurological theory which, if substantiated, would invalidate many of the traditional concepts of brain organization based on orthodox fiber-conduction principles. Proponents of electric field theory hold that a major role in cerebral organization is played by mass electric currents flowing through the cortex as a volume conductor. The subjective aspects of perception are thought to be more satisfactorily correlated with these gross electric currents in the brain than with the orthodox type nerve impulses traveling in discontinuous scattered patterns along discrete fiber pathways. Field theory also purports to account more readily than the fiber circuit schemes for various Gestalt and other relational effects in behavior, particularly in the area of perception.

A partial test of the electric field hypothesis was attempted some years ago in an experiment (34) designed to determine the importance in cerebral organization of horizontal or tangential intracortical conduction over the horizontal fiber systems of the cortex. Numerous subpial knife cuts were made in crisscross patterns throughout the sensorimotor cortex in the monkey (Plate 28). The cuts, extending radially through the depth of the gray matter, would have blocked any tangential intracortical conduction over distances of the kind required to mediate relational interaction between motor and sensory points for different joints of the limb. Presumably the walls of clotted blood and subsequent scar tissue should also have deformed any precise normal patterning of direct-current flow within the subdivided area. Nevertheless, almost no functional disorganization resulted from this extensive cortical parcellation.

A subsequent effort to distort the postulated cortical currents of field theory by short-circuiting them with metallic inserts (16) also failed to produce visual disturbances. From the standpoint of field theorists, however, this first short-circuiting experiment was considered inconclusive because the functional tests had been quite simple and the metallic inserts had left unaffected large portions of the visual cortex corresponding to nearly a quadrant of the visual field. When these were remedied in comparable experiments on the cat (47), there was again no significant functional disturbance. Further, the application of the subpial slicing procedure to the cats' visual cortex (47) similarly failed to disrupt refined visual pattern discriminations (see Plate 28).

Objections that the mass cortical currents might pass undistorted through the above knife cuts and also around the metallic inserts seems to have been answered in a later investigation (46). In this case a large number of small dielectric plates of mica were inserted all through the visual areas of both hemispheres, as illustrated in Figure 122. The object again was to distort, by blocking instead of by shorting, the postulated mass electric currents of visual form perception. In spite of the cortical damage inevitably produced by such inserts, the functional effects again were hardly measurable where the inserts were confined to the depth of the cortex. When the mica plates were pushed deep into the white matter, pronounced visual impairment ensued, but this was followed by recovery of a fair to high level of pattern recognition in the course of two and one-half months. The functional deficits produced by the mica inserts were no greater than those produced by control knife-cut lesions that simulated the tissue damage produced by the inserts.

One can find little justification in the results of this series of investigations for continuing to approach the problems of cerebral function in terms of the electric field theory as it is currently formulated. This conclusion is supported also by considerations of a more theoretical nature (16, 41) that have seemed from the beginning to favor the classic fiber conduction doctrine. Certain other theoretical proposals for cortical integration based on "transcortical irradiation," "scanning in random networks," and "reduplication of interference patterns" are equally difficult to reconcile with the above findings.

SECTION OF CEREBRAL FIBER TRACTS

Deep knife cuts that invade the white matter of the hemispheres to interrupt large bundles of association fibers between cortical areas have been reported to produce amazingly little or no defect in the learning and retention of maze and other trained habits in rats, dogs, and monkeys (15,

53). Perhaps the most dramatic of such findings is the observation that the entire corpus callosum, the largest fiber tract of the brain by many times, can be completely sectioned in man without producing any clear-cut functional symptoms, either overt or introspective. Piano playing, typing, tap dancing, contralateral transfer of learning in mirror drawing and in non-visual stylus maze tasks, binocular depth perception, and apparent movement across the vertical mid-line of the visual field have all been studied (1, 4, 24) and reported to be unimpaired to any significant degree by callosal section. Such findings are difficult to reconcile with the idea that inter-cortical fiber connections are basic to cerebral integration. The results on man in particular have been taken as evidence of the need for an entirely new approach to cortical physiology and the neural basis of learning.

The evidence on cerebral tract section does not all point in the same direction. In our own experience, the surgical invasion of the white matter in cats and monkeys causes much more pronounced functional impairment than do comparable lesions restricted to the gray matter (34, 46, 47). Maspes (17) used tachistoscopic tests on patients with callosal section and found that visual patterns such as letters, numbers, geometric figures, and the like were seen but not comprehended when projected to the nondominant hemisphere in two patients with callosal section. Alexia and tactile agnosia on the nondominant side were mentioned also by Dandy (6). Section of the callosum in dogs is said to prevent the usual transfer of cutaneous conditioned reflexes to contralateral homologous areas (5).

Recent investigations by Myers (22) show that the corpus callosum in the cat is essential for the contralateral transfer of visual learning and memory from one hemisphere to the other. The visual input in these experiments is restricted to one hemisphere by mid-line section of the optic chiasma (Fig. 121) and by placing a blinder over one eye during the training and testing. Under these conditions, it is found that visual discriminations learned with one eye can be performed readily with the untrained eye. This interocular transfer fails, however, with the callosum sectioned. In fact, with the callosum divided, completely opposing and otherwise incompatible discriminations can be trained through the separate eyes with no interference (21). A discrimination task that has already been learned and overtrained with one eye requires as long to relearn with the second eye in chiasma-callosum sectioned cats as if it had never been seen before (48). These animals have no recollection with one eye of what they have been doing with the other eye.

Results of the same kind have been obtained in the tactile sphere. Discriminations for roughness, hardness, and shape learned with one forepaw are found to transfer at a high level to the contralateral untrained paw

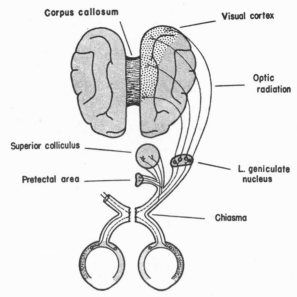

Corpus callosum

Visual cortex

Optic radiation

Superior colliculus

Pretectal area

L. geniculate nucleus

Chiasma

Fig. 121.—After midsagittal section of optic chiasma, visual discrimination habits learned with one eye transfer readily in cats to the untrained eye provided posterior portion of corpus callosum is intact (22). If the callosum is sectioned also, such interocular transfer is completely absent (21, 48).

in normal cats, but in cats with the callosum sectioned, such contralateral transfer fails, and the discrimination has to be relearned from the beginning with the second paw (Stamm and Sperry, unpublished). Even the initial adaptation to the training apparatus, which involved learning to push one of two pedals in the proper manner, and which thus was largely motor, had to be retrained when the cats were shifted to using the second paw.

Perceptual learning and memory seem thus to proceed quite independently in the two hemispheres in the absence of the callosum. It is interesting that in spite of this independence, the learning curves of the two separated hemispheres are strikingly similar in character in the same individual though they differ in the usual way from animal to animal and from problem to problem in the same animal. We have found this to be true both for visual (48) and for tactile discrimination (Stamm & Sperry, unpublished) The fact that the individual variability in perceptual learning runs parallel in the two separated hemispheres indicates that this variability is less a matter of accident and of fortuitous events in the

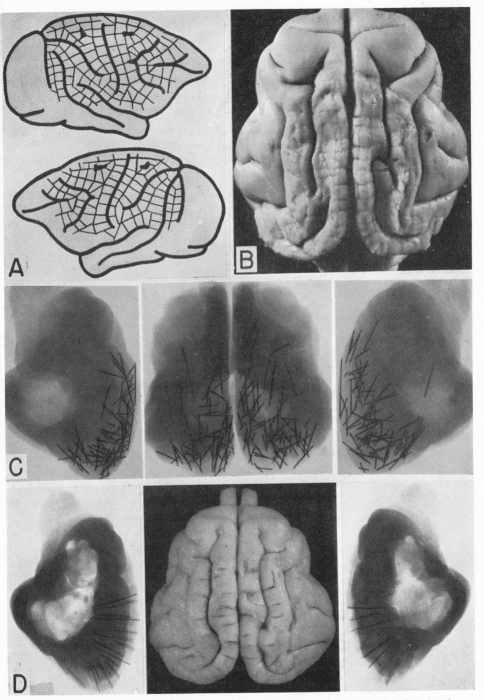

Plate 28.—Failure of the above types of cortical insult to produce major functional disruption is difficult to reconcile with electrical field theory and with any hypothesis based on tangential intracortical conduction. *A.* Multiple subpial knife cuts in sensorimotor cortex of monkey (34). *B.* Same in visual cortex of cat (47). *C.* Lateral and dorsal X-ray views of tantalum wire insertions in visual cortex of cat (47). *D.* Lateral X-ray and dorsal surface views of mica plate insertions in visual cortex of cat (46).

learning process and general training situation than one might have supposed. It appears to be predetermined to a surprising degree by the intrinsic structural and functional organization of the cerebral hemispheres. To what extent this organization is acquired and to what extent inherited remains to be determined.

The studies on callosal section in the cat at least indicate that this structure has an important role in integrating the activity of the two hemispheres. It would appear to follow that a learning task that involves a bilateral influx of learning cues ought to be mastered more rapidly with callosal function intact. To what extent the individual fibers have specific function remains to be determined. Preliminary results of Myers suggest that in the cat transfer of simple visual discriminations can be effected following section of all but a small segment of the callosum about 2 mm. long and that it is not critical which small segment is left so long as it is in the posterior half.

The studies on callosal function show consistently that easily learned discriminations transfer more readily than difficult ones, and that the learning is more rapid and stable on the trained side than on the contralateral side. If there is interference or conflict in one hemisphere between a habit directly trained and one transferred from the other side, the direct training effects are strongly dominant over the transfer effects, other things being equal (22). One gets generalization effects in callosal transfer as in normal learning. If, however, two related patterns are differentiated on one side by long training, the differentiation tends not to transfer although the individual discriminations and generalization effects do so readily (Myers and Sperry, unpublished). We have recently seen this same monocular differentiation fail to transfer to the untrained eye after section of one optic tract, i.e., the differentiation did not transfer from the crossed to the uncrossed fiber systems within the same hemisphere.

With regard to the problem of the localization of memory traces, it is interesting that transfer of visual learning through the callosum can be obtained after removal of the entire occipital, parietal, and temporal lobe cortex on the trained side (Myers and Sperry, unpublished). The cortical removals are made after the completion of training and before switching the blinder. The transfer is erratic under these conditions, occurring in some cases and not others, but the amount of cortex removed beyond the striate area does not seem to have much effect upon the degree of transfer. Easy discriminations transfer much better than difficult ones under these conditions. The same type of result has been obtained (21) when the callosum is sectioned after training is completed and prior to the testing for transfer. The results demonstrate that the memory traces or engrams for these perceptual habits are not confined to the directly trained, receptive area of the cortex. In some form or other they get across to the opposite side. Transfer of a simple but not a difficult discrimination has been observed after removal of the anterior half of the visual cortex of one hemisphere and the posterior half of the other, suggesting that these transfers through the callosum are not just simple mirror images of the sensory input.

It would appear that the callosum operates primarily in the highest-level activities where learning and memory are involved, but is not critical for more basic sensory and motor integration. This is consistent with the recency of its phylogenetic evolution and with the fact that complete section fails to produce any direct symptoms apparent to casual observation.

FUNCTIONAL PLASTICITY THROUGH DIFFERENTIAL PATTERNING OF FACILITATION

Some of the most convincing arguments and bodies of evidence advanced against conventional connectivity theory have failed in the last decade to withstand critical examination and experimental test. The outcome has done more than reflect doubt on the new hypotheses. In a number of respects we have emerged with positive evidence of the direct dependence of normal function upon specific nerve connections. The results favor adherence to traditional circuit theory with allowance for amplifications and revisions where necessary, rather than continued search for some radically new mechanism of integration.

This means that eventually one must be able to find satisfactory connectivity explanations for various other phenomena that heretofore have made the classical theory appear inadequate, i.e., such phenomena as sensory and motor equivalencies, response reversals, equipotentiality and vicarious function of cortical areas, size and shape constancies, perceptual generalization, abstraction, and the like. These and many other forms of functional plasticity will require separate and specific analysis before one can expect any satisfactory understanding. An important advance toward reconciling some of these phenomena with fiber circuit theory has already been made by Hebb (11). I shall only try here to take one more step in the same direction by pointing out the rather general and paramount role that facilitory sets may play in the mediation of much of the plasticity in neural integration.

With facilitory sets operating in a switchboard or fiber circuit system, the functional patterns, though still dependent on specific connections, become much less a direct reflection of the underlying structural design. Given a morphologically rigid circuit system of sufficient complexity, it is possible, for example, to get an almost unlimited variety of different responses from the same invariant stimulus simply by shifting the distribution of central facilitation, i.e., by opening certain central and motor pathways at one time and others at another time. This can be illustrated in simple form at the spinal level. If a spinal salamander is tapped on the tail, the hind leg will respond by retraction or, conversely, by protraction, depending on which of the spinal limb centers happens to be in a state of facilitation and which in a state of inhibition (8). These central states are proprioceptively controlled by the posture of the limb.

The same principle has much wider application at the cerebral level. This can be illustrated with reference to the common voluntary reaction-time experiment: A subject is told to respond as quickly as possible at a certain signal by pushing a key with the finger. When the subject is set for this response, the proper signal triggers off an immediate depression of the key with the short latency of approximately 0.25 sec. However, the same signal may evoke just as rapidly the opposite response if the subject is instructed to pull the key instead of pushing it. Or, the response may be similarly changed to a movement of the foot or of the vocal apparatus without significant increase in latency. By means of fleeting shifts in the central patterns of facilitation and inhibition the same signal can be linked directly to any one of literally hundreds of different responses. No change in brain morphology, no alteration of its wiring plan, is required.

The brain circuits are so constructed that numerous alternative pathways of discharge are available at each integrating center. However, only one or a few of the potential patterns of discharge are open (facilitated) at any one time, the others being closed by inhibitory activity. By this opening and closing of different patterns of circuits at different times, the single morphological network can in effect be transformed into many different types of circuits with widely differing properties and capacities. A very large part of the plasticity and versatility of the nervous system seems to be based on just this principle.

Like a computing machine the neural mechanism can be preset to respond to a given series of numbers by addition, subtraction, or multiplication. Unlike any computors available to date, the same neural mechanism can also be preset at different times for running or walking, typing or piano playing, conversing in French or in Spanish, recording objects by color or by form or by both, and so on and on. By virtue of these different settings, the neural machine becomes many machines in one. We urgently need further analysis and understanding of these differential facilatory sets, how they are controlled, and the principles on which they operate. Possibly some of the recent work on interrelations between cortex and brain stem discussed by Dr. Jasper and Dr. Magoun in this Symposium may lead in this direction.

It might be mentioned in passing that any calculations of the limit of the nervous system's capacity for absorbing and producing information must be made in terms of these multiple settings. When these are taken into account, the full capacity of the brain is infinitely extended beyond the total number of combinations and permutations of cellular and fiber interconnections. In fact, an entirely different formulation of the problem is indicated. On the proposed terms neither the subjective information nor its neural basis is necessarily restricted to any number of "bits," i.e., it is not necessarily quantized at all, but may involve all manner of continuous shades, and intergradations.

With regard to the total brain organization and its enormous efficiency, one could say that the inhibitory aspect of the facilitory set is perhaps even more important than the excitatory. If the hind leg of the decerebrate salamander is placed in an extreme position of protraction, thus facilitating the spinal centers for retraction, all other possible responses, e.g., protraction, adduction, abduction, inversion, eversion, and intermediate combinations are inhibited. Similarly, if the cerebral mechanisms are set for a specific activity, such as card sorting, all the thousands of other activities that might equally well be carried out in the same situation, but which are incompatible with the sorting process, are automatically excluded. Normally the brain does not get confused by activating mixtures of the thousands of settings at its command. Each setting somehow inhibits all other inappropriate excitation patterns.

One can think of the functional settings of the brain as being related to one another in tree-like fashion, each with the same central trunk, but each with an almost infinite array of possible distal ramifications. The motor set for the reaction time experiment, for example, may have subordinate branches, so to say, for movements of the hand or the foot and each of these members further can be preset for movement in a theoretically unlimited number of directions from any given starting posture. Another main branch for movements of the vocal apparatus can be preset to respond with any one of as many different words, phrases, and nonsense syllables as exist in however many languages the subject knows. Perhaps it would be more accurate and fruitful to picture the differentiation and interrelations of facilitory sets, not in terms of tree limbs and branches, but directly in terms of the potential postures and movements of the vertebrate body. The "postural sets" then have direct application to overt movement and, perhaps, more or less direct implication for the implicit operations of perception and thought processes, depending on the closeness or remoteness of these latter to motor adjustment.

MORPHOLOGICAL OVERLAP AND
FUNCTIONAL REINFORCEMENT

The physiological reinforcement obtained through overlap in fiber terminations is an important stabilizing factor in function, particularly in the preservation of organized activity after extensive nerve lesions. This principle is nicely illustrated in some experiments of Gray and Lissman (9, 10): If all the dorsal sensory roots of the spinal cord are transected in the adult toad, all walking is abolished. However, if only one, or to be safe, just two roots are left intact, it does not matter which two, the ambulatory pattern can still be evoked with all four limbs moving in the proper diagonal sequence. After more than two limbs are deafferented there begins a progressive loss of ambulatory coördination that increases with advancing stages of deafferentation. However, reminiscent of cortical mass action, it is the extent and not the site of deafferentation that is important.

By cutting the sensory and motor roots in various combinations, they found that the sensory feedback from any one limb helps to control the direction and timing of movement in all four limbs. This is true during each changing phase of the movement cycle of each limb. In addition there is feedback from the proprioceptors of the trunk that also reinforces the proper pattern of leg and trunk movement. Thus, the walking pattern of the entire trunk and four limbs tends to be reinforced as a whole from the separate movements of all the separate parts. The individual sensory roots transmit specific discharge patterns that spread through the full length of the cord on both sides. This tremendous overlap makes it possible to remove large fractions of the sensory input before the organization begins to fall apart.

We lack similarly clear evidence of this kind of thing in the higher centers. However, it is entirely conceivable that something of the sort is in part responsible for the fact that such large amounts of cortical tissue must often be removed to produce dysfunction and that in some situations it appears to be the quantity of cortex removed that counts regardless of its location. If multiple parts of a going cerebral excitation tend individually to reinforce all other parts and at the same time to inhibit incompatible patterns, many of the neural elements could be removed without destroying the organization of the whole. At least it becomes theoretically possible to account for much of the brain lesion data in these and related terms without relinquishing conventional fiber circuit concepts.

In this connection the brain lesion results also appear less embarrassing for connectivity theory when one views the engram as a co-function of facilitory set, as recently outlined (42), reinforcing expectancies and related high-level phases of cerebral activity rather than direct sensori-motor or sensory-sensory associations. In these terms the engram, even for the simplest of conditioned responses, becomes relatively complex and diffusely distributed through the cortical apparatus.

INTRAHEMISPHERIC ASSOCIATIONS

Our experimental preoccupation with possible new approaches to the physiology of integration has, in one sense, merely led into a series of blind alleys. On the positive side, however, the results give new confidence in the connectivity approach and a conviction that one is not misled, after all, in continuing to search for specific functions in the various centers and connecting fiber systems of the brain, i.e., specific functions at the analytic, neuronal level, not at the level of molar behavior. Much disagreement in the past on questions of cerebral localization and functional specificity stems from a failure to specify the exact level of functional organization to which reference is being made.

It should perhaps be emphasized that there is nothing in the foregoing to detract from the possibility of qualitative differences among nerve impulses, particularly with reference to synaptic transmission. One would infer merely that any such specific nerve energy phenomena would have to be superimposed upon the basic connectivity mechanisms, adding functional refinement and differentiation, but nevertheless operating within the connectivity framework.

In recent efforts to learn more about connectivity principles in perceptual integration, we have been putting to use the demonstrated functional independence of the two hemispheres in what we have come to call the "split-brain" preparation. This is an animal in which the brain has been split down the middle by section of the corpus callosum, the optic chiasma, and usually also the anterior and hippocampal commissures. Such animals, incidently, are indistinguishable from normal to casual examination. The callosum appears to be necessary for the transfer of perceptual discrimination and memory from one hemisphere to the other, but in line with clinical observations, its complete section does not seem to impair immediate perceptual capacities or motor coördination.

In these split-brain animals one can leave intact a whole hemisphere to maintain generalized background functions and to prevent incapacitating paralyses. Cortical lesion and correlated methods of analysis can then be applied to specific learning and. memory functions within the other single hemisphere. In the test hemisphere, instead of the customary small lesions in the critical area, one can use the converse approach, i.e., the greater part of the cortex can be removed to leave intact only the critical area one wishes to test. The functional tests must of course be unilateral.

We have only begun to explore these possibilities in studies on the isolated visual and isolated somatic cortex in the cat. As an important first step in the investigation of perceptual integration, we have tried to determine the extent to which perceptual learning and memory can be mediated by sensory cortical area alone and to what extent it is dependent upon more complex integrations involving the function of other cortical areas. When an island of cortex including the area for central vision is isolated in the manner shown in Figure 122, nearly all previously trained

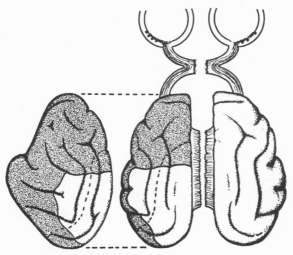

Fig. 122.—With chiasma and callosum sectioned as shown, isolation of left visual cortex in manner indicated severely impairs visual performance with corresponding (left) eye. Lateral tongue of cortex extending into auditory area is left intact to avoid damage to underlying optic radiation.

visual discriminations with the eye on the affected side are lost (Sperry and Myers, unpublished). The simplest discriminations, as between horizontal and vertical stripes, however, survive in the exceptional case and, if lost, can be retrained.

Preoperatively trained discriminations between a cross and a circle and between perfect and imperfect triangles can also be relearned by such animals, but the learning in the latter case fails to progress beyond the lower levels of our test scales for pattern discrimination (46). Preoperative discriminations between upright and inverted **V**'s are lost and cannot be relearned. Such cats tend to bump into objects in walking about a strange room and may have difficulty locating a piece of meat held at close range in front of them. They work slowly in the testing apparatus and will run only about half as many trials as before the cortical removal. These impairments are not evident when the mask over the non-test eye is switched to the operated side or removed entirely.

Degeneration in the lateral geniculate nucleus in these cases is not sufficiently greater on the operated side than on the nonoperated side to account for the functional difference. That the visual impairment is not a result of geniculostriate damage is supported by the results of removing the nonvisual portions of the cortex in two stages. When the first removal includes the temporal lobe and all areas adjacent to the visual island, sparing only the frontal region with somatic sensory and motor areas, the deficit is less severe than if the somatic areas are included. Such animals show definite impairment in visual performance but retain most of their preoperatively trained discriminations at a fairly high level, including that for upright and inverted **V**'s. Subsequent removal of the remaining frontal region, which is too distant to involve the already isolated geniculostriate system, produces an additional marked and permanent lowering of visual performance to approximately the level obtained by making the total removal in one stage. It would thus appear that the somatic areas of the cortex play some important role in visual discrimination.

The results are different for somesthetic discrimination. In this case we are finding good retention of previously trained discriminations and good learning of new discriminations with the only remaining cortex

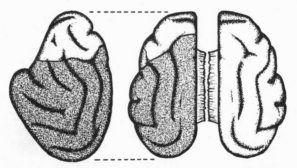

Fig. 123.—After isolation of small sector of left frontal cortex as shown, tactile discriminations with right forepaw are retained at high level and new ones are readily learned. Subsequent removal of remaining cortical island abolishes all discriminative performance with affected paw.

being the small amount shown in Figure 123 (Sperry and Stamm, unpublished). Apparently we are approaching a minimum here, because the most difficult discrimination task, involving choice between a smooth and a sandpaper surface, is not retained in the majority of cases and is relearned with difficulty. Also, an attempt to pare down the size of the remaining cortical island in one case so as to leave only the primary foreleg area, abolished all discriminative performance with the affected forepaw.

Possibly the greater functional efficiency of the isolated somatic cortex, as compared with that of the isolated visual cortex, can be attributed to the inclusion of the motor areas within the intact somesthetic island. At any rate, it would seem safe to infer that the cat is able to perceive, to some extent at least, with only a small island of cortex, and that widespread cortical integration is not essential for perceptual learning and memory. However, we are only just beginning to tangle with these latter problems and are in no position to foresee any definite answers.

REFERENCES

1 Akelaitis, A. J. Studies on the corpus callosum. VII. Study of language functions (tactile and visual lexia and graphia) unilaterally following sections of the corpus callosum. *J. Neuropath.*, 1943, *2*: 226–62.

2 Anokhin, P. Reports on the problem of centre and periphery in the physiology of nervous activity. Gorky, USSR: Gorky State Publishing House, 1935.

3 Bethe, A., and E. Fischer. Die Anpassungsfähigkeit (Plastizität) des Nervensystems. In A. Bethe, G. von Bergmann, G. Embden, and A. Ellinger (Eds.), *Handbuch der normalen und pathologischen Physiologe*. Vol. 15. Berlin: Verlag Von Julius Springer, 1931, pp. 1045–1130.

4 Bridgman, C. S., and K. U. Smith. Bilateral neural integration in visual perception after section of the corpus callosum. *J. comp. Neurol.*, 1945, *83*: 57–68.

5 Bykov, K. Versuche an Hunden mit Durchschneiderd des Corpus callosum. *Zbl. ges. Neurol. Psychiat.*, 1925, *39*: 199.

6 Dandy, W. E. Operative experience in cases of pineal tumor. *Arch. Surg., Chicago*, 1936, *33*: 19–46.

7 Goldstein, K. *The organism*. New York: American Book Co., 1939.

8 Gray, J. Aspects of animal locomotion. *Proc. roy. Soc., Ser. B.*, 1939, *128*: 28–61.

9 Gray, J., and H. W. Lissman. Further observations on the effect of deafferentation on the locomotory activity of amphibian limbs. *J. exp. Biol.*, 1946, *23*: 121–32.

10 ――――. The co-ordination of limb movements in the amphibia. *J. exp. Biol.*, 1946, *23*: 133–42.

11 Hebb, D. O. *The organization of behavior*. New York: Wiley, 1949.

12 Kappers, C. U. A. Principles of development of the nervous system (neurobiotaxis). In W. Penfield (Ed.), *Cytology and cellular pathology of the nervous system*. Vol. I. New York: Hoeber, 1932, pp. 45–89.

13 Lashley, K. S. Brain mechanisms and intelligence. Chicago: Univer. Chicago Press, 1929.

14 ———. The problem of cerebral organization in vision. *Biol. Symp.*, 1942, *7:* 301–22.

15 ———. In search of the engram. *Symp. Soc. exp. Biol.*, 1950, *4:* 454–82.

16 Lashley, K. S., K. L. Chow, and J. Semmes. An examination of the electrical field theory of cerebral integration. *Psychol. Rev.*, 1951, *58:* 123–36.

17 Maspes, P. E. Le syndrome expérimental ches l'homme de la section du splénium du corps calleux: Alexie visuelle pure hémianopsique. *Rev. neurol.*, 1948, *80:* 100–13.

18 Miner, N. Integumental specification of sensory neurons in the genesis of cutaneous local sign. Unpublished doctor's dissertation, Univer. Chicago, 1951.

19 Mishkin, M. Visual discrimination performance following partial ablations of the temporal lobe: II. Ventral surface vs. hippocampus. *J. comp. physiol. Psychol.*, 1954, *47:* 187–93.

20 Mishkin, M., and K. H. Pribram. Visual discrimination performance following partial ablations of the temporal lobe: I. Ventral vs. lateral. *J. comp. physiol. Psychol.*, 1954, *47:* 14–20.

21 Myers, R. E. The corpus callosum and hemispheric interaction. Unpublished doctor's dissertation, Univer. Chicago, 1955.

22 ———. Interocular transfer of pattern discrimination in cats following section of crossed optic fibers. *J. comp. physiol. Psychol.*, 1955, *48:* 470–73.

23 Piatt, J. Regeneration of the spinal cord in the salamander. *Anat. Rec.*, 1955, *121:* 412 (Abstract).

24 Smith, K. U. Learning and the associative pathways of the human cerebral cortex. *Science*, 1951, *114:* 117–20.

25 Sperry, R. W. The functional results of muscle transposition in the hind limb of the rat. *J. comp. Neurol.*, 1940, *73:* 379–404.

26 ———. The effect of crossing nerves to antagonistic muscles in the hind limb of the rat. *J. comp. Neurol.*, 1941, *75:* 1–19.

27 ———. Transplantation of motor nerves and muscles in the forelimb of the rat. *J. comp. Neurol.*, 1942, *76:* 283–321.

28 ———. Functional results of crossing sensory nerves in the rat. *J. comp. Neurol.*, 1943, *78:* 59–90.

29 ———. Effect of 180 degree rotation of the retinal field on visuomotor coordination. *J. exp. Zool.*, 1943, *92:* 263–79.

30 ———. Visuomotor coordination in the newt (*Triturus veridescens*) after regeneration of the optic nerve. *J. comp. Neurol.*, 1943, *79:* 33–55.

31 ———. Optic nerve regeneration with return of vision in anurans. *J. Neurophysiol.*, 1944, *7:* 57–69.

32 ——. The problem of central nervous reorganization after nerve regeneration and muscle transposition. *Quart. Rev. Biol.,* 1945, *20:* 311–69.

33 ——. Nature of functional recovery following regeneration of the oculomotor nerve in amphibians. *Anat. Rec.,* 1947, *97:* 293–316.

34 ——. Cerebral regulation of motor coordination in monkeys following multiple transection of sensorimotor cortex. *J. Neurophysiol.,* 1947, *10:* 275–94.

35 ——. Effect of crossing nerves to antagonistic limb muscles in the monkey. *Arch. Neurol. Psychiat., Chicago,* 1947, *58:* 452–73.

36 ——. Orderly patterning of synaptic associations in regeneration of intracentral fiber tracts mediating visuomotor coordination. *Anat. Rec.,* 1948, *102:* 63–75.

37 ——. Patterning of central synapses in regeneration of the optic nerve in teleosts. *Physiol. Zool.,* 1948, *21:* 351–61.

38 ——. Myoptic specificity in teleost motoneurons. *J. comp. Neurol.,* 1950, *93:* 277–88.

39 ——. Mechanisms of neural maturation. In S. S. Stevens (Ed.), *Handbook of experimental psychology.* New York: Wiley, 1951, pp. 236–80.

40 ——. Regulative factors in the orderly growth of neural circuits. *Growth,* 1951, Suppl. to *15:* 63–87.

41 ——. Neurology and the mind-brain problem. *Amer. Scientist,* 1952, *40:* 291–312.

42 ——. On the neural basis of the conditioned response. *Brit. J. anim. Behav.,* 1955, *3:* 41–44.

43 ——. Problems in the biochemical specification of neurons. In H. Waelsch (Ed.), *Biochemistry of the developing nervous system.* New York: Academic Press, 1955, pp. 74–84.

44 ——. Functional regeneration in the optic system. In W. F. Windle (Ed.), *Regeneration in the central nervous system.* Springfield, Ill.: Charles C Thomas, 1955, pp. 66–76.

45 Sperry, R. W., and N. Deupree. Functional recovery following alterations in nerve-muscle connections of fishes. *J. comp. Neurol.,* 1956, *106:* 143–58.

46 Sperry, R. W., and N. Miner. Pattern perception following insertion of mica plates into visual cortex. *J. comp. physiol. Psychol.,* 1955, *48:* 463–69.

47 Sperry, R. W., N. Miner, and R. E. Myers. Visual pattern perception following subpial slicing and tantalum wire implantations in the visual cortex. *J. comp. physiol. Psychol.,* 1955, *48:* 50–58.

48 Sperry, R. W., J. S. Stamm, and N. Miner. Relearning tests for interocular transfer following division of optic chiasma and corpus callosum in cats. *J. comp. physiol. Psychol.,* 1956, *49:* 529–33.

49 Weiss, P. Erregungsspezifität und Erregungsresonanz. *Ergebn. Biol.,* 1928, *3:* 1–151.

50 ——. Selectivity controlling the central-peripheral relations in the nervous system. *Biol. Rev.,* 1936, *11:* 494–531.

51 ———. Self-differentiation of the basic patterns of coordination. *Comp. Psychol. Monogr.*, 1941, *17:* No. 4 (Whole No. 88).

52 Wiersma, C. A. G. An experiment on the "Resonance Theory" of muscular activity. *Arch. néerl. Physiol.*, 1931, *16:* 337–45.

53 Wing, K. G., and K. U. Smith. The role of the optic cortex in the dog in the determination of the functional properties of conditioned reactions to light. *J. exp. Psychol.*, 1942, *31:* 478–96.

Austin H. Riesen

Plasticity of Behavior: Psychological Aspects

Original data reported in this paper are from investigations supported in part by research grants B-771 and B-772 from the National Institute of Neurological Diseases and Blindness of the National Institutes of Health, Public Health Service.

The evolution of behavior has brought increasing plasticity with increasing complexity. The correlation between plasticity and complexity is not logically necessary, and is far from perfect, but since it is a high correlation the biologist looks for common underlying factors. The system or systems which generate one may well foster the other. Organisms high in the phylogenetic series have developed an exceedingly complicated neurohumoral homeostasis. This development is somehow the physiological counterpart of the psychological trend. Science has entered the period of discovery which is leading to a more adequate explanation for the multiple correlation between neurohumoral complexity, behavioral complexity, and behavioral plasticity.

As a fundamental property of organisms, behavioral modifiability is observed under many conditions and recorded by an astounding variety of techniques. Students of modifiability are nonetheless valiantly seeking to reduce its many manifestations to one or a few simple principles. Whether this effort succeeds or not will depend to a large extent on what is discovered concerning the nature of changes in the nervous system that make alterations of behavior possible and necessary. In other words, we need to find those properties of behavior and those functions of neural transmission systems which insure that the very occurrence of behavior will produce a lasting consequence relative to the responses of the particular organism in question.

Complexities of behavior even in relatively simple organisms may confuse the issue of how to define learning and the still more difficult question of where and how to look for its structural correlates. Nevertheless, enough is known about the properties of behavioral plasticity so that the relationships that are known can give the biochemist or the neurophysiologist clues as to where to look first for the essential alterations. As one of the least understood, and hence most mysterious, of the modes of interaction between organism and environment, the mechanism whereby a lasting change is produced in the behavioral effect of a stimulus deserves a concerted focus of investigation. The psychologist is in a position to contribute a knowledge of critical events quantitatively specified. If he selects his examples with proper consideration for the tools available to men in other disciplines, he cannot fail to pinpoint the problem for them. In what follows I propose to take some steps in thus focusing attention on critical events and relations.

An experimenter who wishes to produce a lasting change in the behavioral effect of a stimulus thinks first of how he may control event-sequences in the environment. He selects stimuli whose effects on the organism he has already discovered. He arranges to present these stimuli in appropriate strengths, under appropriate temporal-spatial relationships, and with the organism in a predetermined state of nutrition and alertness. There exists an optimum range of values for each of these factors within which he tries to work. These ranges have been carefully determined for only a limited number of organisms. Interaction effects of different combinations of values have been measured for an extremely small percentage of the possible combinations. Yet, for purposes of the present discussion it will be necessary to select for careful consideration only a few of the known combinations that make the most difference.

Critical Time Relations in S-R Learning

The cue-reinforcement interval.—The classical conditioning procedure permits fairly accurate control over the time of onset of two central processes by means of the timing of external stimuli—about as accurate control as one can impose on an intact organism whose capacity for behavioral modification is under investigation. When we consider how rapidly a sensory event is transmitted to the primary projection area of the cortex, it is perhaps rather surprising that the optimum interval for the production of an associative modification is so long. To produce such a change with a high degree of efficiency, one does not delay the unconditioned stimulus merely by an interval of a few milliseconds but, rather, for a period of just under a half-second. What has happened to the neural consequences of the stimulus-to-be-conditioned by the time the second stimulus is producing its effects in the central nervous system? This is a crucial question which neurophysiologists should be urged to answer.

Figure 124 presents a summary of several recent studies of this interval to show that results are consistent. Two of these studies measured galvanic skin responses (19, 35) and two, eyelid responses (15, 23) of human subjects. One of each is a trace-conditioning experiment; the others used delayed-conditioning procedures. Eyelid conditioning in monkey and dog requires the same arrangement of the CS–UCS interval, according to all evidence available. In the data for this figure the eyelid responses were measured after 50 to 60 conditioning trials, the galvanic responses after only 5 or 23 trials. Slopes of these curves must therefore be expected to differ. The important point is that, whether measured early or late in the conditioning process, the efficient interval is the same.

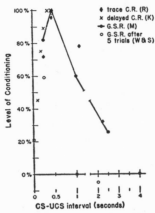

Fig. 124.—The relative effectiveness of varying CS–UCS intervals in eyelid and GSR conditioning.

In discrimination learning procedures the experimenter does not control the (unknown) stimuli that occasion a selective response by the organism. He is limited to controlling the interval between the organism's "spontaneous" action in a predesignated manner and the onset of a differential reinforcement. Whatever neural processes lead to the response being measured are therefore not under control and are presumably quite variable from trial to trial. This is in contrast to the use of an adequate eliciting stimulus, as in classical CR procedures. Under some conditions, then, and particularly in "sophisticated" animals and man, there seems to be little relationship between rate of learning and delay of reinforcement. When the learning task involves naive subjects, a delay-of-reinforcement curve shows a *decay* segment strikingly similar to that found for classical conditioning.

Figure 125 shows such data for rats (9) and for two chimpanzees (24). The associative mechanism rapidly approaches failure as intervals exceed 1 or 2 sec., whether a conditioning or a discrimination learning procedure is employed. The discriminated stimuli in Grice's study with rats were black vs. white alleys, those for the chimpanzees were red vs. green windows. Both studies also showed that if special "meanings" were previously associated with the relevant stimuli, learning efficiency increased and the deleterious effect of a delay interval could be markedly reduced.

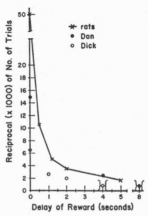

Fig. 125.—The delay-of-reward gradient in visual discrimination learning by rats or by "naive" chimpanzees.

The data of these two figures cut across mammalian species, sensory modalities, and kinds of response indicators. They provide a general confirmation of the principle of contiguity. But the burning question remains: What neural process consequent to the stimulation whose effects will be modified is contiguous with what other neural event that regularly produces the response? Electrophysiological and biochemical studies of the central correlates of auditory or visual stimuli should reveal the location and the nature of processes whose temporal characteristics correspond (i.e., are slow enough) to their interval of effectiveness in conditioning.

The stabilization interval after new learning.—A second example of critical time relations in conditioning comes from studies of the so-called "consolidation interval" that immediately follows the pairing of the stimulus to be conditioned with the originally effective stimulus. The acquisition of a new behavioral effect of any given stimulus is susceptible to drastic interference by events that follow learning "trials." Clinical neurologists have long known that a person who has suffered a blow on the head may not remember events that just preceded the blow. This is a crude source of data. The evidence has been refined by Duncan (6) in his experiment with rats. His animals avoided pain from a charged grid if they moved from a black compartment into a white one within a short safe period after they were put into the apparatus. Different groups of rats received electroconvulsive shock following each training trial, either 20, 40, 60 sec., 4 min., 15 min., 1 hr., 4 hr., or 14 hr. after the animal ran from the grid. In Figure 126 we see the average number of anticipatory runs (shock avoided) made by each group of rats. For each group in which electroconvulsive shock was given less than an hour after a trial, learning was depressed. Control groups were run to ascertain whether or not this result was merely a negative reinforcement (punishment) effect. Such an effect appears to account only for a portion of the depression at the shortest interval.

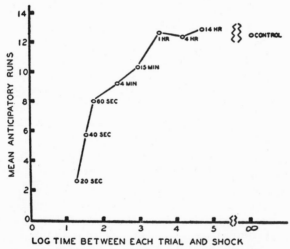

Fig. 126.—The data of Duncan (6) on the interfering effects of electroshock on learning for different intervals between a learning trial and electroconvulsive shock. Each point on the curve is determined by a different group.

THE QUESTION OF STIMULUS-STIMULUS MODIFICATION

The evidence on temporal relations between the critical stimuli, and on the "consolidation" process following the pairing of such stimuli, gives us a quantitative description of certain conditions which must be fulfilled if learning is to occur. Stimulus-response (S-R) behavior modification furnished the experimental paradigm for the investigation of these quantitative laws. Because of the greater ease of control and the facility with which the dependent variable can be recorded, the S-R learning situation has received by far the most emphasis in the experimental psychology of learning. Many functional relations between variation in stimuli have been worked out. Stimulus generalization, stimulus equivalence, concept formation, and transfer of training have been studied as functions of a large variety of stimulus variables. Response strength, response generalization, and other behavioral variables amenable to investigation by the application of different methods of measuring muscular or glandular activity are being studied in detail.

Neuropsychologists (12, 18) have pointed out that there should be nothing sacred about the modifiability of S-R neural sequences as against S-S sequences. If the temporal contiguity between sensorimotor neural events modifies subsequent responses, there is no obvious reason for the absence of modification when two or more sensory processes occur together. It is, however, clearly a much more difficult problem to measure such a modification. It has been necessary to use some behavioral indicator for investigating the results of any change in sensory neural sequences. This kind of measurement always raises the question of whether direct effects on the response measured or earlier sensory modifications were critical. Furthermore, theorists find it easy to propose some hypothetical unmeasured response that may have intervened to mediate the learning. This leads to the claim that so-called sensory preconditioning experiments are inconclusive as evidence for S-S association.

What appears to be crucial evidence for an S-S mechanism in classical and avoidance conditioning has been obtained by Whatmore and Kleitman (34). They extirpated the sensory cortex to which the unconditioned stimulus was projected in their dogs, thereby eliminating the conditioned response. Hemispherectomy which removed the sensory and/or motor cortex involved in other components in the conditioning procedure (the CS and the CR) showed that these areas were not crucial in maintaining the conditioning.

Plasticity in the Visual Sensory System

Experiments in a number of laboratories (cf. 3, 7) are currently providing evidence that S-S modification may be highly characteristic of the early life of mammals. Hebb (12) has already presented detailed considerations of theoretical and experimental arguments to this effect. New data make the conclusion more and more certain that the speed with which particular combinations of sensory inputs can be incorporated into behavior depends upon the degree of prior exposure to such combinations.

A series of studies on infant chimpanzees by Chow, Nissen, Semmes,

TABLE 35

Observations on visual function and structure in dark-reared chimpanzees

	Subject and darkroom period (i.e., age in months)				
Response	Kandy (140) 0–3 mo.	Debi (136) 0–7 mo.	Faik (101) 8–24 mo.	Alfalfa (120) 0–21 mo.	Snark (85) 0–33 mo.
Pupillary reflexes					
Spontaneous nystagmus	none				
Disc pallor	none	temporary	progressive	permanent	progressive
Subsequent loss of pupillary reflexes	none	none	partial	none	total
Follows objects	16 days	13 days	43 days		temporary
Fear of strangers	4 mo.	4 mo.	no. discr.	3 mo.	no. discr.

Animals 140, 136, and 101 were continuously in darkness. Animals 120 and 85 had brief exposures totaling 5 min. per day to age 16 months and 10 to 15 min. per day for the remainder of the light-deprivation period. Absence of an entry in the table indicates the presence of the response at the end of deprivation. The course of the manifestation of pallor is indicated for the period *after* removal from the darkroom. Days or months are also counted from the time of removal into daylight.

and myself, at the Yerkes Laboratories of Primate Biology, has been directed at the determination of how early stimulation of the visual system affects the structure and function of that system. We have found it necessary to break down this general problem into several subproblems (25). We approached it originally by imposing drastic restriction of visual stimulation. This produced extreme dysfunction, by the standard of comparison of normal primate vision. It proved difficult to evaluate the several sources of differences in function or the sites of their physiological substrate. With full daylight stimulation the vision of these early subjects improved, but it never caught up with that of normal animals.

Retina and optic nerve after light deprivation.—We are using a series of five baby chimpanzees to study optic nerve atrophy as it is related to length of light deprivation. With 3 and 7 months of deprivation, respectively, two infants recovered from any such atrophy as may have been produced. Pallor of the optic disc disappeared after 6 to 18 months in Debi. Table 35 summarizes the results with subjects in this series. Sixteen months is a sufficient light-deprivation period, even when begun after normal development to age 8 months, as in Faik, to produce irreversible changes in the ganglion cell layer and optic nerve. Three subjects showed

TABLE 36

A comparison of retinal ganglion cell densities in rabbits living
in daylight or in complete darkness from birth to ten weeks

		Dry weight	PNP fraction	Protein
Rabbits living	Mean	0.78	0.47	0.31
in daylight	SD	0.057	0.055	0.027
Rabbits in total	Mean	0.16	0.00	0.16
darkness	SD	0.042	0.029	0.027

Data from Brattgård (2). Weights are in 10^{-9} mg/u^3 (milligrams
per cubic micron).

continued pallor of the disc after 6 years or more.* Brattgård (2) reports
a parallel finding in rabbits, to the effect that total light deprivation produces atrophy of the retinal ganglion cells. His techniques, which employed X-ray microradiography of the individual cells, provided an assay
of their protein content. Drastic reduction of cell density and the disappearance of the pentose nucleoprotein fraction were found.

One interpretation of these results is that this degeneration of ganglion cells is an example of transneuronal degeneration akin to, and in addition to, the degeneration seen in the next higher order of neurons of
the visual system, those of the lateral geniculate body. I look with favor
on the suggestion (2, 4, 5) that the disturbance is probably related to metabolic insufficiency associated with drastic reduction of stimulation. An
example of the extent and quality of the alteration to be found in rabbits
after 10 weeks in total darkness is given in Table 36, taken from Brattgård's excellent monograph. Additional dark-reared rabbits brought into
daylight at 10 weeks of age showed partial recovery and increased variability in cell densities at 13 weeks of age.

The changes in the PNP (pentose neucleoprotein) fraction in retinal
ganglion cells and in other cells of the central nervous system (2) are so
highly susceptible to *recent* prior stimulation (Table 37) that they hardly
seem to point directly to the mechanism of a durable memory. It is nevertheless encouraging to find a biochemical structural change that responds
promptly to neural function, for this kind of change has until now been
sought with great hope and little success. There is somewhat more reason
to see a promise here of a basis for immediate memory, which in turn

* W. J. Knauer, M.D., W. J. Knauer, Jr., M.D., and Frank W. Newell, M.D. have
evaluated the ophthalmoscopic appearance of the retinae of these and many control
subjects and have performed enucleations. Details of the histological findings will be
reported separately.

TABLE 37

The chemical composition of retinal ganglion cells from eight-month-old rabbits under different conditions of stimulation

	Dark-adapted							
	Stimulated for 6 hr.		Dark-adapted for 10 min.		Dark-adapted for 3 hr.		Dark-adapted for 3 hr. then stimulated for 3 hr.	
	Mean	SD	Mean	SD	Mean	SD	Mean	SD
Total dry weight	0.98	0.137	0.75	0.114	0.53	0.023	0.73	0.027
PNP Fraction	0.49	0.100	0.28	0.118	0.05	0.029	0.24	0.034
Protein	0.49	0.061	0.47	0.077	0.48	0.019	0.49	0.031

From Brattgård (2). Weights in 10^{-9} mg/u^3 (milligrams per cubic micron).

might prove to be an essential step toward a consolidation of some more lasting neural alteration. An examination of Brattgård's data reveals stable protein density to be a variable that responds more slowly to degree of stimulation than does the PNP fraction and it also retains the effects for a longer period.

Vision after patterned and unpatterned light.—We customarily think of the "educative process" in higher primates as one that results in the gradual accumulation of the fruits of earlier experience over the months and the years. Actually, our understanding of how prior learning supplies building blocks for new integrations and discriminations is growing only very gradually. Harlow (11) has provided highly significant evidence that monkeys do "learn to learn." At an earlier age and at a more rudimentary level of discrimination, the cats and the chimpanzees with which we experiment are showing us that a common, everyday, heterogeneously patterned visual environment provides learning opportunities that rather profoundly affect the subsequent discriminations of which the subject may be capable.

Before I draw the comparisons between the effects of different kinds and degrees of early exposure to patterned and unpatterned visual stimulation, let me present a single example in some detail. Our chimpanzee infant, Chow, was separated from its mother shortly after birth on February 5, 1950. On the fifth day after birth it was put into the darkroom, and ten days later daily exposure to diffuse light was begun. It lived 90 min. each day with its head encased in a Plexiglas dome. Cardboard mailing tubes surrounded its arms and allowed some freedom of movement of the arms within the cylinders. Ventilation of the space under the dome was provided through many openings in the supporting surface at the back of the head.

At the age of seven and one-half months Chow was very gradually, over a period of ten days, given more and more light in the form of increased general illumination of the room. We made repeated observations of the infant's visual responses and general behavior during this time. The animal showed lively pupillary constriction to light, both simple and consensual. There were irregular and recurrent episodes of spontaneous nystagmus with both eyes open, and there was a cover nystagmus with either eye. Immediately, and for some days, there was a strong divergent and a slight vertical heterotropia (or squint). Sudden momentary increases of illumination produced a startle response.

There was initially no eyeblink to movement in the visual field or to a threatened blow toward the face. Slow approach and mild contact of the face produced a startle response. Visual fixation and pursuit of objects were conspicuously absent. With repeated testing "pursuit" of a moving light in the darkroom was first seen after 24 hr. of low general room illumination. This consisted of a series of refixations rather than pursuit in the usual sense. After 50 hr. in light (approximately 25 waking hours) the first series of jerky refixations to a moving light in a daylighted room appeared. At this same stage we saw the first sure pursuit in the revolving drum (optokinetic nystagmus), where earlier observations were rendered ambiguous by "spontaneous nystagmus" intermingled with roving movements of the eyes.

On the ninth day we observed the first eyeblinks to movement in the visual field. Hereafter for about two weeks this response occurred on about half the six trials given each day. The response increased in magnitude and frequency until movement toward the face and across the visual field produced gross startle responses on 80 to 100 per cent of trials.

During the second and third weeks we saw an unmistakable predominant use of the right eye in fixation, with occasional use of the other, and with a gradually reducing degree of exotropia. Chow continued to show startle when we approached its face slowly to the point of contact, using either our hand or an object, such as the feeding bottle. It showed no awareness of the feeding bottle until it recognized it by touch.

Chow did not show any emotional disturbance on the tenth day when we moved it and its crib into the daylighted nursery. (But neither did our other subjects which were moved without the gradual transition, so long as their tactual environment remained familiar.) Like our other pattern-vision–deprived or light-deprived animals, Chow was fed occasionally by

a total stranger and showed *no* emotional upset. This is a strikingly different reaction from that of normally reared infants of comparable age.
The result suggests that the common reaction to strangers may be strictly
visual, at least when other sources of stimulation are not grossly deviant
from the usual.

On day 11 Chow gave its first fixation and jerky pursuit responses to
a bright red object (prior pursuit responses were to a light and the object
was ineffective). In three more days Chow responded in like manner to a
person's head and face moving from side to side at the end of the crib.
By day 17 Chow was maintaining fixation on a nonmoving face. Episodes
of the spontaneous nystagmus had meanwhile gradually reduced in frequency so that they were apparent less than one-fifth of the time and entirely absent for long intervals.

During the ten days of gradually increasing illumination Chow took
bottle feedings three times daily while held in Annie-the-nursemaid's lap,
just as it had in the darkroom. Then we began to feed Chow in a chair-
table unit. It was still finding the bottle by feel until, on the nineteenth
day, Chow began to follow it with eye- and head movements. Soon it was
protruding its lips at the "sight" of the bottle, *but* the animal also did
this if I moved my hand or a square white card in similar fashion in front
of it.

Beginning on day 12 training on an avoidance response was begun.
Twice daily, during one of several interruptions in the bottle feeding, a
"shock-plaque" was held in front of Chow for 5 sec. at a distance of 40 cm.
from its face. The plaque was then advanced toward the animal until an
electrode made contact with its chin. The shock delivered was sufficient to
produce whimpering and some generalized emotional disturbance, but
Chow resumed feeding quite promptly when the bottle nipple was put in
its mouth.

Initially, and after each of the first 5 experiences, no observable response occurred to the presentation of the plaque despite its large size and
unique markings. The plywood disc was 38 cm. in diameter, painted in
vertical yellow and black stripes, each 5 cm. wide. After 6 shocks (on trial
7) some sign of general increase in tonus occurred. After 8 shock experiences anticipatory emotional disturbance appeared upon presentation,
prior to actual delivery of the shock. The first effort to pull away from the
plaque occurred after 19 shock experiences. A normally reared control
animal (no. 101) of the same age showed the emotional response after
two trials with shock, and the turning away after trial 4.

This gave us a crude measure of the visually deprived animal's ability
to utilize a gross visual cue in avoidance conditioning. From this point we

attempted discriminative conditioning. We interrupted bottle feedings 12 times daily. During 2 or 3 of these interruptions we showed the shock-plaque, following it by shock if avoidance did not occur. On other occasions four other plaques were used and were always followed after 5 sec. by the food-bottle. The "positive" plaques differed from the shock disc in any one of four respects: size, color (and brightness), direction of stripes, or shape.

Table 38 shows a comparison of the numbers of errors made by Chow and by control infant no. 101 with each of the plaques before a criterion of three errorless feeding sessions (18 errorless trials) was reached. For the first four plaques an error was a false avoidance response; for the shock-disc it was a false approach. Compared with the normal control, Chow required more than twice as many trials and made more than double the number of total errors. Whereas no. 101 ceased to avoid the various "positive" discs after approximately equal numbers of trials, Chow began to make food grunts to the horizontal stripes relatively early (on the ninth

TABLE 38

Number of errors (false avoidance or approach) before performance at the criterion level

Plaque with critical cue	Chow (125)	Faik (101)	Lad (119)
Horizontal	5	16	6
Red	16	17	6
Small	44	13	0
Square	93	20	5
Shock-plaque	9	9	35
Total errors	167	75	52

feeding) but was very late in discriminating the shape of the disc (square vs. circle). A third animal for which data are given in the table is a control that until 7 months of age received only 90 min. of light daily in an artificially lighted room. It saw room patterns, feeding bottle, itself, and caretaker. It received no more light than did Chow, but it made only a third as many errors altogether, most of them failures to avoid the shock-plaque. We will examine other data for Lad (no. 119) a little later in an overview of findings on all subjects.

Having completed these discrimination learning tests, we now proceeded toward a determination of Chow's visual acuity. Retinoscopy at 1 m. had shown a far-sighted index, +2.50, during the discrimination conditioning when Chow reached nine months of age. Acuity tests were done as rapidly as feasible, but the infant was in its eleventh month before a reasonably adequate result could be obtained. The discrimination between horizontal and vertical striations was pushed gradually down to require the resolution of finer striations. Chow continued to differentiate the stimuli down to the limit of our series of discs: striations of 1/3 mm. This is equivalent to resolution of a visual angle of 3 min., which provided assurance that acuity was not grossly defective. (Spence [29] obtained threshold angles of 1 to 4 min. in young chimpanzees and children three to five years of age.)

Throughout these postrestriction months Chow showed steady decrease in the frequency of the episodes of spontaneous nystagmus. Binocular fixation and convergence improved. Chow was nearly a year old—three and one-half months out of the darkroom—before it could converge to an object brought into contact with its upper lip. It still maintained such convergence only briefly.

TABLE 39

Presence (+) or absence (−) of responses on first visual tests at seven months of age

| Response | Condition of rearing to age 7 months and animal number | | | | | |
| | Total darkness | Diffuse light | | Diffuse light with fixation spot | Holder only | Freemoving |
	136	125	142	168	148	119
Pupillary reflex	+	+	+	+	+	+
Startle to sudden light	−	+	+	−	+	+
Optokinetic	?	?(3)*	?(20)*	+	+	+
"Spontaneous" nystagmus	+	+	+	+	−	−
Cover nystagmus	+	+	+	+	+	−
Heterotropia	+	+	+	+	+	−

Animal no. 136 was brought from total darkness into normal daylight at this age. All other subjects had received 90 min. of light per day, three of them through the diffusing dome, the other two in a moderately illuminated room. One of the latter (holder only) was restricted in the same animal holder as was used for the animals receiving diffuse light.

* Numbers in parentheses designate days on which the optokinetic response was first unmistakably observed, following removal of the two infants from the deprivation conditions to normal visual environments.

I have gone into these earlier observations on Chow in case-history detail. Two other chimpanzee infants have given essentially the same results. One of these, however, is so recently out of the darkroom that not all the phases of testing are completed.

Five infants have been followed for from six months to six years after they were reared under four different conditions of light exposure. Chow

TABLE 40

The day of first appearance of recognition responses following move into normal visual environment

Recognition response	Condition of rearing and animal number					
	Total darkness	Diffuse light		Diffuse light with fixation spot	Holder only	Freemoving
	(136)	(125)	(142)	(168)	(148)	(119)
Pursuit of object	13	11	13	9	+	+
Fixation of person	30	17	13	11	+	+
Mouth approach to bottle	27	19	20	11	11	+
Bottle discriminated	48	67	49	50	33	20
Fear of strange object	33	35	38	66	56	298
Fear of unfamiliar person	169	157	never		63	298

Plus sign indicates occurrence of the item before termination of the experimental treatment.

was one of these five. All received 90 min. of light daily from birth to seven months of age. Chow and Kora received only diffuse light; Wenka could look at a black target which intermittently approached and receded, and in darkness could view a pair of blinking "stars"; Mita was supine in the holder and could see ceiling, walls, and light source, and moving persons. Lad was free to live a normal cage life, except that it was in darkness all but 90 min. of the 24-hr. day. The results on first visual test at seven months of age are given in Table 39, along with those for Debi (136), which was in total darkness to that age. (The chimpanzee of seven months is comparable in general maturational level to a human infant of ten months [26].)

Lad, the free-moving animal, was scarcely distinguishable from a normal animal at seven months in its visually guided responses except that it did not show the avoidance of a strange object or the preference for familiar persons that was typical of a score or more of "normal" nursery-reared infants. The "holder only" animal was considerably less advanced in visual development. In Tables 39, 40, and 41 this intermediate performance is shown in comparison with the better responses of Lad and the generally, but not universally, more retarded progress shown by the animals from the "diffuse light" conditions.

For the animals without prior exposure to room patterns a minimum of nine days (approximately a hundred hours) of such exposure was necessary before any selective response (fixation) to such patterns appeared. Recognition behavior in a more discriminative sense developed only after many additional days of exposure (Table 40). When the subjects first approached their feeding bottles with heads moving forward, mouths open, and lips protruding, this was considered the initial "recognition" of the bottle. For several weeks, however, the same response could be elicited by a gray cardboard mailing tube, a person's hand, a square white card, or even a square black card. This result suggests a very broad generalization gradient along several dimensions. The fourth item (bottle discriminated) in Table 40 indicates the day of appearance of significantly less response to each of these four objects than to the feeding bottle.

Fear of strange objects or unfamiliar persons appears "spontaneously" in the nursery-reared infants at the Yerkes Laboratories. After the third and fourth months such fear becomes increasingly prominent until the infants are two years old or more. Our experimental subjects began to show fear of strange objects placed in their cribs early in the second month (age eight to nine months), and it was five months when Chow and Debi (no. 125, 136) avoided unfamiliar persons and went to familiar ones. The testing procedures demanded reliance on visual cues. The data on this test are incomplete for Wenka and Lad (168, 119). Wenka is still too young. Lad showed no preference after 24 days in the normal surroundings. Lad was then not tested until 298 days, at which time it gave clear-cut differential responses. It had developed the reputation in the nursery for having strong preferences for certain individuals. Kora (142) was an unusual chimpanzee youngster in that it always solicited play from any person available. It died of meningitis at two years and nine months of age.

In contrast with this long-delayed appearance of visual recognition in our experimental subjects, one sees very rapid identification of new objects or new faces in mature animals. Earlier I cited the comparison between Chow and a normal seven-month-old in their rate of learning to avoid the shock-plaque. There is much evidence that an "experienced" chimpanzee will discriminate a new human face as quickly as a person can. The integration of such a complex visual form demands an astonishing sensory associative efficiency. Whether the memory for such a spatio-temporal complex can be said to develop in one trial depends on our definition of "trial." Standardized experimental procedures must be brought to bear on this question, and here Professor Harlow's techniques for investigating "learning to learn" should provide one very definitive approach to a developmental study of form vision. It needs to be applied with stimuli varying along readily specified dimensions to subjects whose prior experience along such dimensions has been controlled.

The increase in associative efficiency that comes with the prior use of certain stimulus dimensions must not be attributed solely to sensory-sensory integration. I stress the sensory-sensory aspect because until recently it has been neglected. Learning theorists have lumped complex spatiotemporal patterns of energy in with simple clicks and light flashes to call any of these that are reproducible a "stimulus." This has greatly confused the neuropsychological issues. If we stuck to the newer emphasis on S-S combinations and sequences, we would still be guilty of oversimplification. I believe that any stimulus complex that has been discriminated previously by an organism still tends to arouse orienting and recognition behavior which in turn supplies new sensory input. Central correlates of these processes must certainly lose identifiability in terms of either stimulus or response units. The psychologist is not equipped to identify them directly. He therefore speculates about central autonomous processes as well as cell assemblies and phase sequences, all of which are sometimes under sensory control and sometimes not, with degree of susceptibility varying from moment to moment and even more significantly from stage to stage in the history of the organism as it moves from naive infancy to experienced maturity.

Some anomalies of oculomotor coördination.—Without a patterned visual environment in early infancy the experimental subjects failed to progress beyond infantile types of eyemovement (14, 17). In approximately the fourth month they began to show the maladaptive "spontaneous" nystagmus. At no time during the deprivation period were they capable of sustained *binocular* fixation. Heterotropia not unlike that of the newborn, usually divergent and with a moderate and variable vertical component, persisted until the animals had lived some weeks or even longer in the normal visual environment. Binocular fixation and convergence improved gradually whereas spontaneous nystagmus and heterotropia occurred with decreasing frequency. Table 41 indicates the course of this improvement in terms of improving adequacy of convergence to an approaching object or light.

Where exposure to pattern was prevented either by darkness or diffuse light for seven months or longer, occasional bursts of nystagmus and brief periods of strabismus have persisted. Infant no. 140, in darkness from birth to 3 months, showed an esotropia or cross-eyed squint which disappeared by 5 months. Later, for a short time at 15 months, exotropia occurred episodically, followed by what was thereafter a completely normal binocular performance on all our tests. All infants brought into daylight conditions at 7 months started with alternation of fixation and exotropia.

TABLE 41

Number of days in normal visual environment (after age seven months) until convergence eyemovements could be elicited

Eyemovements	Condition of rearing and animal number					
	Total darkness	Diffuse light		Diffuse light with fixation spot	Holder only	Freemoving
	(136)	(125)	(142)	(168)	(148)	(119)
First convergence	58	40	59	5	8	+
to 5 in.	76	74	59	17	40	+
to 3 in.	93	124	107	63	82–225	+
to lip contact	117	131	385–655	86	301	9

Animal 148 continued to show a strong divergent strabismus with alteration of fixation, and it is doubtful that is would ever achieve the most stringent test for convergence.

It was with a view of minimizing anomalies of fixation that animal no. 168 was given special visual targets during the seven-month diffuse light period. In the darkroom it could look at either one of a pair of blinking "stars," and during the 90 min. under the dome it could fixate a black circular target which intermittently approached and receded. The animal did not utilize these targets as much as we hoped it might. It usually slept part of the time under the dome, but we also observed, by temporarily converting the target in the dome into a peephole, that the subject looked at this intermittently. Occasionally there was binocular fixation, but more frequently there was exotropia with either eye fixating. Bursts of nystagmus occurred, sometimes jerky and sometimes pendular, and after some minutes the lids began to close unless noise or tactual stimulation was given to rearouse the subject. We used a Snooperscope in the darkroom. The eyes remained in slightly divergent position in total darkness, and we rarely saw nystagmus until we turned the blinking "stars" back on, when its frequency increased. (Each star was on for 2 sec. and off 1 sec.) We were never sure that Wenka was successful in fixating these lights. During the seventh month under the dome Wenka was able to hold binocular fixation of the peephole for 2 or 3 sec. in frequently recurring episodes. Conjugate roving eyemovements, monocular jerks, and bursts of nystagmus also continued. When Wenka finally came out into normal surroundings at seven months, it performed just like Chow and Kora and Debi had. Wenka was quite avisual. The comparisons in Tables 40 and 41 do indicate that this subject had some advantage over the others in developing fixation skills.

Monocular "blindness" after monocular form deprivation.—Could these results, this failure of the animals to respond to visual excitation, be a consequence of some motivational quirk, a general visual inattention, or a displaced "cathexis" toward other stimuli? Could the difficulty lie in an inability to make appropriate responses? We have recently obtained good evidence that the form blindness is not an artifact of motivational origin, nor a lack of ability to respond. Chow and Nissen (3) with the chimpanzee, and Riesen, Kurke, and Mellinger (27, 28) with kittens, have shown that these same results are produced *monocularly* in animals that are well motivated and able to utilize the input from the other eye. When one eye is deprived of form stimulation and the other is regularly exposed to room patterns, the usual equivalence does not develop. A discrimination habit learned through either eye remains specific to that eye. The infant chimpanzee, Sally, for example, was put into the darkroom at 1 week of age. Five weeks later the animal was started on a monocular exposure schedule. The left eye received diffused light for 90 min. daily, the right being covered by a patch while the animal was in the dome. With the left eye covered, the right eye was exposed for 90 min. to the patterned light of the nursery. A horizontal-vertical discrimination training procedure was started at 16 weeks, the left eye exposed to the striated plaque. With this eye open there was no blinking to an approaching object, no recognition of the milk bottle, no following of a moving pencil. Sally learned the H-V discrimination habit in 450 trials, exclusive of 50 criterional trials on which performance was better than 90 per cent cor-

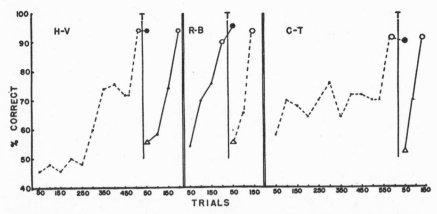

Fig. 127.—(From Chow and Nissen, 3.) Successive habits learned monocularly by an infant chimpanzee after exposure of one eye to patterned light and the other to diffused light. Single vertical lines indicate the beginning of interocular transfer tests. Double vertical lines mark the beginning of each new discrimination. *H-V*, horizontal versus vertical striations; *R-B*, red versus blue squares; *C-T*, circle versus triangle. Performance with the diffused-light eye is indicated by the broken line. There is no immediate transfer in either direction.

rect. At this point Dr. Chow tested for transfer. He exposed each eye alternately in blocks of 10 trials given 20 trials per day for five days. Performance with the left eye continued above 90 per cent while on trials with the right eye exposed performance remained at a chance level. With continued training Sally learned this habit using the second eye after 150 trials (Fig. 127). A color discrimination and a form discrimination also failed to show immediate interocular transfer.

Control infants of comparable age showed immediate interocular transfer, as did one infant to which patterned light had been given for 90 min. daily to each eye separately. Two additional experimental infants, reared as Sally had been, gave results similar to those for Sally, i.e., they showed no immediate transfer, but there were savings in the numbers of trials needed for learning with the second eye. Norma learned a color discrimination with one eye and a horizontal-vertical discrimination with the other eye concurrently and failed to transfer these in either direction.

Our results with young cats (28) are illustrated in Figure 128. Cat P-1 was given only alternating monocular visual exposure, and cat P-3 received patterned light in the "training eye" and diffuse light in the "test eye." Training of both animals in form discrimination began at the age of three months. For cat P-3 learning with the test eye exposed required as many trials as did the initial learning. Earlier results (27) on cats given

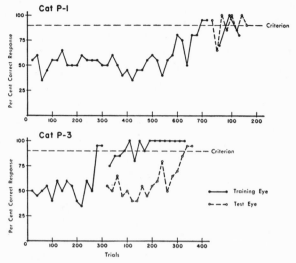

Fig. 128.—Interocular transfer tests showing a high degree of transfer (cat P-1) after early monocular alternating exposure to room patterns and lack of transfer (cat P-3) from training eye to test eye when the test eye has received prior exposure only to diffused light.

all training at a more advanced age showed "savings" with the second eye which reflected the fact that initial training required many more trials.

What is the underlying neurophysiological explanation of these data? We know from other evidence that central excitation from each eye may be relatively independent. Fusion of certain combinations of binocular stimulation is extremely difficult or impossible. There are individuals that do not achieve fusion even under ideal conditions. Binocular cff thresholds are surprisingly little different from monocular thresholds (30, 31). Sherrington chose to discount the slight differences that he obtained, and that more recent work has shown to be real, and to conclude that ocular fusional processes were psychic (or mental) rather than physiological. I choose to think of them as physiological, but requiring a rather high order of neural integration, a portion of which must be developed through stimulation with patterned light.

Discussion: Ontogenesis of Form Vision

In higher mammals form vision is a cortical function that requires activation of projection fibers in and beyond the striate cortex or other primary receiving stations. The conclusion seems inescapable that the form blindness of our experimental animals is related to an inadequate development of the function of this projection system. The interocular transfer studies of Chow and Nissen separate the form-vision mechanisms from reflex-like fixation responses mediated through the midbrain. Inadequacies at the level of fixation reflexes are not necessarily correlated with degree of form blindness.

I conceive of the development of form vision as requiring a sensory-sensory integration that involves learning according to a contiguity principle. My basic premise is in this respect the same as that of Hebb (12). Such development, the evidence reviewed above indicates, must await differential excitation from contours, corners, and edges. These insure that certain loci in the retina, and hence certain cells in the projection areas, are maximally active while others remain relatively inactive. When there is consistency and repetition in the patterns of these loci, sensory-sensory conditioning takes place. The probability of the participation of certain cells in an activation sequence increases, and that of other cells remains the same or decreases. Some relatively permanent structural modifications must result which register the effects of, and *constitute*, the intrasensory associative patterning. Hebb has gone to some pains to develop neuropsychological constructs which are applicable to simultaneous and sequential patterns of this kind.

Since S-S learning is more difficult to measure than S-R learning, psychology with a behavioristic orientation tends to minimize consideration of it or to deny it. Hull's concept of afferent neural interaction would be broad enough to include it, but Hull would prefer to handle any modification of sensory-sensory relationships by inserting a hypothetical response between Ss to provide S-R-S sequences. Lashley (18) has argued that there is not time for all the responses that would be necessary to account for fast-moving behavior in accordance with an S-R-S schema. One reason that sensory-sensory integrations are so slighted in psychology lies in the loose definition of "stimulus" employed. The S-R theorists accept any complex combination of sensory energies, such as is inherent in a visual form or a tactual proprioceptive pattern, as *a* stimulus. Tacit acceptance of the organism's capacity to make unity out of diversity is general, especially since Gestalt psychology asserted that such a capacity is innate. This has not led to an understanding of how the unique interrelations within each unity are integrated into a unique unit.

In responding to the uniqueness of patterns which can only be discriminated (or identified) on the basis of subtle differences in contour, hue, and brightness relationships within the pattern, the sophisticated perceiving organism also *isolates* the pattern within a massive afferent flux. "Meaningful" segments of spatial mosaics in the visual environment are abstracted by selective "attention." Our visually naive subjects are apparently meeting neither the integrative nor the selective requirements of form perception effectively. They do show certain limited, innate predispositions to isolate and unify. They can cope with a "real" environment only after frequent contiguities of specific combinations of sensory energies greatly expand the selective and integrative processes.

With cumulative visual exposure to spatial patterns our chimpanzee subjects show gradually increasing facility for discriminating complex forms. It is highly significant that horizontal vs. vertical striation should have proved relatively easy for Chow to discriminate. These stimuli carry the same differentiating cues repetitively over the visual field. At the other extreme is the very late appearance of discriminations for faces. Here, the discrimination must be based on subtle differences in the relative angular, curvilinear, and areal dimensions. Memories of familiar faces must serve as reference standards. These involve sensory-sensory integrations (associations) developed over many hours of experience. To consider the discrimination aspect of this behavior without regard for the associative integration involved is to focus on only half the problem (8). Loss of the associative integration-over-area function through cortical insult is sometimes seen in relatively "pure" form (1).

The difficulty of the integration over area that is involved in early visual perception can be judged from many examples. The bright 11-year-old operated on for congenital cataract and studied for many months afterward by Weill and Pfersdorff (32, 33) identified a fish as a camel, mistaking the dorsal fin for the hump. *Adult* Africans tested with form-board intelligence tests (22) performed very badly. Geometrical stimuli were foreign to their visual world. As trackers of animals, however, these same individuals apparently could see subtle cues of shading on leaves, twigs, and branches. They outclassed the white man, who found he could not identify the tracks at all. Laboratory studies, carefully controlled with reference to the types of stimulation permitted in pretest periods, are urgently needed to work out the required sensory integrations that will permit rapid discrimination of "new" visual forms. That the prior patterns must resemble the new quite closely is suggested by the statement of a Caucasian: "All Chinamen look alike to me." The skilled microscopist forgets how little he saw when he first examined a slide.

We can draw a few inferences concerning biochemical changes that may or may not underlie the cumulative perceptual changes shown in the behavior of our animals. If we have provided for adequate stimulation of retinal cells and cells of the optic tract, we would expect no further gross change in average cell mass for these nuclear layers when patterned light is substituted for diffuse light, as long as immediately prior conditions of stimulation (i.e., degree of dark adaptation) were the same. The Brattgård (2) and the Hamberger and Hydén (10) studies suggest that the PNP fraction would respond cumulatively to the change in degree of stimulation in the ganglion cells and in cells of the lateral geniculate body, because patterned stimulation would increase frequency of firing by virtue of on-off effects. Our animals also spent more hours per day in the light as soon as diffuse lighting conditions were terminated. Since performance on pattern (and color-brightness) discriminations was relatively independent of numbers of hours in light (most clearly shown in the Chow and Nissen data), the assumed general change in PNP content of cells appears not to be relevant to the discrimination behavior or the sensory-sensory integrations. Here I believe we need to be concerned with more local changes related to individual cells or to substructures of cells. Regions of contact between cells are obvious candidates for study.

We are still groping for suggestions as to how to find local changes that might correlate with visual-memory function. The implication that protein structures in cells of the central nervous system are altered by function, primarily supported by the data from Sweden referred to above, encourages the search for ways of investigating the suggestions of Katz and Halstead (13). They have proposed a number of ways in which protein molecular structures might be involved in the mechanism of neural transmission, with special reference to how changes in transmission could depend upon changes in orientation and periodicity of the molecules. Such a protein lattice would have to be sufficiently stable to account for the remarkable durability of memory and, at the same time, plastic enough to account for rapid impressionability.

In the cortical projection areas a selective facilitation of firing in certain cell groups (or "assemblies," Hebb [12]) by activation of specific patterns of sensory cells should produce a general change in the structural and functional characteristics of the region. In contrast with animals always kept in diffuse light a normal animal ought to have a more readily and more prolongedly activated cortex after brief exposure to a familiar form. An effect should also be picked up in the thalamic diffuse projection system. Perhaps the techniques used by Krech *et al.* (16) would reveal heightened biochemical activity (cholinesterase production) in the visually sophisticated chimpanzees or cats. Measures could be taken at sites localized sufficiently to reveal effects of monocular exposure. This could be done more readily if Sperry's (21) technique for sagittal cutting of the chiasm and the posterior third of the corpus callosum were used to restrict the visual projection to the hemisphere on the side of the open eye.

The functional "demands" of pattern vision presumably alter the general efficiency and the specific integrative-discriminative capacity of the higher-order neural networks by cumulative effects on the microstructure of the cortex. We must also expect to find properties of the midbrain affected by the stimulation which improves "reflex" coördinations of the fixational and fusional mechanisms. Our data on cats and chimpanzees suggest that the gradual improvement in the original crude fixation responses may reflect partly or chiefly a reflex sensitization process. Modification of behavior by sensitization is not necessarily a distinctly different process from that by contiguity conditioning (20, p. 446). At the level of the neural change underlying the consequence of each kind of experimental manipulation, one can easily conceive of an identical mechanism for improved cell-to-cell transmission. Whether the process is one of sensitization or conditioning, it is clear that the visually deprived chimpanzee of seven months is already at some disadvantage relative to one that has received patterned visual stimulation from an earlier age. Fixation and convergence mechanisms fail to develop as readily after seven months as after three months or earlier. The discovery of a neurophysiological basis for such a loss of plasticity during the early months of life would be a major triumph for interdisciplinary research.

CONCLUSIONS

Among the several "laws" of behavioral modification, the law which has been measured with greatest precision is that of temporal contiguity. Studies at the behavioral level have shown that the relevant measurements are reproducible with some generality, but they have not shown exactly what events must be contiguous. These events must be sought in the central nervous system.

Studies of early sensory deprivation, sensory-sensory transfer, and effects of removal of sensory cortex after avoidance conditioning have recently thrown new light on the role of stimulus contiguities in plasticity of behavior. The development of pattern vision is a prime example of intrasensory organization which is dependent upon earlier contiguities of stimulation. Full mediation of visually guided behavior in mammals depends upon sensory-sensory as well as sensorimotor sequences organized centrally in neuroanatomical structures through an associative process. This process is one that underlies permanent sensitization and conditioning to increase the stability and precision of innate visual reflexes and to short-circuit the sensory control of elaborate central redintegrative patterns of activity—patterns originally excited only by the more extensive combinations of environmental stimulus configurations and sequences.

REFERENCES

1 Adler, A. Disintegration and restoration of optic recognition in visual agnosia. *Arch. Neurol. Psychiat., Chicago,* 1944, *51:* 243–59.

2 Brattgård, S. O. The importance of adequate stimulation for the chemical composition of retinal ganglion cells during early post-natal development. *Acta radiol., Stockh.,* 1952, Suppl. 96.

3 Chow, K. L., and H. W. Nissen. Interocular transfer of learning in visually naive and experienced infant chimpanzees. *J. comp. physiol. Psychol.,* 1955, *48:* 229–37.

4 Clark, W. E. Le G. The Doyne Memorial Lecture: The anatomy of cortical vision. *Trans. Ophthal. Soc. U. K.,* 1942, *62:* 229–45.

5 Cook, W. H., J. H. Walker, and M. L. Barr. A cytological study of transneuronal atrophy in the cat and rabbit. *J. comp. Neurol.,* 1951, *94:* 267–92.

6 Duncan, C. P. The retroactive effect of electroshock on learning. *J. comp. physiol. Psychol.,* 1949, *42:* 32–44.

7 Forgus, R. H. The effect of early perceptual learning on the behavioral organization of adult rats. *J. comp. physiol. Psychol.,* 1954, *47:* 331–36.

8 Gibson, J. J., and E. J. Gibson. Perceptual learning: Differentiation or enrichment? *Psychol. Rev.,* 1955, *62:* 32–41.

9 Grice, G. R. The relation of secondary reinforcement to delayed reward in visual discrimination learning. *J. exp. Psychol.,* 1948, *38:* 1–16.

10 Hamberger, C. A., and H. Hydén. Transneuronal chemical changes in Deiters' nucleus. *Acta otolaryng., Stockh.,* 1949, Suppl. *75:* 82–113.

11 Harlow, H. F. The formation of learning sets. *Psychol. Rev.,* 1949, *56:* 51–65.

12 Hebb, D. O. *The organization of behavior.* New York: Wiley, 1949.

13 Katz, J. J., and W. C. Halstead. Protein organization and mental function. In W. C. Halstead, (Ed.), Brain and behavior: A symposium. *Comp. Psychol. Monogr.,* 1950, *20:* No. 1 (Whole No. 103), pp. 1–38.

14 Keiner, G. B. J. *New viewpoints on the origin of squint.* The Hague, Neth.: Martinus Nijhoff, 1951.

15 Kimble, G. A. Conditioning as a function of the time between conditioned and unconditioned stimuli. *J. exp. Psychol.,* 1947, *37:* 1–15.

16 Krech, D., M. R. Rosenzweig, E. L. Bennett, and B. Kruekel. Enzyme concentrations in the brain and adjustive behavior-patterns. *Science,* 1954, *120:* 994–96.

17 Lancaster, W. B. *Refraction and motility.* Springfield, Ill.: Charles C Thomas, 1952.

18 Lashley, K. S. The accuracy of movement in the absence of excitation from the moving organ. *Amer. J. Physiol.,* 1917, *43:* 169–94.

19 Moeller, G. The CS-UCS interval in GSR conditioning. *J. exp. Psychol.*, 1954, *48:* 162–66.

20 Morgan, C. T., and E. Stellar. *Physiological psychology* (2nd ed.). New York: McGraw-Hill, 1950.

21 Myers, R. E. The corpus callosum and hemispheric interaction. Unpublished doctor's dissertation, Univer. Chicago, 1955.

22 Nissen, H. W., S. Machover, and E. F. Kinder. A study of performance tests given to a group of native African Negro children. *Brit. J. Psychol.*, 1935, *25:* 308–55.

23 Reynolds, B. The acquisition of a trace conditioned response as a function of the magnitude of the stimulus trace. *J. exp. Psychol.*, 1945, *35:* 15–30.

24 Riesen, A. H. Delayed reward in discrimination learning by chimpanzees. *Comp. Psychol. Monogr.*, 1940, *15:* No. 5 (Whole No. 77).

25 Riesen, A. H., K. L. Chow, J. Semmes, and H. W. Nissen. Chimpanzee vision after four conditions of light deprivation. *Amer. Psychologist*, 1951, *6:* 282 (Abstract).

26 Riesen, A. H., and E. F. Kinder. *Postural development of infant chimpanzees.* New Haven: Yale Univer. Press, 1952.

27 Riesen, A. H., M. I. Kurke, and J. C. Mellinger. Interocular transfer of habits learned monocularly in visually naive and visually experienced cats. *J. comp. physiol. Psychol.*, 1953, *46:* 166–72.

28 Riesen, A. H., and J. C. Mellinger. Interocular transfer of habits in cats after alternating monocular visual experience. *J. comp. physiol. Psychol.*, 1956, *49:* 516–20.

29 Spence, K. W. Visual acuity and its relation to brightness in chimpanzee and man. *J. comp. Psychol.*, 1934, *18:* 333–61.

30 Thomas, G. J. The effect on critical flicker frequency of interocular differences in intensity and in phase relations of flashes of light. *Amer. J. Psychol.*, 1954, *67:* 632–46.

31 Thomas, G. J. A comparison of uniocular and binocular critical flicker frequencies: Simultaneous and alternate flashes. *Amer. J. Psychol.*, 1955, *68:* 37–53.

32 Weill, G., and C. Pfersdorff. Les functions visuelles de l'aveugle-né opéré. *Ann. méd.-psychol.*, 1935, *93:* Pt. 2, 367–82.

33 ———. Evolution ultérieure des facultés visuelles d'une aveugle-née opérée. *Strasbourg-med.*, 1937, *97:* 272–75.

34 Whatmore, G. B., and N. Kleitman. The role of sensory and motor cortical projections in escape and avoidance conditioning in dogs. *Amer. J. Physiol.*, 1946, *146:* 282–92.

35 White, C. T., and H. Schlosberg. Degree of conditioning of the GSR as a function of the period of delay. *J. exp. Psychol.*, 1952, *43:* 357–62.

Alice in Wonderland
or Psychology Among the Biological Sciences

Alice, as you will recall, was a level-headed sensible girl, with the role of straight man for the remarkable characters in whose company she found herself. She asked the honest questions. They gave the brilliant replies. You will also recall that in her brief visits she was never quite integrated into Wonderland and the Looking-Glass world—in that universe but not of it. If she had been destined to stay permanently with her new playmates, something would have been necessary to correct this state of social maladjustment. Alice had a certain lack of insight, and all hands might have done with some psychotherapy.

I suppose it is because of its history, the course of its earlier development and its origins, that psychology is not yet fully integrated with the realm of biology though, inescapably and permanently, it is now in that realm. We do not communicate well enough: not as geneticist communicates with botanist, or physiologist with biochemist. A psychologist, even a comparative psychologist, could not step into a job in zoology as a physiologist might into pharmacology or neuroanatomy. The clinical neurologist complains that psychologists are complicating the problem of aphasia; the neurosurgeon does not understand what the objections are to localizing a stuff called consciousness or memory or something else in this part of the brain or that. For their part, psychologists too often fail to keep themselves informed about what goes on in the neurological field and, in defence of such ignorance, too often deny that it has any relevance for their work—a position so preposterous and indefensible that it is hard to attack.

There are no tougher problems than ours, nor more urgent ones. If it should be possible to communicate better, we might increase the rate of progress in solving them. I don't hold much with team research, except in the applied field ("team research" here means unified control of what the individual investigator does, either by a director of research or by committee), and this is not what I am talking about, but about the stimulation to new ideas, the criticism and guidance that is possible when workers with different backgrounds and skills effectively understand each other's language and modes of thought.

It may not be bias for me to argue that for such collaboration the electrophysiologist and neurochemist must do more homework in psychology. The converse holds as well, and I have put in a fair amount of effort at persuading psychologists to do more boning up on the biological bases of psychology. To be effective the effort must be two-sided, and "effort" is the right word—what I am talking about is hard work.

Without really stopping to think about it, I have always taken for granted that psychological methods are not particularly hard to understand. Psychologists, it seemed, were open and aboveboard, while to understand that stuff in the *EEG Journal* took sweat and tears, if not blood, and one was lucky to end up understanding it even then. But the Red Queen and the White Rabbit have been taking Alice somewhat more seriously in recent years—let a psychologist say something about consciousness or instinct, and he's likely to hear the baying of a neurologist or geneticist hot on his trail—and from the kind of question, criticism, or even favorable comment that is made one may discover that one's fellow scientists, even those who take a real interest, frequently just don't understand the nature of modern psychology, the changes that have occurred since 1910, the methods that have been developed, the self-imposed limitations as to scope and the kind of problem that can be dealt with.

I don't think it fair to say that a camel will go through the eye of a needle sooner than one could make a psychologist out of an electrophysiologist or an anatomist. That would be inaccurate as well as unfair. I know workers in other biological disciplines who really understand modern psychology, its whys and wherefores. But such understanding demands as much effort—and this is the point—it demands just as much effort as for a psychologist learning the anatomy of the reticular formation or the functioning of the pituitary. My own estimate frankly is that it demands more.

There are of course difficulties on both sides in this interaction. My intention, in making the present survey of our interdisciplinary efforts, is to try to look at both aspects, and then go on to consider the methodological and conceptual problems of physiological psychology, in general terms, having in mind especially the question of research strategy.

RED QUEEN, WHITE QUEEN, MEET ALICE

The source of the difficulty that confronts someone in another discipline, when he tries to find out what goes on in psychology, may simply be an enormous literature; but there may be, also, the idea that the literature is rather superficial or off the main point and thus not worth the labor of getting up. This is the only way I can understand, for example, how an eminent neurophysiologist recently could propose a theory of conditioned reflexes which explained extinction as a simple dropping out of synaptic connections due to disuse—completely unaware, apparently, that extinction does not occur with disuse alone (8). In fact, after extinction has been established, disuse generally results in spontaneous recovery of the conditioned response.

Surely it is time for the work of the CR diagram-makers to stop abandoning the assumption that the CR is the simple prototype of learning and that it depends only on the establishment of a one- or two-step pathway from a sensory to a motor structure. This sort of thing is still being taught in departments of physiology, and medical students are still being presented with an unpalatable mixture of Pavlov and Freud as their introduction to behavioral theory. Just conceivably, this may do the general practitioner no harm; but it is certainly poor intellectual equipment for the medical man who goes into behavioral research.

There is a point that is worth making explicit in this context. Because a simple task could, theoretically, be handled by a simple mechanism does not mean in fact that the brain handles it that way. In an uncomplicated nervous system, yes; but in the complex brain of a higher animal other mechanisms may insist on getting into the act and turn the simple task into a complex one. The animal may learn much more than it has to in order to solve the problem; and in some circumstances the extra may constitute positive interference. This could be the explanation of the extraordinarily slow learning of simple discriminations by the chimpanzee, which takes 200, 300, or 400 trials to learn things for which the laboratory rat, certainly no genius, needs only 10 to 20 trials or (for somewhat more difficult discriminations) 50 to 80 trials.

The same point seems clearly related to certain common difficulties in human learning. Every user of the English language has a handful of intractable words with respect to spelling or pronunciation. Commonly, the difficulty is a choice of alternatives which have been overlearned; instead of failing to remember one pronunciation, the speaker remembers two and cannot choose between them. I first encountered the word *marauder* in print and pronounced it to myself with stress on the first syllable. Later, a teacher corrected me; I had no trouble learning the new pronunciation but at the same time learned something else, namely, that mȳ spontaneous pronunciation of the word was wrong. Then as the new pronunciation became habitual I would start to say *maraud'er*, think to myself, "No, my pronunciation is wrong," and thus return to *mar'auder*. The engine kept on knocking in this way for some twenty years before I found an effective cure. I had exactly the same trouble with (*har'ass* or *harass'*); but it occurred to me one day that *harass* and *harry* are probably related, they have the same stress, and the stress in *harry* is evident. It was easy, too, to associate *harass* with *marauder* and remember that their stresses differ, one on the first, one on the second syllable. Now when I see *marauder* all I need do is take a little thought and its pronunciation becomes obvious, as any fool kin plainly see. (Could any of you supply me next with a key to *vag'ary*, or is it *vagar'y?*)

The widespread difficulty with left and right is probably another form of this problem of choosing between overlearned alternatives. You can easily teach a rat to turn left, and teach a child which is his right hand—except that next day or next week the child is likely to have "forgotten." All the signs of elaborate thought processes can sometimes be observed in the twelve-year-old who is told that the book he wants is at the right of the bookcase. In my own case, until military drill finally made it automatic, I had a mental ritual which worked infallibly. I imagined myself back in the room in which I was first taught left and right, faced toward the fireplace, and thereupon knew that the hand near the window was my left. With much practice this took only about two seconds; though it was still not quick enough for the drill sergeant who subsequently took charge of my education.

These intimacies are not reported just to show that I am confused. They are examples of a common phenomenon which has been extensively disregarded by psychologists and which is, so far as one can see, quite inconsistent with existing stimulus-response or CR formulations of the learning problem. They exemplify an important principle, that the large brain like large government may not be able to do simple things in a simple way. When the adult chimpanzee has finally learned to discriminate a triangle from a circle, it has perceived much more about the triangle than the rat has; when the human infant has passed through the stage of primary perceptual elaboration, he can respond to relations that lower animals cannot; but the fact remains that in either case the lower animal gets there first in a simple learning task. As I have said, because the CR could theoretically be a simple set of connections in the higher brain does not, therefore, mean that it is. The instruction of the young physiologist should not leave him with the idea that learning in mammals can be dealt with by some minor modification of Pavlov's ideas, even though Pavlov's work *is* one of the pillars of modern psychology.

Another example of the lack of familiarity with behavioral facts and methods: Several years ago an investigator working with a nonmammalian species asked me at a public meeting to account for the apparent similarity of the learning he had observed with what had been found in mammals, despite differences in brain structure. In one experiment he had taught the subject to avoid a white square. He described the animal's neural structures and asked, "What pathways are involved in the learning?" My first question concerned the properties of the stimulus that were eliciting the response, whether of form or brightness, so I asked what transfer tests (tests of stimulus equivalence) had been made. But all this was a new idea to the investigator in question, and as I started to outline the necessary experimental steps, he interrupted and said, "Never mind the alibis, stop evading the question, what paths are involved?"

In view of the last thirty years of study of animal learning, and especially Lashley's analysis of the perceptual process, this question was rather premature. Very different pathways must be involved if the animal is responding to relative brightness, on the one hand, or to the pattern on the other. It would be the merest fantasy to speculate about neural mechanisms until one knew what properties of the stimulus object determine the response.

Approach or avoidance responses to the same stimulus object may be made by animals which perceive the object differently, which means that the neural mechanisms involved in the responses are different. We train a rat and a chimpanzee, for example, to look for food behind a white triangle, so that both animals make an adient response to the same object. By testing them with other stimulus objects, however, we find that their perceptions of this object differ: The rat does not recognize and respond to a rotated triangle, nor to a black triangle, whereas either will elicit the response from the chimpanzee (Fig. 129). The mechanisms determining the original response, therefore, are different.

But this is not the place for a disquisition on analyzing learning. The point here is that the complications of learning theory in psychology are based on demonstrable complexities in brain function. We are past the era in which the kind of oversimplification made by Thorndike, Pavlov, and Watson is scientifically fertile. Such theories, all of the stimulus-response type and providing for no autonomy whatever in cerebral processes, were useful and necessary clarifications at one stage in the development of knowledge. They served the function of good theory by leading to their own destruction—they led to new analysis, new data, new ideas, which in their turn make new theoretical formulations possible. The critical level of complexity has gone up if theory is to continue being a guide to research, instead of mere verbal flux.

This is where the mathematical models and factor analysis have also failed us. The long and short of it is that you cannot get out of an equation, or any other mathematical gymnastics, any better ideas than you put in—not even when the mathematics is supplemented by one of those

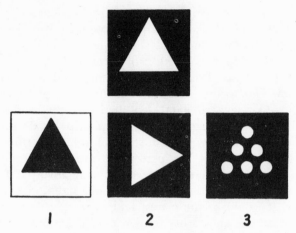

Fig. 129.—Degree of perception of "triangularity." Trained to respond to the top diagram, the rat makes random responses to diagrams 1, 2, 3; the chimpanzee recognizes the same figure in diagrams 1 and 2 and responds selectively to them, but makes random responses to 3; the two-year-old human child recognizes the training figure in all three test diagrams (Fields, Lashley, Gellermann). The cerebral processes involved in the original training to respond to the triangle, therefore, differ in complexity.

fancy network diagrams. What these do is ring the changes on a few ideas, sometimes new ideas, but always at an unrealistic level of over-simplification and with the aim, apparently, of avoiding the structural complexities of the nervous system. Factor analysis remains a powerful tool for simplifying correlational data, but it now seems clearly not to be a means of discovery, and it is not reasonable to expect that it can transcend the limitations of the original test data or be a substitute for new experimental analyses.

THE BEAM IN THINE OWN EYE

Much of what has just been said implies the need of considerable reform for Alice, too, and as one reads some current documents in psychology, one cannot wonder that others sometimes get mistaken ideas about the present state of psychological knowledge. Many psychologists still cling nostalgicly to the oversimplifications of Thorndike and Pavlov, still hope, apparently, for some magical means of evading the next step—analysis of ideational processes, those activities of the brain that are not directly and fully determined by present sensory input.

Sometimes this takes the form of setting up one's experiment so that the animal is simply not permitted to manifest any behavior that would raise awkward questions. Shut your animal up in a box with a lever to press; never look at the animal, but let your data be the ink-written record of the lever-pressing. Or use severe hunger or pain, not to energize the animal (it will show plenty of activity in other circumstances), but to limit the variability of behavior and hold the animal to the single purpose of avoiding electric shock or getting a bite of food. In themselves, such methods can be extremely valuable, and without them psychology would have made much less progress, but they become a liability when the experimenter permits them to limit his own vision as well as the animal's.

Another widespread idea is isolationistic: the idea that the only data and methods for a psychologist to be concerned with are psychological ones. This is not paranoia, though it may seem so to others. It is based on certain positivistic conceptions of the scientific method which, logically sound if you grant the original premises, nonetheless have no detectable relation to the actual processes of scientific discovery (the way in which knowledge is communicated is another matter). Writers intelligent in other respects—highly intelligent—deny that the anatomy and physiology of the brain even have relevance for psychology; not uncommonly it is asserted that the physiological psychologist is not a psychologist at all. (Heaven knows what this makes him, for in most cases he could not qualify as a physiologist.) Others, agreeing that the physiological psychologist may be a member in good standing, still feel that he is a rather limited fellow and that the important problems, which they may refer to as either "molar" or "dynamic," fall outside his scope: the problems of personality, consciousness, thinking, emotions, and so forth. There is a genuine problem of method here, to which we shall return, but it is possible to press a point too far.

The more extreme isolationist is typically a peripheralist, and what we may call a biological hedonist as well. By "peripheralism" I mean the view that behavior can be analyzed in terms of stimulus and response alone: in psychological terms, omitting thought or ideation, attention, and set from the scheme of things; in physiological terms, not denying the importance of cerebral processes but treating them mainly as a transmission of sensory input to motor structures, and so assuming that they need not be taken account of as a separate factor in behavior.

Let me say at once that the extreme form of this view seems to have disappeared. Hull's stimulus trace is of course a process with some autonomy (since it exists after the sensory input has ceased), and it appears also that the "fractional anticipatory goal response" may be treated as either a central or an effector event. Meehl and MacCorquodale (10) have put expectancy, an ideational process, into Hullian coördinates. The "response" that Seward calls "surrogate," Osgood "mediated," and Kendler "mediational" appears to have the same significance.

The day of out-and-out peripheralism seems over, but there is still a certain cramping effect of older ideas. One would think that a central-process postulate added to stimulus-response theory would be treated as a major item of business, worthy of extensive and thorough examination since its implications must affect the whole system of ideas. Instead, it seems regarded as Jane Austen regarded sex: something very important but not to be spoken of openly. The euphemism "response" for an unobservable central process mixes up data with inference but maintains respectability. Thus a thinker as acute as Bergmann refers with approval to a proposal by Berlyne that it is all right to deal with perceptions as long as they are called responses and not intervening variables, "though they do often temporally intervene between the presentation of a stimulus situation and other *possibly more overt responses*" (1, p. 437). My italics here draw attention to words that produce complete disbelief in me. The rat perceives a triangle and jumps toward it: Is there any possible question which of these two "responses" is more overt? If the term response is to be used this way, we have two classes of response to keep distinct: one implicit and inferential, and one overt; and of the two usages, one must be regarded as a purely ritual incantation, warding off lions.

However, terminology is not of the essence; once we are clear about the meaning of terms, the important thing is that the peripheralist-by-preference and the central-process theorist do not any longer differ fundamentally but only in emphasis.

Hedonism may be on its way out also. By this term I mean the position that identifies motivation with the biologically primitive hunger, pain, and sex. We need not go into this in detail. Evidence recently reviewed (6) shows that there is no escaping the addition of an exploratory-investigatory-manipulatory drive at the very least, if we are to theorize in terms of discrete drives at all. The so-called exploratory drive has been known for some time, and the work of Harlow and his associates (5) and of Bexton, Heron, and Scott (2) shows that the scope of the investigatory motive is much broader than "exploratory" would imply and of far greater importance in primate behavior than would be suspected from the earlier work with rodents. But there are many facts, disregarded so far by the hedonist, that are not comprehended even with this addition. These include fear of strangers and strange places; fear of isolation; acute disturbance at sight of a deformed, mutilated, or inert body; capricious refusal to copulate with a particular, biologically adequate partner, for months on end; anger at the sight of sexual stimulation of another; anger induced by another's begging for food, at the same time handing it over compulsively; love of excitement; teasing for its own sake and pleasure at the discomfiture of another; friendliness induced by punishment: all phenomena observed in chimpanzee as well as being familiar in human society (7).

In the chimpanzee they have been seen in circumstances that preclude the explanation by association with the supposedly more primitive hunger, pain, sex gratification. How is all this to be handled? I know of no adequate theory—certainly mine is not sufficient—but we may ask of any theoretical treatment that it should show signs of growth, a capacity for developing into a more adequate one. There appears to be a good case for thinking of a general drive state related to the nonspecific projection system of the brain stem, and of motivation as tending to produce an optimal level of "arousal" in this system, not as an adequate explanation, even of the facts now known, but as one that is both more adequate than existing theories and more capable of development.

At any rate, further persistence in the hunger-pain-sex approach (or still more, in the attempt to reduce everything to pain alone) is open to the strong suspicion that the writer is refusing even to consider the evidence, for this line of theorizing has long been contradicted by the facts and its explanatory value has decreased, instead of increased, with the research of recent years. We must assume that such biological hedonism has seen its day.

Finally, among the motes and beams in Alice's eye, a methodological weakness: The over-formalization of "hypothesis testing" and mathematico-deductive theory are in my estimate a serious impediment not only to collaborative work with other biological scientists, but also to psychological research per se. The point is included here for completeness only; discussion of it is postponed until we come to the question of research strategy.

THE ROLE OF PSYCHOLOGICAL CONSTRUCTS

Let us turn next to an aspect of behavior in research that presents certain possibilities for misunderstanding.

Even a physiologically based or "neuropsychological" theory of behavior remains a *psychological* theory. Its main features must be determined by certain constructs, theoretical conceptions, whose *raison d'être* is behavioral instead of physiological. Such constructs may be presented in anatomical and physiological terms, which on the one hand help communication among biological scientists. On the other hand, however, this seems to mislead both psychologist and nonpsychologist into regarding the theory as neurophysiological instead of psychological. The misunderstanding makes psychologists regard the theory as having narrower application than it really has, and leads the physiologist to expect something more concrete and directly verifiable than is in fact possible.

Let us be clear first that there is no possibility of a physiological psychology that can avoid use of "intervening variables" or "dispositional concepts"—conceptions that refer not to a specific structure, or activity of a specified kind in a specific locus of the nervous system, but to a property of functioning of the whole nervous system which is known from behavior and which must involve such complexities of unit interactions in the nervous system that it would be impossible to specify them in detail.

It is not remotely possible to give an account of the simplest behavior of the whole mammal without making use of such conceptions. Motivation, learning, intelligence, emotional disturbances—we may hope to refine such ideas or to substitute better ones for them, but there is no avoiding terms at this "molar" level of analysis. For them we can give none but the vaguest of physiological referents at present; they must refer to modes or degrees of organization, not to specific structures or processes; and they must consist of fantastically complex interactions, both spatial and temporal. It is chimerical in view of the limits of the human intellect to suppose that we could ever dispense with conceptions at this level in favor of hypotheses stated solely in terms of the activity of specifically named pathways from this nucleus to that. One may take one of these conceptions at a time and try one's hand at reducing it to more "molecular" terms (analyzing it in order to improve it), but one cannot expect in so doing to make psychological conceptions unnecessary—conceptions, that is, that have been found necessary in dealing with behavior instead of deriving from anatomy and physiology. We may say that physiological psychology tries to devise physiological hypotheses about the nature of some of psychology's "intervening variables" with the hope of sharpening the ideas in question, but not of superseding them.

In my own theorizing, to make this more specific, the "phase sequence" is a psychological rather than a physiological conception. Its chief specifications were determined in an effort to account for certain facts of behavior. Further, the "cell-assembly" is more a behavioral than a physiological conception; it was the behavioral data that led to the general idea in the first place, and I had to put some strain on the physiological and anatomical data to make it intelligible in these terms. This then is a case of taking two psychological conceptions, the train of thought and the idea (or image), and attempting to give them neurophysiological specifications. The result of this process was to suggest certain modifications of the psychological conceptions, but not to make them less psychological. They were not made more molecular, less molar; and they were not made less consonant with the psychological data—if, instead, they had not seemed *more* consonant with the data, they would not have been published.

Let us take a clarifying analogy. The engineer who designs a bridge must think at different levels of complexity as he works. His over-all plan is in terms of spans, piers, abutments; but when he turns to the design of a particular span, he starts to think in terms of lower-order units such as the I-beam. This latter unit, however, is still quite molar; any engineer is firmly convinced that an I-beam is just a special arrangement of certain molecules, the molecule in turn being a special arrangement of electrons, protons, and so forth. Now note: At a microscopic level of analysis, a bridge is nothing but *a complex constellation of atomic particles;* and a steel I-beam is no more than a convenient fiction, a concession to the limitations of thought and the dullness of human perception.

At another level of analysis, of course, the I-beam is an elementary unit, obviously real and no fiction. At this level electrons have a purely theoretical existence, which suggests that "reality" is meaningful as designating, not some ultimate mode of being about which there must be argument, but the mode of being which one takes for granted as the starting point of thought: for different problems, different realities.

Now consider the behavioral problem. At a certain level of physiological analysis there is no reality but the firing of single neurons; perception, anxiety, and intention are convenient fictions. But like a steel I-beam, such conceptions are necessary as well as convenient, and they are fiction at the microscopic level only. If at another level steel is reality, so are cognitive and emotional processes. It is not unusual for the biological scientist to feel that the psychologist is animistic when he denies that clinical-psychological problems, for example, can be dealt with solely in physiological terms. This is logically no better than regarding a bridge-builder as indulging in the supernatural if he refuses to design bridges in terms of placing so many molecules here, so many there, and specifies instead steel of such-and-such coefficients of hardness, elasticity, and tensile strength (all fictitious entities, of course). But the psychologist himself, on the other hand, is usually not too clear about the logic of what he is doing in this respect. Otherwise we would not find psychologists divorcing themselves completely from the universe of neuroanatomy and neurophysiology. If we learn more about the qualities of steel beams by relating them to molecular and atomic theory, so we can learn as much or more about our psychological entities by subjecting them to physiological analysis, without suggesting that they could ever be supplanted by purely physiological conceptions.

The physiological psychologist, therefore, bends every effort toward casting psychological conceptions into terms that will be consonant with, or translatable into, the terminology of neurophysiology and anatomy. He finds at once that he cannot fully succeed. But when he asks what "anxiety" is, in such terms, or how "defense" can operate, when one is speaking of the defenses of an "ego-structure" against some unpleasant perception (which must mean the maintenance of stability in one brain-process in the presence of another, disorganizing, process)—when he attempts such translations and attempts to think rigorously in such terms, he will find that he cannot get very far with the sort of statement that would satisfy an anatomist who is asking "Where?" and "How?," but he may find too that his behavioral problem appears in a new light.

We cannot leave this process of refinement to the clinical psychologist and the student of normal man. The onus is on the physiological and comparative psychologist to attempt such clarifications and maintain communication with the clinical psychologist, and it seems to me that we are not meeting our responsibilities in this respect. (Harlow made the same point earlier [4, p. 51].) Too frequently we take a destructively critical attitude, condemning psychoanalytic ideas and Rorschach readings without offering anything in their place. We cannot expect the student of intact human beings to do much "physiologizing"; too many fingers were burnt in the twenties and thirties, and the pessimism engendered by Lashley's destructive critique of simple-minded physiological theory is still with us. At the same time, we have no choice, really, but to physiologize, if we are to have any hope of solving our problems—we cannot ignore any source of new ideas or clarification of old ones. The physiological psychologist must go the second mile in the collaboration with other psychologists; instead of concerning himself solely with the problems that can be handled by physiological methods, he should be worrying *also* about the larger aspects of the problems of behavior. What is the distinction between "conscious" and "unconscious" motivation? How are we to deal with the "body image"? What are the mechanisms of "irrational" angers and fears, or of mental depression?

These are genuine problems and I am somewhat disappointed that they have occupied so little of the space in this Symposium. I do not believe that they are entirely beyond our reach. It is not altogether fanciful to hope that we can make more progress with ideation and the thought process, and when we do, we shall find of these other pieces in the jig-saw puzzle fitting in. It would take too much space to list the various researches that I have in mind, but I would like to point out that in the last ten years, in the period beginning with Harlow's work on learning sets (4) and including Riesen's work on visual learning in chimpanzees reared in darkness (11)—a period seeing also the death of the ill-fated continuity-noncontinuity argument (9)—there has been something like a revolution in psychological knowledge to go with the neurophysiological revolution that began earlier. It is quite true that we must speculate to deal with the thought process; but the scientist who does not speculate is no scientist at all, and new opportunities for controlled speculation are available to us today.

THE STRATEGY OF RESEARCH

We turn now, finally, to the question of strategy in behavioral research. What are the conditions that make for discovery of new properties of behavior and the development of more powerful explanatory ideas?

It may surprise you to learn that I don't have a complete answer to the question. I have, however, made certain empirical observations which I shall be glad to hand on, without prejudice. Some are negative, some positive.

The broad tolerance with which I approach the problem will perhaps become evident with the following propositions. Our current sophistication with respect to the design of experiments, statistically speaking, is a brilliant development of method without which we would be much better off. Hypothesis testing, and the compulsion on graduate students to present their thesis plans in such terms, is naive and a barrier to research. Courses in how to do research before turning the student loose in the laboratory are like teaching a child to swim without letting him get near the pool. The teaching may be worse than useless if it simply produces a fear of making mistakes and the idea that one must swim with perfect style or not at all—and such fear, and such perfectionism, are common results of graduate training in psychology. No research gets done by the man who must do only the experiments that are beyond criticism.

These propositions may be overstated, but they are not entirely ridiculous. There are schools in which research cannot begin until the student has a plausible hypothesis to test. This is unwise, for it rules out the study which starts with the question, "What would happen if I did so and so?" or with the feeling or hunch that there is something of interest to be found out in some particular area. A fertile investigation is more likely to end up with a hypothesis in testable form than to begin with one. The hypothesis, of course, can then be tested; I do not mean to deny that this is part of research. But the more significant and difficult part is arriving at the idea that is to be tested, and what I think bad about the views referred to is that they pay little attention to the way in which ideas are arrived at, overlooking the fact that the better the idea, the more likely it is to have been extremely vague, inchoate, when experimentation began, and to have become definite only as a *result* of the experiment. If this is true of the experienced investigator, as it generally is, how can we demand of the neophyte that he be able to produce a worth-while hypothesis before starting his research? Here, too, lies the weakness of the "design of experiment" approach: It assumes that the thinking is done in advance of experimentation, since it demands that the whole program be laid out in advance; it tends also, in its own Procrustean way, to confirm or deny the ideas with which one began the experiment, but its elaborate mathematical machinery is virtually certain to exclude the kind of unexpected result that gives one new ideas.

There are, of course, two modes of research, one systematic or systematizing with the aim of producing order in existing knowledge, and one exploratory or developmental, which aims at extending and deepening knowledge. None of my objections apply to the first mode. To make knowledge more sytematic is an important objective, especially in the applied field, and the closer one is to application, the more useful the hypothetico-deductive and design-of-experiment approach must be. My objection is to allowing the systematic to overshadow the developmental mode, and allowing students to think that there is only the one way of going at research. An experiment can be set up either to encourage serendipity or to discourage it, to maximize or to minimize the probability of picking up new conceptions in the course of the work. If, as I think, the need of better conceptions is our essential problem, and if the aptitude for developing them is rarer than that for systematizing, then we need a change of emphasis in the text books and journal articles on research methods.

Graduate training as such is not our present concern, but all this is not completely off the mark in view of the proportion of current research that is done by graduate students rather than their seniors, who are busy raising the wherewithal (and giving courses in research methods).

What then do we have to say about strategy? First and foremost, that we must not let our epistemological preconceptions stand in the way of getting research done. We had much better be naive and productive than sophisticated, hypercritical, and sterile.

Order in research is of value, but so is imagination and spontaneity. The plan for the American Psychological Association's current "Project A (Evaluation of Psychological Science)" is based on the idea that the "aimlessness and incoördination of research planning" in psychology needs correction, and that we should try to strengthen "whatever sober and constructive trends toward the rational development of the science already exist." In short, behavioral theory and knowledge are in a terrific muddle.

Now there are two ways of treating the situation. One is to have recourse to our theories of what science is or should be, and stop developing new ideas until we have got the present ones straightened out, with definitions, postulates, and deductions all in order.

The alternative view is this. Psychology and related biological sciences were never in such a healthy state. The differing interpretations of fact, the frequent lack of interlocking research plans, the lacunae of knowledge, all may be signs of present vigor. The situation may be like that of the general whose army is winning a battle and who has lost contact with most of his field officers. This is embarrassing, especially if pockets of resistance remain and the general gets sniped at. But if he has competent officers, capable of independent operations and keeping *some* contact with one another, the confusion may be superficial, and strategy may best be served by letting consolidation wait. It need not be intellectual laziness that leads a researcher to refuse to define his terms in detail, make all his assumptions explicit, and complete all the possible variations on one experiment so that he knows everything about that topic before moving on to the next. At a certain point in theorizing, further elaboration is carrying an answer to too many places of decimals.

I hold firmly to the proposition that theoretical formulations have an essential part in the strategy of research, but I also urge that we temper our enthusiasm, not go to extremes and suppose that theory is always the better for a more formal and systematic development in detail. Including my own, our current theories are not worth more detailed elaboration. What we need from a theory is that it should hold together long enough to lead us to a better one. There is no rule by which one can say when this degree of specificity has been reached, what the fertile degree of elaboration is.

On the positive side, then, it seems evident that research strategy includes a lively, but temperate, interest in theory. We must take it seriously, but not be dominated by it; bend every effort to making it as good as possible, but still avoid having our experiments limited by it.

The psychologist must also take a similar attitude toward current physiological knowledge, and take it seriously but not reverently. When, some time ago, I argued that neurological ideas have an essential role in psychology, I did not mean, as Bronfenbrenner thought, that Klein and Krech were wrong in saying that "the inadequacy of neurology will be remedied in part by . . . attention to psychological data and theory" (3, p. 160). On the contrary, the statement seems sound to me. Psychology cannot stray *far* from the data of anatomy and physiology; but it has in the past been demonstrably right, on occasion, when neurophysiology was wrong.

Our strategy calls for maximal utilization of data and ideas from both sides of this fence; and in fact we must get rid of the fence as far as possible. The only real barrier is that of communication, as I argued earlier. It seems that Alice reached the eighth rank some time ago, and with her new powers acquired some new responsibilities. One of these is to make an attack on the thought process, to formulate the problems in such a way that the neuroanatomist or physiologist can at least see how his data are relevant and how they are being used or abused by psychologists. Another is a more adequate treatment of motivation. I have in mind the probability that the future will see a considerable development of neuro-chemical-psychological analysis—and still without minimizing or neglecting the motivational phenomena brilliantly studied at Wisconsin. The irresponsibility of the empty-organism approach, of continuing with the hedonism of 1911 in spite of all the data to the contrary that have been obtained since, and of closing one's eyes to the existence of set and attention and purpose while making an endless elaboration of methodological notions that clearly have not paid off in the development of new knowledge—this kind of irresponsibility can be avoided at least by the physiological psychologist who is obliged to recognize the real complexities of neural function, and to see that it is unlikely that we shall solve the problems of behavior without the aid of the biochemist, the geneticist, the anatomist, and the physiologist.

REFERENCES

1 Bergman, G. Theoretical psychology. *Annu. Rev. Psychol.*, 1953, *4:* 435–58.
2 Bexton, W. H., W. Heron, and T. H. Scott. Effects of decreased variation in the sensory environment. *Canad. J. Psychol.*, 1954, *8:* 70–76.
3 Bronfenbrenner, U. Personality. *Annu. Rev. Psychol.*, 1953, *4:* 157–82.
4 Harlow, H. F. The formation of learning sets. *Psychol. Rev.*, 1949, *56:* 51–65.
5 ———. Mice, monkeys, men, and motives. *Psychol. Rev.*, 1953, *60:* 23–32.
6 Hebb, D. O. Drives and the C. N. S. (Conceptual nervous system). *Psychol. Rev.*, 1955, *62:* 243–54.

7   Hebb, D. O., and W. R. Thompson. The social significance of animal studies. In G. Lindzey (Ed.), *Handbook of social psychology.* Cambridge, Mass.: Addison-Wesley, 1954, pp. 532–61.

8   Malmo, R. B. Eccles' neurophysiological model of the conditioned reflex. *Canad. J. Psychol.,* 1954, *8:* 125–29.

9   Meehl, P. E., and K. MacCorquodale. A further study of latent learning in the T-maze. *J. comp. physiol. Psychol.,* 1948, *41:* 372–96.

10 ———. Some methodological comments concerning expectancy theory. *Psychol. Rev.,* 1951, *58:* 230–33.

11   Riesen, A. H. The development of visual perception in man and chimpanzee. *Science,* 1947, *106:* 107–108.

Index